PRICE GUIDE TO ANTIQUE
AND CLASSIC CAMERAS
Fifth Edition
1985-1986

Edited by James M. McKeown
and Joan C. McKeown

Fifth Edition on press. Published June 1, 1985

Second Printing October 1, 1985

European Distributors:
Hove Foto Books
Hove, East Sussex, U.K.

Library of Congress Catalog Card Number: 85-070917

ISBN 0-931838-08-8

ON THE COVER

This book is dedicated
to the fact
that the price of
an antique camera
is entirely dependent
upon the moods
of the buyer and seller
at the time of
the transaction.

CONTENTS

ACKNOWLEDGEMENTS

This book has grown tremendously since its first edition twelve years ago, not only in the number of cameras included, but also in the amount and accuracy of the information on each. Obviously this has not been the work of a single individual. This current edition has benefitted greatly from the knowledge and research of many authorities in specialized areas of the camera collecting field. The depth of information in these specialty areas would not have been possible without their generous sharing, for while the job of editing this guide requires a broad interest in the field, this wide interest is necessarily shallow overall.

The largest single contribution to this edition is the revised and expanded section on Minolta, which is primarily the work of *Jack & Debbie Quigley* of Quigley Photographic Services. They provided dates and technical information as well as photographs for nearly every Minolta model up to about 1965. The Quigleys are well known authorities on Minolta. Debbie runs the mail order end of their business and teaches photography. Jack takes time from his career in commercial photography, camera repair and custom crafting to write the "Minolta Mania" column for Photographic News.

The Zeiss-Ikon section is the work of *Mead Kibbey*. Mead is widely recognized as one of the world's leading authorities on Zeiss-Ikon.

Peter Dechert is responsible for the Canon section. Dr. Dechert is well known as a leading authority in the field of Canon rangefinder cameras, and author of the book *Canon Rangefinder Cameras* published by Hove Foto Books.

Bob Rotoloni, who literally wrote the book on Nikon, was the major contributor for that section. His new book called *Nikon Rangefinder Cameras* is published by Hove Foto Books.

Paul-Henry van Hasbroeck contributed historical information, photographs, and some useful pricing data for the Leica section. Paul-Henry is the author of several books on Leica cameras, the latest of which is entitled *Leica: A History Illustrating Every Model and Accessory*. See the advertising section at the back of this guide for further information on his books.

Art Evans was extremely generous in supplying information for the Franke & Heidecke (Rollei) section. He took time from his busy schedule and shared information from his forthcoming book, *Collectors Guide to Rollei Cameras*, to be published soon by Centennial Photo Service.

Dick Paine was kind enough to let us use material from his book, *Graflex, The All American Cameras*. Further help in the Graflex area was provided by *Roger Adams*, who is currently working on a book on the subject.

Jim Stewart provided help in several areas, of which the Alpa section is only the most obvious. Many other details and bits of information provided by Mr. Stewart are scattered throughout the book, in areas including 35mm and subminiature cameras.

Bill Carroll, made numerous additions throught the guide. His particular interests are early shutters, small format rollfilm cameras, mechanically complex cameras (built-in motor drives or other unusual features), camera look-alikes (flasks, compacts, etc.), and non-photo-electric exposure determining devices. Contact him at 8500 La Entrada, Whittier, CA 90605, (213)-693-8421.

Mike Kessler is particularly interested in unusual 1880-1890's disguised or detective cameras and Simon Wing cameras. He may be reached at 25749 Anchor Circle, San Juan Capistrano, CA 92675, (714)-661-3320.

George Kirkman provided information on many early stereo cameras. He will field questions on (or buy) stereo cameras (1900-1940) and would appreciate hearing from you at: P.O. Box 24468, Los Angeles, CA 90024, (213)-208-6148.

The Western Photographic Collectors Society volunteered to respond to any questions on collectible cameras. If they don't have the answers, they will find someone who does. Write: WPCA, P.O. Box 4294, Whittier, CA 90607.

In addition to the historian/collectors, we are indebted to another group of friends who are the market specialists. These are primarily dealers or very active collectors who review the price data from a viewpoint based on extensive experience in the general market or specialized areas thereof. While the majority of the prices in this book are derived from our database of worldwide sales records, it is of critical importance that these figures be reviewed for possible errors. We communicate regularly with many of the top dealers and collectors in the field to constantly verify our statistics.

Jay Tepper has always been willing to help in this area. Jay and his wife Bobby publish a monthly list and are among the world's largest dealers in collectible cameras. Jay regularly purchases large numbers of cameras worldwide to maintain his extensive inventory. He may be contacted at 313 N. Quaker Lane, West Hartford, CT 06119 U.S.A. Tel: 203-233-2851.

Dr. Burton Rubin was especially helpful in the area of 35mm cameras. His interest and knowledge span many manufacturers to help keep the various specialty areas in perspective.

Don Chatterton and *Bob Sperling* are both specialists in the Leica field, and we greatly appreciate their help with the nuances of Leica pricing.

Bob Barlow helped eliminate some of the confusion among the various Contax-type cameras made in post-war East Germany. Bob specializes in East German Contax cameras, and welcomes the exchange of information and/or equipment. Contact him at P.O. Box 76, Livingston, NJ 07039.

Ron Anger contributed to the Ernemann section from the market and historical viewpoints.

Subminiature camera collecting has its specialists who were also very cooperative, including *Bob Johnson, Jay Tepper, Jim Stewart,* and *Dick Sanford.*

Allen Weiner was called upon for his respected opinion on relatively unusual cameras for which there are always inadequate sales figures to make a good average. Allen & Hilary Weiner are well established and respected dealers who are always interested in buying entire collections or fine individual items. They may be contacted at 80 Central Park West, New York City 10023. Tel: 212-787-8357.

Thurman F. (Jack) Naylor of Cameras & Images International Inc. has always been generous in sharing his knowledge in both the historical and pricing areas. Certainly one of the world's leading collectors, Jack keeps abreast of the latest price trends on significant cameras, and has also been thoroughly cooperative in providing needed information on many of the rare items from his collection.

Camera manufacturers are in business to sell cameras, not to provide historical information to those of us who live with one foot in the past. In spite of the sometimes cold push toward productivity so prevalent in today's world, there are a few camera manufacturers who took time from their schedules to provide us with information and/or photographs. Included are *Agfa-Gevaert, Eastman Kodak Co., Ernst Leitz GmbH, Victor Hasselblad Aktiebolag, VEB Pentacon, Robot Foto & Electronic GmbH, Rollei-Werk, Ehrenreich Photo Optical Industries, and Durst S.A.* We would like to thank them for the help they have provided.

Numerous other people and organizations have helped, and unfortunately they can not all be listed here. Even the list of contributors at the front of the book is not nearly complete. This book has become a depository for useful information, and we are often approached by collectors at camera shows who fill in bits and pieces of information gleaned from new purchases and discoveries. We receive many letters and postcards with contributions of historical, technical, or pricing information. All of this is greatly appreciated. While we have tried to list the major contributors, I am sure that there are omissions, and I would like to thank especially those whose contributions are going temporarily without recognition.

INTRODUCTION

The first edition of *Price Guide to Antique & Classic Still Cameras* was published in 1974, shortly after the camera collecting hobby came out of the closet. Since that time, this guide has been the single most complete and accurate reference guide to cameras in the entire field. With this new edition, we make another giant step ahead. This edition lists over 5000 camera models. Not only has it been expanded to include more camera models, but we have made every effort to expand the information given for the individual cameras, providing dates and historical information wherever possible. Each new edition of this guide has made significant improvements over the last, and with your support we hope to continue this tradition.

WHERE ARE PRICES GOING?

In our fourth edition we had noted the overall change in prices from ascending patterns through 1981 to a leveling off about 1982-83 with some items beginning to drop. In 1983 and 1984, camera prices dropped considerably, especially in reference to the American Dollar, which is our basis. Partially this is due to the general softening of the market and of course a good portion of the loss is due to the rapid rise in the value of the dollar compared to other currencies.

Extremely rare, important, and unique cameras in the higher price ranges (over $10,000) have experienced the least depression. The small number of collectors active in that segment of the market are not generally as susceptible to short-term fluctuations in the economy. Prices in the $3,000-10,000 range had softened as we entered the 1983-1984 period as the collectors who purchase cameras in that range tightened the purse-strings. This is an area of the market which is still limited to a rather small group of collectors. Since the cameras in that range are few, and those who seek them are few, the entire market can be affected by a much smaller number of people. This area of the market seems to have leveled off somewhat, and many changes in price figures are due only to currency fluctuation.

The most drastically affected by the softened market are the low and medium priced cameras which are not in perfect condition. As camera sales slowed, collectors were able to be more selective in their purchases. From a wider selection of offerings, they were able to purchase those items in better condition and pass up anything which showed heavy signs of use or abuse. And so while some of the prices of cameras did not drop as much as one would have expected, during the 1982-83 slump, the toll was paid by the models in lesser condition to maintain the prices of those in better shape. It is still true that there "ain't no such thing as a free lunch".

This pattern of lower prices has continued through 1984 and 1985. It should be emphasized that these are generalities, and that each camera must be individually considered. Obviously a low-priced camera which is rare will not suffer like a common one, and some types of cameras will be affected more than others by these conditions.

One phenomenon which has been noted by many dealers is the continual fluctuation within the market. Some have compared it to the stock market and insist that the only ones who know the value of a camera are those who are in the market daily. There is a certain element of truth in this. Those who are in the market as a daily way of life can spot a chance to pick up a few percentage points by trading or buying the right camera at the right time. To the normal collector, however, this is not of great importance, since these fluctuations are both up and down. The long range graph for any particular camera is generally quite steady. As a matter of fact, from an investment standpoint, cameras have been a relatively stable investment. Our statistics show that over the broad range of collectible cameras, the appreciation rate is surprisingly similar. From the perspective of fifteen years of keeping records of the values of collectible cameras, we find that the most rapid changes in values are usually due to the "fad factor" or readjustment of priorities among collectors.

WELCOME BACK, COLLECTORS! BON VOYAGE, SPECULATORS!
When camera collecting was experiencing a boom in the late 1970's, speculators began buying heavily and indiscriminately, which fanned the flames of inflation and drove prices to the breaking point. Some collectors left the field as they saw the commercial aspect of collecting overshadow the historians and hobbyists who truly appreciated the cameras and not only their price tags. The slump of 1982-83 was a cloud with a silver lining. Many speculators have left the field, and new collectors are joining our ranks. While prices may not be as high as they once peaked, the field is stronger and more stable than it was just two years ago.

ADVICE TO NEW COLLECTORS
Our advice to collectors would depend entirely on your motives for collecting. If you are concerned with collecting as an investment, you should concentrate on the more rare and unusual camera models, which will naturally require more capital and expertise. If you are collecting primarily for the enjoyment of it, you should follow the dictates of your interest and budget. Many of the lower-priced cameras offer an inexpensive hobby, and often this is a good place to start. Most collectors start out with a general interest which often becomes more defined and specialized as they continue in collecting. If you are dealing in cameras to make a profit, you must maintain close contact with the market, and remain within your area of expertise. By following the market closely, you can make a profit from its ordinary fluctuations, and by knowing your customers' interests.

All prices in this edition have been updated. They are as current as possible, and data has been weighted toward the most recent figures. However, we have also retained the stabilizing influence of the 10 year price record of each camera to prevent the "overshooting" which can occur in a less researched effort. Our prices tend to follow the long-term trends more accurately in the same way that a viscous-damped compass maintains a smooth heading.

The information and data in this edition is based on hundreds of thousands of verifiable sales, trades, offers, and auction bids. It lists cameras from over 1000 manufacturers. It contains thousands of little bits and pieces of photographic history and trivia, many of which are not to be found in other reference works. It is a reference work -- a research report. The prices do not tell you what I think the camera is worth, but they tell you what a lot of former owners and present owners thought it was worth at the moment of truth. That is the esence of "McKeown's Law" which states: **"The price of an antique camera is entirely dependent upon the moods of the buyer and seller at the time of the transaction."**

Two other observations have been added to this general philosophy of collecting.
1. "If you pass up the chance to buy a camera you really want, you will never have that chance again."
2. "If you buy a camera because you know you will never have the chance again, a better example of the same camera will be offered to you a week later for a much lower price."
These observations should always be taken into account when applying McKeown's Law.

INSTRUCTION FOR USE OF THIS GUIDE

All cameras are listed by manufacturer, and manufacturers are listed in alphabetical order. A few cameras are listed by model name if we were not sure of the manufacturer. Generally, we have listed the cameras under each manufacturer in alphabetical order, but occasionally we have grouped them by type, size, or date of introduction or other sequence appropriate to the situation.

Photos appear immediately above the listing which describes them. In a few cases, the photographs have been positioned nearby and identified with a caption.

We have used different type faces to make the guide easier to follow. The pattern is as follows:

MANUFACTURER NAME (all caps)
Historical notes or comments on the manufacturer.
Camera Name - Description of camera and current value data.
Special notes regarding camera or price.

CAMERA NAME - If the camera model name is in all caps, it is a separate listing, not related to the previous manufacturer. We use this style usually when the manufacturer is unknown.

CONDITION OF CAMERAS
Two recent trends in describing condition should be noted. The first is a rather alarming number of people who consistently describe the condition while looking through rose-colored glasses. One dealer, speaking of his printed ads, recently said to me: "If I don't put it down as Excellent, I can't sell it." Personally, I disagree with that policy and attitude. In the short term, he may sell a few overrated cameras, but eventually will lose his entire business. I once bought by mail from another dealer a camera which was described as "excellent". It was not only less than excellent, but had parts missing. That was my first and last mail transaction with that dealer. I know of many other people who have had the same type of experience with the same dealer. In order to maintain any stability in the collecting field, we would recommend that buyers insist on a return privilege for any items purchased unseen by mail or phone. Any reputable dealer will allow this, but some individuals may not. If you find a dealer or collector who consistently exaggerates condition, we would recommend that you confront him with the problem or perhaps stop dealing with him. There are various sets of standards in use, but none that should allow a dented, scratched or non-functioning camera to be described as "excellent".

The second trend in describing condition is a reaction against the earlier system of misleading word descriptions in which a camera described as "good" really means it is "poor" and a camera described as "very good" is really only "fair". The more recent approach is to separately describe the cosmetic and functional attributes of the camera. We feel strongly that the field should adopt a universally accepted standard which would allow for this flexibility. A camera in mint cosmetic condition, but not functioning may be perfectly acceptable to a collector who will put it on the shelf. On the other hand, a user may not care much about the appearance as long as it works. We strongly support such a system, and recommend that it be implemented on a world-wide scale with the cooperation of pricing guides, collector publications and societies, auction houses and dealers.

In an effort to establish an international standard for describing condition, we are proposing the following scale. We have purposely used a combination of a number and a letter to avoid any confusion with other grading systems already in use. Condition of a camera should be given as a single digit followed by a letter. The number represents cosmetic condition and the letter gives functional condition.

GRADE---COSMETIC CONDITION

0---New merchandise, never sold. In original box, with warranties.
1---AS NEW. Never used. Same as new, but not warrantied. With box or original packaging.
2---No signs of wear. If it had a box, you wouldn't be able to tell it from new.
3---Very minimal signs of wear.
4---Signs of light use, but not misuse. No other cosmetic damage.
5---Complete, but showing signs of normal use or age.
6---Complete, but showing signs of heavy use. Well used.
7---Restorable. Some refinshing neccessary. Minor parts may be broken or missing.
8---Restorable. Refinishing required. May be missing some parts.
9---For parts only, or major restoration if a rare camera.

GRADE---FUNCTIONAL CONDITION

A---AS NEW. Everything in perfect working order, with factory warranty.
B---AS NEW. Everything in perfect working order, but not warrantied by factory. Seller fully guaranties functioning.
C---Everything working. Recently professionally cleaned, lubed, overhauled and fully guaranteed.
D---Everything working. Recently professionally cleaned, or overhauled, but no longer under warranty.
E---Everything working. Major functions have recently been professionally tested.
F---Not recently cleaned, lubed, or overhauled. Fully functioning, but accuracy of shutter or meter not guaranteed.
G---Fully fuctioning. Shutter speeds and/or meter probably not accurate. Needs adjusting or cleaning only.
H---Usable but not fully. Shutter may stick on slow speeds. Meter may not work.
J---NOT USABLE without repair or cleaning. Shutter, meter, film advance may be stuck, jammed, or broken.
K---Probably not repairable.

In this system, an average camera would be rated as 5F. A camera rated as 3G would mean cosmetically showing minimal signs of wear, but with questionable accuracy of meter or shutter. Thus a very specific description of condition fits in a small amount of space, and eliminates the problems which have been associated with word or letter descriptions which do not allow distinctions between cosmetic and functional condition. To be even more specific, users may wish to expand the cosmetic grade by using a second digit. Thus "56B" would mean cosmetic condition somewhere between grade 5 and 6, guarnteed to be functioning properly.

Sometimes collectors are more lenient in applying these standards to older and more rare cameras, and more strict in applying them to newer or more common models. This is somewhat self-defeating. If you describe a camera as "very good condition considering its age", you are adding a personal judgement that old cameras should be judged by a different set of standards. Even though most cameras of that age may show some signs of age, the fact that it is old does nothing to improve its condition.

COMPARISON WITH OTHER GRADING SYSTEMS:
The following table compares the Cosmetic portion of the condition grading system with some of the common word or letter descriptions currently in use. These comparisions are approximate and are provided only to help users move to the new system more easily. The last column in the table shows in general terms how condition will affect prices. However, these are only approximations. Condition affects price differently on various types and ages of cameras. The suggested allowances below are given as percentages of the listed price.

McKeown	SA	Cornwall	Percent of listed price
0	N	-	150-200%
1	LN	-	130-150%
2	M	A	120-140%
3	M-	AB	115-130%
4	E+	B	110-120%
5	E	C	95-115%
6	VG	CD	80-110%
7	G	D	55-85%
8	F	E	30-60%
9	P	-	10-30%

Any missing or loose parts should be specifically noted. Use of a (-) after a condition number or letter means that it meets the standard except for minor condition AS DESCRIBED in adjoining comment. Use of a (+) means it exceeds this condition standard, but doesn't qualify for next higher rating.

INTERPRETATION OF PRICE FIGURES:
All price figures are in United States Dollars. A table of conversions to other currencies may be found at the back of the book. Prices apply to cameras in condition range 5 to 6 according to the standards previously set forth. This is the most common condition in which cameras are found and collected, and makes the most useful standard. To determine the value of a particular camera, the user of this guide should consider any variation from this condition when assessing it and vary his value estimate accordingly.

The lower priced items in this guide and on the market tend to be slightly over-priced, simply because the cost and bother of advertising, selling, and shipping an $5.00 item is not much different from the same costs and efforts to sell an item valued for hundreds or thousands of dollars. The middle priced items show the most accurate and stable prices. They are the most commonly traded; they are in large supply; and thus the market is very stable. The higher priced cameras of any particular style, brand, or age tend to be the most volatile, because there is both limited supply and limited demand.

ACCURAFLEX - c1950's. TLR, 2¼x2¼" on 120 rollfilm. Accurar Anastigmat f3.5/80mm lens. Accurapid 1-300,B,ST sync shutter. Semi-automatic film transport. Original price was $60 in 1957. Current value: $20-30.

ACMA (Australia)
Sportshot - 620 or 120 film. $15-25.

ACRO - Brown bakelite minicam for 16 exposures on 127 rollfilm. Identical to Photo Master. $4-8.

ACRO SCIENTIFIC PRODUCTS CO. (Chicago)

Acro Model R - Black plastic and metal camera for 16 exp. on 127 rollfilm. Built-in rangefinder & extinction meter. Styled similar to the Detrola. f3.5 Wollensak lens in Alphax shutter. $15-25.

ADAMS & CO. (London)
Challenge - Half-plate mahogany tailboard-style camera. With Dallmeyer landscape lens. $400-500.

De Luxe - c1898. A deluxe variation of the earlier Adams Hand Camera for 3¼x4¼" plates. Spanish mahogany with sealskin covering. Rack and pinion focusing. $350-500.

Hand Camera - c1891-96. Leather covered hand camera with detachable 12-plate magazine. Rising, shifting front, double swing back. Ross Rapid Symmetrical f8

lens, Iris T,I shutter. 3¼x4¼" or 4x5" size. Rare. $350-500.

Hat Detective Camera - c1892-96. Camera fits into a bowler-style hat. Bayonet mount Rapid Rectilinear f11 lens and T,I between-the-lens shutter are in the crown of the hat. ¼-plate is secured in a strut folding mechanism inside the hat. Advertised as a "secret Camera that defies detection". Made from Jekeli & Horner's patent of the Chapeau Photographique; Adams had sole rights in Great Britain. Hat had to be removed from the head to be used. Extremely rare. No known sales. Would command a very high price, easily over $10,000.

Idento - c1905. Folding camera with side

panels supporting the lensboard, similar to the Shew Xit. Ross Homocentric or Zeiss Protar f6.3/5" lens. Between-the-lens ½-100, T shutter. Leather covered. Made in 5 sizes 2½x3½" to ½-plate. $200-300.

Minex - Single lens reflex cameras similar to the Graflex, made in various sizes. $150-200.

Minex Stereoscopic Reflex Deluxe - A deluxe stereo version of the Minex, with brown leather bellows & focusing hood. With a Ross Xpres f4.5 lens, one of these sold at auction in mid-1982 for $8600.

Minex Tropical - 2½x3½, 3¼x4¼, 4x5, 4¾x6½" sizes. Teakwood SLR with brass binding. With film holders, lens, and crocodile leather case. $2000-3000.

Vesta - c1930's. Folding bed and strut cameras. Ross Xpres f4.5/4¾" lens. Two versions:
Focal Plane Vesta - For 9x12cm plates. $200-300.
Rollfilm Vesta - Compound 1-200,T,B shutter. Takes 6.5x9cm plates and 6x9cm on 120 rollfilm. $200-300.

Videx - c1909. SLR, usually found in the 3¼x4¼" size. $125-175. The 4¼x6½" size is less common. $175-225.

Yale No. 1, No. 2 - c1895, Detective magazine camera for 12 plates 3¼x4¼". Adams Patent Shutter ½-100. Focus by internal bellows. No. 1 has Rapid Rectilinear f8 lens, No. 2 has Cooke f6.5/5" lens. $150-200.

Yale Stereo Detective No. 5 - Leather covered body. Zeiss 7½" lenses. Internal bellows with rack focusing. Leather plate changing bag. $450-550.

ADAMS & WESTLAKE CO. (Chicago)

Adlake Cameras - c1897. Manual plate changing box cameras for 12 plates in 3¼x4¼" & 4x5" sizes. $40-60.

ADINA - Folding 6x9cm rollfilm camera. f6.3/105mm Rodenstock Trinar lens in Adina or Compur shutter. $15-20.

ADOX KAMERAWERK (Wiesbaden)
Adox, Adox II, Adox III - c1936-1950. 35mm cameras with extensible front. Made by Wirgin, styled like the Wirgin Edinex. $25-35.

Adox 66 - Bakelite box camera for 6x6cm on 120. $8-12.

Adox 300 - The first German 35mm camera with interchangeable magazine backs. Large film advance & shutter cocking lever concentric with lens. BIM. Synchro-Compur to 500. Steinheil Cassar or Schneider Xenar f2.8/45mm lens. Originally supplied with 3 magazines in 1957. $100-125.

Adrette - 35mm camera with extensible front. Identical to the Wirgin Edinex. Front focus Steinheil Cassar f3.5/50mm,

Schneider Radionar f2.9/50mm, or Xenon f2/50mm lens in Prontor, Prontor II, or Compur shutter. $30-45.

Adrette II - Same as the Adrette, but with helical focus. Prontor II, Compur, or Compur Rapid shutter. $40-60.

Blitz - Bakelite box camera for 6x6cm on 120 film. f6.3/75mm lens. Styled like the Adox 66. $8-12.

Golf - 6x6cm folding camera. Adoxar or Cassar f6.3 lens. Vario sync shutter. Rangefinder model: $20-25. Simple model without rangefinder: $10-20.

Juka - c1950. A postwar version of the Junka-Werke "Junka" camera for 3x4cm on special rollfilm. Achromat f8/45mm lens. Single speed shutter. $50-75.

Polomat - Rigid body 35mm camera with BIM. f2.8 lens. Pronto LK shutter 15-250. $25-30.

Sport - Folding dual-format rollfilm cameras for 6x9 or 4.5x6cm on 120 film. Steinheil Cassar f6.3 or Radionar f4.5. Vario shutter. Optical or folding viewfinder models. Common. $15-20.

AFIOM (Italy)
Kristall - c1955. Leica copy. Elionar f3.5/5cm lens. $125-165.

Wega II, IIa - Leica copies which accept Leica screw-mount lenses. CRF. Synchronized FP shutter to 1000. Trixar f3.5/50mm. $125-165.

AGFA KAMERAWERKE (Munich)
Originally established in 1867. "Aktien Gesellschaft fuer Analin-Fabrikation" was formed in 1873. AGFA is an abbreviation from the original name. Rietzschel merged with Agfa in 1925, at which time the Rietzschel name was no longer used on cameras and the first Agfa cameras were produced. Agfa's USA operations joined forces with Ansco in 1928 to form Agfa-Ansco, which eventually became GAF. Agfa also continued operations in Germany both in the production of cameras and films. After the war, Agfa abandoned its Wolfen factories, and in 1952 founded "Agfa AG fuer Photofabrikation" in Leverkusen and "Agfa Kamerawerk AG" in Munich. These merged in 1957 to become Agfa AG, which soon acquired Perutz Photowerke, Leonar-Werke, Mimosa, and others before merging with Gevaert of Belgium in 1964.

Agfaflex - c1959. SLR cameras. Models I-IV. Prontor 1-300. Apotar or Solinar f2.8 lens. $50-65. Model V with f2 lens: $60-85.

Ambiflex - c1959. SLR. Coupled meter. Interchangeable prism & WL finders. f2.8/50mm Color Solinar in Prontor Reflex 1-300. $60-90.

Ambi-Silette - 35mm. 2.8/50 Solinar in Synchro-Compur to 500. Interchangeable lenses available include f4/35mm Ambion, f4/90mm, and 135mm. With normal lens: $35-45. Extra lenses: $30-50.

Automatic 66 - c1956. Horizontally styled folding camera for 6x6cm on 120. CRF. Fully automatic metering with manual override. Color Solinar f3.5/75mm in Prontor-SL shutter. Helical focusing. $200-325.

Clack, Click - c1954-59. Box cameras. $4-7.

Billy (O,I,II,III,Clack,Record,etc.) - A series of folding rollfilm cameras produced from 1929-1960, usually encountered in 6x9cm size with f4.5 Apotar or Solinar or f6.3 Agnar or Igestar. Shutters include Automat and Prontor. A few of the better models: $16-22. Most models: $8-12.

Billy I Luxus - c1930's. Igestar f8.8/100 in Billy 25-100 shutter. $60-90.

Billy Compur - Like the Billy, but with Compur shutter and f4.5 or f3.9 Solinar or f4.5 Apotar. $20-35.

Billy Optima - c1930's. 7.5x10.5cm. Solinar f4.5/120mm in Compur 1-250. $50-75.

Box cameras - misc. sizes, styles. $5-10.

Cadet B-2 - c1939. Made by Agfa-Ansco in Binghamton, New York. After 1943, sold under the Ansco Cadet name. Metal box camera. $4-8.

Captain - 6x9cm art-deco folding camera. Captain lens in Agfa T,I shutter. $6-10.

Chief - c1940. Metal eye-level box camera. Similar to the Pioneer, but with zone focus and built-in finder. $4-8.

Clipper PD-16 - c1938. Metal bodied camera with extensible rectangular front section. Takes 16 exp. on 616 film. Single speed shutter & meniscus lens. Made in U.S.A. $1-5.

Clipper Special - Like the Clipper, but with f6.3 Anastigmat and 25-100 shutter. Optical finder. $4-7.

Flash Champion - Metal-bodied camera

with rectangular extensible front. Similar to the Clipper cameras. $1-5.

Flexilette - c1960. 35mm TLR. Color Apotar f2.8/45mm in Prontor 1-500. Unusual design has viewing lens above taking lens in a round front panel. $50-100.

Folding Rollfilm cameras - Common models for 116 and 120 films. $8-12.

Iso Rapid I, IF, IC - Compact cameras resembling the 126 cartridge type, but for Rapid 35mm cassettes. I has hot shoe. IF has AG-1 flash. IC has flashcube socket. $1-5.

Isoflash Rapid - Similar to the Iso Rapid IF. Isoflash Rapid C uses flashcubes. $1-5.

Isola - c1950's. 2¼x2¼". Agnar f6.3/75mm in Single shutter. $7-11.

Isolar - c1927-35. 9x12cm folding plate camera. Solinear f4.5/135mm. Dial Compur to 200. DEB. GGB. Metal body. $35-50.

Isolette I & II - Folding rollfilm cameras

for 6x6cm & 4.5x6cm on 120 film. Original model 1939-1949 with Igestar f6.3 in Vario. Model I c1952-1957 with f4.5 Agnar in Vario or Pronto. Model II c1948-1950 has f4.5 Agnar or Apotar or f3.5 or 4.5 Solinar in Vario, Pronto, Prontor-S, Compur, Synchro-Compur. $12-18.

Isolette III - c1952. Non-coupled rangefinder. f4.5 Apotar or f3.5 Solinar in Pronto, Prontor, SV, SVS, or Synchro-Compur. $20-30.

Isolette L - 1957-1960. 6x6cm or 4.5x6cm on 120 film. Apotar f4.5/85mm in Pronto. BIM. $30-40.

Isolette Super - c1954. Folding camera for 6x6cm on 120 film. Solinar f3.5/75mm. Shutter to 500. MXV. $100-125.

Karat - *A long-lived series of cameras for 24x36mm exp. on 35mm film in Karat-cassettes, the original design which eventually led to the international standard "Rapid Cassette" system. The pre-WWII models, officially named by their lens aperture, all have the same body style with tapered ends and with the viewfinder protruding from the slightly rounded top.*
Karat 6.3 - 1938-1940. Igestar f6.3 in Automat shutter. $35-45.

Karat 3.5 - 1938-1940. Solinar f3.5 in Compur Rapid shutter. $25-32.
Karat 4.5 - 1939-1950. Oppar f4.5 in Pronto shutter. $20-25.
Karat - *Postwar models have a new body style with beveled ends and viewfinder incorporated with rangefinder in the top housing.*
Karat 12 - 1948-1950. Solinar f3.5 or Xenar f2.8 lens in Compur-Rapid shutter (1948). Apotar f3.5 in Prontor-S (1948-1950). $20-30.
Karat 36 - (also called Karomat 36) 1949-1952. Xenar f2.8/Compur Rapid or Xenon f2/Synchro-Compur (1949). Xenon or Heligon f2/Synchro-Compur (1950). Solinar or Soligon f2.8/Synchro-Compur (1952). $35-45.
Karat IV - 1950-1956. Identifiable by the equally sized and spaced finder windows on the front. Solinar f2.8 (1950). Solagon f2 or Apotar f3.5 (1955-1956). Prontor SV or SVS. $30-50.

Karomat - Also called Karat 36. f2.8 Xenar or f2 Xenon. $30-40.

Major - folding bed camera for 6x9cm exp. on 120 film. $10-15.

Memo (full frame) - c1939. Horizontally styled folding bed camera for 24x36mm exposures on 35mm Agfa Rapid cassettes. Rapid advance lever on back. Made in U.S.A. Agfa Memar f3.5, 4.5, or 5.6 lens. $25-40.

Memo (half-frame) - Similar to the above, this single-frame (18x24mm) model was added in 1940. $35-50.

Motor-Kamera - c1951. Unusual 35mm camera for remote control use. Agfa Color Telinear f3.4/90mm. Large electric motor built on to front of camera and externally coupled to the advance knob. (A rather clumsy arrangement when compared with modern mass-marketed autowinders.) $300-400.

Nitor - 1927-1930. 6x9cm on plates, pack, or rollfilm. Helostar f6.3/Pronto or Linear f4.5/Compur to 250. $25-40.

Optima - A series of 35mm cameras. Original model 1959-1963 has left-hand shutter release, Color Apotar f3.9 in Compur. Claimed to be the first fully automatic camera in the world. Model I 1960-1964 has Color Agnar f2.8/45mm in Prontorlux. Right-hand release. Mod. IA c1962 has an advance lever on top and removable back. Model II 1960-1964. IIS 1961-1966 is like the II but with CRF. Model III (1960) has meter and IIIS (1960) includes meter & CRF. Prices range from $15-25 for the simpler models to $35 for a nice IIIS.

Optima Reflex - c1963-1966. 35mm TLR with eye-level pentaprism, meter, matched Color Apotar f2.8/45mm lenses. An unusual design, and not commonly found. $75-125. *(illustrated top of next column)*

Paramat - c1960. Like the Parat but with meter. $20-35.

Optima Reflex

Parat, Parat I - c1960. Half-frame 35mm. Color Apotar f2.8/30mm. $30-45.
PD-16 - This was Agfa's number for the same size film as Kodak 116. Several of the Agfa cameras use this number in their name, but they are listed by their key word (Clipper, Plenax, etc.)

Pioneer - c1940. Metal & plastic eye-level box camera with tapered ends in both PD-16 and PB-20 sizes. Made in the USA by Agfa-Ansco. After 1943, sold as "Ansco" Pioneer. Very common. $2-5.

Plate cameras - 6x9cm with f4.5/105 and 9x12cm with f4.5/135mm Double Anastigmat or Solinar lenses. Compur shutters. $20-40.

Plenax - c1935-. Folding rollfilm cameras made in U.S.A. Models PD-16 & PB-20. Antar, Tripar, or Hypar lens. $8-12.

Preis-Box - c1932. Box camera which originally sold for 4 marks. $7-12.

Schul-Praemie Box - Originally given out as a school premium in Germany, which accounts for the inscribed title. A blue metal and plastic box for 6x9cm rollfilm. $20-30.

Selecta-Flex - c1964. Pentaprism 35mm SLR. Interchangeable f2.8 Solinar or f2 Solagon. $45-60.

Selecta-M - c1965. Fully automatic motor camera for 24x36mm. Shutter regulated by BIM. Solinar f2.8/45mm in Compur 30-500. $75-125.

Shurflash, Shurshot - Made in USA by Agfa-Ansco. Common box cameras. $4-8.

Silette (I), II, L, LK, SL, Super - A series of 35mm cameras introduced in 1956 and ranging from the simple viewfinder model to the metered rangefinder models. Common. $12-20.

Solinette, Solinette II - c1952. Folding 35mm cameras. Solinar or Apotar f3.5/50 in Prontor-SVS or Synchro-Compur. $20-30.

--Super Solinette - c1953-1957. Similar but with CRF. $30-45.

Speedex 6x9cm - c1936. Folding rollfilm camera. f4.5 in Compur. $12-18.
(illustrated top of next column)

Agfa Speedex, 6x9cm

Speedex B2 6x6cm - c1940. Horizontally styled rollfilm camera made in USA. f4.5 Anastigmat in ½-250 shutter. $12-18.

Speedex Jr. - Similar to the Speedex B2, but with fixed-focus lens in T&I shutter. $5-10.

Speedex 0 - c1938. Vest pocket (127 film) size folding bed camera of vertical style. Solinar f3.9 lens in Compur. Leather covered with chrome and enamel side panels. $40-60.

Standard - c1927-1931. *A series of folding cameras in various models for rollfilm or plates.*

Rollfilm models - Made in both 6x9cm and 6.5x11cm sizes. Various lenses and shutters. $15-25.

Plate models - For 6.5x9cm or 9x12cm plates. Various f4.5 or f6.3 lenses in Automat or Compur shutter. $20-35.

Deluxe plate models - Brown leather covering and brown bellows. Original price was only about 10% higher than standard plate model. Current collectors pay $50-80.

Superior - 1930-32. A deluxe folding camera for 8x14cm "postcard size" photos. Reddish-brown leather, brown bellows. Trilinear f6.3 or Solinear f4.5 in Compur. $175-200.

Synchro-Box - c1952. Metal box camera for 6x9cm on 120 film. Plastic covering and art-deco front. $1-5.

Trolix - c1937. Bakelite box, 2¼x3¼". $20-30. (illustrated top of next column)

Ventura 66 - c1950. Among the first postwar products of Agfa Camerawerk. Horizontal style folding camera for 6x6cm

Agfa Trolix

on 120. Agnar f4.5 in synchronized Vario to 200. $12-18.

Ventura Deluxe - similar to the regular 66, but with Apotar f4.5, Prontor-S or Compur and double exposure prevention. $12-18.

Ventura 69 - c1950. Vertically styled folding rollfilm cameras for 6x9cm on 120 film. $12-18.

View cameras - Various models in 3¼x4¼ to 5x7 inch sizes. As collectible cameras, these do not create as much interest as they do for studio use. Collector value $40-75 with shutter and lens. If the camera has full movements, it is a usable item for commercial photographers and will fetch $100-250 without lens or shutter.

Viking - c1940. Folding cameras for 120 or 116 rollfilms. f6.3 or 7.7 lens. $8-12.

AGILUX LTD. (Croydon, England)
A subsidiary of Aeronautical & General Instruments, Ltd., from which the AGI names originate.
Agiflex - 6x6cm SLR originally made for the Royal Navy during WWII. Focal plane shutter 25-500. Styled similar to the Reflex Korelle. $50-75.

Agifold (rangefinder model) - c1955. Folding camera with built-in uncoupled rangefinder and extinction meter. Agilux anastigmat f4.5/75mm. $30-50.

AIGLON - c1934. French subminiature. All metal, nickel-plated body with removable single-speed shutter attached to the lens cone. Special rollfilm records 8 exposures with meniscus lens. $150-200.

AIR KING PRODUCTS (Brooklyn, NY)
Air King Camera Radio - The perfect marriage of a red reptile-skin covered radio and concealed novelty camera. $100-150.

AIRES CAMERA IND. CO. LTD. (Tokyo)

Aires 35-III - c1957-1958. 35mm RF. f1.9/45mm in Seikosha MX. Single stroke lever advance. Bright frame finder. $20-30.

Aires 35-IIIC - c1958-59. Improved version of III & IIIL, incorporating coupled LVS system, self-timer, and automatic parallax correction. Strongly resembles the Leica M3 from a distance. It was designed to accept Aires or Leica M3 cassettes. $30-45.

Aires 35-IIIL - c1957-1959. Similar to III, but with LVS shutter 1-500. Rewind knob has crank. $30-40.

Aires 35-V - c1959-1962. BIM, bayonet mount interchangeable lenses, fast f1.5 normal lens. Also available were f3.5/100mm and f3.2/35mm. With three lenses $75-100. With normal lens only $35-55.

Airesflex - c1953-55. 6x6cm TLR. Coral f3.5/75mm in Seikosha-Rapid to 500. $35-50.

Penta 35 - c1960. Low-priced 35mm SLR. Non-interchangeable Q Coral f2.8/50mm lens accepts supplementary wide angle & telephoto lenses. Seikosha SLV 1-500. $40-60.
Penta 35 LM - c1961. Similar to Penta 35, but with f2 lens and BIM. $40-60.

Viscount - c1962. Low-price 35mm RF camera. Even with its fast f1.9 lens, it sold new for under $40. $20-35.

AIVAS (A. Aivas, Paris)
Beginner's Camera - c1910. ¼-plate tailboard camera. Mahogany body, blue cloth bellows. Brass barrel lens, gravity guillotine shutter. $125-150.

ALFAX MODEL I - Japanese camera for 4x4cm on 127 film. Recta Anastigmat f3.5/60mm in New Alfa shutter. $25-40.

ALIBERT (Charles Alibert, Paris)

Kauffer Photo-Sac a Main - c1895. Folding plate camera disguised as a handbag. Several models were made. One is styled like a square-cornered case which hinges from the middle and a strut-upported front extends. A similar model uses the strut-supported front but in a smartly styled handbag with a split front door hinged at the top and bottom. The other variation has the handbag shape but uses the bottom door as a bed to support the lens standard. Designed by Bernard Kauffer of Paris. Estimated: $2000-3000.

ALLIED Carlton Reflex - Bakelite 6x6 TLR. $5-10.

ALSAPHOT (France)
Dauphin, Dauphin II - Pseudo-TLR, 2¼x2¼". $15-25.

ALTHEIMER & BAER INC.
Photo-Craft - Black bakelite minicam, 3x4cm on 127 rollfilm. $4-8.

ALTISSA KAMERAWERK - B.Altmann (Dresden). *Also associated with E. Hofert of Dresden, eventually becoming Eho-Altissa. See Eho-Altissa.*

AMCO - Japanese paper "Yen" box camera for single exposures on sheetfilm in paper holders. The Amco is larger than most cameras of this type, taking 4.5x6.5cm exposures. It is covered in brown & tan rather than the normal black. An unusual item for a collection of novelty cameras. $25-35.

AMEREX - Early Japanese 16mm subminiature of the Hit type. One of very few marked "Made in Occupied Japan". $25-30.

AMERICAN ADVERTISING & RESEARCH CORP. (Chicago)
Cub - c1940. Small plastic camera for 28x40mm exposures on 828 film. All plastic construction, similar to the Scenex. Simple lens & shutter. Toothpaste premium. (Original cost was 15 cents and a

American Advertising Cub

Pepsodent box.)Common but cute. $10-15.

AMERICAN CAMERA CO. (London)
Demon Detective Camera - Small metal camera for single round exposures on dry plates. Originally introduced in 1889 for 2¼ inch diameter photos on 2¼x2¼ inch plates (later called No. 1 size). A larger model (No. 2 Size) for 3¾ inch plates was introduced in 1890. Funnel-shaped front with flat, rectangular back. The striking design of the back stamping (by W. Phillips of Birmingham) makes the back view more interesting than the front view of these cameras. $800-1200.

AMERICAN CAMERA MFG. CO. (Northboro, Mass. USA) *This company was founded in 1895 by Thomas Blair, who had previously founded the Blair Tourograph & Dry Plate Co. in 1881 (later changed to Blair Camera Co.). He still held partial interest in the Blair Camera Co. until 1898, but internal difficulties had prompted him to leave the Blair organization about 1892. The American Camera Mfg. Co. was in business for only a short time, since Thomas Blair sold out to George Eastman about 1897. The company was moved to Rochester about 1899 and continued to operate under the American Camera Mfg. Co. name at least through 1904, even though owned by Kodak. By 1908, the catalogs showed it as the American Camera Division of Eastman Kodak Co. If all of this seems confusing, remember also not to confuse this with the American Optical Co., which is a completely different company.*

Buckeye Cameras:
No. 2 Buckeye - c1899-1908? Box camera for 4x5" exposures. Similar to the Blair Hawk-eye box cameras. $40-60.

No. 3 Buckeye - c1895. Folding rollfilm camera. Maroon leather bellows. f8 lens. $40-60.

No. 8 Folding Buckeye - 4x5" rollfilm camera. Rollholder lifts up to focus on ground glass. $250-350.

Buckeye Special - Like the No. 2 Buckeye, but for rollfilm or glass plates. $75-100.

No. 1 Tourist Buckeye - c1895. Folding rollfilm cameras in sizes for 3½x3½" or 3¼x4½" exposures. Maroon bellows, wooden lens standard. $125-150.

Long Focus Poco - 4x5". Folding camera

with maroon leather bellows. $75-100.

AMERICAN FAR EAST TRADING CO.

Santa Claus Camera - c1980. Novelty camera for 126 film. Santa Claus face forms the front of the camera. $15-20.

AMERICAN MINUTE PHOTO CO. (Chicago)
American Sleeve Machine - A street camera for tintypes, similar to the more common models by the Chicago Ferrotype Co. $75-125.

AMERICAN OPTICAL CO. (New York)
Acquired the John Stock Co. (including the C.C. Harrison Co.) in 1866 and was then bought out by Scovill Mfg. Co. in 1867.
Flammang's Patent Revolving Back Camera - c1886. Tailboard style view camera, with patent revolving and tilting back. Tapered bellows, rising front. Mahogany body with brass fittings. Usually found in 5x7" and 6½x8½" sizes. $150-175.

Henry Clay Camera - c1892. 5x7 inch folding plate camera. A well-made hand camera with many desirable features, such as double shift and swing front, fine focusing, etc. Somewhat uncommon and quite distinctive. Originally with Wale shutter. $350-450.

Plate camera 5x8" - horizontal format. Complete with lens, back, holder. $125-175.

AMERICAN RAND CORP.
Photo Binocular 110 - c1980. A pair of 4x30mm binoculars with a built-in camera with 80mm telephoto lens for 110 cartridge film. $35-45.

AMERICAN RAYLO CORP. (New York)

Raylo Color Camera - c1925. Magazine-loading color separation camera for 4.5x8cm plates. Automatic clockwork mechanism apportions the time through each color filter in the correct ratio to produce three negatives of even scale. Rare. $1500-2000.

AMERICAN SAFETY RAZOR CORP. (NY)
ASR Fotodisc - c1950. A small cast metal

camera with eye-level finder. A film disc in a special holder fastens by bayonet mount to the back of the camera. Takes 8 exposures 22x24mm on a film disc. $400-500.

AMICA INTERNATIONAL (Japan)

Eyelux - c1966. 35mm RF. f1.8/45mm lens in Citizen MVE shutter. $15-25.

ANNY - "Diana" type rollfilm camera. $1-5.

ANSCO (Binghamton NY USA) *Formed by the merger of the E.& H.T. Anthony Co. and Scovill & Adams in 1902. The name was shortened to Ansco in 1907. A merger with the American interests in the German firm of Agfa in 1928 formed Agfa-Ansco. In 1939, Agfa-Ansco changed its name to General Aniline & Film Corporation, but still used the Agfa-Ansco name in advertising until 1943 when the Agfa name was dropped. The Ansco Division of General Aniline kept its name as the main banner of the company until the company name was officially shortened to GAF in 1967. More recently, GAF withdrew from the consumer photographic market but the Ansco name continues as part of Haking International. See also Agfa, Anthony, Scovill.*
Admiral - Black plastic twin lens box camera, 2¼x2¼". $1-5.

Anscoflex, Anscoflex II - c1954. All metal

6x6cm reflex-style camera. Gray & silver color. Front door slides up and opens finder hood. Model II has closeup lens and yellow filter built in and controlled by knobs on the front. $10-15. Slightly higher in Europe.

Anscomark M - c1960-1963. 35mm RF camera. Interchangeable bayonet mount Xyton f1.9/50mm or f2.8/50 Xytar lens. Viewfinder has frames for 100mm & 35mm lenses. Coupled meter. With 3 lenses: $60-85. With normal lens only: $25-35.

Anscoset - c1960. 35mm RF. BIM with match-needle operation, f2.8/45mm Rokkor. Made by Minolta for Ansco. $25-30.

Automatic - c1925. Folding rollfilm camera

for 6 exp. 2½x4¼ inches in six seconds. Required a new film "No. 6A Automatic" since the regular 6A film only allowed 5 exposures. Spring-wound automatic film advance. Designed and patented in 1915 by Carl Bornmann, who had also designed the 1888 Antique Oak Detective Camera for Scovill & Adams and was still designing for the company. f6.3 Anastigmat lens. Orig. price about $75. $100-150.

Automatic Reflex - High quality TLR introduced in 1947 at the healthy list price of $262.50. This original model did not cock the shutter with the film advance, and was lacking flash sync. The improved model (sometimes called Model II, although not marked as such) has a sync post in the lower corner of the front plate, and features automatic shutter cocking. By 1950, the list price had dropped to $165. Ansco Anastigmat f3.5/83mm lens. f3.2/83mm viewing lens. Shutter to 400. Ground glass focusing screen and optical eye-level finder. $75-125.

Autoset - c1961. 35mm RF camera. Similar to the Anscoset, but fully automatic shutter speed control rather than match-needle. $20-30.

Box cameras - Colors other than black: $8-12. Black models: $3-6.

Buster Brown Box Cameras:
No. 0 Buster Brown - 4x6.5cm on 127 $5-10.
No. 2 Buster Brown - 6x9cm on 120 (4A) film. $5-10.
No. 2A Buster Brown - 2½x4¼" on 118 film. $5-10.
No. 2C Buster Brown - 2⅞x4⅞". $5-10.
No. 3 Buster Brown - 3¼x4¼. $5-10.
Buster Brown Special, Nos. O, 2, 2A - Box cameras with red covering and lacquered brass trim. $10-20.

Folding Buster Brown Cameras:
No. 1 Folding Buster Brown -$10-15.
No. 2A Folding Buster Brown - $10-15.
No. 3 Folding Buster Brown - $10-15.
No. 3A Folding Buster Brown - Postcard size. Deltax or Actus shutter. $12-18.
Buster Brown Junior - Folding camera for 116 roll. $8-12.

Cadet cameras:
Cadet B2 and D-6 box cameras - c1947. Basic rectangular box cameras. $1-5.
Cadet (I) - c1959. Black plastic camera with metal faceplate. $1-5.
Cadet Flash - c1960. Similar to the Cadet (I) but with large built-in flash on top. $1-5.
Cadet II, Cadet III - c1965. Horizontally styled gray plastic cameras with aluminum faceplate for 127 film. Originally came in hard plastic carrying case. $1-5.
Cadet Reflex - c1960. Reflex brilliant finder version of the Cadet. 4x4cm on 127. $4-8.

Century of Progress - Cardboard box camera with art-deco style World's Fair design on metal front. Made for the 1933 World's Fair at Chicago. $50-75.

Clipper, Color Clipper, Flash Clipper, Clipper Special - A series of metal

cameras with rectangular extensible front. $3-7.

Commander - Mid-1950's folding rollfilm camera. Agnar f6.3 zone focusing lens in Vario sync shutter. $15-20.

Craftsman - c1950. A construction kit to build your own 6x9cm box camera. The camera kit was pre-tested by Ansco for several months before the decision was made to market it. Over 100 grammar school children participated in the tests. Current value of an original unused kit with assembly instructions $40-50. Assembled Craftsman $4-8.

Dollar Box Camera - c1910-1928. A small 4x3½x2½" box camera for 127 film. Available in black or green. No strap. Some are identified "Ansco Dollar Camera" on the front. The same camera in red and with a strap was sold as the Kiddie Camera c1926-29. $10-15.

Folding Ansco cameras: *(There is a certain amount of confusion over the correct name for some of these cameras, since Ansco catalogs called them by different names even within the same catalog. For example, the No. 4 Folding*

Pocket Ansco is the same as the No. 4 Ansco Model B, or the No. 4 Folding Ansco.)

No. 1 Folding Ansco - c1920's. Folding bed camera for 6x9cm. Anastigmat f7.5 in Ilex General shutter 1/5-100. $10-15.
No. 1 Special Folding Ansco - $10-15.
No. 1A Folding Ansco - 116 film. Anastigmat f7.5 in Ilex. $10-15.
No. 3 Folding Ansco - 118 film. $12-18.

No. 3A Folding Ansco - common postcard size. Lenses: Wollensak, RR, Ansco Anast. Shutters: Ilex, Deltax, Bionic, Speedex. $10-20.
No. 4 Folding Ansco - c1905. Models C & D. 3¼x4¼ on 118 film. Horizontal format. Mahogany drop bed. Wollensak lens, Cyko Auto shutter. Nickel trim. $15-25.
No. 5 Folding Ansco - c1905. Wollensak lens. Cyko Automatic shutter. Black bellows. $15-25.

No. 6 Folding Ansco - c1907. Models C & D. 3¼x4¼. Wollensak f4 lens. Red leather bellows. For roll or cut film. $20-30.
No. 7 Folding Ansco - (Anthony & Scovill

Co.) Postcard sized rollfilm camera. Last patent date 1894. Red bellows, brass barrel Wollensak lens. $20-30.
No. 9 Ansco, Model B - Horizontal style folding camera for 3¼x5½ on rollfilm. Cherry wood body, leather covered. Red bellows. Cyko shutter in brass housing. (Later models had black bellows & nickeled shutter.) $20-35.
No. 10 Ansco - pat. Jan. 1907. Folding camera for 3½x5 on 122 film. (Model A has removable ground glass back. Ansco Automatic shutter.) $20-30.

Goodwin cameras *Named in honor of the Rev. Hannibal Goodwin. Dr. Goodwin invented the flexible transparent rollfilm which has become the standard of the photographic industry. His 1887 patent application took over 11 years to process, by which time his idea was already in widespread use.*
No. 1 Goodwin Jr. - c1925. Folding camera. Strut-supported front pulls straight out. $15-25.
No. 1A Folding Goodwin - Folding bed rollfilm camera for 116 film. "Goodwin Film & Camera Co." on the shutter face. $10-20.
No. 2, 2A, 3 Goodwin - Box cameras. $5-9.

Junior - *A series of folding rollfilm cameras, beginning with the Model A about 1910. At first horizontally styled, the later models switched to the vertical styling.*
Ansco Junior (Model A & Model B) - c1910. Horizontal style folding camera. 2½x4¼" exposures. RR lens. $15-25.
No. 1 Ansco Junior - c1917. 2¼x3¼" on 120 rollfilm. Vertical style. Originally with Achromatic, Rectilinear, or Modico Anastigmat lens in Actus or Bionic shutter. Later versions had other options. $10-15.
No. 1A Ansco Junior - c1917. Like the No. 1, but 2½x4¼ on 116 film. $10-15.
No. 2C Ansco Junior - 2⅞ x 4⅞" on 130 film, otherwise like the No. 1 above. $15-25.
No. 3 Ansco Junior - 3¼x4¼ on 118 film. Introduced somewhat later than the other sizes, in the early 1920's. $10-18.
No. 3A Ansco Junior - 3¼x5½" on 122 film, otherwise like the No. 1 above. $15-25.

Karomat - c1951-56. 35mm strut-folding

rangefinder camera, identical to the Agfa Karat 36. Early models have hinged knob on advance lever, and a depth of field calculator on top. Beginning about 1953, the advance lever has a fixed knob, and there is no longer a depth calculator. Schneider Xenon f2.8 or f2.0 in Synchro-Compur. $30-40.

Kiddie Camera - c1926-29. Listed in the catalogs along with the Dollar Camera, with shared description and photo. It is the same cardboard box camera, but with red covering and a strap. $10-15.

Lancer - c1959. Streamlined cast metal camera made for Ansco by Bilora. Identical in style to the Bilora Bella 44. Simple f8 lens in 2-speed shutter. Takes 12 exposures 4x4cm on 127 film. $10-15.
Lancer LG - c1962. Identical, but with uncoupled meter attached to the front. $15-25.

Memar - c1954-1958. Basic 35mm camera. Apotar f3.5/45 in Pronto. $12-18.

Super Memar - Similar to the Memar, but with CRF and f3.5 lens. $15-25.

Super Memar LVS - CRF, Synchro-Compur LVS shutter, and f2 Solagon lens. $25-35.

Memo cameras - The Memo cameras have presented a problem to some collectors who advertise one for sale and do not indicate which model they are selling. Ansco sold several different cameras which were simply called "Memo" with no further designation. In recent years, serious collectors and dealers have tried to identify them further by using the year of introduction along with the name.

Memo (1927 type) - intro. 1927. Half-frame 35mm camera. Wooden vertical box body with leather covering. Tubular optical finder on top. Makes 50 exposures 18x23mm on 35mm film in special cassettes which were originally made of wood. Wollensak Cine-Velostigmat f6.3/ 40mm or Ilex Cinemat lens. Sliding button on back for film advance, automatic exposure counter. Some models focus, others are fixed focus. A shutter release guard was added to later models. Although these sometimes sell for slightly more in Europe, they are fairly common in the U.S.A. $45-60.

Memo (Boy Scout model) - The "Official Boy Scout Memo Camera" has a wooden body painted olive-drab color and has a special nameplate with the official insignia, and comes in a matching olive-drab case. Much less common than the normal models. Camera only: $125-150. With case: $150-200.

Memo (Wood finished) - The earliest variation of the 1927 type Memo, this had varnished wood and brass trim rather than leather covering. Less common than the others of the series. (Original ads in December 1926 and January 1927 illustrate this wood model.) $200-250.

Memo (1940 type) - see AGFA Memo.

Memo Automatic - c1963. Single frame (18x24mm) camera for standard 35mm cartridges. Features spring-motor film advance. Made by Ricoh for Ansco, and identical to the Ricoh Auto Half. Also continued as the Memo II under the Ansco and GAF labels. $25-35.

Memo II - see Memo Automatic, above.

Memory Kit - A specially packaged outfit including a folding camera in a fitted polished wood box with 4 rolls of film. A metal plate on the box is suitable for engraving. Came with No. 1 Ansco Junior, No. 1 Folding Ansco, or No. 1 Readyset Royal. Complete with camera and original boxes of film: $50-75. Camera and presentation box only: $40-60.

Panda - Small black plastic camera with white trim for 6x6cm exposures. Ansco's answer to Kodak's Baby Brownie cameras. $2-6.

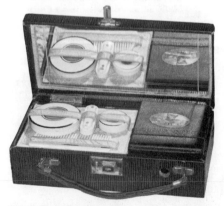

Photo Vanity - A small Ansco box camera

concealed in one end of a case. May be operated from the exterior with the case closed. The case also contains art-deco designed lipstick, powder, rouge & comb, and a mirror in the lid. Apparently the vanity case was made by Q.L.G. Co. and fitted with an Ansco camera, so only the camera itself is actually on Ansco product. $650-1000.

Pioneer - c1947-1953. Plastic eye-level cameras in PB-20 and PD-16 sizes. Formerly called Agfa Pioneer. Common. $1-5.

Readyflash - A low-priced plastic eye-level camera for 6x9cm on 620 film. Sold new in 1953 for $14 with a flash, 6 bulbs, gadget bag & film. $2-6.

Readyset (No.1, 1A, Eagle, Special, etc.) - folding cameras. $10-15.

Readyset Royal, Nos. 1, 1A - Folding cameras with special leather coverings, usually brown, including pigskin & ostrich skin. These are not rare, and although they are seen advertised for sale at higher prices, they are generally available for $15-20. Somewhat higher in Europe.

Readyset Traveler - Folding cameras in #1 & 1A sizes (for 120 & 116 film). These are covered in canvas with colored stripes and have a matching canvas case. $15-20.

Rediflex - c1950. Plastic twin lens box camera, 6x6cm on 620 film. $2-7.

Regent - c1953. Identical to the Agfa Solinette. Horizontally styled folding bed 35mm camera. Apotar f3.5 in Prontor-SV to 300. $15-25.

--Super Regent - intro. 1954. The Ansco equivalent of the Agfa Super Solinette.

CRF. Solinar f3.5 lens in Synchro-Compur shutter. $35-50.

Vest Pocket No. 0

Semi-Automatic Ansco - c1924. Folding rollfilm camera. A lever on the operator's right rear of the drop bed actuates a spring-wound advance system. It differs from the Automatic model which further couples the winding mechanism to the shutter release. Ansco Anastigmat f7.5/30mm in Ilex shutter. $100-150.

Shur-Flash - Basic box camera with flash attachment. $1-5.

Shur-Shot - A basic box camera with vertically striped aluminum front. Perhaps the most common of the Ansco box cameras. $1-5.

Speedex *(See the listing of Speedex cameras under Agfa. Essentially the same cameras were marketed under both the Agfa and Ansco names.)*

Speedex 1A - c1916. Folding camera for 116 film. Anastigmat f6.3 in Ilex Universal shutter. $12-20.

Vest Pocket Ansco: *(While we tend to think that all vest pocket cameras are for 4x6.5cm exposures on 127 film, Ansco called its No. 1 and No. 2 models "Vest Pocket" even though they were larger cameras.)*

Vest Pocket No. O - The WWI model for 4x6.5cm exposures on 127 film. Ansco Anastigmat f6.3 or Modico Anastigmat f7.5. Strut-supported front pulls straight out. $30-50. *(illustrated top of next column)*

Vest Pocket No. 1 - Folding camera for 6x9cm. Strut-supported front. Patents to 1912. Actus shutter. $15-25.

Vest Pocket No. 2 - Similar to the No. 1 and also for 6x9cm. The unusual feature of this camera is the hinged lens cover. Ansco Anastigmat or f7.5 Modico Anast. Bionic or Gammax shutter. $20-30.

Vest Pocket Model A - Designed with a folding bed, unlike the other vest pocket models above. B&L Zeiss Tessar lens. Ansco shutter. $20-30.

Vest Pocket Junior - Introduced c1920. Folding bed camera for 6x9cm on 4A (120) film. $12-20.

Vest Pocket Readyset - Folding bed style camera for 4x6.5cm exposures on 127 film. Early models are covered with leather. Later models c1930 are enameled in a number of colors. $20-35.

Viking - c1946-56. Folding bed camera for 6x9cm on 120 film. Agnar f6.3 or f4.5 lens in Pronto shutter to 200. $10-15.

Ansco View - View cameras are difficult to price as collectibles because their main value lies in their usability. Any usable view camera with tilts and swings generally exceeds the price collectors would pay. Shutter & lens are even more important in estimating the value, since a good lens has more value than the camera itself. Collectible value, with older type lens & shutter $50-100. Usable value with full movements, not including lens $75-125.

ANTHONY *The oldest American manufacturer of cameras and photographic supplies. Begun by Edward Anthony in 1842 as E.Anthony. Edward's brother Henry joined him in 1852, and in 1862 the firm's name was changed to E. & H.T. Anthony & Co. In 1902, they merged with the Scovill & Adams Co. to form Anthony & Scovill, and five years later the name was shortened to Ansco, a contracted form of the two names. At the same time, they moved from their original location on Broadway to Binghamton, N.Y. (See also Agfa, Ansco, Scovill.)*

Ascot - c1899. Folding plate cameras. *Note: The plate & hand camera division of E.& H.T. Anthony Camera Co., which made the Ascot Cameras, merged with several other companies in 1899 to become the Rochester Optical & Camera Co. Ascot cameras are quite uncommon, since they were made for such a short time.*

Ascot Cycle No. 1 - 4x5" size. Orig. price $8 in 1899. $45-60.

Ascot Folding No. 25 - 4x5" size. $45-60.

Ascot Folding No. 29 - 4x5" size. Original price $15 in 1899. $45-60.

Ascot Folding No. 30 - The big brother of the above cameras, this one takes 5x7" plates. Like the others, it has a side door for loading and storage of plate holders. $60-75.

Box cameras -
- c1903-1906. Leather covered box for 3¼x4¼ on rollfilm. $20-30.
- Focusing model for 4x5" exposures on plates or with rollholder. $30-50.

Buckeye - c1896. Box cameras for 12 exp. on daylight-loading rollfilm sold by Anthony. (Some models equipped for either plates or rollfilm.) Made in 3¼x4¼" & 4x5" sizes. These were probably by American Optical Co. with Anthony acting as a sales agent. These cameras were the competition for the Boston Bullseye and the Eastman Bullet cameras of the day. $30-50.

Champion - c1890. A series of mahogany field cameras, in sizes from 4x5" to 8x10". Folding bed with hook-shaped "patent clamps" to hold it rigid. Rising front, swing back. Originally supplied with cone-shaped brass barrel single achromatic lens, case, holder, and tripod. $150-200.

Clifton - c1901. A series of view cameras with a great variety of movements including double-swing back and front, rising/shifting front, reversible back, front & rear rack focus. Made in 6 sizes from 5x7" to 14x17". $100-200. *(illustrated top of next page)*

Anthony Clifton

Climax Detective - A rather large wooden box "detective" camera from the late 1880's for 4x5" plates. It was called a detective camera because it didn't look like the large tripod-mounted bellows style view cameras which were the order of the day. It could be operated hand-held, and all the shutter controls could be operated without opening the box. A removable rear storage compartment holds five double plateholders. Available in polished wood or leather covered models. At least one dealer asked $2500 for a complete example, but more realistically these fall into the range of $1200-1500.

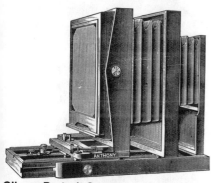

Climax Portrait Camera - c1888. A large studio view camera, usually found in the 11x14" size, but made up to 25x30". Two sets of bellows allow long extension with telescoping bed. With brass barrel lens: $200-300.

Compact Camera - A compact folding field camera based on English designs of the time. The lensboard folds flat against the bed using its center tilt axis. A rotating tripod top is built into the bed. The lens must be removed to fold the camera, and

unfortunately many cameras of this style have become separated from their original lenses. Made in sizes from 5x7" to 8x10". $150-225.

Daylight Enlarging Camera - c1888. A view camera & enlarger for plates to 11½x11½". Rotating back & bellows. Masking back for enlarging. Without lens $150-175.

Fairy Camera - c1888. A lightweight folding view camera. Similar in design to the more common Novelette camera, it featured a revolving back & bellows combination for horizontal or vertical orientation. It also offered rack & pinion focusing while the Novelette employed a sliding back with a fine-focus screw. The Fairy camera has a walnut body with nickel plated fittings. Made in 6 sizes from 4x5" to 8x10". $175-275.

Gem Box - c1877. A series of cameras for making multiple "gem" tintypes by using from 4 to 12 lenses on Anthony's Universal Portrait & Ferrotype Camera. Camera sizes from 3¼x4¼" to 6½x8½". Quite rare. We would recommend consultation with several reputable dealers or advanced collectors, since these would interest only a small group of collectors in the estimated price range of $1000-3000.

Klondike - c1898. Fixed focus 3¼x4¼" plate box camera Adjustable shutter speeds & diaphragm. $50-75.

Lilliput Detective Camera - c1889. A detective camera in the shape of a miniature satchel. Takes 2½x2½" plates in double plateholders. A rare item. $2000-3000.

Normandie - According to the Anthony 1891 catalog, this was the "lightest, most compact, and easily adjustable, reversible back camera in the market." The spring-loaded ground glass back was a relatively new feature at that time. Made in sizes from 4x5 to 14x17". Current value with original lens $125-175.

Novel - A family of view cameras from the 1880's with a rotating back & bellows combination. Although 4x5" & 5x7" sizes were made, by 1888 the Novel cameras were made only in sizes 8x10" and larger. The smaller sizes were replaced by the Novelette. With brass barrel lens: $125-175. *(illustrated top of next column)*
Novelette, Duplex Novelette - c1885. View cameras. Similar in design to the

Anthony Novel

Novel, with the rotating back & bellows unit. The Duplex Novelette carried this idea one step further by allowing the bellows to be easily released from the lensboard. This permitted the user to convert from a 5x8" to an 8x10" back in seconds. Made in all standard sizes from 4x5" to 11x14" in basic, single swing, and double swing models ranging from $12 to $54. Current value with lens $175-250.

Novelette Stereo - Essentially the same camera, but fitted with twin lenses to make stereo views to enchant the pre-TV generation. $350-500.

Anthony PDÇ

PDQ - c1890. A detective box camera for 4x5" plates or films. Original price $20. Currently $600-850. *(illus. on previous page)*

Satchel Detective Camera - Consists of a Climax Detective camera in a special covering designed to look like a satchel with a shoulder strap. The bottom of the satchel is completely open to allow access to the camera's controls. This outfit was called the "Climax Detective Satchel Camera" in the 1893 catalog, although earlier catalogs used the "Satchel Detective Camera" name. This is an extremely rare camera, and obviously the price would be negotiable. One sold at auction a few years ago in the range of $15,000-$20,000.

Schmid's Patent Detective Camera -The

first hand-held instantaneous camera produced in America. Although two years earlier the Englishman, Thomas Bolas, produced and patented two hand-made prototype cameras which were hand-held with viewfinders, these were never commercially produced. Therefore the Schmid was the world's first "commercially produced" hand-held camera. Patented January 2, 1883 by Wm. Schmid of Brooklyn, NY. The earliest model for 3¼x4¼" plates featured a rigid one-piece carrying handle formed from a brass rod. The second model featured a folding handle. Later models had the focusing scale on the right side, and leather covering was optional. The 1891 catalog offers 6 sizes from 3¼x4¼" to 8x10", sizes above 4x5" on special order only. $3000-4000.

Stereo Solograph - c1901. Well-crafted lightweight folding-bed stereo camera for 4½x6½" plates. Mahogany body with morocco leather covering. Polished wood interior. Red Russian leather bellows. Rack & pinion focus. $300-350.

Marlborough View

View cameras - Anthony made a variety of view cameras, most of which can be identified with a certain amount of research. However, it is relatively safe to say that most do not fall into the category of useful equipment today, and therefore can be classified strictly as collectible cameras. While some of the earlier models stir more interest, the later, more common types can generally be found in very good condition, with an original vintage lens, for $125-175.

APeM (Amalgamated Photographic Manufacturers, London)
Rajar No. 6 - Folding camera with 4 cross-swing struts. Body and front plate made of bakelite. Its 1929 introduction makes it one of the earliest bakelite rollfilm cameras. $10-17.

APOLLO - c1951-54. Horizontal folding camera for 16 exposures 4.5x6cm on 120 film. Westar Anastigmat f3.5 lens. $20-30.

APPARATE & KAMERABAU
(Friedrichshafen, Germany)
Akarelle - c1954. Unusually designed 35mm camera with two side-by-side finder windows. Lever wind. Prontor shutter. Various interchangeable lenses f2 to f3.5. $30-50.

Akarette - c1949. Similar to Akarelle. Model 0 is basic black enameled model with Radionar f3.5 lens. Model I has chrome faceplate, self-timer, and film reminder in advance knob. Model II has metal parts chromed, is leather covered, has strap lugs, and one of the following lenses: Radionar f3.5, Xenar f3.5, 2.8, or f2. $30-50.

Akarex (Models I & III) - c1953. 35mm. Rangefinder and lens are interchangeable as a unit. Normal lens: Isco Westar f3.5/45mm. Also available: Schneider Xenon f2/50mm, Tele-Xenar f3.5/90, Xenagon f3.5/35mm. Camera with 3 lenses: $100-125. Camera with normal lens only: $50-75.

Arette - 35mm cameras of the late 1950's.

Model A is basic. Model IA early models c1957 are basic. Later variation c1959 has bright frame. Model IB has meter. Model IC has CRF. Model ID has meter & rangefinder. $15-20.

ARCOFLEX - Japanese "Hit" type novelty camera. Not a reflex camera as the name would imply. An uncommon name. $15-25.

ARGUS, INC. (Ann Arbor, Michigan & Chicago, Illinois.) *Originally founded as International Research Corp., Ann Arbor. The name was changed to "Argus, Inc." in 1944, the new name coming from their popular Argus cameras.*

A - 1936-1941. 35mm cartridge camera with bakelite body. Argus Anastigmat f4.5/50mm in collapsible mount. Early models have fixed pressure plate, sprockets on one side of film. Later models have floating pressure plate and sprockets on both sides. Originally advertised in the following color combinations: Black/chrome, gray/gunmetal, ivory/gold, and brown/gold. In actual practice, the "gunmetal" may be chrome and the "gold" is definitely brass. Gold: $100-150. Gray: $25-35. Black: $10-20.

A (126 cartridge) - To avoid confusion with the original Argus A above: This is a recent 2-tone gray plastic camera for 126 "Instamatic" film. $1-5.

AF - 1937-1938. Same as A, but lens mount focuses to 15". $15-20.

A2 (A2B) - 1939-1950. Similar to the A,

but with extinction meter. Two position focus. Coated lens after July 1946. $12-18.

A2F - 1939-1941. Like A2 with extinction meter but also close focusing to 15". $15-25.

AA (Argoflash) - 1940-1942. Synchronized for flash, otherwise similar to the "A". However, it has a simpler f6.3 lens and T&I shutter. $20-30.

FA - 1950-1951. The last of the "A" series with the original body style. Large flash socket added to the left end of the body. Argus Anastigmat f4.5/50mm. Two position focus. 25-150,B,T. $20-30.

A3 - 1940-1942. A streamlined version of the A series, with fully rounded body ends and a chrome top housing incorporating an extinction meter. Exposure counter on front. Body shutter release. $15-25.

A4 - 1953-1956. Body style completely different from the earlier "A" cameras. Boxy black plastic body with aluminum faceplate. Cintar f3.5/44mm. Sync. $10-17.

K - 1939-1940. One of the more desirable Argus cameras, the Model K is assumed to be a simplified version of the legendary Model D (a spring-motor autowind camera announced in 1939 but apparently never marketed). The Model K retained the same body style, but without the autowind feature. It did include a COUPLED extinction meter for its $19.50 original price. $175-200.

C - 1938-1939. The original brick-shaped camera with a non-coupled rangefinder. With speed range select switch: $40-60. Without speed range select switch, as in C2: 30-45.

CC (Colorcamera) - 1941-1942. Streamlined camera based on the A3 body, but with uncoupled selenium meter instead of extinction type. $35-50.

C2 - 1938-1942. Like the "C", but the rangefinder is coupled. Introduced just after the model C in 1938. An early "brick". $15-25.

C3 - 1939-1966. The most common "brick". A solid, durable, and well-liked camera, like the C2, but with internal synch. $10-15.
C3 Matchmatic - 1958-1966. Basically a face-lifted C3 in two-tone finish. Designed for use with a non-coupled clip-on selenium meter. Must be complete with meter to be valued as a collectible. $10-20.

C4 - 1951-1957. Similar to the Model 21 Markfinder of 1947, but with coupled rangefinder rather than bright frame viewfinder. Cintar f2.8/50mm. $15-25.

C4R - 1958. Like the C4, but with rapid film advance lever. $30-45.

C44 - 1956-1957. Similar to the C4 series, but with interchangeable lens mount. Three-lens outfit: $50-85. With Cintagon f2.8/50mm normal lens: $20-35. **C44R -** 1958-1962. Like the C44 but with rapid advance lever. Three-lens outfit: $60-90. With normal lens: $35-45.

C20 - 1956-1958. Replaced the A4, using the same basic body style but incorporating a rangefinder. Brown plastic body. $15-20.

C33 - 1959-1961. A new design incorporating features of the C3 and C4 series in a boxy body even less appealin than the famous brick. It did have a combined view/rangefinder and interchangeable lenses, and accepted an accessory coupled meter. Shutter cocking is coupled to the film advance lever. Wit█ normal lens: $15-25. Extra lenses $15-2█

21 (Markfinder) - 1947-52. A reincarnati█ of the A3 body style, with interchangeab█ lenses and a bright-frame finder. Cintar f3.5/50mm coated lens. $15-20.

Argoflex - *There are a number of Argoflex twin-lens cameras, none of which cause any great excitement among collectors.*

Argoflex E - 1940-1948. Focusing 3-element f4.5/75mm Varex Anastigma█ Shutter b-200. $15-20.
Argoflex EM - (Also called Argoflex II) 1948. Metal body. $15-20.
Argoflex EF - 1948-1951. Flash model. $15-20.

Argoflex 40 - 1950-1954. Beginning wi█ this model, the lenses are no longer externally coupled, and the viewing lens does not focus. $10-15. (illustrated top █ next page)
Argoflex Seventy-five - 1949-1958. Bla█

Argus 40

plastic body. Fixed focus. $5-10. Slightly higher in Europe.

Argus 75 - 1958-1964. Brown plastic body. Continuation of the Argoflex Seventy-five with minor cosmetic changes. $5-10. Slightly higher in Europe.
Argus Super Seventy-five - 1954-1958. Focusing Lumar f8/65mm coated lens, otherwise like the Argoflex Seventy-five. $5-10.

Autronic I, Autronic 35, Autronic C3 - 1960-1962. Although the camera bore several designations during its short life, it was really just one model. Similar in appearance to the C33, but incorporating a meter for automatic exposure with manual override. Cintar f3.5/50mm. Synch shutter 30-500, B. $15-25. (Often found with inoperative meter for about half as much.)

Camro 28 - Same camera as the Minca 28, but with a different name. $20-30.

Delco 828 - Same camera as the Minca 28, but with a different name. $20-30.

Model M - 1939-40. Streamlined bakelite camera for 828 film. Argus anastigmat f6.3 lens in a collapsible mount. For 8 exp. 24x36mm or 16 exp. 19x24mm. $40-60.

Minca 28 - (also called Model 19) 1947-1948. A post-war version of the Model M camera. Lunar f9.7 lens. (Also sold under the names "Camro 28" and "Delco 828".) $20-30.

V-100 - 1958-59. Rangefinder camera made in Germany for Argus. f2/45mm Cintagon II or f2.8/50mm Cintar II in Synchro-Compur. BIM. $20-30.

ARNOLD, KARL (Marienberg) *Producer of KARMA cameras, an abbreviation of KArl ARnold, MArienberg.*

Karma - 6x6cm rollfilm camera for 120 film.

Trapezoid-shaped body with black leather. Eye-level telescopic finder and uncoupled rangefinder. Meyer Trioplan f3.5/75mm lens, helix focus. Focal plane shutter 25-500, T. $200-250.

Karmaflex, 4x4cm - c1932-1937. SLR for 127 film. Ludwig Vidar f4.5/60mm or Laack Ragolyt f4.5/60mm. Guillotine shutter 25-100. Black leather covered metal body. $300-400.

Karmaflex, 6x6cm - Rare model resembling the Karma camera with a reflex finder perched on top almost as if an afterthought. This is much less common thatn the 4x4cm models. $700-900.

Noviflex - c1935. German SLR, 6x6cm on 120 film. Schneider Radionar f2.9/75mm or Victor f3.5/75mm lens. FP shutter 1/20-1/1000. $150-200.

ARROW - Novelty camera of "Hit" type for 14x14mm on 16mm paper-backed rollfilm. $5-10.

ARROW - Plastic 120 rollfilm camera of the Diana type. $1-5.

ARS OPTICAL CO. LTD.
Acon - c1956-1958. Japanese 35mm RF cameras. f3.5/45mm Vita lens. Models I, II, & IIL. $15-25.

ARSEN - c1938-1942. Similar to the more common Gelto, but for 12 exp. 4x4cm on 127 film rather than 16 exp. Collapsible front. f3.5 or f4.5/50mm lens in 5-250 shutter. $50-70.

ASAHI KOGAKU (Tokyo) *Founded in 1919, the Asahi Optical Co. began making projector lenses in the 1920's and camera lenses in 1931. During the war, Asahi production was strictly military. Their claim to fame is the introduction of the first Japanese 35mm SLR, the Asahiflex I of 1951, followed shortly in 1954 by the world's first instant-return mirror. The Asahiflex line became the Pentax line which remains among the major cameras of today.*

Asahiflex Cameras *The early Asahiflex cameras made from 1951-1957 are considerably different from the later Pentax models. Aside from the fact that they are boldly marked "Asahiflex" on the front, there are several other features which distinguish them. The reflex viewing is waist-level only, and there is a separate eye-level finder. The lens mount is a screw-thread, but not the standard 42mm size.*

Asahiflex I - 1951. FP shutter 25-500. Single X-synch post on front. Takumar f3.5/50mm normal lens. $75-120.

Asahiflex Ia - 1953. Similar to model I, but with F and X synch posts on front. $75-120.

Asahiflex IIB - 1954. The world's first instant-return mirror. Takumar f2.4/58mm or f3.5/50mm. $95-130.

Asahiflex IIA - 1955. Slow speed dial added to front. Also sold in USA by Sears as Tower 22. $60-100.

Pentax (original) - 1957. In a completely new design from the earlier Asahiflex cameras, the Pentax incorporated an eye-level pentaprism, standard 42mm threaded lens mount, rapid advance lever, crank rewind, etc. This is the only Pentax which

retains the slow-speed dial on the front. $200-250.

ASIA AMERICAN INDUSTRIES LTD. (Tokyo)

Orinox Binocular Camera Model AAI-720 - c1978. Camera for 110 film built into binoculars. $60-100.

ASIANA - Plastic 120 novelty camera of the Diana type. $1-5.

ASTORIA OPTICAL (Japan)
Astoria Super-6 IIIB - Super Ikonta B copy. Lausar f3.5/85mm. $150-175.

ASTRA - Japanese novelty subminiature of the Hit type. $10-15.

ASTROPIC - Japanese novelty subminiature of the Hit type. $10-15.

ATLAS-RAND
Mark IV - 126 cartridge camera with electronic flash. Made by Keystone. $4-8.

ATOM-6 - Folding camera for 120 rollfilm. Eye-level and waist-level finders. Japan. $40-50.

ATOM-SIX-II - Similar, but dual-format for 6x6cm or 4.5x6cm on 120. Separate finder for each size. $50-60.

ATOMS (St. Etienne, France) *The ATOMS name is an abbreviation of "Association de Techniciens en Optique et Mecanique Scientifique", a company founded in 1946 to build twin-lens reflex cameras.*

Aiglon - A series of TLR style cameras in which the finder lenses are fixed focus, and the objective focuses by turning the front element. Various lenses in Atos I or II shutters. $30-40.

Aiglon Reflex - c1950. A better quality model with coupled Angenieux, Berthiot or Roussel f4.5 lenses. $35-45.

Atoflex - The best of ATOMS' TLR cameras with externally gear-coupled lenses. Angenieux f4.5 or f3.5 objective. Shutter 10-300. $40-50.

ATTACHE CASE CAMERA 007 - c1960's. Sophisticated toy from Japan. A James Bond style attache case with a spy camera, radio, telescope, and de-coder. Advertised a few years ago at $475, gradually dropping to $150 in new condition. We suspect that supply would exceed demand at that price, and that perhaps $75-100 might be more realistic.

AURORA PRODUCTS CORP.
Ready Ranger Tele-photo Camera Gun - c1974. A thoroughly modern collectible with some interesting features. The actual camera is a "Snapshooter" slip-on camera for 126 cartridges, which is little more than a lens and winding knob. The most interesting part is the outlandish telephoto attachment, shaped like a giant blue bazooka with a folding stock. While it may some day sell for ridiculous prices like the Attache Case camera above, it can usually be found today in new condition with the original box for $10-20.

AUTOMATIC RADIO MFG. CO. (Boston)
Tom Thumb Camera Radio - c1948. A

great combination of a 4-tube portable radio and a plastic reflex novelty camera, all in a wooden body with gray and red exterior. Identical in appearance to the "Cameradio" of Universal Radio Mfg. Co. $95-125.

B & R Manufacturing Co. (NY)

(Photoette, rear view)

Photoette #115 - Small metal box camera with cardboard back. Covered with leather-pattern black fabric. 4.5x6cm on 127 film. Not common. $35-50.

B & W Manufacturing Co. (Toronto, Canada)

Press King - c1948-50. 4x5" press camera, similar to the Crown Graphic. Lightweight metal body, double extenion bellows, drop-bed, revolving spring back. $100-150.

BABETTE - Hong Kong novelty camera for 127 film. Also sold with the "Bazooka" name as a chewing gum premium. Various colors. $2-6.

BABY CAMERA - Small novelty "Yen" camera, available in both folding style and box type. Paper covered wood with ground

glass back. Takes single sheets of film in paper holders for 3x4.5cm negatives. Folding style: $15-25. Box style:$10-20.

BABY FINAZZI - c1950. Made in Baden, Switzerland. Box camera for 6x9cm on 120 rollfilm. Red leatherette, red lacquered metal parts. $25-40.

BABYFLEX - Japanese subminiature TLR for 13x14mm exp. on rollfilm. Sanko f3.5/20mm lens in Peace shutter. A rare subminiature. $400-600.

BABY-MAX - Novelty subminiature, similar in construction to "Hit" types, but different shape. $20-30.

BAIRD (A.H. Baird, Edinburgh, Scotland)
Single lens stereo camera - Tailboard style camera with sliding lensboard to allow either single or stereo exposures. Mahogany with brass fittings. Roller-blind shutter. $450-500.

Tropical Field Camera 5x7" - Brass bound field camera of light wood. Square-cornered bellows. $300-400.

BALDA-WERKE (Max Baldeweg, Dresden)
Baldalette - c1950. Folding 35mm. Schneider Radionar f2.9/50. Compur Rapid or Pronto shutter. $30-40.

Baldalux - c1952. Folding camera for 6x9cm or 4.5x6cm on 120 film. Radionar f4.5 lens in Prontor SV shutter with body release and DEP. Eye level and reflex finders. $20-35.

Baldamatic I - c1959. 35mm rangefinder camera with non-changeablef2.8/45mm Xenar in Synchro-Compur. Bright frame finder with auto parallax correction. Match-needle metering. $20-30.

Baldamatic II - $20-30.

Baldamatic III - Similar, but interchangeable lenses. $45-65. (extra lenses additional).

Baldax 6x6 - Folding camera for 6x6cm on 120 film. Trioplan f2.9/75mm in Compur or Compur-Rapid. Newton finder with manual parallax adjustment. $25-35.

Baldax V.P. - c1930's. Compact folding camera for 16 exp. 4.5x6cm on 120 film. Available in a large variety of lens/shutter combinations, f2.8-f4.5. $30-40.

Baldaxette - f2.9/75 Hugo Meyer Trioplan or f2.8/80 Zeiss Tessar. Rimset Compur or Compur Rapid shutter with self-timer.
Model I - For 16 exp. 4.5x6cm on 120 film. $50-75.
Model II - For 12 exp. 6x6cm on 120 film. $50-75.

Baldessa Ib - c1958. 35mm, BIM, CRF, bright frame finder. f2.8 Isco lens and meter. $25-35.

Baldi - c1930's. For 16 exp. 3x4cm on 127. f2.9 or 3.5/50mm Trioplan. $35-50.

Baldina - c1930's. Folding 35 (similar to the early folding Retina Cameras). Common combinations include:f3.5/50 Baldanar, f2/45 Xenon, f2.9/50 Xenar. Prontor-S or Compur Rapid shutter. $30-45.

--Super Baldina (bellows style) - c1937-40. Folding "Retina-style" 35mm with CRF. Trioplan f2.9, Tessar f2.8, Xenon f2. Compur or Compur Rapid. $60-90.

--Super Baldina (telescoping front) - c1955. 35mm cameras, with or without RF. $30-45.

Baldinette - ca. late 1930's. Retina-style 35mm. Various shutter/lens combinations. $25-40.

--Super Baldinette - c1950. CRF, f2 lens. Also sold as Hapo 35 by Porst. $35-50. *(illustrated top of next column)*

Baldini - c1950. Retina-style folding 35mm camera, similar to the Baldinette. $15-30.

Gloria - c1936. Folding camera for 6x9cm or 4.5x6cm on 120 film. Folding eye-level finder and small reflex finder. Trioplan f3.8 in Compur. $15-25.

Jubilette - c1938 (the 30th anniversary of Balda-Werk, thus the name). Folding 35mm similar to the Baldina. f2.9/50mm Baltar or Trioplan. Compur shutter. $15-30.

Juwella - 6x9cm folding rollfilm camera. f4.5 Juwella Anast. Prontor T,B, 25-125, self-timer. $10-15.

Piccochic - Vest-pocket camera for 16 exp. 3x4cm on 127 film. Normal lens: Ludwig Vidar f4.5/50mm. Also available: f3.5Trioplan, f2.9 Vidonar, f2.9 Schneider Xenar. Compur, Prontor, or Ibsor shutters. New prices ranged from $12.50 to $37.50. $30-40.

Pierrette - c1934. Unusual folding 4x6.5cm rollfilm camera with leather covered "clam-shell" front doors and strut-supported front. Trioplan f3.5/75 in

Super Baldinette

Compur 1-300 or Pronto 25-100. Folding optical finder. Uncommon. $75-150.

Poka - Metal box camera, 6x9cm exp. on 120. Meniscus lens, simple shutter. $8-12.

Rigona - c1937. Folding camera for 16 exp. 3x4cm on 127 film. Similar to the Baldi. Normal lenses: f4.5 Vidanar, f2.9 Schneider Radionar, f2.9 Meyer Trioplan. Prontor shutter. $35-50.

Rollbox 120 - all metal 6x9cm box. $8-12.

Super Pontura - Folding camera for 8 exp. 6x9cm on 120 film, adaptable for 16 exp. 4x6cm. f3.8 or 4.5 Meyer Trioplan. Compur Rapid to 400. CRF, automatic parallax compensation. $40-60.

BALNET BABY - Japanese copy of Zeiss Baby Ikonta. $75-125.

BANIER - Plastic Diana-type novelty camera. $2-6.

BANNER - Novelty camera of Diana type. $2-6.

BARCO - Japanese novelty subminiature of the Hit type. Unique construction: front half is cast aluminum. Shutter housing appears to be copper, not brass. In colors. $10-15.

BAUCHET (France)

Mosquito I - Plastic camera with rectangular telescoping front. Made by Fex for the Bauchet firm. Similar to the Ultra Fex. No sync or accessory shoe. $10-15.

Mosquito II - Like the Mosquito I, but with accessory shoe and flash sync. $10-15.

BAUDINET INTERNATIONAL
Pixie Slip-On - Lens & shutter assembly which snaps onto a 126 film cartridge to form a camera. $1-3.

BAUER - folding camera for 8 exposures 6x9cm or 16 exposures 4x6cm on 620 rollfilm. Schneider Radionar f4.5/105. Vario sync. shutter. $15-25.

BAZIN & LEROY (Paris)
Le Stereocycle - c1898. Jumelle-styled stereo camera for 12 plates 6x13cm. Ross Rapid Rectilinear lenses. Guillotine shutter. $250-300.

BEAR CAMERA - Camera shaped like a bear's head. In brown and yellow or white and black panda colors. Uses 110 film. Made in Taiwan. $15-20.

BEAURLINE INDUSTRIES INC.
(St. Paul, Minnesota)

Imp - c1951-54. A disposable mail-in camera, factory loaded. Plastic body covered with bright red or yellow paper. Camera is self-addressed to the processing lab. $10-15.

Pro - c1951-54. Disposable mail-in 35mm plastic camera, factory loaded with 12 exposure Ansco film. $10-15.

BEAUTY - Occupied Japan subminiature. Eye-level and deceptive angle finders. $50-75.

BECK (R & J Beck, Ltd., London)

Frena - c1897. Detective box magazine cameras for special sheetfilms. Made in three sizes:2-5/8x3½, 3¼x4¼, 4x5". $100-125.

Frena Deluxe - c1897. For 40 exp. 6.5x9cm on special perforated sheet film. Covered with brown calves leather. Metal parts gold plated. $350-475.

BEDFORDFLEX - Twin lens novelty camera for 4x4cm on 127 film. $1-5.

BEICA - Japanese "Hit" type novelty camera. $10-15.

BEIER (Kamera-Fabrik Woldemar Beier, Freital, Germany) *Several major reference books have misspelled the name of this company. In an effort to keep the incorrect spellings from proliferating, we would like to affirm that the first name is spelled with an "o" and that the last name is NOT "Bayer".*

Beier folding sheet film cameras - 3¼x4¼" or 9x12cm sizes. Rodenstock Trinar Anast. f4.5 or Betar f4.5 in Compur shutter. $25-35.

Beier-Flex - c1938. 2¼x2¼" SLR, similar to the Reflex Korelle. FP shutter to 500. Xenar f3.5/75mm lens. $175-225.

Beira - c1930. 35mm camera. f2.7/50mm Dialytar. Originally for non-standard film and without rangefinder. Later modified for standard 35mm film and unusual prismatic telescopic rangefinder added. Compur or Compur Rapid. Rangefinder model: $250-350. Without RF: $125-175.

Beirax - c1930's. Folding 6x9cm rollfilm camera. E. Ludwig Victar f4.5/105. Prontor or Vario shutter. $15-20.

Beirette (folding type) - ca. late 1930's compact, horizontal style folding 35mm camera. Cast metal body with leather bellows. Rodenstock Trinar lens: f2.9, 3.5, or 3.9 in Compur or Compur Rapid shutter. $150-200.

Beirette (rigid type) - c1966-on. Low cost East German 35mm cameras, various models, which were sold new as late as 1981 for $24. Used value $10-20.

Precisa - folding camera for 6x6cm on 120. 75mm lenses range from f2.9 to f4.5. AGC, Compur, or Compur Rapid shutter. $15-30.

Rifax - 6x9cm rollfilm. Rodenstock Trinar f3.8/105. Prontor II, 1-150. $20-30.

Rifax (Rangefinder model) - c1937. Vertical style folding-bed camera for 6x6cm or 4.5x6cm on 120 film. CRF. $50-75.

BEIL & FREUND (Berlin)
Plate Camera, 9x12cm. - c1890. f8 Anastoskop Meniscus lens. $75-125.

BELCA-WERKE (Dresden)

Belfoca - c1955. Folding camera for 8 exp. 6x9cm on 120. Prontor shutter, f4.5 Ludwig Meritar lens. $20-30.

Belplasca - c1955. Stereo 24x36mm on 35mm film. f3.5/37.5 Jena lenses (Tessar formula). Shutter 1-200, sync. $300-375.

Beltica - c1951. Folding 35mm. Ludwig Meritar f2.9/50 or Zeiss Tessar f2.8/50. Ovus or Cludor shutter. $15-25.

BELCO - Small black-enameled cast metal camera for 36x36mm exposures on 127 film. Extinction meter. $35-50.

BELL-14 - Novelty 16mm subminiature camera styled like a 35mm. $8-12.

BELL CAMERA CO. (Grinnell, Iowa)
Bell's Straight-Working Panorama Camera - c1908. Panoramic camera in which neither the film nor lens swings, pivots, or moves, which justified the cumbersome name. This camera is basically an extra-wide folding camera for 5 exp. 3¼x11½ on rollfilm. On some models, knobs on top of camera allow the user to change format in mid-roll to 3¼x5½" postcard size, 10 exposures per roll. $400-500.

BELL KAMRA- Model KTC-62 - Combination 16mm cassette camera & shirt-pocket sized transistor radio. Identical to the Kowa Ramera, but not often found under this name. $100-125.

BELL & HOWELL (Chicago)

Colorist I (TDC Stereo Colorist) - Stereo camera for 35mm film. f3.5 Rodenstock Trinar lenses. Made in Germany for Bell & Howell. $75-90.

Colorist II - Similar, but with rangefinder. $75-110.

Dial 35 - Half-frame 35mm. Auto wind. Same as Canon Dial 35, but sold under B&H label. With unique molded plastic case: $50-70.

Electric Eye 127 - (originally announced in late 1958 under the name "Infallible".) A heavy all-metal box camera with an automatic diaphragm and a large eye-level optical finder. Normally with silver enamel and black leatherette, but also with black enamel and grey covering. 4x4cm on 127 film. $8-12.

Foton - c1948. 35mm spring-motor driven, 6 frames per sec. CRF. Original price of $700 (subsequently reduced to $500) made it a marketing failure and it was discontinued in 1950. With Amotal f2.2/ 50mm normal lens: $300-425. *(illus. on front camera with accessory finder)*

Vivid (TDC Stereo Vivid) - Leather covered cast aluminum body. Combined rangefinder-viewfinder with spirit level. f3.5/35mm Steinheil Trinar Anastigmats, focus to 2½'. Shutter 1/10-1/100, MFX sync. Front squeeze shutter release. Common. $75-100.

BELLCRAFT CREATIONS
Can-Tex - Plastic "Cardinal" type novelty camera for 16 exp on 127 film. $3-6.

BELLIENI (H. Bellieni & Fils, Nancy, France)
Jumelle - for 36 plates 9x12cm. Zeiss Protar f8/136mm. Leather covered wood body. $150-200.

Stereo Jumelle - c1894. 6x13cm or 9x18cm stereo plate cameras, magazines backs. Some versions could also take panoramic exposures. Goerz or Zeiss lenses in aluminum barrel with brass diaphragm ring. 6 speed shutter. $150-200.

BENCINI (Italy)
Animatic 600 - c1955. Cassette camera for 126 film. $1-5.

Comet II

Comet, Comet II, Comet S - A series of cast aluminum cameras for 4x4cm & 3x4cm on 127 film. Model II has telescoping front. $12-25.

Comet 3, III - c1950. Unusual 3x4cm rollfilm camera styled vertically like a movie camera. Model 3 is fixed focus, Model III has helical focus. $30-50.

Cometa - Cast aluminum camera for 4x4cm on 127 film. Integral accessory shoe cast into bottom. $20-35.

Eno - Inexpensive 6x9cm rollfilm camera. $15-25.

Koroll - Cast aluminum camera for 6x6cm on 120 film. Telescoping front. $15-25.
Koroll 24 - For 16 exposures on 120 film. $20-30.

BENETFINK (London)
Lightning Detective Camera - c1895. ¼-plate. Ilex string-cock shutter. $75-100.

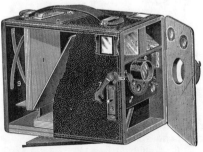

Lightning Hand Camera - c1903. Falling-plate magazine camera for 12 plates, 3¼x4¼". $35-50.

Speedy Detective Camera - Falling

plate box camera with unusual 10-plate changing mechanism & counter. Guillotine shutter attached to inner side of hinged front. $75-100.

BENSON DRY PLATE & CAMERA CO.
Victor - Street Camera with cloth sleeve, tank, and tripod. $100-150.

BENTZIN (Curt Bentzin, Goerlitz, Germany) *(Succeeded by VEB Primar)*

Planovista - c1930. Twin-lens folding camera (NOT a reflex). A "taking" camera topped by a second "viewing" or "finder" camera. Separate lens and bellows for each half. For 8 exp. 4x6.5cm on 127 film. Meyer Trioplan f3.5/75mm, Pronto shutter, 25-100, T, B. Top lens tilts down for automatic parallax correction. $500-700. *(The Planovista was made by Bentzin to be marketed by the Planovista Seeing Camera Co. Ltd. of London. The design is that of the Primarette, but with a new name.)*

Primar (Plan Primar) - 6.5x9cm folding plate/sheetfilm camera. Meyer Trioplan f3.8 or Zeiss Tessar f4.5. Rimset Compur. $50-75.

Primar Reflex - 6.5x9 or 9x12cm. Tessar f4.5 lens. $125-175.

Primar folding (Klapp) Reflex - 9x12 cm. Meyer Trioplan or Tessar f3.5/210mm. Focal plane shutter 1-300, T, B. $150-200.

Primarette - c1933-37. Compact twin-lens folding camera as described above under "Planovista". Tessar f2.8 lens. $600-800.

Primarflex (Primar Reflex) - c1936. SLR, 6x6cm. f3.5/105 Tessar. FP shutter. Uses rollfilm or single glass plates. Style similar to the Hasselblad, although pre-dating it by over 10 years. (Primar Reflex name appears to have been used after WWII for the same camera which was formerly called Primarflex.) $150-225.

Primarflex II - c1951. Similar to the Primarflex, but with interchangeable finder hood and optional pentaprism. Also sold under the name "Astraflex II". Both this and the earlier model tend to have shutter problems. $150-200.

Stereo Reflex - 6x13cm stereo reflex. GGB. FP shutter 20-1000. f6 Roja Detective Aplanat. $400-450.

BERA - see Maschpriborintorg

BERMPOHL & CO. K.G. (Berlin, Germany) *Two distinctive designs in color-separation cameras were produced by Bermpohl. Miethe's Three-color camera took succesive exposures on a shifting plate. Bermpohl's Naturfarbenkamera (natural color camera) used beam-splitting mirrors to expose three plates at the same time.*

Bermpohl's Naturfarbenkamera - A beautifully constructed teakwood beam-splitting tri-color camera made in 9x12cm, 13x18cm (5x7"), and 18x24cm sizes. These rarely appear on the market, and are of interest to a limited number of collectors. Sales in the early 1980's were $1800-2200, but recent auction sales have been as low as $1100. Current estimate: $1000-1500.

BERNARD PRODUCTS CO.

Faultless Miniature - Boxy bakelite minicam for 3x4cm on 127 film. Metal art-deco faceplate. $1-5.

BERNING (Otto Berning & Co., Duesseldorf, Germany) *Currently known as Robot Foto & Electronic GmbH & Co. K.G., the company was founded in 1933 and its first camera was presented at the 1934 Leipzig Spring Fair.*

Robot I - c1934. For 1"x1" exp. on 35mm film. Spring motor automatic film advance. Zeiss Tessar f2.8/32.5mm lens. Rotating shutter 2-500. Robot I cameras require special supply and take-up cassettes which open automatically inside the camera, and close when the camera is opened. Includes built-in lever-actuated green filter. Serial numbers below 30,000 with no letter prefix. (We see these advertised occasionally at prices over $125, but those ads are repeated for months on end without result.) $85-115.

Robot II - c1939-1950. Improved model of Robot I. Built-in flash synchronizer, but no filter. Enlarged finder housing includes right-angle finder. Various lenses f1.9, f2.8, f3.8, in 37.5 or 40mm focal lengths. Serial number has "B" prefix. $75-100.

Robot IIa - c1951-53. Similar to II, but takes standard 35mm or special Robot cartridges. Has accessory shoe. Double flash contacts on front. Available with tall double spring. "C" serial numbers. $95-125.

Robot Junior - c1955-58. Similar to IIa, but without right-angle viewing. Schneider Radionar f3.5/38mm. "J" serial prefix. $75-100.

Robot Luftwaffe Model - 1940-45. Most commonly found with 75mm lens. Pictured here with 40mm lens. Note the tall winding grip. "F" serial prefix. Not uncommon, but often overpriced by hopeful sellers. $125-175.

Robot Royal 24, III - c1954. Newer style but still for 24x24mm exposures. 24 has "G" serial prefix; III has "H" prefix. $175-275.

Robot Royal 36 - c1956. 24x36mm full-frame size, rather than the 24x24mm format of the other models. "Z" serial prefix. $250-300.

Robot Star - c1952-59. f1.9 Xenon. MX sync. "D" serial prefix. $100-140.

Robot Star II - c1960. New body style. "L" serial prefix. $100-150.

BERTRAM (Ernst & Wilhelm Bertram, Munich, Germany)

Bertram-Kamera - c1954-56. Press-type camera for 2¼x3¼" exposures. Unusual design for a press camera, with no bed. CRF. Parallax compensation. Tilt and swing back. Rack & pinion focus. Lenses are bayonet-mounted, rather than using interchangeable lensboards as did most contemporary press cameras. Lenses included Schneider Angulon f6.7/65mm wide angle, Xenar f3.5/105mm normal, and Tele-Xenar f5.5/180mm. Synchro-Compur 1-400 shutter. With normal, WA, and tele lenses: $400-600. With normal lens only: $300-350.

BERTSCH (Adolphe Bertsch, Paris) Chambre Automatique - c1860. A small brass box camera with fixed-focus brass barrel lens, and a permanently attached wooden plateholder designed for 2½x2½" wet plates. The camera case also housed the equipment and chemicals to prepare and develop plates in the field, while an outer case served as a darkroom. A museum-quality collectible. Estimated value $5000. Stereo version (c1864) would likely bring $6000-7000.

BESTA - Bakelite minicam for 3x4cm on 127 rollfilm. $3-7.

BIFLEX 35 - An unusual Swiss subminiature for 11x11mm exposures in staggered vertical pairs on 35mm wide rollfilm. Quite rare. $600-900.

BILORA (Kuerbi & Niggeloh)

Bella 44 - Cast metal camera for 4x4cm exp. on 127 film. Styled like a 35mm camera. $5-10.

Bella 66 - c1956. Aluminum body. 6x6cm exposures on 120 film. $5-10.

Bellina 127 - Compact camera for 4x4cm on 127. Rectangular collapsible front. Introduced ca. 1964, but still being sold as late as 1980 for $18 new. $10-15.

Bonita 66 - c1953. Twin-lens box camera covered with imitation reptile skin. $10-15.

Box Cameras - c1950's. Simple lenses and shutters, some with sync. $4-9.

Boy - c1950. Small round-cornered bakelite box camera. Black: $10-18. Brown with gold trim: $15-25.

Radix - c1947-51. Small 35mm camera for 24x24mm on rapid cassettes. Biloxar f5.6/38mm lens. Simple model has rotary B&I shutter. Better model has f3.5 lens, 5 shutter speeds, plus accessory shoe. $20-35.

BINOCA PICTURE BINOCULAR - Japan. c1950. 16mm subminiature built into 2.5x opera glasses. Formerly sold higher, but is now settling in at $400-500 for white model. Red or blue somewhat higher.

BIOFLEX - c1965. 6x6cm TLR-style

plastic novelty camera. Hong Kong. Two-speed shutter. $8-12.

BIRDSEYE CAMERA CORP. (New York City)
Birdseye Flash Camera - c1954. Plastic eye-level box camera similar to the Herbert-George Co. Savoy. $5-10.

BIRMINGHAM PHOTOGRAPHIC CO. LTD. (London)

Criterion - c1897. Simple box camera for ¼-plates. $75-100.

BISCHOFF (V. Bischoff, Munich)

Detective camera - c1890. Box camera for 9x12cm plates. Polished wood body. Aplanat lens, iris diaphragm. Two-speed shutter. $600-800.

BLAIR CAMERA CO. *Thomas H. Blair applied for a patent in 1878 for a unique camera which included its own miniature dark-tent for in-camera processing of wet collodion plates. This camera, called the Tourograph, was built for him by the American Optical Division of Scovill Mfg. Co. In 1879, Blair incorporated as "Blair Tourograph Co." in Connecticut. In 1881, he moved to Boston and reincorporated as the Blair Tourograph & Dry Plate Co. (shortened to*

Blair Camera Co. in 1886). In 1890, Blair absorbed the Boston Camera Co., manufacturer of the Hawkeye cameras. In 1899, Eastman Kodak Co. bought Blair Camera Co., moving it to Rochester, N.Y. Beginning in 1908, it was no longer operated independently, but as the Blair Camera Division of Eastman Kodak Co.

Baby Hawk-Eye - 1896-98. A small 7 ounce box camera similar to Kodak's Pocket Kodak cameras. Takes 12 exposures 2x2½" on daylight-loading rollfilm. Much less common than the comparable Kodak cameras. $150-175.

Century Hawk-Eye - 1895-96. A leather covered wooden folding camera for 6½x8½" plates. Nearly identical to the Folding Hawk-Eye cameras of the same vintage, but the opening for plate holders is at the side instead of at the top. $250-300.

Columbus - Box camera similar to the '95 Hawk-Eye Box, but with integrated rollfilm system and not for plates. $300-375.

Combination Camera - c1882. A 4x5" view camera with an accessory back in the shape of a truncated pyramid which allows it to use 5x7" plates. $250-350.

No. 3 Combination Hawk-Eye Model 1 - 1904-1905. Replaced the No. 3 Focusing Weno Hawk-Eye. This camera is nearly identical to the better known Screen Focus Kodak Camera of the same year. The rollfilm back hinges up for focusing on the ground glass. $275-350.

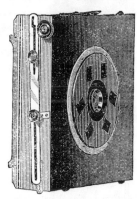

English Compact Reversible Back Camera - c1888-98. Very compact view camera, made in 7 sizes from 3¼x4¼" to 10x12". Sunken tripod head in bed of camera. Mahogany body, brass trim. Double extension. $150-250.

Focusing Weno Hawk-Eye No. 4 - 1902-03. (Advertised as the "Focussing Weno

Film Camera" in England). Allowed use of No. 103 rollfilm or 4x5" plates. Groundglass could be used with either. Rollfilm holder pulls out from the top like a drawer. This design was probably the inspiration for the Screen Focus Kodak and Combination Hawk-Eye cameras which appeared in 1904. Double extension red bellows. Wood interior. B&L RR lens. Blair/B&L pneumatic shutter. $325-375.

Folding '95 Hawk-Eye - c1895-1898. A 4x5 folding plate camera, basically a cube when closed. Similar to the No. 4 Folding Kodak Camera of the same period. Top back door for loading plate holders. Could also use roll holder. $225-275.

Folding Hawk-Eye 5x7 - c1892. Again, a cube-shaped camera when closed. Black lacquered wood with brass trim. Top back door accepts plate holders or Eastman Roll Holder. Model No.1 has built-in shutter. Model No.2 has exterior shutter and more movements. $275-350.

No. 3 Folding Hawk-Eye, Model 3 - 1905-1907. Horizontal format folding camera, for 3¼x4¼" exposures on rollfilm. Wood interior. Maroon bellows. B&L

No. 3 Folding Hawkeye

Rapid Rectilinear lens. $35-50.

No. 4 Folding Hawk-Eye, Models 3 & 4
- 1905-13. Horizontal format folding rollfilm camera for 4x5" exp. Red double-extension bellows. Rapid Symmetrical lens. Hawk-Eye pneumatic shutter. Nickel trim. Wood focus rails. $30-50.

No. 4 Folding Weno Hawk-Eye - 1902. Horizontal style folding camera. Polished mahogany interior, leather exterior. Meniscus, R.R., or Plastigmat lens in B&L automatic shutter. $30-50.

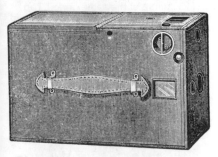

Hawk-Eye Camera (Also called **Hawk-Eye Detective Camera or Detective & Combination Camera)** - 1893-1898. Originally made by Boston Camera Co., then continued by Blair. A large polished light wood box camera with brass fittings. Internal bellows focus. No leather covering. Takes 4x5" plates.

--First Blair version - Self-capping shutter cocked by a knob. Just below the knob on the side is a hole through which tension strengths of 1, 2, and 3 can be read. The distance scale window has become a small slit. Time release button on the front, instant release on top. $175-225.

--Improved model - Separate releases on top for time and instant. Distance scale is on the focusing knob on top. $125-175.

Hawk-Eye Camera (Leather Covered) - 1893-98. Box camera for 4x5" plates in plate holders. Top back door hinges forward to change holders. Leather covered wood construction. Essentially the same as the Hawk-Eye camera above except for the leather covering. $100-150.

'95 Hawk-Eye Box - c1895. Box camera for plates, or will accept Blair rollholder. $300-350.

Hawk-Eye Junior - 1895-1900. Box for 3½x3½" on rollfilm or plates. $40-65.

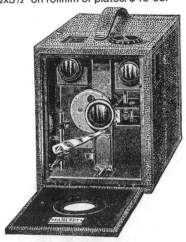

L Lens.
R R Film Rolls.
F F Focal Plane.

Kamaret - intro. 1891. This large box camera (5½x6½x8¾") was advertised as being "one-third smaller than any other camera of equal capacity" because it was the first American box camera to move the film spools to the front of the camera. Made to take 100 exposures 4x5" on rollfilm.

Other features included double exposure prevention, automatic film counter, and an attachment for plates or cut film. $350-450.
- 5x7 size - Relatively rare, valued up to $650.

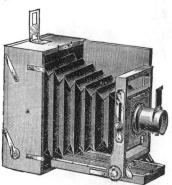

Lucidograph - c1885-1886. A folding plate camera with all wood body. Front door hinges to side, bed drops, and standard pulls out on geared track. Tapered black bellows. Brass-barrel single achromatic lens with rotating disc stops. Made in several sizes: No. 1 for 3¼x4¼, No. 2 for 4¼x5½, No. 3 for 5x8". 5x8" model also has sliding front. These are not found often. $650-750.

Petite Kamarette - c1892. Small box camera, like the Kamaret but in a "petite" size for 3½" round exposures. $400-500.

Stereo Weno (1902-03),
Stereo Hawk-Eye (1904-07) - Leather covered, wood bodied stereo rollfilm cameras for 3½x3½" exp. Blair Hawk-Eye models 1 & 2 are from 1904-06. Later models by EKC/Blair 1907-16. Maroon bellows, simple B&L stereo shutter in brass housing. $150-225.

Tourist Hawk-Eye - 1898-1904. Folding rollfilm camera. 3½x3½ or 4x5" size. Plain-looking wooden standard conceals lens and shutter. $120-140. (With optional accessory plate attachment add $50.)

Tourist Hawk-Eye Special - 1898-1901. Horizontally styled folding rollfilm camera, 4x5" (or plates with accessory back.) Unicum shutter. $100-140.

View cameras:
4x5, 5x7 or 5x8 field type - with lens. $150-200.
6½x8½ - with lens. $175-225.
11x14 - $150-250.

No. 2 Weno Hawk-Eye - 1904-1915. Box camera for 3½x3½" on 101 rollfilm. Similar to the "Bulls-Eye" series of the Boston Camera Co. $18-25.

No. 3 Weno Hawk-Eye - (3¼x4¼") box. $18-25.

No. 4 Weno Hawk-Eye - 1904-15. Large box camera, 4x5". Single speed shutter. Two finders. $18-25.

No. 6 Weno Hawk-Eye - 1906-07. Box for 3¼x5½" on 125 film. $18-25.

No. 7 Weno Hawk-Eye - 1908-1915. Box camera for 3¼x5½" on 122 rollfilm. $18-25. (Most commonly found model of the Weno Hawk-Eyes.)

BLAND & CO. (England) *Manufacturers of a variety of cameras for wet collodion plates. Bland & Co. cameras should be individually evaluated. We have seen examples sold at prices ranging from $395 to $3000. The large stereo, sliding-box, and collapsible types are obviously of much greater value than the more common view cameras.*

BLOCH (Edmund & Leon Bloch, Paris, France) *Leon was the manufacturer, while Edmund was the designer.*

Photo-Bouquin Stereoscopique - c1904. Stereo camera disguised as a book with the two objectives and the finder lens in the spine. For 45x107mm stereo plates. The camera is operated with the book cover open, and operating instructions in French are on the "first page". $3000-4000.

Photo Cravate - c1890. An unusual camera designed to be concealed in a necktie, with the lens masquerading as a tie-pin. The body of the camera is a flat metal box with rounded ends. Six 23x23mm glass plates are advanced on a roller-chain controlled by an exterior knob, and the shutter is released by a concealed bulb release. Estimated current value: $3000-6000.

Physio-Pocket - c1904-1907. Camera disguised as a monocular, with deceptive right-angle viewer in eyepiece. Krauss Tessar f6.3 lens is concealed behind a small round hole in the side. This monocular camera was later sold with the Physiographe name. This basic design was later used in the Nettel Argus, Zeiss Ergo, etc. $900-1100.

Physiographe (monocular) - see description and price under Physio-Pocket above.

Physiographe (binocular) - A "binocular" version of the Physio-Pocket. The second side is actually a plate changing magazine for 12 plates, 4.5x6cm. $700-1000.

Physiographe Stereo - (Also sold in England as "Watson's Stereo Binocular".) Patented in 1896 and sold until the 1920's, the Physiographe Stereo camera resembles a pair of binoculars (slightly larger than the regular Physiographe). Incorporating the deceptive angle viewfinder in one eyepiece, the other is used as a handle to slide out the plate magazine which is hidden in the second half. Takes 45x107mm plates. Current value: $1000-1500. *Note: the first two models of the Stereo Physiographe used 5x12cm plates, with the earliest model using a leather bag for plate changing rather than the magazine. These early models would naturally be more valuable. *(Magazine model illustrated on rear cover.)*

BOBBY - Cast metal subminiature, similar to the Aiglon, but with black enamel finish. $125-175.

BOCHOD (VOSKHO) - c1970. Cyrillic letters look like Bochod, while Roman-lettered models read "Voskho". Unusual vertically styled 35mm camera from Russia. Nomo f2.8/45mm lens. Shutter to 1/250. BIM. $75-125.

BOLLES & SMITH (L.M.Bolles & W.G. Smith, Cooperstown, NY)
Patent Camera Box - c1857. An unusual sliding-box style camera for in-camera processing of single 4¼x6½" wet collodion plates. With this camera, the photographer could sensitize, expose, and develop wet plates entirely within the camera. Patented in 1857, this pre-dates the famous (and less complicated) Dubroni camera. It is also more rare. $4000-6000.

BOLSEY CORP. OF AMERICA
(New York) *See also Pignons for Alpa cameras which were designed by Jacques Bolsey before his move to the United States. Cameras designed in the U.S.A. by Bolsey were manufactured by the Obex Corporation of America, Long Island, NY. and distributed by Bolsey. After June 1, 1956, all distribution was also taken over by Obex.*

Bolsey B - c1947-1956. Compact 35mm camera with CRF. f3.2/44mm Anastigmat in helical mount. Shutter to 200, T, B. $20-25. Often found with inoperative shutter for $5-10.

Bolsey B2 - c1949-1956. Similar to the B, but with double exposure prevention and sync shutter. $15-25.

Air Force model - Identical to the B2, except for the top plate which, in typical government language says "Camera, Ground, 35mm" and "Property USAF". $75-100.

Army model, PH324A - An olive-drab and black version made for the U.S. Army Signal Corps. $75-100.

Bolsey B22 - Set-O-Matic. Wollensak Anastigmat f3.2 lens. If working $15-22.

Bolsey B3 - 1956. Similar to the 1955 Jubilee, but without the Set-O-Matic system. $20-30.

Bolseyflex - 6x6cm TLR. 120 film. f7.7/80mm lens. Made in Germany by Ising for Bolsey. The earlier model has a smaller finder hood and "Bolsey-Flex" is hyphenated.

The later model has a larger finder hood which covers the shutter release, and "Bolseyflex" is not hyphenated. The same camera models were also sold by Sears under the Tower name. $15-20.

Bolsey C - c1950-1956. 35mm TLR. f3.2/44mm Wollensak Anast. Wollensak shutter, 10-200, B,T, synch. $25-45.

Bolsey C22 - Similar to C, but with Set-O-Matic. $40-60.

Explorer - f2.8 lens. Rapid wind. $20-30.

Explorer "Treasure Chest" outfit - In special display box with flash, case, instructions, guarantee, etc. $45-60.

Jubilee - c1955-1956. 35mm camera with coupled rangefinder. Steinheil f2.8/45mm. Gauthier leaf shutter 10-200, B. $25-35.

La Belle Pal - c1952. A simplified and restyled 35mm camera without a rangefinder. Manual front-element focusing. Wollensak f4.5/44mm anastigmat in Wollensak Synchro-Matic shutter. Originally was to be called Bolsey Model A, but apparently it was only marketed by La Belle as the Pal. Formerly sold in excess of $200. Currently: $75-125.

Bolsey Reflex - Original model, c1938. Mfd. by Pignons SA, Balaigues, Switzerland. This camera is identical to the Alpa I, both cameras being developed by Jacques Bolsey shortly before he moved to the United States. 35mm SLR. 24x36mm format. Interchangeable lens. Focal plane shutter 25-1000. Focus with ground glass or split-image RF.
-Model A - c194?. Bolca Anastigmat f2.8/50mm. $800-1200.
-Model G - c1942. Angenieux f2.9/50mm. $150-250.
-Model H - c1942. Angenieux f1.8/50mm. $200-300.

Bolsey 8

Bolsey Uniset 8

Bolsey 8 - 1956. Still or motion picture camera. Shutter speed variable from 1/50-1/600. Stainless steel body, size of cigarette pack. $100-150. *(illustrated in previous column)*

Bolsey Uniset 8 - 1961. Similar to Bolsey 8 but without variable shutter speeds. Rare. $175-275. *(illustrated in previous column)*

BOLTA-WERK (later called **Photavit-Werk GmbH. Nuernberg, Germany)**

Boltavit - c1936. A small cast metal camera for 25x25mm exp. on rollfilm. Doppel Objectiv f7.7 or Corygon Anastigmat f4.5/40mm lens. $75-125.

Photavit - A compact 35mm camera for 24x24mm exposures on standard 35mm film, but in special cartridges. Film advances from one cartridge to the other. No rewinding needed; the old supply cartridge becomes the new take-up cartridge. Wide variety of shutter & lens combinations. Standard model is black enameled with leather covering. Deluxe model is chrome plated with leather covering. Also made in version for 828 film after WWII. $50-75.

BOREUX (Armand Boreux, Basel, Switzerland)
Nanna 1 - intro. 1909. Folding stereo camera for 45x107mm plates. Streamlined

body with rounded edges and corners.
Clamshell-opening front with struts to
support lensboard. Suter Anastigmat f6.8/
62mm lenses. 3-speed guillotine shutter.
Folding frame finder. Unusual design.
$300-450.

BORSUM CAMERA CO. (Newark, N.J.)
see also Reflex Camera Co.— post 1909.
5x7 Reflex - patents 1896-1897. c1900.
A very early American SLR. Measures
15x11x8½" when closed. Goerz Dagor
Ser. III f7.7/16½" lens. Focal plane
shutter. $300-350.

5x7 New Model Reflex - Large box with
internal bellows focus. Small front door
hinges down to uncover lens. Identical to
the 5x7 Reflex of the Reflex Camera Co.
$300-350.

BOSTON CAMERA CO. (Boston, Mass.)
*Founded in 1884 by Samuel Turner, who later
invented numbered paper-backed rollfilm.
Boston Camera Co. began marketing the
Hawk-Eye detective camera in 1888. In 1890, it
was purchased by the Blair Camera Co., which
continued to market improved versions of the
Hawk-Eye cameras. About 1892, Turner left the
Blair Co. and started a new company named
"Boston Camera Manufacturing Co." which
made "Bulls-Eye" cameras. Thus there are two
separate "Boston" companies, both founded by
Samuel Turner. The first made "Hawk-Eye"
cameras and the second made "Bulls-Eye"
cameras. It was this second company which held
the rights to Turner's numbered rollfilm, and
George Eastman purchased the company in
1895 to secure those rights.*

Hawk-Eye "Detective" box cameras -
c1888-1890 as a "Boston" camera, but
continued by Blair after 1890. Large
wooden box camera for 4x5" plates.
Rotating brass knob at rear focuses
camera by means of internal bellows.
Certain features distinguish it from the
later Blair models: Wire tensioning device
on the side; small shutter cocking lever in
a curved front depression; top front

shutter release; distance scale window on
side near center. All wood box model:
$200-250. Leather covered model:
$150-200.

BOSTON CAMERA MFG. CO. *(see
historical note above under Boston Camera Co.)*

Bull's-Eye box cameras - intro c1892.
Simple, wooden, leather-covered box
cameras for rollfilm. Very similar to the later
Blair and Kodak Bull's-Eye cameras, but
easily identified by the "D"-shaped red
window. Historically important as the first
cameras to use numbered paper-backed
rollfilm and red windows. $75-125.

BOUMSELL (Paris)

Azur - A series of folding rollfilm cameras
for 6x9cm on 120 film. $15-25.

Box Metal - Basic metal box camera for
6x9cm on 120 film. Imitation leather
covered. $5-10.

Longchamp - Simple bakelite reflex-style camera for 3x4cm on 127 film. Similar to Clix-O-Flex. $8-12.

Photo-Magic - Small bakelite eye-level camera similar to the MIOM. Black or wine-colored. Takes 4x6.5cm on 127 film. $15-25.

BOWER (Saul Bower Inc., NYC)
Bower 35 - c1952-1958. Basic 35mm viewfinder camera. Steinheil Cassar f2.8 or Meritar 45mm lens. Prontor-S or SV shutter. $20-25.
Bower-X - c1951-1958. Folding camera for 620 rollfilm. Models I, II, and 63: $10-15. Colored models: $40-60.

BOX CAMERAS *The simplest, most common type of camera. Box cameras have been made by most camera manufacturers, and of most common materials from paper to plastic to metal. Many models are listed in this guide under the manufacturer, but to save you the trouble of looking, common boxes sell for Five Dollars or less, including sales tax, postage, and green stamps. They can make a fascinating collection without straining the average budget.*

BRACK & CO. (Munich)
Field camera 18x24cm - square cloth bellows (black with red corners) extend backwards. A fine wood and brass camera with Rodenstock WA Bistigmat 24x30 lens with brass revolving stops. $175-225.

BRAUN (Carl Braun, Nuernberg, Germany)

Gloriette - Non-RF 35mm camera, 24x36mm. f2.8/45mm Steinheil Cassar, Prontor SVS shutter. $15-25.

Norca - 6x9cm folding rollfilm camera with cast aluminum body. $12-18.

Pax - c1950. Compact metal camera with square extensible front. For 6x6cm on 120 film. Identical to the Paxina I. $10-20.

Paxette I - c1950's. Compact 35mm RF camera. Various models. $15-25.

Paxette Automatic Super III - BIM.

Interchangeable f2.8/50 Color Ennit. $25-35.

Paxina I - Metal camera with square telescoping front. Paxanar f7.7/75mm lens. Shutter built into front has 30, 100, T. $5-10.

Paxina II - 6x6cm rollfilm camera. Round telescoping front. f3.5/75Staebler Kataplast lens in Vario shutter. $5-10.

Super Colorette - c1957. 35mm RF cameras.
I - CRF, f2.8, rapid advance. $15-20.
Ib - Meter, 4-element lens. $20-25.
II - Interchangeable lenses. $25-30.
IIb - Like II, but with meter. $30-35.

Super Paxette - 35mm RF cameras, various models. Interchangeable lenses. Xenar f2.8/50mm or Enna Color Ennit. Prontor shutter. $30-45.

BRIN'S PATENT CAMERA - London, c1891. A miniature detective camera hidden in an opera glass. Takes 25mm circular plates. f3.5/30 lens, simple front shutter. Very rare. $3000-4500. Replica recently made. $850.

BRIOIS (A. Briois, Paris)
Thompson's Revolver Camera - intro. 1862. Designed by Thompson. Brass pistol-shaped camera with scope, wooden pistol grip, but no barrel. Takes four 23mm dia. exposures in rapid succession on a 7.5cm circular wet-plate. Ground glass focusing through the scope which is above the cylindrical plate chamber. Petzval f2/40mm lens, single speed rotary behind-the-lens shutter. The lens is raised and sighted through to focus, then dropped into place in front of the plate, automatically releasing the shutter. The circular plate was then rotated a quarter turn and was ready for the next exposure. Rare. Estimated value about $15,000.

BRITISH FERROTYPE CO. (Blackpool, England)
Telephot Button Camera - c1911. Like the Talbot Errtee Button Tintype Camera. For 1" dia. ferrotype dry plates. Rapid Rectilinear lens, between-the-lens shutter. $350-650.

BROOKLYN CAMERA CO. (Brooklyn, NY)
Brooklyn Camera - c1885. ¼-plate (3¼x4¼) collapsible-bellows view camera with non-folding bed. $200-250.

BROWNELL (Frank Brownell, Rochester, NY)
Stereo Camera - c1885. A square bellows dry-plate camera for stereo exposures. Historically significant, because Frank Brownell made very few cameras which sold under his own name. He made the

first Kodak cameras for the Eastman Dry Plate & Film Co., and was later a Plant Manager for EKC. Rare. No recent sales.

BRUMBERGER 35 - 35mm RF camera designed to look like a Nikon S2. Non-changeable f2.8 or f3.5/45mm coated lens in leaf shutter to 300. Probably made by Nicca for Brumberger. $35-50.

BRUNS (Christian Bruns, Munich)
Detective camera - c1893. An unusual wooden box detective camera for 9x12cm plates. The unique design incorporates an auxiliary bellows with ground glass which mounts piggy-back on top of the camera. The camera lens slides up to double as a lens for this full-size ground glass viewer. $1000-1200.

BUDWEISER - Can camera. $15-25.

BUENA 35-S - Japanese 35mm. f3.5/45mm Buena lens. $25-35.

BUESS (Lausanne)
Multiprint - A special camera for 24 small

exp. on a 13x18cm plate which shifts from lower right to upper left by means of a crank on the back. Corygon f3.5/105mm lens, rotating shutter 1-100. Reflex finder. *(Only 25 of these cameras were made. We know of only 2 examples. One sold at a German auction in 1976 for $820, the other in late 1984 for $450.)*

BULLARD CAMERA CO. (Springfield, MA) *Founded c1895 by Edgar R. Bullard, and absorbed into the Seneca Camera Co. c1902.*

Folding Magazine Camera - c1898. For 18 plates in 4x5" format. First models (rare) were made in Wheeling, West Virginia and were heavier and better made than the later ones made in Springfield, MA. Push-pull action of back advances plates. Front bed hinges down and bellows extend. Unusual, because the majority of the magazine cameras were box cameras, and did not employ folding bed or bellows. $250-275.

Folding plate camera, 4x5" - c1900. Wood interior. Red bellows. Reversible back. B&L or Rauber Wollensak lens. Victor shutter. $75-125.

BURKE & JAMES, INC. (Chicago)
Cub - c1914. Box cameras. They stand out in a collection of box cameras because they load from the side. Made in 2A, 3, & 3A sizes. $5-10.

Grover - Monorail view cameras in 4x5", 5x7", and 8x10" sizes. Valued as usable equipment rather than collectible, the most important consideration is the shutter and lens, which can vary greatly in value. Without lens or shutter $75-125.

1A Ingento Jr. - f6.3 lens. $15-20.

3A Ingento Jr. - Vertical format. Ilex lens. Ingento shutter. $15-25.
3A Folding Ingento, Model 3. - Horizontal format. Ilex lens. Ingento shutter. $15-25.

Korelle - *Marketed by Burke & James, but manufactured by Kochmann. See Kochmann.*

Panoram 120 - c1956-1971. Wide angle camera for 4 exposures 6x18cm (2¼x7") on 120 film. Originally available with Ross f4/5" lens in focusing or fixed focus mount, single speed shutter, 1/100. With detachable ground glass back and magazines, we've seen them from $100-550.

PH-6-A - U.S. Signal Corps special wide angle camera for 5x7" filmholders. Wollensak f12.5 Extra Wide Angle lens in Betax No. 2 shutter. $75-100.

Press 4x5 - f4.7/127 Kodak Ektar. $90-110.

Rexo cameras:
Box camera - for 6x9cm rollfilm. $4-8.

1A Folding Rexo - for 2½x4¼ on 116 film. Anastigmat lens. $12-18.

1A Rexo Jr. - Folding camera for 2½x4¼ on 116 film. Single Achromatic or RR lens. Ilex shutter. $12-18.

2C Rexo Jr. - folding camera. $12-18.

3 Rexo - folding 3¼x4¼ rollfilm. RR or Anastigmat lens. Ilex shutter. $12-18.

3 Rexo Jr. - 3¼x4¼, single achromatic lens. Ilex shutter. $12-18.

3A Rexo - folding camera. $15-20.

Vest Pocket Rexo - Wollensak Anastigmat lens in Ultex shutter. $15-20.

Rexoette - c1910. Box camera 6x9cm. $8-10.

Press/View cameras: 2¼x3¼ & 3¼x4¼ - with lens: $40-60.
4x5 Watson Press - with lens: $60-80.
5x7 view - without lens: $60-100.
8x10 view - without lens: $100-150.

Watson-Holmes Fingerprint Camera -A special purpose camera for making 1:1 reproductions of fingerprints or small objects. Front of camera rests on object being photographed and interior bulbs provide illumination. (Military version is called PH-503A/PF). $50-75.

BURLEIGH BROOKS INC. (Englewood, NJ)

Bee Bee - c1938-1941. German folding plate cameras sold in the USA under the "Bee Bee" name (for Burleigh Brooks). Model A for 6.5x9cm, Model B for 9x12cm. Bayonet mount for easy changing of lens and shutter. Identical to the Certo Certotrop cameras. $25-40.

Brooks Veriwide - Wide angle camera using the Schneider Super Angulon 47mm lens (f8 or f5.6 versions) on a thin camera body compatible with the Graflex

XL system. Price includes any one of the normal backs. f5.6: $550-650. f8: $450-550.

BURR, C.
Stereo camera - Mahogany tail board camera with square leather bellows, twin brass-barreled Burr lenses and Thornton-Pickard roller blind shutter. $500-750.

Wet plate camera - c1860. Sliding-box style. Polished mahogany with brass barrel lens and brass fittings. Sliding back allows three exposures on a single 3¼x4¼" plate. $2500-3000.

BUSCH CAMERA CORP. (Chicago)

Pressman 4x5 - f4.7 Ektar, Optar, or Raptar lens. Press camera styled like Graphic. $125-170.

Pressman 2¼x3¼ - Miniature press camera. Although sometimes offered at higher prices, there is usually no shortage in the normal range of $50-90.

Verascope F-40 - c1950's. Stereo camera for 24x30mm pairs of singles. f3.5/40mm Berthiot lens. Guillotine shutter to 250. RF. Made by Richard in France but sold under the Busch name in the U.S.A. Generally considered to be one of the best stereo cameras, and not often found for sale. $350-475.

BUTCHER (W.Butcher & Sons, London) *Founded by William Butcher in 1866, and operated as a family business. Although the Butcher firm joined forces with George Houghton, and eventually became a part of Ensign Ltd., it still remained a family tradition, and two of Butcher's grandsons were still associated with the Ensign firm in the 1930's. Check Houghton-Butcher for cameras not listed here.*

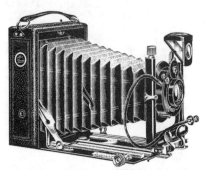

Cameo - A series of folding cameras for plates, introduced around the turn of the century and continuing for many years in all sorts of variations. In the common sizes with normal lens and shutter: $20-35.

Cameo Stereo - Folding bed style stereo camera for plates. The No. 0 and No. 1 models are simpler, with T,B,I shutter. The No. 2 features rack focusing, DEB, rising front, and shutter speeds to 1/100. Aldis, Beck, or Cooke lens. $125-160.

Carbine cameras - A series of folding cameras primarily for rollfilm, but most models have a removable panel in the back which allows the use of plates as well. Quite a variety of models with various lenses and shutters. The models with better lenses and shutters obviously bring the better prices. $20-40.

Klimax - Folding camera for plates. Aluminum body covered with Morocco leather. In various sizes from ¼ to ½ plate. Model I is single extension, while Model II is double extension. A great variety of shutter and lens combinations were available. $20-30.

Little Nipper - c1900. Simple box cameras for glass plates. One model for 4.5x6cm plates, and the larger model for 6.5x9cm plates. Add-on finder is similar to that of the original Brownie camera of the same era. $50-75.

Maxim No. 1 - c1903. A leather covered wooden box camera for 6x6cm exposures on rollfilm. A rather scarce box camera from the days of the first "Brownie" cameras. $50-75.

Midg - A series of drop-plate magazine box cameras in 3¼x4¼" or postcard (3¼x5½") sizes. The No. 0 is the simplest, with built-in shutter and lens. Shutter speed dial is low on the front. The models 1, 2, 3, & 4 have a hinged front which conceals the better lens and shutter. We have seen these advertised at quite high prices, but they generally sell with difficulty in the range of $25-30.

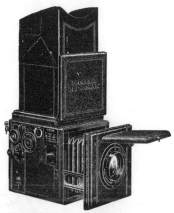

Popular Pressman - Butcher's entry into the field of reflex cameras, in 3¼x4¼" & 3¼x5½" sizes. Focal plane shutter. Generally found with f4.5 lens by Beck, Aldis, Cooke, Dallmeyer, or Ross. $75-115.

Butcher Stereolette

Reflex Carbine - 6x9cm 120 film SLR. Aldis Uno Anastigmat f7.7/4¼". Two separate releases for T & I. Body of wood covered with black leather. $90-120.

Royal Mail Postage Stamp Camera - c1907-1915. Wooden box camera for multiple exposures on a single 3¼x4¼" plate. Two major variations exist. The 3-lens model will take 3 or 6 exposures on a plate by shifting the lensboard. Current value of 3-lens model: $750-1000. The 15-lens model simultaneously exposes 15 stamp-sized images on the plate. The 15-lens models previously sold as high as $1500-2000. Recent auction prices have been in the $750-1000 range.

Stereolette - c1910-1915. Miniature folding-bed stereo camera for 45x107mm plates. Zeiss Tessar f6.3 or f4.5 in Compound Shutter. $350-500. *(illustrated in previous column)*

Watch Pocket Carbine - c1920. Compact folding rollfilm cameras, horizontal or vertical styles, in 6x6cm, 6x9cm, and 6.5x11cm exposure sizes. Leather covered metal body. Normally with f7.7 Aldis Uno Anast. in Lukos II shutter. $40-50.

Tropical Watch Pocket Carbine - Like the regular models, but with black unleathered body and Russian leather bellows. $100-150.

BUTLER (E.T. Butler, England) Patent Three-Colour Separation Camera - A mahogany camera for three exposures on separate plates through the use of semi-silvered mirrors. The front and focusing mechanism are very similar to the Butcher Popular Pressman reflex, but with an additional cube on the back. Made in sizes for 2¼x3¼", 3¼x4¼", and 4¼x6½" plates. $2000-3500.

CADOT (A. Cadot, Paris) Scenographe Panoramique - Jumelle style 9x18cm plate camera. One lens rotates to center position to change from stereo to panoramic mode. $250-350.

CAILLON (Paris)

Bioscope - c1915-25. Rigid-bodied jumelle style sterso cameras in 6x13 and 8x16cm sizes. Convertible for use as a panoramic camera. $150-200.

Megascope - c1915. Jumelle style stereo with changing magazine for 12 plates, 6x13cm. Rising/falling front. Folding frame viewfinder. Leather covered metal body. Hermagis f6.3/85mm lenses, guillotine shutter ½-200. $100-150.

CAM-O CORP. (Kansas City, MO) Ident - 35mm TLR "school camera" for bulk rolls of 46mm film. Wood body. f9.5/ 114mm $50-75.

CAMERA - Yes, that's the full name of this small Japanese paper "Yen" box camera for single exposures on sheetfilm in paper holders. Ground glass back. Black: $10- 15. Colored: $25-35.

CAMERA CORP. OF AMERICA

(Chicago) *Original name "Candid Camera Corp. of America" 1938-1945 was shortened to "Camera Corp. of America" in 1945. Ceased operations about 1949 and sold its tools and dies to Ciro Cameras Inc. This is not the same company as the Camera Corp of America (Detroit) which sold the Camcor camera c1956- 1959, and also not the same as the Camera Corp. of America (Hicksville, NY) also known as Chrislin Photo Industry, which sold the Chrislin Insta Camera c1966-71 (see listing under Chrislin).*

Cee-Ay 35 - 1949-1950. Wollensak Anastigmat f4.5 in Synchro Alphax 25-150, T,B or Wollensak Anastigmat f3.5 in Synchro Alphax 10-200,T,B. $40-55.

Perfex Cameras (listed chronologically) *Note: Perfex cameras are often found with inoperative or sticky shutters, usually at about half the normal prices listed below.*

Perfex Speed Candid - 1938-1939. Bakelite-bodied 35mm camera. Non-coupled RF. Interchangeable f3.5/50mm or f2.8 Graf Perfex Anastigmat. Cloth focal plane shutter 25-500, B. $45- 60.

Perfex Forty-Four - 1939-1940. Aluminum-bodied 35mm CRF camera. Interchangeable f3.5 or 2.8/50mm Graf Perfex Anastigmat. Cloth FP shutter 1-1250, B, sync. Extinction meter. $30-40.

Perfex Thirty-Three - 1940-1941. f3.5 or f2.8/50mm Scienar Anastigmat. FP shutter 25-500, B, sync. CRF. Extinction meter. $35-45.

Perfex Fifty-Five - 1940-47. f3.5 or 2.8 Scienar or Wollensak Velostigmat lens. FP shutter, 1-1250, B, sync. CRF. Extinction meter-exposure calculator to 1945. $25-35.

Perfex Twenty-Two - 1942-45. f3.5 Scienar Anastigmat. FP shutter 1-1250, B, sync. CRF. Extinction meter. Black or aluminum body. $35-45.

Perfex DeLuxe - 1947-1950. The first of the post-war Perfex models, it introduced the stamped metal body to replace the original die-cast design. Wollensak f2.8 or f2.0 lens. $30-40.

Perfex One-O-One - 1947-1950. With Ektar f3.5 or f2.8 lens in Compur Rapid shutter: $40-50. With Wollensak Anast. f4.5/50mm lens in Alphax leaf shutter 25-150, T, B: $30-40.

Perfex One-O-Two - 1948-1950. With Ektar f3.5 or f2.8 lens in Compur Rapid shutter: $40-50. With Wollensak f3.5/50mm lens in Alphax shutter: $30-40.

CAMERA MAN INC. (Chicago)
Champion - Black plastic "minicam" for 16 exp. on 127 film. $8-12.

Silver King - An art-deco styled plastic minicam with a metal back. $10-15.

CAMERA OBSCURA - Pre-photographic viewing devices used to view or to trace reflected images. While technically these are not cameras, they did indeed lead to the development of photography in an attempt to fix their image. Original examples which pre-date photography are highly prized, but to a small group of collectors, and they vary widely in price depending on age, style, and condition. $750-3000.

CAMERETTE - Japanese novelty box camera for single exposures on sheet film in paper holders. $10-15.

CAMOJECT LTD. (England)
Camoject - Unusual bakelite subminiature for 14x14mm exposures. $100-150.

CANADIAN CAMERA CO. (Toronto, Canada)
Glencoe No. 4 - 4x5" folding plate camera. Leather covered, red bellows, reversible back. Brass-barrel lens and brass trim. Wollensak shutter. $60-90.

CANDID CAMERA SUPPLY CO.
Minifoto Junior - Black plastic minicam for 127 film. Identical to the Falcon Miniature. (Actually made by Utility Mfg. Co. for Candid Camera Supply Co.) $5-10.

CANON

CANON INC. (Tokyo) *Originally established in 1933 as Seiki-Kogaku (Precision Optical Research Laboratory), this firm concentrated on 35mm cameras. (There is a rare Seiki subminiature for 16mm film which was made by a different company also named Seiki-Kogaku.) The Seiki-Kogaku name was used through the end of WWII. In 1947, the company name was changed to Canon Camera Co., and the Seiki-Kogaku name was dropped. The Canon name was derived from the first 35mm cameras designed by the company in 1933, which were called Kwanon.*

Most of the historical and technical information, photographs, and structuring of this section are the work of Dr. Peter Dechert, who is widely regarded as one of the world's leading collectors and historians in the field of Canon rangefinder cameras. His special interest is now the Seiki-Kogaku cameras and accessories. Dr. Dechert has graciously volunteered to help other collectors with questions if they will enclose a self-addressed stamped envelope with their queries, or call 5:00-9:00 PM Mountain Time or on weekends. You may contact him at: P.O. Box 636; Santa Fe, NM 87504 USA. Telephone: 505-983-2148. Dr. Dechert is the author of Canon Rangefinder Cameras: 1933-1968, *published by Hove Foto Books. It is available in the U.S.A. at $22.95 list, imported by H.P. Books in Tuscon.*

PRODUCTION QUANTITIES of CANON RANGEFINDER CAMERAS: *Altogether approximately 600,000 Canon Leica-derived RF cameras were made between 1935 and 1968. About half this total was composed of the four most common models: IID, IVSB, P, and 7. The following table groups RF Canons according to the number produced.*
1-99 - Kwanon, JS, S-I, 1950, IIA, IIAF, IIIA Signal Corps.
100-999 - Hansas, Original, J, NS, J-II, Seiki S-II, IIC.
1000-2999 - S, IV, IID1, IIS, IIF2.
3000-9999 - Canon S-II, IIIA, IVF/IVS, VT-Deluxe, VT-Deluxe-Z, VT-Deluxe-M, VL, VL-2, VI-T.
10000-19999 - IIB, III, IIF, IVSB2, IID2, IIS2, L-1, L-2, L-3, VI-L, 7s.
20000-35000 - IID, IVSB.
90000-95000 - P.
135000-140000 - 7

SERIAL NUMBER RANGES of CANON RANGEFINDER CAMERAS: *Rangefinder Canons after the Hansa/Original and J series were numbered more or less consecutively as they were produced (with many large gaps) and, until #700,001, without regard for model identification. The next table shows the models produced within the several serial number ranges.*
Kwanon, Hansa, Original - No top serial number; use the number on the lens mount.
1000-3000 - J, JS (1938-42)
8000-9000 - J-II (1945-46)

10001-15000 - S, NS, S-I (1938-46)
15001-25000 - Seiki S-II, Canon S-II (1946-49)
25001-50000 - IIB, IV trial models (1949-51)
50001-60000 - IIC, III, 1950, IV (1950-51)
60001-100000 - IIA, IIAF, IID, IID1, IIF, III, IIIA, IIIA Signal Corps, IV, IVF, IVS, IVSB (1951-53)
100001-169000 - IID, IID1, IIF, IIS, IVSB, IVSB2 (1953-55). REUSED for 7s and 7sZ (1964-68)
170001-235000 - IID2, IIF2, IIS2, IVSB2 (1955-56)
500001-600000 - VT, VT-Deluxe, VT-Deluxe-Z, VT-Deluxe-M, L-1, L-2, L-3, VL, VL-2 (1956-58)
600001-700000 - VI-L, VI-T (1958-60)
700001-800000 - P (1958-61)
800001-999000 - 7 (1961-64)
Various prototypes and trial models were numbered outside the above ranges.

SEIKI-KOGAKU CANONS - *Canon cameras made between 1933 and 1947 were manufactured by Seiki-Kogaku. Their early lenses, lens mounts, and finder optics were designed and in most cases manufactured by Nippon Kogaku. Serenar lenses made by Seiki-Kogaku were phased in slowly during WWII on Model J and X-Ray Canons, and on other Canons from 1946. Prices on all Canons marked "Seiki-Kogaku" are quite variable, depending on demand, supply, and location world-wide, and are best considered negotiable.*

KWANON SERIES (1934-1935) - These were largely mock-ups and a few working prototypes. The only working Kwanon known today is a very roughly-made Leica II copy repurchased by Canon Japan from a private owner in the 1960's. Canon has made one or more inexact copies of this Kwanon for promotional purposes.

ORIGINAL SERIES (1935-1940) - *The only Canons with the exposure counter on the front face of the body. Speeds 25-500. Nikkor f3.5 lens (early ones have black face without serial number). Pop-up finder. Serial numbers on lens mount and inside of baseplate. Wide variation in details, especially in early production.*

Canon / NK Hansa - 1935-1937. Original series features, but occasionally with random parts originally made for use on Kwanon cameras. The earliest Hansa cameras were assembled at Seiki Kogaku Kenkyujo under the supervision of Nippon Kogaku managers between 10/1935 and 8/1937, and these were marked "Nippon Kogaku Tokyo" next to the camera serial number on the focusing mount. Design elements came from both companies, and these cameras can be considered fore-runners of both "Nikon" and "Canon" descendents. Recent prices start at about $1700 and can go much higher for examples with identifiable Kwanon-associated parts.

Canon Hansa - 1937-1940. In August 1937 Seiki Kogaku Kenkyujo was reorganized and refinanced as Seiki Kogaku K.K.K. Shortly thereafter the "Nippon Kogaku Tokyo" name was dropped from the camera body. Although the camera remained essentially the same, it was hereafter primarily a "Canon" product and not directly a "Nikon" predecessor; nor did these later cameras incorporate Kwanon parts. Recent prices range between $1250 and $2250 depending on cosmetic values.

Original Canon - Most Canon Hansas were sold through Omiya Trading Co. and marked with Omiya's "Hansa" trademark. A smaller number were sold directly and not so marked; for some years collectors used to call the latter the "Original Canon." Both Canon/NK Hansas and Canon Hansas are found without "Hansa" logos, and since they are less common than the "Hansa" marked versions they may bring somewhat

increased prices. Hansas and non-Hansas of equal vintage are, however, essentially identical cameras and all varieties were known at the time simply as "the Canon Camera." The type designation "Original Canon" is now outmoded and should not be used except to describe the non-Hansa variation.

J SERIES (1939-1946) - *None has rangefinder. Viewfinder is built into top housing. "Canon", "Seiki-Kogaku", and serial number on top.*

J - 1939-1944. Speeds 20-500. No cover patch on slow dial area. Finder housing cut straight from front to backbeside a large rewind knob. Nikkor f4.5 or f3.5 in screw mount similar to but not interchangeable with Leica mount. Price negotiable. $2000 and up.

JS - 1941-1945. Identical to J except for slow dial on front face, speeds 1-500. Limited production, most for armed forces. Some were modified after manufacture from model J cameras, either by the factory or elsewhere. Price negotiable. $2000-??

J-II - 1945-1946. Like the J, but finder housing nests around smaller rewind knob similar to Leica. No slow speeds. Slow dial area usually covered by metal patch, sometimes by body covering material. Nikkor or Seiki-Kogaku Serenar f3.5 in same mount as J and JS. Price negotiable. VG: $1250+. Excellent $2500+.

S SERIES: *Retained the Hansa pop-up finder until 1946, but moved the frame counter to the top beneath the advance knob, like Leica. Retained the Original Series' bayonet lens mount until 1946.*

S - 1938-1946. Slow dial on front, lever-operated to avoid fouling focusing mount. Considerable detail variation in cameras and lenses, particularly during wartime. Canon records use the designation "S-I" for a small number made after the war, but these were assembled from left-over parts and are hard to distinguish from wartime production. A Japanese Navy version, marked entirely in Japanese, was made c1942. Nikkor f4.5, f3.5, f2.8, and f2 lenses. $1200+

NS - 1940-1942. Like the S, but no slow speeds. Considerable construction variation, but none with patch over slow dial area. Nikkor f4.5 and f3.5 lenses. $1500 and up.

Seiki S-II - 1946-1947. "Seiki-Kogaku"

marked on the top plate. Combined single-stage rangefinder-viewfinder. Speeds 1-500. Formed metal body (a few late ones were die-cast). Earliest production retained the J-type lensmount. Slightly later production had a lensmount with sufficient "slop" to accomodate J-lenses or Leica-derived lenses. Final version has Leica thread mount. Nikkor f3.5, Seiki-Kogaku f3.5 and f2 lenses in versions to fit all three mounts. With "Seiki-Kogaku" markings: $250-450. (If not marked "Seiki", see Canon S-II below.)

X-RAY CANONS: *Dr. Mitarai, one of the early Canon founders, was especially interested in making cameras to record the images on X-ray screens, and these formed a considerable part of Canon's early production. Three versions of the earliest model were produced, marked as "Seiki" with bird logo, "X-Ray Canon 35", and "Canon CX-35", from about 1939 until 1956, when more elaborate units in 35mm, 60mm, and 70mm were substituted. The three early versions are interesting because they used Nikkor and Seiki-Kogaku Serenar (later Canon Serenar) f2 and f1.5 lenses. Most X-ray cameras were scrapped when replaced, and are hard to find. On the other hand, most collectors are not particularly interested in finding them. Prices negotiable. VG, complete with lens and mount: $500+.*

CANON CAMERA CO. CANONS: *In September of 1947, the company name was changed from Seiki-Kogaku to Canon Camera Co. At the same time, the lens names were changed from Seiki-Kogaku Serenar to Canon Serenar. In 1952, the Serenar lens name was dropped and they were called simply "Canon" lenses.*

CANON II SERIES (1947-1956): *All Canon II cameras have a top speed of 500 and film loading through the baseplate. Nikkor lenses were discontinued in 1948.*

Canon S-II - 1947-1949. Like the Seiki S-II, but almost all have die-cast bodies, later production with thicker wall than early production. No finder magnification adjustment. Nikkor f3.5, Canon Serenar f3.5 and f2 lenses. $200-250.

IIB - 1949-1952. First 3-way magnification control of combined rangefinder-viewfinder operated by 2-piece lever under rewind knob. Speed dials split at 20. No flash synch rail or original factory synch. Serenar f3.5 & f1.9 collapsible lenses. $125-200.

IIC - 1950-1951. Like IIB, but speed dials split at 25. Same lenses. $100-175.

IIA - 1952-1953. No slow speeds. Slow dial area covered by metal patch with body covering insert. No synch. Price negotiable, very rare. $1000+

IIAF - 1953. Like IIA, but with flashbulb

synch by side rail. Canon f3.5 or f2.8 lenses. Price negotiable, extremely rare.

IID - 1952-1955. Like IIC, but one-piece VF selector lever. No flash synch or film reminder dial. Speed dials split at 25. Canon f3.5, f2.8, f1.8 lenses. $90-140.

IID1 - 1952-1954. Like IID, but with film speed reminder built into wind knob. $90-140.

IID2 - 1955-1956. Like IID1, but speed dials split at 30. Canon f2.8 or f1.8 lenses. $90-140.

IIF - 1953-1955. Fast and slow speed dials split at 25. Side synch rail. No X-synch position on speed dials. Top speed 500. Some examples model-identified on loading diagram. Canon f3.5, f2.8, f1.8 lenses. $80-125

IIF2 - 1955-1956. Like IIF, but speed dials split at 30. $100-150.

IIS - 1954-1955. Like IIF, but includes X-synch setting on slow dial at 1/15 area. Lock on slow speed dial. Some examples model-identified on loading diagram. $90-140.

IIS2 - 1955-1956. Like IIS, but speed dials split at 30 and X-synch also marked on top dial at 1/45 area. $100-150.

CANON III SERIES: *All Canon III cameras have speeds 1-1000 on two dials, film loading through baseplate, and NO flash synch.*

III - 1951-1952. Two-piece finder selector lever. No film speed reminder. Canon Serenar f1.9 lens. $80-125. *(illustrated top of next page)*

Canon III

IIIA - 1951-1953. Like III but one-piece finder selector lever, and film speed reminder in wind knob. There are many varieties of III/IIIA hybrids. These are not uncommon and not greatly more valuable than true examples of either type. $80-125.

IIIA Signal Corps - 1953. A small run of very late IIIA cameras marked on the baseplate "U.S. ARMY. SIGNAL CORPS". 50mm, 28mm, 135mm, and 800mm Canon Serenar lenses for these cameras were also so marked. Cameras and lenses were otherwise identical to the standard model, and their current prices depend on demand and supply. $250-450.

CANON IV SERIES: *All Canon IV cameras have two-dial speeds 1-1000, film loading through baseplate, and side-mounted flash synch rails. (Note: Hybrid variations of models IV through IVSB exist, partly because of running changes during manufacture and partly because of authorized updating. These are not uncommon and are not greatly more valuable than true examples of each type.)*

Canon 1950 - 1950. An early version of the Canon IV, marked "Canon Camera Co. Ltd." and with other cosmetic and mechanical differences. Serenar f1.9 lens, serial numbers between 50000 and 50199. Only 50 were made; most were sold by C. R. Skinner, San Francisco, as model "IIC" (Canon's original short-lived designation) or "IVM" (Skinner's own later designation). Few remain; when found they command $1200 or more.

Canon IVF

IV - 1951-1952. Two-piece finder magnification lever. No film speed reminder. No X-synch. Serenar f1.9 lens. "Canon Camera Co. Inc." logo. $150-200.

IVF - 1951-1952. One-piece finder selector lever. Film speed reminder in wind knob. No X-synch. No lock on slow dial. Built-up interior wall next to film supply chamber. Serenar f1.8 lens. $90-140. *(illustrated in previous column)*

IVS - 1952-1953. Like IIF but flat die-cast wall next to film supply chamber. $90-140.

IVSB (IVS2) - 1952-1955. X-synch marked on slow dial at 1/15 area. Slow dial locks at 25, at which speed dials are split. Canon f1.8 lens. Model IVSB was known as IVS2 in many countries including USA, but IVSB is proper factory manufacturing designation. $90-140.

IVSB2 - 1954-1956. Like IVSB but speed dials split at 30 and X-synch also marked on top dial at 1/45 area. $100-150.

CANON V SERIES: *All Canon V cameras load through a hinged back, have two speed dials split at 30, and wind with a trigger that folds into the baseplate. Normal lenses were 35mm and 50mm in speeds between f2.8 & f1.2.*

VT - 1956-1957. Identified on front of

baseplate (a few prototypes marked simply "Model V"). Numerous small manufacturing variations during production. $125-175.

VT-Deluxe - 1957. Identified on front of baseplate. No baseplate opening key. Cloth shutter curtains. Chrome or black enameled bodies. Chrome $125-175. Black $300-500.

VT-Deluxe-Z - 1957-1958. Like VT-Deluxe but with baseplate opening key. Prices as VT-Deluxe.

VT-Deluxe-M - 1957-1958. Marked simply "VT-Deluxe", but with factory-installed metal shutter curtains and silver-coated finder optics. Prices as VT-Deluxe.

CANON L SERIES: *All Canon L cameras have back loading, thumb lever wind on top, two speed dials split at 30. Lenses as on V cameras.*

L-1 - 1956-1957. Identified on bottom. Cloth shutter curtains. No self-timer. Some metal-curtained VL prototypes may be marked "L-1". Chrome $125-150. Black $250-450.

L-2 - 1956-1957. Identified on bottom. Common in Japan; scarcer in USA. $150-225.

L-3 - 1957-1958. Identified on bottom. Common in Japan; scarcer in USA. $150-225.

VL - 1958. No model identification on body. Like L-1 but has metal shutter curtains and self-timer. Speeds to 1000. X & FP synch. $225-250. *(illustrated top of next column)*

VL-2 - 1958. No model identification on body. Like VL but has speeds to 500 only. Common in Japan; rare in USA. $175-250.

LATE CANON RF SERIES: *These cameras all have back loading, single speed dial on top with 1-1000 range. Lenses varied, the 50mm*

Canon VL

f1.4 and f0.95 (on 7 & 7s only) are most desirable.

VI-L - 1958-1960. No model identification on body. Top lever wind. Single speed dial. Chrome $175-225. Black $425-550.

VI-T - 1958-1960. Identified on front of baseplate. Last baseplate trigger wind model. Chrome $175-225. Black $400-500.

P - 1958-1961. Identified on top, this model also exists with special 25th anniversary and Japanese army markings. Chrome $125-175. Black $400.

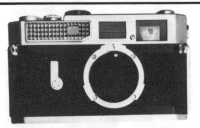

7 - 1961-1964. Identified on top. The most common of all RF Canons, and usually overpriced. Reasonable prices:
Black $300-450; with f0.95 add $90-150.
Chrome $110-175; with f0.95 add $75-125.

7s - 1964-1967. Identified on top, with RF adjustment port in front of shutter speed dial: $200-250.

7sZ - 1967-1968. Also marked "7s" but with RF adjustment port above second "n" in "Canon" logo on top of camera. $225-300.

BLACK RF CANONS: *The following models are known to exist with black enameled bodies: IVSB (never commercially available), L-1, VT-Deluxe, VT-Deluxe-M, VI-L, VI-T, P, and 7. Produced in relatively small quantities, these black Canons usually command higher prices n the equivalent chrome versions, on the order of two-times with considerable paint wear to 3-times in excellent condition.*

EARLY CANON SLR CAMERAS: *This list includes all Canon SLR's produced during the period that Leica-mount RF's were still being made. Each model is identified on its body. Some were issued in black as well as chrome.*

Canonflex - 1959-1960. $75-125.
Canonflex RP - 1960-1962. $75-100.
Canonflex R2000 - 1960-1962. $100-150.
Canonflex RM - 1961-1964. $60-125.
Canonex - 1963-1964. The first auto-exposure Canon SLR. $65-85.
FX - 1964-1966. $75-90.
FP - 1964-1966. $75-90.
Pellix - 1965-1966. $100-140.
Pellix QL - 1966-1970. $100-140.
FT - 1966-1972. $85-125.
TL - 1968-1972. $85-110.
EX-EE - 1969-1973. Interchangeable front elements. $75-90.

CANONET CAMERAS - A long-lived and very popular series of rangefinder cameras with non-changeable lenses. The first Canonet was introduced in 1960 and the series continues through the current G-III models. Sometimes with f2.8 lens, but more commonly found with f1.7 or f1.9 lenses. $30-50.

DEMI CAMERAS - A series of half-frame cameras initiated in 1963-64 with the Demi and continued as the Demi II (1964-65), Demi S (1964-66), Demi C (1965-66), Demi EE17 (1966-71), Demi EE28 (1967-70), Demi Rapid (1965-66). $40-60.

Dial 35 - 1963-67 (Model 2: 1968-71). Half-frame 35mm camera with spring actuated motor drive. Unusual styling with meter grid surrounding the lens and round spring housing extending below the body to serve as a handle. $30-55.

CAPITOL 120 - 2¼x3¼" metal box camera. Body identical to Metropolitan Industries

Chix 120, but no B,I. U.S. Capitol dome pictured on front plate. $15-25.

CARDINAL CORP. (U.S.A.)

Cardinal, Buckeye, Photo-Champ, & Cinex - All are nearly identical small plastic novelty cameras for 16 exp. on 127 film. Similar cameras by other manufacturers include "Halina-Baby", "Can-Tex" etc. $4-6.

CARMEN (France) - c1930's. Small black enameled stamped metal camera for 24x24 exp. on 35mm wide paper backed rollfilm on special spools. Meniscus lens, simple shutter. Also sold under the name "Pygmee". $75-125.

CARPENTIER, Jules (Paris)

Photo Jumelle - c1890's. Rigid-bodied, binocular styled camera. One lens is for viewing, the other for taking single exposures. This is not a stereo camera, as many jumelle-styled cameras are. Magazine holds 12 plates. To change plates, a rod extending through the side of the camera is pulled out and pushed back in. Various models in 6x9cm and 4.5x6cm sizes. $125-175. (There is also a very rare Stereo version of this camera. Price would be negotiable.)

CENTURY CAMERA CO. *Century began operations in 1900, which probably explains the company name well enough. In 1903, George*

Eastman bought controlling interest in the company. In 1905, Century took control of the Rochester Panoramic Camera Company, which had recently introduced the Cirkut camera. In 1907 it became "Century Camera Div., EKC". Following that, it was in the Folmer-Century Division of EKC which became Folmer Graflex Corp. in 1926.

Copying/Enlarging/Reducing Camera - c1900-1910. Professional studio camera for copying photographs. Front & rear bellows. $75-125.

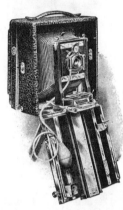

Field cameras - Since many of the Century cameras are not fully identified, this listing is provided as a general reference. Classified by size, with normal older lens & shutter. A good usable lens in a synchronized shutter will add to the values given here:
4x5 - (including models such as #40, 41, 42, 43, 46.) $75-125.
5x7 - (including model 15, etc.) $60-110.
6½x8½ - $85-125.
8x10 - $110-170.
11x14 - $150-250.

Grand - c1908. Folding cameras for plates. Leather covered wood body. Red bellows. 4x5", 5x7" or 6½x8½" size with normal lens and shutter. $75-100. With triple convertible lens: $125-150.
Grand Sr. - Deluxe model plate camera in 5x7" or 6½x8½" size. $100-150.

Long Focus Grand - Similar, but with additional rear track for extra bellows extension. $150-200.

Stereo plate camera - 5x7 folding style. $325-375.

CERTO KAMERAWERK (Dresden, Germany)
Certix - c1930's. 6x9cm folding rollfilm camera. Various shutter/lens combinations cause prices to vary widely. $15-50.

Certonet - c1926. 6x9cm folding 120 film camera. f4.5/120mm Schneider Radionar. Vario or Pronto shutter, T, B, 25-100. $20-30.

Certo-phot - Rigid bodied simple 120 rollfilm camera for 6x6cm exposures. $10-15.

Certo Six - c1950's. 6x6cm folding rollfilm camera for 120 film. Tessar f2.8/80mm lens, Synchro Compur or Prontor SVS shutter. CRF. $125-175.

Certosport - c1930's. Folding plate cameras. 6.5x9 & 9x12cm sizes. Double extension bellows. Normally with f4.5 lens (Meyer or Schneider) in Compur or Ibsor shutter. $30-45.

Certotix - Folding camera for 6x9cm on 120 rollfilm. $15-20.

Certotrop - folding plate cameras, 6x9 & 9x12cm sizes. $30-45.

Damen-Kamera - c1900. Lyre-shaped body covered in alligator skin. Looks like a stylish woman's handbag when closed.

¼-plate size. Same camera was sold by Lancaster as the Ladies Gem Camera and by Dr. Adolf Hesekiel & Co. as the Pompadour. (See Lancaster for illus.)Rare, price negotiable. Estimate: $7500+.

Dollina - *Folding 35mm cameras made from the 1930's to the 1950's. Since the various models are not well identified on the camera body, there has been a certain amount of confusion among buyers and sellers. Hopefully the distinguishing features and illustrations here will help sellers to correctly identify their cameras.*

Dollina "0" - c1937. No rangefinder. Certar f4.5 in Vario or f2.9 in Compur. $40-50.

Dollina I - 1936-39. No rangefinder. All black or with chrome metal parts. Compur 1-300 or Compur Rapid 1-500 shutter. Radionar f2.9, Xenar f2.9 or f3.5, or Tessar f2.8 lens. $35-60.

Dollina II - c1936. Rangefinder above body and focus knob above rangefinder. Compur or Compur Rapid shutter. Various lenses including f2 Xenon, f2.8 Tessar and f2.9 Radionar. $45-60. (Somewhat lower in Europe.)

Dollina III - c1938. Separate eyepiece rangefinder incorporated in body. Focus knob on same plane as advance and ewind knobs. $60-90.

Dolly 3x4 (miniature) - Compact strut camera for 16 exp. 3x4cm on 127 film. f2.9, 3.5, or 4.5 lens. Vario, Pronto, or Compur shutter. Deluxe models have radial focusing lever and optical finder. Original prices ranged from $11 to $70. Currently: $40-50.

Super Dollina - c1939. Rangefinder incorporated in body. Focus knob on right side. Separate eyepiece for rangefinder. Tall knobs sit above flat top plate. Not synchronized. Compur Rapid shutter with f2 Xenon or f2.8 Xenar or Tessar. $50-70.

Super Dollina II - c1951. (Also called Super Certo II, Certo Super 35, and Certo 35.)Like pre-war Super Dollina, but with single eyepiece for viewfinder & rangefinder. Flat knobs recessed into chrome top housing. Compur Rapid MX sync shutter with f2.8 or f3.5 coated Tessar or f2 Heligon. $45-75.

Dolly Vest-Pocket cameras - c1934-40. *There are two major styles produced concurrently. The "miniature" or 3x4cm model has a straight pop-out front with scissor-struts. The V.P. or 4.5x6cm model is a self-erecting bed type capable of taking either 4x6.5cm or 3x4cm size on 127 film.*

Dolly Vest Pocket - Also called Dolly Model A. Self-erecting bed style. 8 or 16 exp. on 127 film. A variation of this camera, marketed as the "Dolly Model B" had interchangeable backs for plates or rollfilm. The same camera, in both rollfilm & combination models was sold under the name "Sonny". $40-50.

Doppel Box - c1935. Box camera for 8 exp. 6x9cm or 16 exp. 4.5x6cm on 120 film. Format changeable by turning a dial. Certomat lens, single speed shutter. $25-35.

KN35 - c1973. Inexpensive 35mm VF camera. Non-changeable Kosmar f2.8 lens. $10-15.

Plate camera - 9x12cm. DEB. $35-50.

Super 35 - c1956. Like the Super Dollina

II above, but with Light Value Scale (LVS) and MXV shutter. $40-70.

Supersport Dolly without and with RF.

Supersport Dolly - ca. late 1930's. Folding camera for 12 exp. 6x6cm or 16 exp. 4.5x6cm on 120 film. Available with or without CRF. After November 1938, an extinction meter was built into the rangefinder housing. Various lenses f2, f2.8, f2.9. Rimset Compur. With Rangefinder: $50-75. Without RF: $40-60.

CHADWICK (W.I. Chadwick, Manchester, England)
Hand Camera - c1891. Black-painted mahogany box camera for single plates. Externals controls. Rack & pinion focusing. Kershaw shutter. Rotating waterhouse stops. $150-225.

Stereo Camera - c1890. ½-plate tailboard stereo. Mahogany body, rectangular bellows, brass trim. Accepts single or stereo lensboard. Brass barrel Chadwick 5" lenses, rotating waterhouse stops. Thornton-Pickard roller-blind shutter. $400-500.

CHADWICK-MILLER
Fun-Face Camera - c1979. Novelty cameras for 126 cassettes. Little boy's or girl's face on front of camera with lens in nose. $10-15.

CHAPMAN (J.T. Chapman, Manchester, England)
The British - c1900. ¼-plate magazine camera. f8 Wray Rapid Rectilinear lens, rollerblind shutter. $100-150.

The British - c1903. ½-plate folding camera. Brass lens, waterhouse stops. Red double extension bellows, brass trim. $100-150.

CHARMY - "Hit" type novelty camera. $15-25.

CHASE - Novelty camera of "Cardinal" type for 16 exp. on 127 film. Identical to the Wales-Baby and Halina-Baby. Made in Hong Kong. $5-8.

CHASE MAGAZINE CAMERA CO., (Newburyport, Mass. USA)
Chase Magaazine Camera - c1899. For 12 plates 4x5". Plates advanced (dropped) by turning large key at side. Variable apertures. Shutter speeds I & T. $75-125.

CHICAGO CAMERA CO. (Chicago, Ill.)
Photake - c1896. A seamless cylindrical camera made to take 5 exposures on 2x2" glass plates. f14/120mm achromat lens, Guillotine shutter. A very unusual camera which originally sold for a mere $2.50. $1200-1400.

CHICAGO FERROTYPE CO. (Chicago, Ill.) *Founded by Louis & Mandel Mandel, the Chicago Ferrotype Co. was the United States' leading producer of direct positive "street" cameras for tintypes, button tintypes, paper prints, and post cards. See also "PDQ Camera Co."*

Mandel No. 2 Post Card Machine -

c1913-1930. A direct positive street camera for five styles of photos from postcards to buttons. $75-125.

Mandelette - Direct positive street camera. 2½x3½" format. Camera measures 4x4½x6". Sleeve at rear, tank below. Simple shutter and lens. A widely publicized camera which sold for about $10.00 in 1929. $50-75.

PDQ Street Camera - including models G & H. For direct positive 6x9cm paper prints. $60-90.

Wonder Automatic Cannon Photo Button Machine - c1910. An unusual all-metal street camera for taking and developing 1" dia. button photographs. $400-700.

CHILD GUIDANCE PRODUCTS INC.
Mick-A-Matic - Camera shaped like Mickey Mouse's head. Lens in nose. Original model uses the right ear for a shutter release. Later models have a shutter release lever between the eye and ear. Although these cameras took a speculative jump a few years ago, they have settled

back to a more normal price range. Actually, they are not hard to find at these prices. Original (ear shutter) model: $40-60. Later models: $20-30.

CHIYODA KOGAKU SEIKO CO. LTD.

Chiyoka 35 - Rare Japanese copy of the Leica Standard camera. Hexar 50mm f3.5 lens in collapsible mount. $500-700.

Chiyoko - 6x6cm TLR. Seikosha MX shutter. f3.5 Rokkor lens. $35-50.

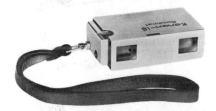

Konan-16 Automat - c1950. 16mm subminiature. The precursor of the Minolta-16. Very similar in style, but much heavier. "Made in Occupied Japan." $60-90.

Minolta - *Although the Minolta cameras were made by Chiyoda, we have listed them under the more widely recognized name- Minolta.*

CHRISLIN PHOTO INDUSTRY
(Hicksville, NY) *Also DBA Camera Corporation of America, but not related to the other companies which also used that name.*

Chrislin Insta Camera - c1965-69. Blue plastic box camera for 8 self-developing 60 sec. prints per roll. Eye level viewfinder in handle. This was in direct competition with the Polaroid Swinger camera, and never got off the ground. $60-100.

CHURCHIE'S OFFICIAL SPY CAMERA - Hong Kong novelty 127 rollfilm camera with tiny adhesive label advertising Churchie's. $1-5.

CHURCHILL - Black bakelite minicam, 3x4cm on 127 film. $5-10.

**CIRO CAMERAS, INC.
(Delaware, Ohio)**

Ciro 35 - c1949-1954. Basically the same camera as the Cee-Ay 35 camera from the Camera Corp. of America. Ciro bought the design and dies and made only minor cosmetic changes. It still did not fare well, and soon was in the hands of Graflex. Graflex sold the Ciro 35, then modified it to make the Graphic 35. The Ciro 35 is a 35mm RF camera. Three models: R- f4.5, S- 3.5, T- f2.8. $15-25.

Ciroflex - c1940's. Common 6x6cm TLR, models A through F, all similar, with each

new model offering a slight improvement. Models A-D: $15-25. Models E,F (better, less common): $25-35.

**CLARUS CAMERA MFG. CO.
(Minneapolis)**

MS-35 - 1946-1952. Rangefinder 35mm camera. Interchangeable f2.8/50mm Wollensak Velostigmat lens. Focal plane shutter to 1000. At least two versions made. (Shutters tend to be erratic and sluggish, which would decrease the value from the listed price.)$25-45.
Note: The Clarus company never did well, because they could not escape their reputation, although they finally managed to make their camera work.

CLASSIC 35 - *This name has been applied to several entirely different cameras, the earliest of which is a tiny die-cast aluminumcamera with black horizontal stripes, made by Craftsmen's Guild. The others were imported to the USA and sold by Peerless Camera Co. of New York. To avoid further confusion, we are listing these full-frame models here.*

Classic 35 - c1956. Made by Altissa-Werk in USSR occupied Germany. Trioplan f2.9 coated lens. $15-20.

Classic II - c1957-58. Made in Japan. Original price $18. $15-20.

Classic III - c1959. Made in Japan. Orig. price $18. $15-20.

Classic IV - c1960. Fujita Opt. Ind., Japan. Orig. price of $20 reduced to $14. $15-20.

CLICK - "Hit" type subminiature. $10-15.

CLOPIC "REPORTER" - Paris, c1903. Strut-folding camera for 9x12cm plates or magazine back. Flor Berthiot f4.5 or Tessar f3.5/135mm. FP ½-200 shutter. $150-200.

CLOSE & CONE (Chicago, Boston, & NY)

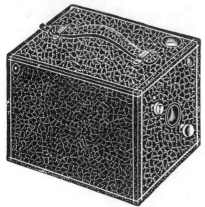

Quad - c1896. Box-plate camera. The

only camera using the new "Quadruple plateholder", an unusual mechanism which turned the four plates into the focal plane. The camera which measured 4⅝x4⅝x6" for 3½x3½ plates was advertised in 1896 as "the largest picture and smallest camera combined ever made", and it cost $5.00 new. $100-125.

CLOSTER (Italy)
IIa - Bottom loading 35mm VF camera. Mizar f4.5/50mm lens. Closter shutter to 300. $30-40.

C60 - 35mm. $15-25.

Olympic - 127 rollfilm. $5-10.

Princess - RF. f3.5/50mm lens, Rimset 1-300 shutter. $25-40.

Sport - 35mm. Closter Anastigmat f8/50mm. $10-20.

Sprint - Inexpensive 35mm with f7/50mm lens in Sincro-Closter shutter to 150. $10-20.

CLOVER SIX - Folding camera for 6x6cm on 120 film. Venner f4.5/80mm Anastigmat in Vester shutter. $25-40.

CMC - Japanese novelty camera of "Hit" type. With gold colored metal parts: $35-50. With colored leatherette: $30-40. Chrome with black leatherette: $8-12.

COLIBRI - Subminiature plastic camera for 13x13mm on special rollfilm. Post-war Germany, U.S. Zone. $75-100.

COLLEGIATE CAMERA NO. 3 - Small Japanese novelty box camera for single paper film holders. $15-20.

COLLINS (C.G.Collins, London) "The Society" - c1886. Full plate compact mahogany field camera produced under license as an improved version of McKellin's Treble Patent Camera of 1884. $175-225.

COLLY - Japanese novelty camera. Takes 14x14mm exp. on 16mm film. Simple shutter, Meniscus lens. $10-15.

COLUMBIA OPTICAL & CAMERA CO. (London)
Pecto No. 1A - 4x5 plate camera. Red bellows. $50-75.

Pecto No. 5 - c1897. Folding bed camera

for 9x12cm plates. B&L RR lens. Unicum shutter Double extension bellows. Rising front. Leather covered wood body. $50-75.

Pecto No. 7 - c1900. 5x7" leather covered hand and stand camera. Double extension red bellows. RR lens, shutter 1-100. $75-125.

C.O.M.I.

Luxia, Luxia II - Small 35mm half-frame cameras. Chrome trim. Colored: $400-600. Black: $350-400.

COMPAGNIE FRANCAISE DE PHOTOGRAPHIE

Photosphere - c1888. One of the first all-metal cameras. For 9x12cm plates, or could take special roll back for Eastman film. Shutter in the form of a hemisphere. Smaller size for 8x9cm plates: $800-1200. Unusual 13x18cm (5x7") size: $1000-1600. Stereo model (world's sexiest camera, according to an expert on the subject): $4000-6000.

COMPASS CAMERAS LTD. (London)
Mfd. by Jaeger LeCoultre & Cie., Sentier, Switzerland for Compass Cameras Ltd.

Compass Camera - The ultimate compact 35mm rangefinder camera system. A finely machined aluminum-bodied camera of unusual design and incorporating many built-in features which include: f3.5/50mm lens, RF, right-angle finder, panoramic & stereo heads, level, extinction meter, filters, ground glass focusing, etc. For 24x36mm exposures on glass plates, or on film with optional roll back. The high prices in the current market are due primarily to collector enthusiasm, not rarity, since they are regularly offered for sale. Complete outfit: $800-1100. Camera only: $500-700.

COMPCO Miraflex & Reflex cameras - Low-cost twin lens box cameras of the 1950's. $5-8.

CONCAVA S.A. (Lugano, Switzerland)

Tessina - c1960. For 14x21mm exp. on 35mm film in special cartridges. The camera, about the size of a package of regular-sized cigarettes, is a side-by-side twin-lens reflex. One lens reflects upward to the ground glass for viewing. The other lens, a Tessinon f2.8/25mm, reflects the image down to the film which travels across the bottom of the camera. Shutter speeds 2-500. Spring-motor advance for 5-8 frames per winding. Available in Chrome, Gold, Red, Black. Camera: $150-200. Various accessories, including wrist strap, prism finder, meter, watch, etc. will add to the value.

CONLEY CAMERA CO. (Rochester, MN)
In addition to the cameras marketed under their own label, Conley also made many cameras for Sears, Roebuck & Co. which were sold under the Seroco label, or with no identifying names on the camera.

Kewpie box cameras:
No. 2 - For 120 film. Loads from side. Rotating disc stops on front of camera. $12-18.
No. 2A - for 2¼x4½ exp. $12-18.

No. 2C - for 2⅞x4⅞" exposures. $12-18.
No. 3 - 3¼x4¼ exp. $12-18.
No. 3A - 3¼x5½ "postcard" size. $15-20.

Folding plate cameras:
3¼x5½ postcard size - c1900-1910. Vertical folding camera. Fine polished wood interior. Double extension red bellows. f8/6½" lens in Wollensak Conley Safety Shutter. $35-50.

4x5 Folding Plate Camera - c1900-10. Black leathered wood body. Polished cherry interior. Red bellows. Usually with Conley Safety Shutter and one of the following lenses: Wollensak Rapid Symmetrical,

Rapid Orthographic, Rapid Rectilinear, or occasionally with the Wollensak 6"-10"-14" Triple Convertible (worth more). Normally found in case side by side with holders "cycle" style. The 4x5 is the most commonly found size of the Conley folding models. $50-75.

5x7 Folding Plate Camera - Similar to the two previous listings. $60-100.

Folding rollfilm camera - 3¼x5½", postcard size, on 122 film. Vitar Anastigmat f6.3 in B&L Compound shutter. Similar to the Kodak folding rollfilm cameras which are much more common. $15-25.

6½x8½ View Camera - The least common size among Conley cameras. $125-175.

8x10 View Camera - Prices vary depending on accessories, particularly lens and shutter, since large format shutters and lenses still have some value as useful equipment. $125-175.

Conley Junior - folding rollfilm cameras, similar in style to the better known Kodak folding rollfilm cameras. $15-25.

Magazine Camera - 4x5" leather covered

wooden box camera for 12 plates. Plates advanced by crank on right side of camera. $45-60.

Snap No. 2 - Strut-type folding camera for 6x9cm on 120 film. Design with cross-swing struts is more typical of Ansco than Conley cameras. $15-25.

Stereo box camera - For 4¼x6½" plates in plateholders. Simple shutter, I & T. Meniscus lenses. $200-225. °(illus. on rear cover)

Stereo Magazine camera - Drop-plate magazine box camera for stereo images on glass plates. $250-300.

Stereoscopic Professional - Folding plate camera for stereo images on 5x7" plates. Wollensak Regular double valve stereo shutter. Rise and shift front. (Note: similar models without full movements are of nearly equal value.) $300-350.

CONTESSA, CONTESSA-NETTEL (Stuttgart) *Contessa merged with Nettel in 1919. In 1926, a large merger joined Contessa-Nettel with Ernemann, Goerz, Ica, and the Carl Zeiss Optical Co. to form Zeiss-Ikon. See also Nettel, Zeiss.*

Contessa Citoskop

Adoro - 6.5x9cm and 9x12cm folding plate cameras. f4.5 Tessar in Compur. Double extension bellows. $25-40.

Tropical Adoro - Like the regular model, but teak wood, brown leather bellows, nickeled trim. $225-300.

Altura - 3¼x5½". Citonar 165mm lens in dialset Compur shutter. $40-60.

Citoskop Stereo - c1924. 45x107mm. f4.5/65mm Tessar lenses. Stereo Compur. $235-275. *(illustrated in previous column)*

Clarissa (Tropical model) - 4.5x6cm plate camera. Light colored wood body with red bellows. Brass struts, standard, and lens barrel. Focal plane shutter 1/20-1000. Meyer Goerlitz Trioplan f3/75mm. $800-1200.

Cocarette - c1930's. Folding bed rollfilm cameras made in 2 sizes,6x9cm on 120 film & 2½x4¼" on 116 film. Many combinations of shutters & lenses. $20-30.

  - Luxus model with brown leather and bellows. $50-90.

Deckrullo-Nettel - Folding plate camera with focal plane shutter. 6.5x9cm with Tessar f4.5/120mm, 9x12cm size with Tessar f4.5/150mm, or 10x15cm size with Tessar f4.5/180mm. Black leather covered body. Ground glass back. $75-130.

Deckrullo (Tropical model) - c1927. Folding 9x12cm plate camera. Teakwood body partly covered with brown leather. Light brown bellows. f4.5/120mm Tessar. FP shutter to 1/2800 sec. Often advertised for higher prices, but at auction they consistently sell at: $425-500.

Deckrullo-Nettel Stereo - 6x13cm size. Focal plane shutter. Tessar f4.5/90mm. $250-300.

Deckrullo Stereo (Tropical model) - Folding teakwood bodied stereo camera for 9x12cm plates. f2.7/65mm Tessars. FP shutter to 2800. GG back, brown bellows, nickel trim. $850-1100.

Donata - c1920's. Folding plate or pack camera, 6.5x9cm and 9x12cm sizes. f6.3 Tessar or f6.8 Dagor. Compur shutter. GG back. $25-45.

Duchessa - c1920's. 4.5x6cm folding plate camera. f6.3/75mm Citomar Anastigmat, Compur 1-100. $200-250.

Duroll - Folding cameras 6x9, 9x12, & 9x14cm sizes. Interchangeable plate or roll backs. $25-35.

Ergo - Monocular-shaped camera for 4.5x6cm plates. Tessar f4.5, Compur 25-100, B. Right angle finder. $750-950. *(Earlier model was the Nettel Argus, later model was the Zeiss-Ikon Ergo.)*

Miroflex - c1924. Single lens reflex for 9x12cm plates. Tessar 4.5/150mm lens. FP shutter to 2000. $225-275. *The later Zeiss-Ikon Miroflex is more often found than the Contessa models.*

Onito - 9x12cm. Nettar Anast. f4.5/135mm. Ibsor 1-100. $20-35.

Piccolette - 1920's folding vest-pocket camera for 4x6.5cm exp. on 127 film. f4.5/75mm Tessar, f6.3 Triotar, or f11 meniscus lenses. Dial Compur or Achro shutter. $35-55.

Picolette Luxus - Brown leather covering and tan bellows. $175-225.

Recto - Small lazy-tong strut camera for 4.5x6cm plates. (A low-priced version of the Duchessa.) Acro shutter 25, 50, 75. $125-175.

Sonnar - folding 9x12cm plate camera. Double extension bellows. f4.5/135mm Contessa-Nettel Sonnar. Compur 1-200. $25-40.

Sonnet - c1920's. Tropical folding plate cameras, 4.5x6cm and 6.5x9cm sizes. Light brown bellows. Teakwood bodies. f4.5 Zeiss lens. Dial Compur 1-300. $400-475.

Stereax, 45x107mm - c1912-19. Stereo camera with folding bed and struts. 60mm Choroplaste lens. Focal plane shutter 1/5-1/1200. $200-300.

Stereax, 6x13cm - c1919-1930. Strut-folding stereo in leather covered and tropical versions. Tessar f4.5/90mm lens. Focal plane shutter 1-1200. Wire sports finder with side pieces that expand the view for panoramic exposures. Tropical: $450-650. Leathered: $200-350.

Steroco - A cheaply made stereo camera for 45x107mm. f6.3 Tessars, Compur. $150-250.

Taxo - 9x12cm folding plate camera. f8/135 Extra Rapid Aplanat. Duvall shutter to 100. $25-35.

Tessco - Folding plate cameras in 6.5x9, 9x12, & 10x15cm sizes. Double extension bellows. GG back. Contessa-Nettel Sonnar f4.5 or Citonar f6.3. Dial Compur 1-200. $35-50.

Tropical model plate cameras - c1920's. 6x9cm size. Zeiss Tessar f4.5/120. Compur shutter 1-250. Finely finished wood, reddish-brown bellows, brass trim or combination of brass and nickel trim. General guidelines: Single lens reflex: $1500-2500. Strut-type with focal plane shutter: $400-700. Bed-type with front shutter: $300-400.

CORFIELD (England)
66 - c1962. SLR for 6x6cm on 120 film or cut film backs. FP sh. 1-500. Lumax f3.5/95mm interchangeable lens. $125-160.

Periflex - c1950's. 35mm Leica copies for 36 exp. 24x36mm. Interchangeable Lumax f1.9 or f2.8/45mm. Focal plane shutter to 1000. Unusual through-the-lens periscope reflex rangefinder. Various models. $75-115.

Periflex "Gold Star" - c1961. (There is a gold star on the front.) Periscope viewfinder. Interchangeable Lumax f1.9 or f2.8/50mm lens, Focal Plane shutter 1-300. $125-175.

CORNU CO. (Paris)
Fama - Small cast-metal 35mm camera with interchangeable shutter and lens mount. Normally found with Flor f2.8/50mm lens. $30-45.

Ontobloc - c1935. 35mm compact camera. Dark grey hammertone painted cast metal body. Som Berthiot Flor f3.5/50mm lens in Prontor II, T, B, 1-200. $30-50.

Ontoflex - c1938. TLR for 6x9cm on 120 film. Rotating back for horizontal or vertical format. Model A is for rollfilm only. Model B has interchangeable rollfilm and plate backs. Berthiot f3.5, Tessar f3.5 or f3.8 in Compur. $250-300.

Ontoscope - Rigid-body stereo cameras, made in the popular 45x107mm and 6x13cm sizes in a number of variations: Focusing/non-focusing, Magazine back/ plate back, Panoramic/non-panoramic. $150-175.

Ontoscope 3D - Stereo camera for 24x30mm frames on 35mm film. Cast metal body, Flor Berthiot f3.5/40mm lenses. Shutter speeds 1-100 set by knob between the lenses. Additional speeds of 200 and 400 by employing a supplementary spring controlled by another knob. Very rustic in comparison with the contemporary Richard Verascope F40, and much more rare. Probably only a few hundred made. $375-500.

Reyna II - Telescoping front 35mm camera. Berthiot Flor f3.5/50mm. Compur Rapid to 500. Front lens focus. Black hammertone painted cast metal body. $20-30.

Reyna Cross III - (Made now by P. Royet, Fontenny-sous-Bois.) Black painted cast aluminum bodied 35mm. f3.5 Berthiot or f2.9/45mm Cross. Two blade shutter 25-200, B. $20-30.

CORONET CAMERA CO. (Birmingham, GB)

Box cameras - Coronet made a great variety of box cameras, most of which are common and not in great demand by collectors. Some were made in France after WWII because of French import restrictions. $5-15.

Cameo - Bakelite subminiature for 13x18mm on rollfilm. Meniscus lens, simple shutter. $50-75.

Midget - A small colored bakelite 16mm novelty camera. Taylor Hobson Meniscus lens f10. Single speed 1/30. Six exposures per special roll. (Original price $2.50.) Current values (in order by rarity)- Brown or black: $65-80. Red or Green: $70-85. Blue: $125-150.

Rapide - Folding 6x9cm rollfilm camera. Body release. Eye-level optical finder. Made in France by Tiranty under license from Coronet. $10-15.

"3-D" Stereo Camera - Inexpensive plastic stereo camera for 4 stereo pairs or 8 single exp. 4.5x4.5cm on 127 film. Single speed shutter, 1/50. Twin f11 meniscus fixed focus lenses. $25-35.

Victor - Black bakelite eye level camera for 4x4cm on 127 film. Focusing f11 lens in synch shutter. $8-12.

Vogue - A brown bakelite-bodied folding camera which uses "Vogue 35" film, a spool film similar to Eastman Kodak 828. Fixed focus lens. Simple B&I shutter. $60-80.

COSMIC - Mid 1960's Russian 35mm. f4/40mm lens, shutter 1/5-1/250. $20-30.

COWI - German plastic camera for 3x4cm on rollfilm. $15-25.

CRAFTEX PRODUCTS
Hollywood Reflex - (Including models A-E, Sportsman, Sightseer, etc.) Cast metal twin-lens reflex style cameras. Generally simple construction, although at least one model had externally coupled lenses for true reflex focusing. $10-15.

CRAFTSMAN SALES CO.

Cinex Candid Camera - Black plastic

"minicam" for 16 exp. on 127. $3-7.

CROMA COLOR 16 - Japanese subminiature nearly identical to the Mykro Fine Color 16, but in green, red, brown, or black bakelite. (Styled like the Whittaker Pixie cameras.) Often chipped where the front section attaches to the back, and sometimes at the latch cogs. Mint: $100-125. Chipped: $40-60.

CROWN CAMERA - Japanese novelty subminiature of the Hit type. $15-20.

CROWN CAMERA CO. (NY)
Dandy Photo Camera - intro. 1910. Simple paper-covered box camera for 1½" circular plates in paper holders. Meniscus lens, simple shutter. Originally sold in an outfit with developing tank, chemicals, lifting spoon, and illustrated instructions, all in a cardboard carton. Full outfit: $250-300. Camera only: $75-100.

CRUVER-PETERS CO. INC. *Later called Palko, Inc.*

Palko camera - c1918-1930's. The only folding rollfilm camera with provision for ground glass focusing without film removal. Based on a 1912 patent of W.A. Peters. Production was apparently started during

WWI with the U.S. Government as the primary customer. Adjustable image size of ⅓, ⅔, or full postcard size. B&L Tessar f4.5 lens in Acme to 300. Original price from $70 in 1918 to $122 in the early 1930's, but closed out at $65 with case. $600-750.

CRYSTAR - "Hit" type novelty camera for 14x14mm exposures on 16mm film (paper-backed rollfilm). $8-12. With colored leatherette: $25-35.

CRYSTARFLEX - c1955. Japanese TLR. Magni Anast. f3.5/80mm in Magni synch shutter. $20-28.

CURTIS (Thomas S. Curtis Laboratories, Huntington Park, CA)
Curtis Color Scout - c1941. Tri-color camera, 2½x3". Ektar f4.5/80mm, Compur 1-200 shutter. CRF. $325-375.

Curtis Color Master - c1948. 4x5" tri-color camera. Ilex Patagon f4.5/5½" lens, Acme shutter. CRF. $325-375.

CYCLONE *Western Camera Co. manufactured Cyclone cameras until about 1899, when it was taken over by the Rochester Optical Co., which continued to produce Cyclone models. We have* *listed Cyclone models under each of these makers.*

CYCLOPS - c1950's. 16mm Japanese binocular camera, identical to the Teleca. f4.5/35mm lens. Shutter 25-100. $300-400.

DACORA KAMERAWERK (Reutlingen & Munich) *Originally located in Reutlingen, the company name went through several changes including: Dangelmaier (1952), Daco Dangelmaier (1954), Dacora Kamerawerk (1970), and then Dacora Kamerawerk at Munich (1972-1976). For the sake of unity, we are listing all cameras here regardless of the company name at the time of manufacture.*

Daci - Metal box camera for 12 exp. 6x6cm on 120 film. Red, grey, or green: $10-20. Black: $8-10.

Dacora I - Folding camera for 12 exp. 6x6cm on 120. Eunar f3.5/75mm. Prontor 1-100. $15-20.

Dacora-Matic 4D - c1961-66. 35mm with coupled meter. Four shutter release buttons for focus zones. Lens rotates to proper focus as release button is pushed. $20-25.

Digna - Simple camera with tubular telescoping front for 6x6cm on 120. $5-10.

Dignette - c1957-1959. Basic 35mm VF camera with f2.8 lens, 1/300 sh. (Orig. price $18.) $10-15.

Instacora E - c1966. A high-quality camera for 126 cartridges. Electric eye, 1/30-1/125 speeds, zone focusing f3.5/45mm Color Dignar lens. $15-20.

Royal - c1955. Folding camera for 6x6cm on 120. Uncoupled RF. Ennagon f3.5 or 4.5 lens in Pronto. (Orig. $31-34.) $30-40.

DAGUERREOTYPE CAMERAS - *The earliest type of camera in existence, many of which were one-up or limited production cameras. Since so few of even the commercially made models have survived time, most Daguerreotype cameras are unique pieces, and price averaging is senseless. However, to keep the novice collector or casual antique dealer from making any big mistakes before consulting with a recognized authority, we will give one example: A half-plate American sliding-box-in-box style is likely to be in the $5000 & up range.*

DAIICHI KOGAKU (Japan)
Zenobia - c1949. Folding camera, 16 exp. 4.5x6 cm on 120 film. Styled like the early Zeiss Ikonta cameras. f3.5/75mm Hesper Anastigmat. DOC Rapid shutter 1-500, B. (Similar to the Compur Rapid.) $25-35.

Zenobiaflex - c1952. Rollei-style TLR. Neo-Hesper f3.5/75mm in Daiichi Rapid shutter. $35-50.

DAISHIN SEIKI K.K.
Hobby Junior - 24x36mm on paper-backed "Bolta" size film. $15-25.

DALE - Japanese "Hit" type novelty subminiature. $10-15.

DALLMEYER (J. H. Dallmeyer, London)
Founded c1860 by J.H. Dallmeyer.
Naturalist - c1900. Long extension bellows attached to front of cubical body. Tube with eye-piece extends from top of body for critical focusing. Long focus lens. ¼-plate. $550-600.

Sliding Box Wet Plate Camera - mid-1860's. $1000-1500.

Snapshot Camera - c1929. Folding camera for 6x9cm filmpacks. Cross-swinging strut design. Two-speed shutter built into front. $70-100.

Speed Camera - mid-1920's. Press-type camera equipped with the Dallmeyer Pentac f2.9 lens, the fastest anastigmat lens of its time. This lens, as well as the ⅛ to 1/1000 sec. FP shutter, account for the camera's name. Small 4.5x6cm size: $250-325. 6x9cm: $175-225.

Stereo Wet Plate camera - c1860. Sliding box style. Brass bound corners on finely crafted wood body. Brass barrel Dallmeyer lenses (consecutively numbered) with wooden flap shutter. $2000-2600.

DAME, STODDARD & KENDALL (Boston)
Hub (Box camera) - Top loading box camera for 4x5 plates. $25-40.

Hub (Folding) - Late 1890's leather covered folding camera for 4x5" plates. Side door at rear for inserting and storage of plateholders. Rotary shutter built into wooden lensboard. Simple lens. $50-60.

DAMOIZEAU (J. Damoizeau, Paris)
Cyclographe a foyer fixe - c1894. An early panoramic camera which revolves on its tripod while the film is transported in the opposite direction past the focal plane slit. Capable of exposures up to 360 degrees (9x80cm). $7500-8500.

DAN CAMERA WORKS (Tokyo)
Later became Yamato Camera Industry (Yamato Koki Kogyo Co. Ltd.) which made the Pax cameras.
Dan 35 Model I- c1946-48. Japanese compact camera, 15 exposures 24x24mm on paper backed 35mm wide Bolta-sized rollfilm. Removable top. Dan Anastigmat f4.5/40mm. Shutter B, 25-100. $50-75.

Dan 35 Model II - c1948-50. Similar, but with body serial number, automatic frame counter, removable bottom. $50-75.

Dan 35 Model III - For 24x32mm exposures on 35mm film in special cassettes. $50-75.

DANCER (J. B. Dancer, Rochester, England)
Stereo Camera - c1856. For stereo pairs on 12 plates 3½x7". A nicely finished wooden stereo camera which set a new record for the highest price paid for an antique camera. $37,500.00 in 1977.

DANGELMEIER - see Dacora

DARIER (Albert Darier, Geneva, Switzerland)
Escopette - c1888. Invented by Darier, manufactured by E.V. Boissonas (Geneva). Wooden box camera with wooden pistol grip, giving it the general appearance of a pistol. The grip and two small brass front legs serve as a tripod. Brass metal parts. This was one of the first cameras to use the same rollfilm as the #1 Kodak Camera, taking 110 exposures, 68x72mm. Steinheil Periscopic f6/90mm lens. Spherical shutter with trigger release. Speeds variable by adjusting spring tension. Rare. Estimated: $5000+

DAVY CROCKETT - Not the box camera

from Herbert-George, but a black plastic minicam style for half-frame 127. $30-40.

DAYDARK SPECIALTY CO. (St. Louis, MO)
Photo Postcard Cameras - "Street" cameras for photo postcards or tintypes, complete with developing tank, dark sleeve, RR lens, and Blitzen Daydark shutter. $100-150.

Tintype Camera - small amateur model. Measures 4½x5x7¼. $50-100.

DBGM, DBP, DBPa: *The "DB" stands for "Deutsches Bundesrepublik". The endings of the abbreviations are: "Gebrauchs Musterschuetz", "Patent", and "Patent Auslegeschrift", trade mark and patent notices which would indicate West German post-war construction.*

DEARDORFF (L.F.) & SONS (Chicago, IL) *Established as camera builders in 1923, the company name goes back to 1893 when Laben F. Deardorff started a camera repair company. In 1923 Laben was commissioned by a group of Chicago architects to build 10 cameras to photograph that new Chicago wonder, the skyscraper. Amazingly enough, five of the first 10 cameras built still exist, four of them in daily studio use! To this day, a member of the Deardorff family is involved in the daily production of cameras. These cameras are primarily "user" cameras though there are a few who collect them avidly. There were no serial numbers until 1951. The condition of these cameras can vary greatly because those sold to studios generally have seen very hard use, while those sold to individual users may have been "babied" and may remain in mint condition even though they are 20-40 years old. Check over the camera, bellows and all metal parts.*
The "refinished" price reflects a camera that has been PROFESSIONALLY restored by Ken Hough Photographic Repair Service, the only authorized Deardorff service center in the USA. Fully restored cameras include new bellows, wood work and parts where needed, and a duplicate of the factory finish. These cameras may be rated as LN-. All prices were compiled by Ken Hough. He may be reached for any questions regarding the Deardorff camera at 219-464-7526. We are also indebted to Jack Deardorff for the history of the early cameras, and to Merle Deardorff for the history of the Baby Deardorff.

8x10" Cameras
The early (pre-1926) cameras are of a light colored, finished mahogany. This wood was taken from the bar tops of Chicago taverns that were closed down during prohibition. Beginning in 1926, the wood was a deep red color.

First series - 1923. Ten cameras. Parquet style bed. Lensboard opening measures 5½x6". Only the first series had this size lensboard. No recent reported sales.

DEARDORFF (cont.)

Second series - 1924. 25 cameras. Parquet style bed. Standardized 6x6" lensboard. Wood and aluminum front standard. Current value: Refinished: $1600. Good condition: $400.

Third series - 1924. 25 cameras. Same as the Second series, but all aluminum front standard. Refinished: $1550. Good: $400.

Fourth series - 1925. 75 cameras. Same as the Third Series, above.

Standardized 8x10" View

- 1926-1937. Wood is deep red in color. Standardized construction with familiar four piece bed, narrow knobs with fine knurling, all brass parts painted with a special gold lacquer. Refinished: $1000. VG: $400. Fair: $200. This style may be seen with front swings added. Refinished: up to $1550. EX: $1000. Good: $500.

- 1938-1948. Same as above but brass parts are nickel plated and knobs are wider. Refinished: $1000. EX: $700. VG: $550. Good: $300. With front swings added. Refinished: $1550. VG: $800. Good: $650.

- 1949. Front swings are standard as is the round bed plate. Nickel plated parts. Refinished: $1500-1600. EX+: $1200. VG: $800. Good: $400. Serial numbers began in 1951 with #100; it was then called the 8x10 View.

AN Series - A large group of 8x10" cameras made for the Army and Navy. There is no difference in these cameras from the standard models except for a small rectangular plate on the bottom of the bed that gives a government number and model number, and lensboards have a thinner rabbet on the front.

5x7" Cameras

- 1929-1937. Basically the same construction as the 8x10" cameras of this time. Red finish on wood. Original square cornered 4½x4½" lensboard, or factory modified 4x4" lensboard. Refinished: $600. VG: $350. Fair: $200.

- 1938-1948. Same construction as the 8x10" cameras of this time. Original round or square cornered 4½x4½" lensboard, or factory modified 4x4" lensboard. Refinished: $650-800. EX: $350-400. VG: $250-350. Good: $150-250. Fair: $100. *Note: This camera may also be seen in a "yellow" colored wood. These were made of Spanish cedar wood because of the wartime shortage of mahogany that was being used in PT boats. Prices may be slightly lower.*

- 1949-present. Redesigned camera body. Front swings, round bed plate, and nickel plated parts are standard. Square cornered 4x4" lensboard. Serial numbers began in 1951 with #100; it was then called the 5x7 View. Refinished: $800-1200. EX: $600. VG: $450. Good: $350.

4x5" Cameras
- 1929-1937. Same as the 5x7" camera, but with a 4x5" reducing back.

- 1938-1948. Same as the 5x7" camera, but with a 4x5" reducing back.

- 1949-present. Redesigned camera body. Front swings, round bed plate, and nickel plated parts are standard. Square cornered 4x4" lensboard only. Serial numbers began in 1951 with #100. Since that time it has been known as the 4x5 Special. Refinished: $900-1200. EX: $650. Good: $400-500.

Baby Deardorff - Designed by Merle Deardorff, this camera looks like a miniature 4x5" or 5x7" camera. It takes up to a 4x5" back. 3½x3½" lensboard only.

First style - 1937-1939. Wood separator strips on bed between front and rear extension. Refinished or EX: No reported sales. VG: $400. Good: $350. Fair: $200.

Second style - 1940-1945. Extruded extension guides, L-shaped guides on front sliding panel. Refinished: $1200-1400. EX: $1000. VG: $450. Good: $400.

Third style - 1945-49. Same as the Second style, but with U-shaped guides on front sliding panel. Refinished: $1200-1450. EX: $1100. VG: $500. Good: $450.

- Backs available for the Baby Deardorff:
- Standard 4x5" still manufactured.
- 3¼x4¼" Graflex style: $60-80.
- 2¼x3¼" standard CFH type: $80-100.
- 35mm back. This was a Kodak 35 body that was mounted on a sliding panel with a ground glass focusing screen, similar to a Leica Focoslide, but vertical in normal operation. Only reported sale: $120.

Triamapro - An ultra precise 4x5" Press style camera, featuring a rotating back, front and rear swings, front rise, and lateral sliding front. May be seen with Kalart rangefinder. The word Triamapro means TRIple extension, AMAteur, and PROfessional. Usually seen in good to VG condition. EX: $1000. G-VG: $350-500. Note: there were also two 5x7" Triamapro cameras built. No reported sales.

11x14" Cameras:
Early style - Looks like a giant 8x10" view camera. Has no front swings. Many were built for the US Marines for "on the beach" photo reconnaissance. Came with tripods whose legs could be used as bayonets!

EX: $1200. VG+: $800.

Second style - Similar to the Early style, but with front swings. Made in small numbers since 1951. In 1985, it sells new for $5500. Refinished: $3500. EX+: $2550. EX: $2000.

Commercial Cameras - 8x10" or 11x14" cameras that must be used on 700 lb. Bi-post stands, 8', 10', or 12'. Also known as the "Dog house type". It is almost always found in large studios.
- 8x10", seldom found for sale. Refinished: $2100. VG: 1500. Good: $900.
- 11x14" Refinished: $2600. EX: $2000. VG: $1600. Good: $1000. Fair: $400.
- Bi-post stands: $900-1600.

16x20" View - Only two were made. No reported sales.
12x20" View - Special order only. One sold in 1983, EX+, for $3200.

5x7" Home Portrait - 1940-present. Still in stock, new. EX: $75. Good: $50.

DEBONAIR - Hong Kong 120 rollfilm novelty camera of the Diana type. $1-5.

DEBRIE (Ets. Andre Debrie, Paris)
Sept - c1923-27. Spring motor drive camera for still, rapid sequence, or cine.

18x24mm on 5m cartridge of 35mm film. Roussel Stylor f3.5/50mm. First model has square motor housing with single spring. Later, the double-spring model with a round motor housing was added. (Burke & James Inc. of Chicago was selling both models as late as 1940!) Not hard to find. $100-150.

DEFIANCE MFG. CO.

Auto Fixt Focus - c1916-20. Well-made folding camera with bed and lazy-tong strut construction. Focusing can be done with the camera in the open or closed position. Self-erecting front assumes correct focus when opened. Goerz f4.8 or f6.8 lens in Acme shutter. $25-30.

DEJUR-AMSCO CORP. (New York)
DeJur D-1 - c1955-57. 35mm VF camera, imported from Germany. Lever film advance cocks shutter. DEP. Interchangeable Staeble-Kata f2.8/45mm normal, f5.6 tele, or f3.5 W.A. lens. (Orig. price for the 3-lens outfit was under $100.) With normal lens: $15-20. Tele & W.A. lenses each: $15-20.

Dejur Reflex - c1952. TLR. DeJur Chromtar

f3.5 lens. Wollensak Synchromatic 10-200 shutter. $30-45.

DELOYE (Paris)
le Prismac - c1905. Built by A. Devaux. Early rollfilm stereo camera. Two 90 degree prisms reflect the image at right angles from the lenses onto the film, allowing for a more compact body than usual. Used Pocket Kodak Camera size #102 rollfilm. Kenngott Anastigmat f8/54mm lenses, 5-speed guillotine shutter. Rare. Estimate: $1500-2500.

DELTAH CORPORATION
Deltah Unifocus - Unusual folding vest-pocket camera for 127 film. $15-25.

DELUXE PRODUCTS CO. (Chicago)
Delco 828 - Streamlined bakelite camera for 828 film. Identical to the Argus Minca 28, this camera merely sports the name of its distributor. $20-25.

Remington - Plastic "minicam" for 3x4cm on 127. $5-10.

DELUXE READING CORP. (Topper Toy Div.)

Secret Sam Attache Case - c1960's. Plastic attache case containing a take-apart pistol and a 127 film camera which can be used with the case closed. (Although this cute novelty item has been advertised for sale at prices over $150, the recent statistics show it continuing to drop to a stable level.) $50-90.

Secret Sam's Spy Dictionary - c1966. Novelty which incorporates a camera in a plastic "book" which also shoots plastic bullets (ouch!). The camera takes 16 exp. on 127 film. (This camera has also dropped in price.) $75-95.

DEMARIA (Demaria Freres, Demaria-LaPierre, Paris)
Dehel - Folding 120 rollfilm cameras. f4.5 or f3.5/75mm lens. AGC shutter. $15-25.

Jumelle Capsa - (Demaria Freres) - 6x13mm stereo camera. $175-225.

Stereo camera for 45x107mm - c1910. RR lenses. $200-250.

DEROGY (Paris)
Single lens stereo camera - Light walnut view camera with sliding front panel and slotted back for single or stereo exposures. Entire bellows rotates to change from horizontal to vertical exposures. Brass trim and brass barrel Derogy lens. $375-425.

Wooden plate camera - c1880. 9x12cm. Derogy Aplanat No. 2 brass barrel lens. Black tapered bellows, polished wood body, brass trim. $175-200.

DETECTIVE CAMERAS - *The earliest "Detective" cameras were simply designed as a box or case. Before long, they were disguised in all shapes and sizes. The original box, case, and satchel cameras are commonly referred to by the name "detective" cameras, while the later disguised/concealed varieties normally are not. Disguised cameras seem to have a special appeal and therefore the prices have remained strong despite the ups and downs of our economy. The magic of the mere name "detective" for an otherwise ordinary-looking box camera has worn thin in the current market and those prices have softened. In any case, they are listed by name of manufacturer.*

DETROLA CORP. (Detroit, Mich. c1939-40) *All letter models listed below are similar "minicam" type cameras for 3x4cm on 127 film. Except for Model A, all have rectangular aluminum plate in center of front. The "W" in models GW, HW, and KW indicates the Wollensak lens.*
Model A - Basic minicam. Meniscus fixed focus. $10-20.

Model B - Duomicroflex f7.9 lens. Extinction meter. $12-18.
Model D - similar, f4.5 lens. $10-20.
Model E - similar, f3.5 lens. $15-20.

Model G - Ilex Anastigmat f4.5. No meter. $15-20.
Model GW - Basic model with Wollensak Velostigmat f4.5. $12-18.

Model H - extinction meter. $15-20.
Model HW - similar to GW, but with meter. $15-20.

Model K - Detrola Anastigmat f3.5, extinction meter. $15-20.
Model KW - Wollensak anastigmat f3.5 lens. $15-20.

Model 400 - c1939-40. A Leica-inspired CRF 35mm camera with interchangeable Wollensak Velostigmat f3.5 or f2.8 lens. Focal plane shutter to 5000. Sync. (Original cost about $70.) $325-375.

DEVIN COLORGRAPH CO. (New York)
After 1940, Devin-McGraw Colorgraph Co., Burbank California. All rights sold c1950 to Bob Frazer of Altadena, CA.
Tri-Color Camera - for making color separation negatives. Original professional size for 5x7". Apo-Tessar f9/12" lens. Dial Compur shutter. $450-550.
- - 6.5x9cm size - intro. c1938. Goerz Dogmar f4.5/5½" lens. Compound shutter. $450-550.

DEVRY - see QRS DeVry Corp.

DEVUS - c1950. USSR. 6x6cm TLR. Copy of the Voigtlander Brillant, similar to the Lubitel. Momo f4.5/75mm, 1/15-250. $30-40.

DEYROLLE (France)

Scenographe (Original model) - c1876. A very early collapsible bellows camera. Wooden body with green silk bellows. Gate-type wooden struts support wooden front with sliding lensboard. Takes single or stereo exposures on 10x15cm plates. Very unusual. We have seen only one offered, in mid-1984 with original wooden case, holder, and ground glass for $5000. Later models with cloth bellows have been offered for half that amount.

DIAMOND JR. - c1898. Top loading box camera for 3¼x4¼" plates. $50-75.

DIANA - Novelty camera for 4x4cm on 120 film. The same camera exists under many other names with only minor variations in style. (Diana-F is synchronized for flash.) $1-5.

DIONNE F2 - Hong Kong "Diana" type novelty camera. $1-5.
DIPLOMAT - "Hit" type novelty camera. $8-12.
DORIES - "Diana" type novelty camera. $1-5.

DORIS - Folding 120 camera, "Occupied Japan". f3.5/75mm lens, NKS shutter. $15-20.

DORYU-2 FLASH CAMERA - c1955. Unusually designed subminiature camera disguised as a pistol. Flash cartridges are shaped like bullets. $2500-3000. (illustrated top of next column)

DOSSERT DETECTIVE CAMERA CO.

Detective Camera - c1890, NYC. 4x5 box-plate camera. Leather covered to look like a satchel. Sliding panels hide lens and

Doryu-2 Flash Camera

ground glass openings. Entire top hinges forward to reveal the plate holders for loading or storage. $750-950.

DOVER FILM CORP.
Dover 620 A - c1950. A plastic & chrome camera for 16 exp. 4.5x6cm on 620 film. Somco f9 meniscus lens. 5 rotary disc stops. Single speed shutter. Built-on flash. $10-15.

DRGM, DRP: *"Deutsches Reichs Gebrauchs Musterschuetz", "Deutsches Reichs Patent", trademark and patent notices which would indicate German construction before WWII.*

DRUOPTA (Prague, Czechoslovakia)
Druoflex I - c1950's. 6x6cm bakelite TLR. Druoptar f6.3/75mm, Chrontax 1/10-200. Copy of Voigtlander Brillant. $35-45.

DUBRONI (Maison Dubroni, Paris) *The name Dubroni is an anagram formed with the letters of the name of the inventor, Jules Bourdin. Although anagrams and acronyms have always had a certain appeal to writers, and inventors, the story in this case is quite interesting. It seems that young Jules, who was about twenty-two years old when he invented his camera, was strongly influenced by his father. The father, protective of*

*the good reputation of his name, didn't want it
mixed up with this new-fangled invention.*

Dubroni camera - c1860's. Wooden box
camera with porcelain interior (earliest
models had amber glass bottle interiors
and no wooden sides on the body) for in-
camera processing. Five models were
made, the smallest taking photos 5x5cm.
Previously sold easily at $3000-3500.
Recent auction sales have been in the
$1500-2200 range.

**DUCATI (Societa Scientifica Radio
Brevetti Ducati - Milan, Italy)**

Ducati - c1938. For 15 exp. 18x24mm on
35mm film in special cassettes. Better
models have interchangeable lenses.
Normally with f3.5 or 2.8 Vitor, or f3.5
Ducati Etar lens, 35mm focal length. FP
shutter to 500. Two major variations are
rangefinder and non-RF models.
$200-300.

DUCHESS - c1887. British ½-plate field
camera. Mahogany body, brass trim,
maroon bellows. RR brass barrel lens.
$150-200.

DURST S.A. *Most photographers know Durst
for their enlargers. However, at one time they
made some solid, well-constructed, innovative
cameras.*

Automatica - 1956-1963 for 36 exp.
24x36mm on standard 35mm cartridge
film. Schneider Durst Radionar
f2.8/45mm. Prontor 1-300, B, and Auto.

(Meter coupled to shutter by pneumatic
cylinder.) $100-125.

Duca - 1946-50. Vertically styled 35mm
camera for 12 exp. 24x36mm on Agfa
Karat Rapid cassettes. Ducan f11/50mm.
T & I shutter. Zone focus. Rapid wind.
Aluminum body. Made in black, brown,
blue, red, & white with matching colored
pouch. $65-85.

Durst 66 - 1950-1954. Compact camera
for 12 exp. 6x6cm on 120 film. Light grey
hammertone painted aluminum body with
partial red or black leather covering. Durst
Color Duplor f2.2/80mm lens. Shutter ½-
200, B, sync. $30-50.

EARL PRODUCTS CO.

Scenex - c1940. Small plastic novelty camera for 3x4cm exposures. Similar to the Cub. $8-12.

EASTERN SPECIALTY MFG. CO.
(Boston, MA)

Springfield Union Camera - c1899. Premium box camera for 3½" square plates. Four plates could be mounted on the sides of a cube, and each exposed, in turn, by rotating the cube inside the camera. An unusual design from a technical standpoint, and visually appealing with the boldly lettered exterior. $350-450.

EASTMAN DRY PLATE & FILM CO.
EASTMAN KODAK CO.

After designing the Eastman-Cossitt detective camera which was not marketed, the first camera produced by the Eastman Dry Plate & Film Co. was called "The Kodak", and successive models were numbered in sequence. These numbers each introduced a specific new image size and continued to represent that size on many cameras made by Kodak and other manufacturers. The first seven cameras listed here are the earliest

Kodak cameras, and the remainder of the listings under Eastman Kodak Co. are in alphabetical order by series name and number. Some of the Eastman models listed are continuations of lines of cameras from other companies which were taken over by Eastman. Earlier models of many of these cameras may be found under the name of the original manufacturer.
For more detailed information on Kodak cameras including production dates, original prices, identification features, and photographs of each model, see "Collectors Guide to Kodak Cameras" by Jim and Joan McKeown. $12.95 at bookstores, camera stores, or by mail from Centennial Photo, Rt. 3, Grantsburg, WI. 54840, USA.

The Kodak Camera (original model) - ca. June 1888 through 1889. Made by Frank Brownell for the Eastman Dry Plate & Film Co. Factory loaded with 100 exposures 2½" diameter. Cylindrical shutter, string set. Rapid Rectilinear lens f9/57mm. This was the first camera to use rollfilm, and is a highly prized collectors' item. $2400-2800.

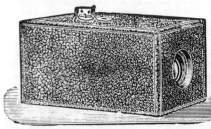

No. 1 Kodak Camera - 1889-1895. Similar to the original model, but with sector shutter rather than cylindrical. Factory loaded for 100 exp. 2½" dia. RR lens f9/57mm. $575-700.

No. 2 Kodak Camera - Oct. 1889-1897. Also similar and still quite rare, but more common than the previous models. Factory loaded for 60 exp. 3½" dia. $275-325.

No. 3 Kodak Camera - Jan. 1890-1897. A string-set box camera, factory loaded for either 60 or 100 exp. 3¼x4¼. Bausch & Lomb Universal lens, sector shutter. $325-400.

No. 3 Kodak Jr. Camera - Jan. 1890-97. A relatively scarce member of the early Kodak family. Factory loaded with 60 exp. 3¼x4¼ on rollfilm. Could also be used with accessory plate back. B&L Universal lens, sector shutter. Overall size: 4¼x5½x9. $300-350.

No. 4 Kodak Camera - Jan. 1890-1897. String-set box camera, factory loaded for 48 exp. 4x5", but with capacity for 100 exp. for prolific photographers. B&L Universal lens. Sector shutter. $250-325. *Despite its rarity, we saw a No. 4 advertised in "Shutterbug" for a year at $315 before it finally was reduced to $275 to sell.)*

No. 4 Kodak Jr. Camera - Jan 1890-97. Similar to the No. 3 Kodak Jr. Camera, but for 4x5". Factory loaded for 48 exp. on rollfilm. B&L Universal lens, sector shutter. Can also be fitted for glass plates. $350-400.

ANNIVERSARY KODAK CAMERA -

A special edition of the No. 2 Hawk-Eye Camera Model C, issued to commemorate the 50th anniversary of Eastman Kodak Co. Approximately 550,000 were given away to children 12 years old in 1930. Covered with a tan colored reptile-grained paper covering with a gold-colored foil seal on the upper rear corner of the right side. (On a worn example, the gold coloring of the foil seal may have worn off and left it looking silver.) Like New w/Box: $25-35. Mint, but without box: $20-25. VG to Excellent: $15-20.

AUTOGRAPHIC KODAK CAMERAS *The Autographic feature was introduced by Kodak in late 1914, and was available on several lines of cameras. Listed here are those cameras without any key word in their name except Autographic or Kodak.*

No. 1A - 1914-1924. For 2½x4¼" exp. on A116 film. Black leather and bellows. $10-15.
No. 3 - 1914-1926. 3¼x4¼" on A118 film. $15-20.
No. 3A - 1914-1934. 3¼x5½" (postcard size) on A122 film. This is the most common size of the Autographic Kodak Cameras. $15-25.

No. 4 - This is actually a No. 4 Folding Pocket Kodak Camera with a retrofit back, available in 1915. A No. 4 Autographic Kodak Camera was never made. *See No. 4 Folding Pocket Kodak Camera.*
No. 4A - This too is not an Autographic Kodak Camera, but simply a 1915 retrofit back on a No. 4A Folding Kodak Camera. *See No. 4A Folding Kodak Camera.*

AUTOGRAPHIC KODAK JUNIOR CAMERAS

No. 1 - 1914-1927. 2¼x3¼ on 120 film. $14-20.
No. 1A - 1914-1927. 2½x4¼ exp. on A116 film. Very common. $12-18.
No. 2C - 1916-1927. 2⅞x4⅞. A very common size in this line. $15-20.
No. 3A - 1918-1927. 3¼x5½" on A122. $12-18.

AUTOGRAPHIC KODAK SPECIAL CAMERA

No. 1 - 1915-1926. No CRF. $35-50.

No. 1A - (2½X4¼"). 1914-16 without CRF: $30-40. 1917-1926 with CRF: $40-60.

No. 2C - 1923-1928. CRF. $40-60.
No. 3 - 1914-1924. No CRF. 3¼x4¼ on A118. Uncommon size, fairly rare. $35-55.

No. 3A - 3¼x5½" on 122. 1914-16 without CRF: $30-40. 1917-33 with CRF (including the common Model B): Although sometimes advertised at higher prices, these are nearly always available for $40-60.

No. 3A Signal Corps Model K-3 - A specially finished version of the 3A Autographic Kodak Special Camera with coupled rangefinder. Body covered with smooth brown leather with tan bellows. Gunmetal grey fittings. B&L Tessar f6.3 in Optimo shutter. Name plate on bed says "Signal Corps, U.S. Army K-3" and serial number. One hundred of these cameras were made in 1916. Rare. $350-600

Kodak Automatic 35

AUTOMATIC 35 CAMERAS *An improved version of the Signet 35 Camera design. Built-in meter automatically sets the diaphragm when the shutter release is pressed.*
Automatic 35 Camera - 1959-64. Flash sync. posts on side of body. $20-30.

Automatic 35B Camera - 1961-1962. Kodak Automatic Flash shutter. $20-30.

Automatic 35F Camera - Built-in flash on top for AG-1 bulbs. $20-30.

Automatic 35R4 Camera - Built-in flashcube socket on top. $20-30.

BANTAM CAMERAS *For 28x40mm exp. on 828 rollfilm.*

(Original) - 1935-38. Rigid finder. $20-30.

f8 - 1938-42. Kodalinear f8/40mm. Rectangular telescoping front rather than bellows. $15-20.

f6.3 - 1938-47. Kodak Anastigmat f6.3/53mm. Collapsible bellows. Like original model, but has folding optical finder. $15-25.

f5.6 - 1938-41. Kodak Anastigmat f6.3/50mm Collapsible bellows. $20-30.

f4.5 - 1938-48. Kodak Anastigmat Special f4.5/47mm. Bantam shutter 20-200. Bellows. The most commonly found Bantam. $15-25.
--Military model - Signal Corps, U.S. Army PH502/PF, Ord. No. 19851. $150-200.

Bantam Colorsnap - Made in London by Kodak Ltd. Kodak Anaston lens, single speed shutter. $5-10.

Flash Bantam Camera - 1947-53. Early model (1947-48) has Kodak Anastigmat Special f4.5/48mm. Shutter 25-200. $25-35. Later model 1948-53 with Kodak Anastar f4.5/48mm is more common. $20-25.

film; in 1933-1934 for 620 film. $50-75.

Bantam RF Camera - 1953-57. Non-interchangeable f3.9/50mm Kodak Ektanon Anastigmat. Shutter 25-300. Coupled rangefinder 3' to infinity. $15-30.

Bantam Special Camera - Compur Rapid shutter (1936-40) is more common that the Supermatic shutter (1941-48). CRF 3' to infinity. With Supermatic: $140-160. With Compur Rapid: $100-125.

BOY SCOUT BROWNIE CAMERA, SIX-20 BOY SCOUT BROWNIE CAMERA - Simple box cameras. Special metal faceplate with Boy Scout emblem. Made in 1932 for 120

BOY SCOUT KODAK CAMERA - 1929-33. For 4.5x6cm on 127 rollfilm. This is a vest-pocket camera in olive drab color with official Boy Scout emblem engraved on the bed. With matching case. $65-95. With replacement black bellows: $50-60.

BROWNIE CAMERAS
(Original) - Introduced in February, 1900, this box camera was made to take a new size film, No. 117 for 2¼x2¼ exposures. The back of the camera fit like the cover of a shoe-box. Constructed of cardboard, and measuring 3x3x5" overall, this camera lasted only four months in production before the back was re-designed. A rare box camera. With accessory waist-level finder. $475-550.
(illustrated top of next page)

The Brownie Camera (original)

No. 0 - A small (4x3¼x6cm) box camera of the mid-teens for 127 film. Slightly larger than the earlier "Pocket Kodak" of 1895. Cute, but not scarce. $15-20.

No. 1 - In May or June of 1900, this improved version of the original Brownie Camera was introduced, and became the first commercially successful Brownie camera. Although not rare, it is historically interesting. $35-45. With accessory finder, winding key and orig. box. $75-100. *The earliest examples of this camera were marked "The Brownie Camera". When additional sizes were introduced, the designation was changed to "No. 1". The early examples would bring an extra $25-35.*

No. 2 - 1901-33. Cardboard box camera, 6 exposures 2¼x3¼" on 120 film, which was introduced for this camera. Mensiscus lens, rotary shutter. (An early variation had smooth finish and the same rear clamp as the No. 1. This variation has an estimated

value of $20-25. Most have grained pattern cloth covering. Later models, some of which were also made in London, came in colors. Black: $3-8. Colored: $12-18.

No. 2A - 1907-33. Cardboard box camera for 2½x4¼" on 116 film. Later models in colors. Black: $3-8. Colored: $10-16.

No. 2C - 1917-34. Box camera for 2⅞x4⅞" on 130 film. $3-8.

No. 3 - 1908-34. Box camera for 3¼x4¼" on 124 film. $3-8.

Brownie 127 Camera - 1953-59. Bakelite body with rounded ends, as if slightly inflated. Made in England. $5-8.

Brownie Auto 27 Camera - 1963-64. Electric-eye version of Brownie Super 27. $7-10.

No. 2A Beau Brownie Camera

Baby Brownie was made in 1939-1940 for the World's Fair, with a special New York World's Fair faceplate. $100-150.

Baby Brownie Special - 1939-54. Bakelite box camera for 4x6.5cm exp. on 127 film. Rigid optical finder. $3-8.

Beau Brownie Camera - 1930-33. A No. 2 or No. 2A Brownie (box) camera, but in classy two-tone color combinations of blue, green, black, tan, or rose. Either size in rose: $60-100.
No.2 - Color other than rose: $25-40.
No. 2A - Color other than rose: $30-45.
(illustrated top of previous column)

Brownie Bull's-Eye Camera - 1954-60. Vertically styled bakelite camera with metal faceplate, Focusing Twindar lens. For 6x9cm on 620 film. Black: $3-8. Gold: $5-12. *See also "Six-20 Bull's-Eye Brownie Camera" below.*

Baby Brownie Camera - 1934-41. Bakelite box camera for 4x6.5cm exp. on 127 film. Folding frame finder. $3-6.

Baby Brownie, New York World's Fair Model - 1939. A special version of the

Brownie Bullet Camera - 1957-64. A premium version of the Brownie Holiday Camera. 4.5x6cm on 127 film. $1-5.

Brownie Bullet II Camera - 1961-68. Similar to the Brownie Starlet camera (USA type). Not like the Brownie Bullet Camera! 4.5x6cm exp. on 127 film. $1-5.

Brownie Chiquita Camera - Same as the Brownie Bullet Camera, except for the faceplate and original box which are in Spanish. With original box: $10-20.

Brownie Fiesta Camera - 1962-66; Fiesta R4- 1966-69. $1-5.

Brownie Flash Camera - Black bakelite box camera identical to the Brownie Hawkeye Flash Model. Made in France for the French market. "Brownie Flash Camera Made in France" on front plate. $10-20.

Brownie Flash B - Metal box camera from Kodak Ltd. in London. Shutter B, 40, 80. Brown and beige color. $10-20. Add $5-10 for original canvas case.

Brownie Flash IV - London-made brown metal box camera with tan covering. Built in close-up lens and yellow filter. Camera only: $10-20. Add $5-10 for original canvas case.

Brownie Flash 20 Camera - 1959-62. Styled like the Brownie Starflash Camera, but larger size for 620 film. $4-8.

Brownie Flash Six-20 Camera - Post-war name for Six-20 Flash Brownie Camera. Trapezoidal metal body. With flash: $4-8.

Brownie Flashmite 20 Camera - 1960-65. $1-4.

FOLDING BROWNIE CAMERAS
Identifiable by their square-cornered bodies and horizontal format. The No. 3 and No. 3A are at least ten times more commonly found for sale than the No. 2, although prices are much the same. These cameras sell in Europe for about double the USA price.
No. 2 - 1904-07. Maroon bellows, wooden lens standard. For 2¼x3¼ on 120 film. $20-30.

No. 3 - 1905-15. 3¼x4¼ on 124 film. $20-30.
No. 3A - 1909-15. 3¼x5½ "postcard" size. Maroon bellows. The most common size. $20-25.

FOLDING AUTOGRAPHIC BROWNIE
CAMERAS *These are a continuation of the Folding Brownie Camera series, but with the addition of the "Autographic" feature. Some of the earlier examples still have the square corners of the earlier style. About 1916, when the 3A size*

was introduced, they were all given the new rounded corners. Square cornered models with the autographic feature could be worth a few dollars more to a serious collector of Kodak cameras.

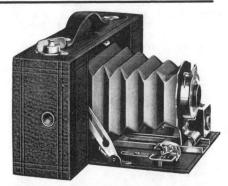

No. 2A - 1910-15. 2½x4¼" on 116 film. With red or black bellows. $15-22.

No. 2 - 1915-26. 2¼x3¼" on 120 film. Very common. $8-16.

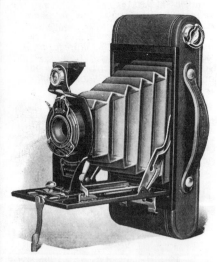

No. 2A - 1915-26. 2½x4¼". By far the most common size of this line. $8-16.
No. 2C - 1916-26. 2⅞x4⅞" exp. $15-22.
No. 3A - 1916-26. 3¼x5½". $10-20.

FOLDING POCKET BROWNIE CAMERAS *Horizontal style folding rollfilm cameras. Square-cornered bodies.*
No. 2 - 1907-15. 2¼x3¼". A continuation of the No. 2 Folding Brownie, but with metal not wooden lensboard. $12-20.

Brownie Hawkeye Camera - 1949-51; Flash Model, 1950-61. Molded plastic box camera for 2¼x2¼" exp. on 620 film. $1-3.

Brownie Holiday Camera - 1953-57; Flash model, 1954-62. 4x6.5cm exp. on 127 film. $1-5.

Brownie Junior 620 Camera - 1934-36. Metal box camera. Made by Kodak A.G. Dr. Nagel-Werk and not imported to the U.S.A. $15-25.

Popular Brownie Camera - 1937-40. Made by Kodak Ltd., London. Box camera for 6x9cm on 620 film. $8-12.

Portrait Brownie Camera, No. 2 - Kodak Ltd. 1929-35. 6x9cm on 120 film. $15-25.

Brownie Reflex Camera - 1940-41; Synchro model, 1941-52. 1⅝x1⅝" exp. on 127 film. $1-5.

Brownie Reflex 20 Camera - 1959-66. Reflex style like the Brownie Starflex Camera, but larger for 620 film. $1-5.

Six-16 or Six-20 Brownie Cameras - 1933-41. Cardboard box cameras with metal art-deco front. $1-5.

Brownie Six-20 Camera Models C,D,E - 1950-59. 2¼x3¼" exp. on 620 film. Made by Kodak Ltd., London. $5-10.

Six-16 or Six-20 Brownie Junior Cameras - 1934-42. Box cameras with art-deco front. $1-5.

Six-16 or Six-20 Brownie Special Cameras - 1938-42. Trapezoid-shaped box. $1-5.

Six-20 Bull's-Eye Brownie Camera - 1938-41. Black bakelite trapezoidal body with eye-level finder above top. Braided strap on side. For 2¼x3¼" exp. on 620 film. $10-20.

Six-20 Flash Brownie Camera - 1940-46. Metal trapezoidal box camera, 2¼x3¼" exp. on 620 film. $1-5.

Brownie Starlet Camera, Kodak Ltd.

Brownie Starflash Camera - 1957-65. Black, blue, red, or white. $1-5.

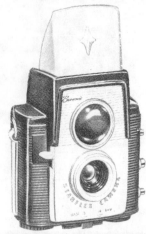

Brownie Starflex Camera - 1957-64. $1-5.

Brownie Starlet Camera (USA) - 1957-62. 4x4cm on 127. $1-5.

Brownie Starlet Camera (Kodak Ltd.) - 1956. 4x6.5cm on 127. $5-10. *(illustrated on previous page)*

Brownie Starmatic Camera - 1959-61; Starmatic II, 1961-63. 4x4cm on 127 film. Built-in automatic meter. $5-10.
Brownie Starmeter Camera - 1960-65. Uncoupled selenium meter. $5-10.
Brownie Starmite Camera - 1960-63; Starmite II, 1962-67. $1-4.

No. 2 Stereo Brownie Camera - 1905-10. Similar to the Blair Stereo Weno Camera. For 3¼x2½" exposure pairs on rollfilm. Red bellows. Stereo Brownie Cameras are much less common than comparable Stereo Hawk-Eye Cameras. $250-350.

Brownie Super 27 - 1961-65. $3-8.

Target Brownie Six-16 and Six-20 Cameras and **Brownie Target Six-16 and Six-20 Cameras** - Metal and leatherette box cameras. Introduced in 1941. Name changed from Target Brownie to Brownie Target in 1946. Six-16 discontinued in 1951; Six-20 in 1952. $1-5.

Brownie Twin 20 Camera - 1959-64. Waist level and eye-level finders. $1-5.

Brownie Vecta - Grey plastic 127 camera made in England. $10-15.

BUCKEYE CAMERA - c1899. Eastman Kodak Co. purchased the American Camera Mfg. Co., which originated this model. The Eastman camera is nearly identical to the earlier version. A folding bed camera of all wooden construction, covered with leather. Lens standard of polished wood conceals the shutter behind a plain front. An uncommon rollfilm model. $75-125.

BULL'S-EYE CAMERAS *After Kodak took over the Boston Camera Manufacturing Co., it* *continued Boston's line of cameras under the Kodak name. (See also Boston Bull's-Eye.) Bull's-Eye cameras are often stamped with their year model as were other early Kodak cameras. Leather exterior conceals a beautifully polished wooden interior.*

No. 2 - 1896-1913. Leather covered wood box which loads from the top. 3½x3½" exposures on 101 rollfilm or double plateholders. Rotary disc shutter. Rotating disc stops. $20-35.

No. 3 - 1908-1913. This model loads from the side. 3¼x4¼" on No. 124 film. Less common than the No. 2 and No. 4. $30-40.

No. 4 - 1896-1904. Nine models. Side-loading 4x5" box for 103 rollfilm. Internal bellows focus by means of an outside lever. $40-55.

No. 2 Folding Bull's-Eye Camera - 1899-1901. For 3½x3½" exposures. Scarce. $100-125.

BULL'S-EYE SPECIAL CAMERAS *Similar to the Bull's-Eye box cameras above, but with higher quality RR lens in Eastman Triple Action Shutter. 1898-1904*
No. 2 - 3½x3½" exp. on 101 rollfilm. $50-75.

No. 4 - 4x5" exposures on 103 rollfilm. $60-80.

BULLET CAMERAS

Bullet Camera (plastic) - 1936-42. A cheap & simple torpedo-shaped camera with fixed focus lens mounted in a spiral-threaded telescoping mount. Common, inexpensive, yet novel. $6-12.

Bullet Camera, New York World's Fair Model - 1939-40. A special World's Fair version of the Bullet camera, marked "New York World's Fair" on a metal faceplate. In colorful original box: $150-175. Camera only: $80-100.

No. 2 Bullet Camera - 1895-1896, improved model 1896-1900, double plateholder option 1900-1902. Box camera for 3½x3½" exposures on glass plates or rollfilm which was first introduced in 1895 for this camera and later numbered 101. Measures 4½x4½x6". Some models named by year and marked on the camera. $25-35.

No. 4 Bullet Camera - 1896-1900. For 4x5" exposures on No. 103 rollfilm (introduced for this camera) or could be used with a single plateholder which stores in the rear of the camera. A large leather covered box. $50-75.

BULLET SPECIAL CAMERAS *Similar to the No. 2 and No. 4 Bullet Cameras above, but with a higher quality RR lens in Eastman Triple Action Shutter. 1898-1904.*

No. 2 - $50-80.
No. 4 - $100-150.

CAMP FIRE GIRLS KODAK - 1931-34. A brown olding vest-pocket camera with Camp Fire Girls emblem on the front door and "Camp Fire Girl's Kodak" on the shutter face. This is a very rare camera, unlike the less rare Girl Scout or the common Boy Scout models. With matching case: $250-350. *(illustrated on top of next page)*

Camp Fire Girl's Kodak Camera

CARTRIDGE KODAK CAMERAS *Made to take "cartridge" film, as rollfilm was called in the early years.*

No. 3 - 1900-1907. For 4¼x3¼" exp. on No. 119 rollfilm, which was introduced for this camera. This is the smallest of the series. Various shutters and lenses. $60-75.

No. 4 - 1897-1907. For 5x4" exp. on 104 rollfilm (introduced for this camera). This is the first of the series. Leather covered wood body, polished wood interior. Red bellows. Various shutters/lens combinations. (Orig. price was $25.) $60-75.

No. 5 - 1898-1900 with wooden lensboard and bed; 1900-1907 with metal lensboard. For 7x5" exp. on No. 115 rollfilm or on plates. (No. 115 rollfilm, introduced for this camera, was 7" wide to provide the 7x5" vertical format.) Red bellows. Various shutters/lens combinations. $70-90.

CENTURY OF PROGRESS, WORLD'S FAIR SOUVENIR - Made for the 1933 World's Fair. Box camera for 2¼x3¼" exp. on 120 film. $100-150.

CHEVRON CAMERA - 1953-1956. For 2¼x2¼" on 620 film. Kodak Ektar f3.5/78mm lens. Synchro-Rapid 800 shutter. $140-175.

CIRKUT CAMERAS, CIRKUT OUTFITS
Manufactured by the Rochester Panoramic Camera Co. 1904-05; Century Camera Co. 1905-07, Century Camera Division of Eastman Kodak Co. 1907-1915; Folmer & Schwing Div. of EKC 1915-17; F&S Dept. of EKC 1917-26; Folmer Graflex 1925-45; Graflex, Inc. (sales only) 1945-49. For obvious reasons of continuity, we are listing all Cirkut equipment under the Eastman Kodak heading rather than split it among all these various companies.

Basically, a Cirkut OUTFIT is a revolving-back cycle view camera with an accessory Cirkut back, tripod, and gears. A Cirkut CAMERA is designed exclusively for Cirkut photos and cannot be used as a view camera. Both types take panoramic pictures by revolving the entire camera on a geared tripod head while the film moves past a narrow slit at the focal plane and is taken up on a drum. These cameras are numbered according to film width, the common sizes being 5, 6, 8, and 10 inches.

NOTE - All prices listed here are for complete outfits with tripod and gears.

No. 5 Cirkut Camera - 1915-1923. With Turner Reich Triple Convertible lens. $500-650.

No. 6 Cirkut Camera - 1932-1949. Triple convertible lens. $800-1000.

No. 6 Cirkut Outfit - 1907-1925. (5x7 RB Cycle Graphic). With Series II Centar lens: $450-700. With Graphic Rapid Rectilinear convertible 5x7 lens: $500-750.

No. 8 Cirkut Outfit - 1907-1926. Based on 6½x8½ RB Cycle Graphic. Uses 6" or 8" film. With Triple Convertible lens: $700-900.

No. 10 Cirkut Camera - 1904-1941. Uses 10", 8", or 6" film. This is the most desirable as a usable camera. With Triple Convertible lens: $1500-2000.

No. 16 Cirkut Camera - 1906-1924. Takes 16", 12", 10", or 8" film. Quite rare. Limited production. $2500-3000.

NO. 1 CONE POCKET KODAK - c1898. A very unusual early Kodak camera which is essentially a non-folding box camera version of the Folding Pocket Kodak camera. Early records indicate that 1000

were shipped to London, from where they were apparently shipped to France. Since 1981 at least two examples have surfaced. Price negotiable. Rare.

COQUETTE CAMERA - 1930-31. A boxed Kodak Petite Camera in blue with matching lipstick holder and compact. Art-deco "lightning" design. $500-750.

DAYLIGHT KODAK CAMERAS *The Daylight Kodak Cameras are the first of the Kodak string-set cameras not requiring darkroom loading. All are rollfilm box cameras with Achromatic lens and sector shutter. Made from 1891 to 1895, each took 24 exposures on daylight-loading rollfilm.*

"A" - 2¾x3¼". (Orig. cost- $8.50). $750-1000.

"B" - 3½x4". (Orig. cost- $15.00). $425-525.

"C" - 4x5". (Orig. cost- $25.00). $400-500. (Also available in a plate version called "C" Special Glass Plate Kodak Camera.)

DUAFLEX CAMERAS - 1947-60. Models I-IV. Cheap TLR's for 2¼x2¼" on 620 film. $4-7. (Add $2-4 for focusing models.)

DUEX CAMERA - 1940-42. 4.5x6cm on 620 film. Helical telescoping front. Doublet lens. $10-15.

DUO SIX-20 CAMERA - 1934-37. Folding camera for 16 exposures 4.5x6cm on 620 film. Made in Germany. f3.5/70mm Kodak Anastigmat or Zeiss Tessar lens. Compur or Compur Rapid shutter. $35-50.

DUO SIX-20 SERIES II CAMERA (without RF) - 1937-39. Folding optical finder on top. No rangefinder. $35-45.

DUO SIX-20 SERIES II CAMERA w/RANGEFINDER - 1939-40. Rangefinder incorporated in top housing. Kodak Anastigmat f3.5/75mm lens in Compur Rapid shutter. $225-300.

EASTMAN PLATE CAMERA, No. 3, No. 4, and No. 5 - c1903. No. 3 in 3¼x4¼", No. 4 in 4x5", and No. 5 in 5x7". Folding bed cycle style plate cameras with swing back more typical of some of the Rochester Optical Co. earlier models. Double extension bellows. RR lens. Kodak shutter. $65-100.

KODAK EKTRA - 1941-48. 35mm RF camera. Interchangeable lenses & magazine backs. Focal plane shutter to 1000. A precision camera which originally sold for $300 with the f1.9/50mm lens. Current value with f1.9/50mm: $375-450.
Ektra accessories:
- 35mm f3.3: $90-125.
- 50mm f1.9: $60-75.
- 50mm f3.5 (scarce): $100-150.
- 90mm f3.5: $90-120.
- 135mm f3.8: $100-125.
- 153mm f4.5: $750-1000.
- Magazine back: $100-125.
- Ground glass back: $175-225.

KODAK EKTRA II - Yes, there is an Ektra II, c1944. Apparently made as an experimental model. We know of only one extant example (Ser. #7021), which also had a spring-motor auto advance back. Price information not available.

KODAK EKTRA 1, 2, 200 CAMERAS -

1978-. Simple 110 pocket cameras for 13x17mm exposures. $1-5.

EMPIRE STATE CAMERAS - c1893-1914. View cameras, usually found in 5x7", 6½x8½", and 8x10" sizes. With original lens and shutter: $100-150.

KODAK ENSEMBLE - 1929-33. A Kodak Petite Camera with lipstick, compact, and mirror in a suede case. Available in beige, green, and old rose. $350-450.

EUREKA CAMERAS *1898-99. Box cameras for glass plates in standard double holders which insert through side door. Storage space for additional holders. Achromatic lens, rotary shutter.*

No. 2 - 3½x3½ exp. on plates or on No. 106 Cartridge film in rollholder. $45-70.

No. 2, Jr. - same size, but cheaper model for plates only. $50-75.

ends, made by Kodak for Fisher-Price. New: $20-30.

No. 4 - 1899 only. For 4x5" exposures on No. 109 Cartridge film in rollholder. $50-75.

THE FALCON CAMERA - 1897-98. Style similar to the Pocket Kodak Camera, but larger. 2x2½" exposures on special rollfilm. $50-75.

NO. 2 FALCON CAMERA - 1897-99. Box camera for 3½x3½" exposures on No. 101 rollfilm. Knob on front of camera to cock shutter. Leather covered wood. $40-60.

FIFTIETH ANNIVERSARY CAMERA (see Anniversary Kodak Camera)

FISHER-PRICE CAMERA - c1984. Pocket 110 cartridge camera with cushioned

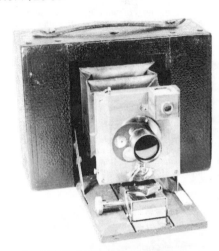

FLAT FOLDING KODAK CAMERA - 1894-95. Kodak's first folding camera with integral rollfilm back. Marketed only in England. RARE. Very few exist. $800-1200.

FLEXO KODAK CAMERA, No. 2 - 1899-1913. Box camera for 12 exp. 3½x3½" on No. 101 rollfilm. The most unusual feature is that the sides and back come completely off for loading, and are held together only by the leather covering. It is very similar in outward appearance to the Bull's-Eye series, but was slighty cheaper when new. The same camera was marketed in Europe under the name "Plico". Achromatic lens, rotary shutter. (Orig. cost-$5.00). $25-35.

FLUSH BACK KODAK CAMERA, No. 3 - 1908-15. A special version of the No. 3 Folding Pocket Kodak Camera for 3¼x4¼" exposures on 118 film, or for glass plates. B&L RR lens in B&L Auto shutter. Made for the European market and not sold in the U.S.A. $40-60.

FOLDING KODAK CAMERAS *There are two distinct styles of "Folding Kodak" cameras which share little more than a common name. The earlier models, numbered 4, 5, and 6 by size, resemble a carrying case when closed, and are easily identifiable by the hinged top door which hangs over the sides like a box cover. The later model can be distinguished by its vertical format and rounded body ends in the more common style. We are listing the early models first followed by the later one.*

FOLDING KODAK CAMERAS (early "satchel style") *There are three variations of the No. 4 and No. 5: Sector shutter in 1890-91; Barker shutter, 1892; and the Improved version with B&L Iris Diaphragm shutter and hinged drop bed, 1893-97.*

*No. 4 Folding Kodak Camera
with early sector shutter*

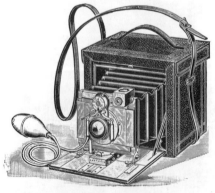

*No. 4 Folding Kodak Improved Camera
with B&L Iris Diaphragm shutter*

No. 4, No. 4 Improved - 1890-1897. For 48 exp. 4x5" on glass plates or rollfilm in rollholder. $350-450.

*No. 5 Folding Kodak Camera
with Barker Shutter*

No. 5, No. 5 Improved - 1890-1897. Similar specifications, but for 5x7" film or plates. $450-550.

No. 5 Improved with stereo lensboard - The same camera as the No. 5 Folding Kodak Improved Camera, but with a stereo lensboard and a partition for stereo work. RARE. No recent sales.

No. 6 Improved - 1893-1895. Similar, but for 6½x8½". Since the No. 6 was not introduced until 1893, it was only made in the "Improved" version with B&L Iris Diaphragm shutter. This size is even less common than the others. $700-1000.

NO. 4A FOLDING KODAK CAMERA -
1906-1915. Vertical folding-bed camera similar to the "Folding Pocket" series. For 6 exp., 4¼x6½" on No. 126 rollfilm. (126 rollfilm, made from 1906-1949, is not to be confused with the more recent 126 cassettes.) Red bellows. $50-90.

FOLDING POCKET KODAK CAMERAS

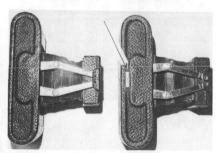

Folding Pocket Kodak Cameras:
Original model (left) has 4 round openings on front, lens cone, and no backlatch slide. Second model (right) has only two finder openings, no lens cone, and has metal backlatch slide.

The Folding Pocket Kodak Camera
Renamed No. 1 after 1899. For 2¼x3¼" exp. on No. 105 rollfilm. Leather covered front pulls straight out. Double finders concealed behind leather covered front. Red bellows. The earliest production models (c1897-1898) included a sequence of changes which led to the more standard "No. 1". The true "Original" had ALL of these features, and later models had some.
1. Recessed lens opening, a wooden "cone" shape (the shutter is quite different from later versions because of this odd opening.)
2. All brass metal parts are unplated.
3. There are four small openings on the face, two of which are used for finders.
4. No locking clasp for the back.
5. Patent pending.
6. Flat bar provided for horizontal standing, but no vertical stand.

--Original model - all features above: $150-200.
--Transitional models - Brass struts, but not all of the above features: $125-150.
--Nickeled struts - c1898-99: $60-80.

No. 0 - 1902-1906. Similar in style to the original. For 4.5x6cm exposures on No. 121 film which was introduced for this camera. It is the smallest of the series, but by no means the first as some collectors have been misled to believe. $70-90

No. 1, (pull-out front) - 1899-1905. Nickeled struts. Similar to the original model. $30-50.

No. 1 with twin-finders

No. 1, (bed-type) - 1905-1915. For 2¼x3¼" exposures. Recognizable by the domed front door, red bellows, and twin sprung struts for the lensboard. Self-erecting bed. Various models. With twin-finders (made briefly): $40-60. With single, reversible finder: $20-35.

No. 1A, (pull-out front) - 1899-1905. Similar to the original FPK, but for 2½x4¼" exposures. $35-50.

No. 1A, (bed-type) - 1905-1915. For 2½x4¼" exposures on 116 rollfilm. Domed front door, twin sprung struts, red bellows. Self-erecting bed. Various models. With twin-finders (made briefly): $40-55. With single, reversible finder: $20-35.

No. 1A Folding Pocket Kodak Camera R.R. Type - (1912-1915) and **No. 1A Folding Pocket Kodak Special Camera -** (1908-1912) Similar to the regular "1A" but with better lenses and shutters. $25-40.

No. 2 - Horizontal style camera for square exposures 3½x3½ on No. 101 rollfilm. Front

is not self-erecting. Bed folds down, and front standard pulls out on track. Flat rectangular front door. First model (1899-1905) has leather covered lensboard with recessed lens and shutter: $50-70. Later models (1905-1915) have wooden standard with exposed shutter and lens: $35-45.

No. 3 - Vertical style folding-bed camera for 3¼x4¼" exposures on 118 rollfilm. Flat rectangular front door. Early models (1900-1903) with leather covered lensboard concealing the rotary shutter: $35-65. Later models (1904-1915) with exposed lens and shutter: $15-25.

No. 3, Deluxe - 1901-03. A No. 3 Folding Pocket Kodak in Persian Morocco covering and brown silk bellows. Rare. Price negotiable. Estimate: $200-400.

No. 3A - 1903-1915. Vertical folding-bed camera for 3¼x5½" exposures on 122 rollfilm (introduced for this camera). Flat, rectangular front door. Red bellows. Polished wood insets on bed. By far the most common model of the FPK series. $18-28.

No. 4 - 1907-1915. Vertical folding-bed camera for 4x5" exposures on 123 rollfilm. Red bellows, polished wood insets on bed. $45-60.

GENESEE OUTFIT - c1886. An early and relatively unknown 5x7" view camera made by Frank Brownell for the Eastman Dry Plate & Film Co. Complete with plateholders, brass-barrel R.R. lens with waterhouse stops, etc. $200-250.

which repeats the art-deco design of the camera. Original price in the 1930 Christmas season was just $15.00. A few years ago these brought a bit more, but enough have appeared to fill the demand and reduce the price. Camera only: $50-75. With gift box: $150-225.

GEORGE WASHINGTON BICENTENNIAL CAMERA - c1932. One of the rarest of Kodak box cameras. This one, like the 50th Anniversary of Kodak camera is based on the No. 2 Rainbow Hawk-Eye Model C, but with special colored covering and a seal on the side. This camera is a very attractive blue, with an art-deco front plate with an enameled red, white, and blue star. Unfortunately, due to the depressed economy in 1932, Kodak decided not to market the camera, and only a few examples are known to exist. You will probably never find one, but if you do, the authors and many of their friends would like very much to get into a bidding war over it.

GIFT KODAK CAMERA, No. 1A - 1930-1931. A special rendition of the No. 1A Pocket Kodak Junior Camera. The camera is covered with brown genuine leather, and decorated with an enameled metal inlay on the front door, as well as a matching metal faceplate on the shutter. The case is a cedar box, the top plate of

GIRL SCOUT KODAK CAMERA - 1929-1934. For 4.5x6cm exposures on 127 film. Bright green color with official GSA emblem engraved on the bed. $75-100.

HAPPY TIMES INSTANT CAMERA -
1978. A special two-tone brown premium
version of "The Handle" camera with
Coca-Cola trademarks. Originally sold for
$17.95 with purchase of Coca-Cola
products. Current value: $30-35.

HAWKETTE CAMERA, No. 2 - c1930's.
British made folding Kodak camera for
2¼x3¼" exposures on 120 rollfilm. Folding
style like the Houghton Ensignette with
cross-swinging struts. Body of bakelite
plastic. These cameras were used as
premiums for such diverse products as
Cadbury Chocolates and Australian
cigarettes. The mottled brown version is a
very attractive camera. Fairly common.
Colored: $25-35. Black: $15-25.

HAWK-EYE CAMERAS *The Hawk-Eye line
originated with the Blair Camera Co. and was
continued by Kodak after they absorbed the
Blair Co. See also Blair Hawk-Eye.*

**CARTRIDGE HAWK-EYE CAMERAS
(Box cameras)**
No. 2 - 1924-1934. 2¼x3¼". $4-8.
No. 2A - 1924-1934. 2½x4¼". $4-8.

FILM PACK HAWK-EYE CAMERAS
No. 2 - 1922-1925. Box camera for
2¼x3¼" film packs. All metal construction.
$8-15.
No. 2A - 1923-1925. Box camera for
2½x4¼" film packs. $8-15.

**HAWKEYE FLASHFUN, FLASHFUN II
CAMERAS -** $3-6.

FOLDING HAWK-EYE CAMERAS

No. 1A - 1908-19. 2½x4¼". Red bellows.
Various lens and shutter combinations.
With Meniscus or RR lens in Kodak Ball
Bearing or pneumatic shutter: $15-25.
With Zeiss-Kodak Anastigmat or Tessar
IIB lens in Compound shutter: $20-30.

No. 3 - 1904-1915. Models 1-9. 3¼x4¼"
exposures on 118 film. Horizontal format.
$20-30.

No. 3A - 1908-1915. Models 1-4. 3¼x5½"
exposures on 122 film. Horizontal format.
$25-30.

No. 4 - 1904-1913. Models 1-4. 4x5"
exposures on 103 rollfilm. $30-40.

Six-16 or Six-20 - 1933-1934. $15-25.

**FOLDING HAWK-EYE SPECIAL
CAMERAS -** In four sizes, with Kodak
Anastigmat f6.3 lens.
No. 2 - 1928-1933. $10-20.
No. 2A - 1928-1930. $10-20.
No. 3 - 1929-1934. $10-20.
No. 3A - c1929. $15-20.

**FOLDING CARTRIDGE HAWK-EYE
CAMERAS**
No. 2 - 1926-1933. 2¼x3¼" on 120 film.
Kodex shutter. Colored models: $15-25.
Black: $6-12.
No. 2A - 1926-1934. 2½x4¼" on 116 film.
Single Achromatic or RR lens. $9-18.
No. 3A - 1926-1935. 3¼x5½" on 122 flm.
Kodak shutter. RR or Achromatic lens.
$10-15.

FOLDING FILM PACK HAWK-EYE CAMERA, No. 2 - 1923. Hawk-Eye shutter. Meniscus Achromatic lens. 2¼x3¼" exposures on film packs. $12-18.

RAINBOW HAWK-EYE CAMERAS *Box cameras, similar to the Cartridge Hawk-Eye, but in colors: blue, green, maroon, vermillion.*

No. 2 - 1929-1933. 2¼x3¼" exposures. Colors: $10-18. Black: $4-8.
No. 2A - 1931-1932. Same, but in 2½x4¼" size. Colors: $10-18. Black: $4-8.

FOLDING RAINBOW HAWK-EYE CAMERAS *Similar to the Folding Hawk-Eye Cameras, but available in black and colors: blue, brown, green, old rose. (Subtract 35% for black replacement bellows.)*
No. 2 - 1930-1934. 2¼x3¼". $18-25.
No. 2A - 1930-1933. 2½x4¼". $18-25.

FOLDING RAINBOW HAWK-EYE SPECIAL CAMERAS *1930-1933. Available in black and colors: black, blue, brown, green, maroon.*
Nos. 2, 2A - $50-80.

HAWK-EYE SPECIAL CAMERAS -

Deluxe model box cameras with embossed morocco-grain imitation leather.
No. 2 - 1928-1933. $12-18.
No. 2A - 1928-1930. $12-18.

STEREO HAWK-EYE CAMERA - A continuation of the Blair Stereo Hawk-Eye series produced through 1916, and labeled "Blair Division of Eastman Kodak Co." A folding stereo camera taking twin 3½x3½" exposures. Various models, numbered in sequence, offered various lens/shutter combinations. Mahogany interior, brass trim, red bellows. $150-250.

TARGET HAWK-EYE CAMERAS, No. 2, No. 2 Junior, No. 2A, Six-16, and Six-20 - Simple box cameras. No. 2 available in black only, others available in black, blue, and brown. 1932- 1933. Black: $1-5. Colors: $12-18.

VEST POCKET HAWK-EYE CAMERA - 1927-1934. 4.5x6cm exposures. Single or Periscopic lens. $15-25.

VEST POCKET RAINBOW HAWK-EYE CAMERA - 1930-1933. Same as the V.P. Hawkeye, but in black or colors: blue, green, orchid, and rose. Black: $20-30. Colors, with original colored bellows: $50-70.

WENO HAWK-EYE CAMERAS *Box cameras originally made by Blair Camera Co. and continued by Eastman Kodak Co. until 1915. See also Blair Weno Hawk-Eye Camera.*

EKC HAWKEYE (cont.) - INSTAMATIC

No. 2 - 3½x3½". $20-25.
No. 4 - 4x5". $20-25.
No. 5 - 3¼x4¼". $20-25.
No. 7 - 3¼x5½". Introduced in 1908 after Blair became a part of EKC. $25-35.

INSTAMATIC CAMERAS *Introduced in 1963, using the new 126 cartridge. A variety of models made, most of which are still too new and common to be collectible. To give a fairly complete list in a small space, we have grouped them together by features.*

Basic models - 100, 104, 124, 44, X-15, X-15F: $1-3.

With meter - 300, 304, 134, 314, X-30, X-35, X-35F: $5-10.

Spring motor models - 150, 154, 174, X-25: $10-20.
Spring Motor & meter - 400, 404, 414, X-45: $15-25.

f2.8 metered models - 324, 500, 700, 704, 714: $25-50.

f2.8, meter, motor, RF - 800, 804, 814, X-90: $25-50.

Instamatic Reflex - 1968-74. SLR for 126 cartridges. Interchangeable lenses. With Xenar f2.8/45mm or Xenon f1.9/50mm lens: $45-80.

Instamatic S-10 & S-20 - 1967-71/72. Compact models with rectangular pop-out front. Advance knob on end. S-20 has meter. $5-10.

JIFFY KODAK CAMERAS *Common rollfilm cameras with pop-out front, twin spring struts. The vest pocket model has a Doublet lens, other models have Twindar lens, zone focus. Note: Back latch is often broken which reduces the value by 40-50%.*

Six-16 - 1933-37. Art-deco enameled front. 2½x4¼" on 616 film. $10-15.

Six-16, Series II - 1937-42. Similar to the Six-16, but with imitation leather front instead of the art-deco. Not as common. $12-18.

Six-20 - 1933-37. Art-deco front. 2¼x3¼" on 620 rollfilm. $10-15.

Six-20, Series II - 1937-48. Similar to the Six-20, but with imitation leather front. $12-18.

Vest Pocket - 1935-42. 4.5x6cm on 127 rollfilm. Black plastic construction. $10-15.

KODAK BOX 620 CAMERA - 1936-37. All black metal box camera with leatherette covering. Made by Kodak A.G., Stuttgart. $12-18.

KODAK JUNIOR CAMERAS *Two of Eastman's first cameras bore the name Junior along with their number. They are the No. 3 Kodak Jr., and the No. 4 Kodak Jr. Both are box cameras with string-set shutters, and are listed at the beginning of the Eastman Kodak section. The models listed here are folding-bed cameras. Nos. 1 and 1A were introduced in 1914 shortly before the Autographic feature became available. These cameras had a short life-span, with the Autographic Kodak Junior Cameras taking their place. (See Autographic Kodak Junior Cameras.)*

No. 1 - 2¼x3¼" on 120 rollfilm. $12-18.
No. 1A - 2½x4¼" on 116 film. $12-18.

Six-16 - 1935-37. 2½x4¼" in 616 film. Octagonal shutter face. Self-erecting bed. $15-25.

Six-16, Series II - 1937-40. Similar. $12-18.

Six-16, Series III - 1938-39. Self-erecting. Streamlined bed supports. $12-18.

Six-20 - 1935-37. Octagonal shutter face. Self-erecting bed. $15-20.

Six-20, Series II - 1937-40. Similar. $12-18.

Six-20, Series III - 1938-39. Self-erecting. Streamlined bed supports. $12-18.

KODAK REFLEX CAMERAS - Twin lens reflex cameras with Kodak f3.5 lens in Flash Kodamatic shutter.

Kodak Reflex (original) - 1946-49. $25-35.

Kodak Reflex II - 1948-54. $30-40.

KODAK SERIES II, SERIES III CAMERAS
Folding rollfilm cameras from the same era as and similar in appearance to the Pocket Kodak folding cameras.

No. 1 Kodak Series III Camera - 1926-1931. 2¼x3¼" exp. on 120 film. $15-20.

No. 1A Kodak Series III Camera - 1924-1931. 2½x4¼" exp. on 116 film. $12-18.

No. 2C Kodak Series III Camera - 1924-1932. 2-7/8x4⅞" exp. on 130 film. $12-18.

No. 3 Kodak Series III Camera - 1926-1933. 3¼x4¼" exp. on 118 film. $20-30.

No. 3A Kodak Series II Camera - 1936-1941. 3¼x5½" exp. on 122 film. $30-45.

No. 3A Kodak Series III Camera - 1941-1943. 3¼x5½" exp. on 122 film. $30-45.

KODAK 35 CAMERA - 1938-48. For 24x36mm exposures on 35mm cartridge film. Various lens/shutter combinations. No rangefinder. Very common. $10-20.

KODAK 35 CAMERA (Military Model PH-324) - Olive drab body with black trim. PH-324 printed on back. $75-100.

KODAK 35 CAMERA, with Rangefinder - 1940-51. f3.5 Kodak Anast. Special or Kodak Anastar lens. Kodamatic or Flash Kodamatic shutter. Very common. $20-25.

KODET CAMERAS
No. 3 Folding Kodet Camera - Vertically styled folding bed camera, similar to the No. 4 but slightly smaller. Probably sold only in England. Rare. Estimated value: $400-450.

No. 4 Kodet Camera - 1894-97. For 4x5" plates or rollfilm holder. Leather covered wooden box. Front face hinges down to reveal brass-barrel lens and shutter. Focusing lever at side of camera. $250-300.

No. 4 Folding Kodet Camera - 1894-97. Folding-bed camera for 4x5" plates or special rollholder. Basically cube-shaped when closed. Early model with variable speed shutter built into wooden lens standard. Brass barrel lens with rotating disc stops. $300-400. Later models with

No. 4 Folding Kodet Camera

Gundlach or B&L external shutters: $250-350.

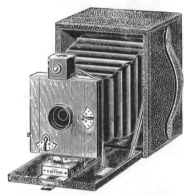

No. 4 Folding Kodet Junior Camera - 1894-97. Rare. Negotiable. Estimate: $300-450.
No. 4 Folding Kodet Special Camera - 1895-97. $250-350.

No. 5 Folding Kodet Camera - 1895-97. $250-350.
No. 5 Folding Kodet Special Camera - 1895-97. $250-350.

MATCHBOX CAMERA - 1944-45. Simple metal and plastic camera shaped like a

127

matchbox. Made for the Office of Secret Services. ½x½" exposures on 16mm film. Rare. $1500-2200.

MEDALIST CAMERAS *2¼x3¼" on 620 film. Kodak Ektar f3.5/100mm. Split image RF.*

Medalist I - 1941-48. Supermatic shutter to 400, B. No sync. $75-100.

Medalist II - 1946-53. Flash Supermatic shutter. $100-150.

MONITOR CAMERAS - 1939-48. Folding rollfilm cameras, available in two sizes:
Six-16 - 2½x4¼" on 616 film. f4.5/127mm lens in Kodamatic or Supermatic. 10-400. (Less common than the Six-20.) $15-25.

Six-20 - 2¼x3¼" on 620 film. f4.5 lens. $18-25.

MOTORMATIC 35 CAMERAS *Similar to the Automatic 35 series, but with motorized film advance. Made in 3 variations:*
Motormatic 35 Camera - 1960-62. Flash sync. posts on end of body. $25-40.

Motormatic 35F Camera - 1962-67. Built-in flash on top for AG-1 bulbs. $20-40.

Motormatic 35R4 Camera - 1965-69. Built-in flashcube socket on top. $20-35.

NAGEL *Some cameras made by Kodak A.G. in Stuttgart (formerly Dr. August Nagel Werk) are continuations of cameras which were formerly sold under the Nagel brand. These cameras may be found under their model name in both the Eastman and Nagel sections of this guide. (e.g. Pupille, Ranca, Regent, Vollenda.)*

ORDINARY KODAK CAMERAS *A series of low-priced wooden Kodak box cameras without leather covering made from 1891-1895. They were called "Ordinary" to distinguish them from the Daylight, Folding, Junior and Regular Kodaks, as they were called at that time. All are made for 24 exposures on rollfilm. All have Achromatic lens, sector shutter. They differ only in size and price.*

A, B, and C Ordinary Kodak Cameras

"A" - 2¾x3¼". (Original cost $6.00.) $1000-1400. *(illus. on front cover.)*

"B" - 3½x4". (Original cost $10.00.) $800-900.

"C" - 4x5". (Original cost $15.00.) $700-1000. (Also available in the plate version called the "C" Ordinary Glass Plate Kodak Camera.)

PANORAM KODAK CAMERAS *A series of rollfilm panoramic cameras in which the lens pivots and projects the image to the curved focal plane. Although designed basically for wide views, it could also be used vertically.*

No. 1 - April 1900-26. For 2¼x7" exposures on No. 105 rollfilm for an angle of 112 degrees. (Original cost $10.) Model A: $160-200. Models B, C, D: $125-175.

No. 3A - 1926-28. Takes 3¼x10⅜" exposures on 122 rollfilm. This is the least common of the series, having been made for only two years. $160-220.

No. 4, (Original Model) - 1899-1900. Has no door to cover the swinging lens. For 3½x12" on No. 103 rollfilm. 142 degree angle. Rapid Rectilinear lens. (Original cost $20.) $175-225.

No. 4, Models B, C, D - 1900-1924. Same as the original model, but with a door over the lens. $120-160.

PEER 100 - c1974. An Instamatic 92 camera whose exterior is designed to look like a package of Peer cigarettes. Used as a sales promotion premium. $275-325.

Petite Camera with "step pattern"

PETITE CAMERA - 1929-33. A Vest Pocket Kodak Model B in colors: blue, green, grey, lavender, and old rose. For 4.5x6cm on 127 film. Meniscus lens, rotary shutter. With original bellows and matching case: $65-75. With black replacement bellows: $40-50. *see also Kodak Ensemble, Coquette.*

--"Step Pattern" - Rather than the normal fabric covering on the front door, some of the Petite cameras had an enameled metal front in an art-deco "step" pattern. These currently bring from $125 for a nice example with replacement black bellows to $175 for an excellent example with original colored bellows, original box and instructions. *(illustrated bottom of previous page)*

PIN-HOLE CAMERA - ca. late 1920's and early 1930's. This is a small kit which consists of 5 cardboard pieces, gummed tape, a pin to make the hole, and instuction booklet. These were given to school children for use as science projects. We have seen a number offered for sale in 1984 at prices from $195 to $350. Obviously these are no longer for kids to play with.

POCKET INSTAMATIC CAMERAS - Introduced in 1972 for the new 110 cartridge. 13x17mm exposures. Most models are too new to be collectible. $1-5. *Better models (40, 50, 60) have more value as usable cameras.*

POCKET KODAK CAMERAS *Except for the first camera listed here, the Pocket Kodak cameras are of the common folding rollfilm variety.*

The Pocket Kodak (box types) - 1895-1900. A tiny box camera for 1½x2" exposures on No. 102 rollfilm which was introduced for this camera. An auxiliary plateholder could also be used. Single lens; pebble-grained leather. Earliest 1895 model has a separate shutter board with sector shutter and round viewfinder. Later models have the shutter mounted on the inside of the camera, and it is removed when loading film. Shutter type changed from sector to rotary in 1896. Identified by model year inside bottom. $75-100.

No. 1A Pocket Kodak Camera

Pocket Kodak Cameras (folding types)
All of these incorporate the Autographic feature, but the word Autographic does not form part of the name.
No. 1 - 1926-31, black; 1929-32, colors. 2¼x3¼" on 120 film. Black: $7-12. Colors (blue, brown, green or grey): $12-20.

No. 1A - 1926-31, black; 1929-32, colors. 2½x4¼" on 116 film. Black: $8-13. Colors (blue, brown, green, grey): $15-25. *(illustrated on bottom of previous page)*

No. 2C - 1925-32. 2⅞ x 4⅞" on 130 film. Black only. $10-15.

No. 3A - 1927-34. 3¼x5½" on 122 film. Black only. $12-20.

POCKET KODAK JUNIOR CAMERAS - 1929-32. Folding bed camera available in black, blue, brown, and green. Meniscus lens in Kodo shutter.

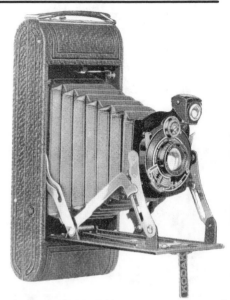

Originally came with matching carrying case. $15-25.

No. 1 - 2¼x3¼" on 120 film. Black: $7-12. Colors: $12-20.

No. 1A - 2½x4¼" on 116 film. Black: $8-13. Colors: $12-20.

POCKET KODAK SERIES II CAMERAS - Folding bed cameras.
No. 1 - 1922-31. Focusing and fixed-focus models. Black only. $10-15.

No. 1A, (black) - 1923-31. Focusing and fixed-focus models. $10-15.

No. 1A, (colors) - 1928-32. Available in beige, blue, brown, green, and grey. Meniscus Achromatic lens in Kodex shutter.

No. 3 Pocket Kodak Special Camera

POCKET KODAK SPECIAL CAMERAS - Folding bed cameras. Kodak Anastigmat f6.3, f5.6, f4.5 lenses in Kodamatic shutter. (No. 2C not available with f6.3 lens.) Black only. *Models with f4.5 lens are hard to find and would be worth about 30-40% more.*

No. 1 - 1926-34. 2¼x3¼" on 120 film. $15-25.

131

No. 1A - 1926-34. 2½x4¼" on 116 film. $15-25.
No. 2C - 1928-33. 2⅞x4⅞" on 130. $15-25.
No. 3 - 1926-33. 3¼x4¼" on 118. $15-25.

PONY CAMERAS
II - 1957-62. 24x36mm exposures on 35mm film. Non-interchangeable Kodak Anastar f3.9/44mm lens. Bakelite body. $10-15.

IV - 1957-61. 35mm. Non-interchangeable Kodak Anastar f3.5/44mm lens. $10-15.

135 - 1950-54; Model B, 1953-55; Model C, 1955-1958. The first Pony Camera for 35mm film. Non-interchangeable Kodak Anaston f4.5 or f3.5 lens in focusing mount. $8-12.

135 (Made in France) - 1956. 24x36mm on 35mm film. Angenieux f3.5/45mm lens. Shutter 1/25-1/150, B. $12-18.

828 - 1949-59. The first in this series, it took No. 828 film. Easily distinguished from the later 35mm models by the lack of a rewind knob on the top right side of the camera next to the shutter release. $10-15.

PREMO CAMERAS *The Premo line was taken over by Eastman Kodak from the Rochester Opt. Co. and was a very popular line of cameras. See Rochester for earlier models.*

PREMO BOX FILM CAMERA - 1903-08. Box camera for filmpacks. 3¼x4¼" or 4x5" sizes. Achromatic lens, Automatic shutter. $8-15.

CARTRIDGE PREMO CAMERAS - *Simple rollfilm box cameras.*

No. 00 - 1916-22. 1¼x1¾". Meniscus lens. $30-55.

No. 2 - 1916-23. 2¼x3¼". $10-16.

No. 2A - 1916-23. 2½x4¼". $10-16.

No. 2C - 1917-23. 2⅞ x 4⅞. $10-16.

FILM PREMO CAMERAS - Wooden-bodied folding bed cameras for filmpacks. Four sizes, 3¼x4¼ through 5x7", usually found in the 3¼x4¼" & 3¼x5½" sizes.

No. 1 - 1906-16. Simple lens and shutter. $20-30.

No. 3 - 1906-10. Various lens/shutter combinations. $25-40.

FILMPLATE PREMO CAMERA - 1906-1916. Folding camera for plates or filmpacks. 3¼x4¼, 3¼x5½, 4x5" sizes: $30-45. 5x7" size: $40-60.

FILMPLATE PREMO SPECIAL - 1912-1916. This is the same camera as the one above. The Filmplate Premo Camera with the better lens/shutter combinations was called the Filmplate Premo Special after 1912. (Only the version with the Planatograph lens was still called the Filmplate Premo.) $40-60.

PREMO FOLDING CAMERAS *Folding cameras for plates or filmpacks.*
Premo No. 8 - 1913-22. Planatograph lens (or Anastigmat on the 3¼x5½") in Kodak Ball Bearing shutter. Made in 3 sizes: 3¼x5½" or 4x5": $25-35. 5x7": $30-50.

Premo No. 9 - 1913-23. Various lens/shutter combinations. 3 sizes: 3¼x5½": $25-35. 4x5": $25-35. 5x7": $30-50.

Premo No. 12 - 1916-26. 2¼x3¼" on plates, packs or rollfilm. Various lens/shutter combinations. $25-35.

FOLDING CARTRIDGE PREMO CAMERAS *Folding-bed rollfilm cameras. Meniscus Achromatic or Rapid Rectilinear lens.*

No. 2 - 1916-26. 2¼x3¼" on 120 film. $7-10.

No. 2A - 1916-26. 2½x4¼" on 116 film. $8-12.

No. 2C - 1917-23. 2⅞x4⅞" on 130 film. Uncommon size. $12-18.

No. 3A - 1917-23. 3¼x5½" on 122 film. $8-12.

PREMO JUNIOR CAMERAS *Filmpack box cameras. Simple lens and shutter.*

No. 0 - 1911-16. 1¾x2¼". $15-20.

No. 1 - 1908-22. 2¼x3¼". The first model to be introduced, in 1908 it was called simply Premo Jr. $12-18.

No. 1A - 1909-21. 2½x4¼". $15-20.
No. 3 - 1909-19. 3¼x4¼". $15-20.
No. 4 - 1909-14. 4x5". $15-20.

POCKET PREMO CAMERAS

Pocket Premo, 2¼x3¼" - 1918-23. Self-erecting, folding bed camera for filmpacks only. Mensicus Achromatic lens, Kodak Ball Bearing shutter. $20-30.

Pocket Premo, 3¼x4¼" - 1903-05. Folding bed camera for plates or filmpacks. Various lenses in B&L Automatic or Volute shutter. $20-30.
Pocket Premo C - 1904-16. 3¼x4¼ and 3¼x5½" sizes. Uses plates or filmpacks. Black or red bellows. $20-30.

PONY PREMO CAMERAS *Folding plate cameras. The 4x5" and 5x7" sizes could also use filmpacks or rollfilm.*
Pony Premo No. 1 - 1904-12. 4x5". Inexpensive lens and shutter. $30-50.

Pony Premo No. 2 - 1898-1912. Inexpensive lens/shutters. 3 sizes: 3¼x4¼": $30-50. 4x5": $35-55. 5x7": $60-90.

Pony Premo No. 3 - 1898-1912. With inexpensive lens/shutter combinations. 3¼x4¼": $35-45. 4x5": $35-60. 5x7": $60-90.

Pony Premo No. 4 - 1898-1912. Various lens/shutter combinations. 4x5", $35-50. 5x7", $60-100.

Pony Premo No. 5 - 1898-1903. Various lens/shutter combinations. For plates. 4x5": $40-60. 5x7": $60-90. 6½x8½" (much less common): $75-125.

Pony Premo No. 6 - 1899-1912. Various lens/shutter combinations. For plates. 4x5": $40-60. 5x7": $60-90. 6½x8½", much less common: $75-125. 8x10": $75-125.

Pony Premo No. 7 - 1902-1912. Various lens/shutter combinations. For plates. 4x5": $40-60. 5x7": $60-90. 6½x8½", much less common: $75-125.

STAR PREMO - 1903-08. Folding bed

camera for 3¼x4¼" exposures on plates or filmpacks. Various lens/shutter combinations. $35-50.

PREMOETTE CAMERAS *Leather covered wood-bodied "cycle" style cameras in vertical format. For filmpacks.*

(no number) - 1906-08. 2¼x3¼". Became the No. 1 in 1909 when the No. 1A was introduced. $25-35.

No. 1 - 1906-12. 2¼x3¼". (Models with better lens/shutter combinations were referred to as Premoette Special No. 1 for a few years.) $20-30.
No. 1A - 1909-12. 2½x4¼". (Models with better lens/shutter combinations were referred to as Premoette Special No. 1A for a few years.) $20-35.

PREMOETTE JUNIOR CAMERAS
Leather covered aluminum-bodied folding bed cameras for filmpacks. The bed folds down, but not a full 90 degrees. There is no track on the bed, but the front standard fits into one of several slots at the front of the bed for different focusing positions. These cameras, although not terribly uncommon in the USA, are currently worth about double the US price in Europe.
(no number) - 1911-12. 2¼x3¼". Became the No. 1 in 1913 when the No. 1A was introduced. $15-25.

No. 1 - 1913-23. 2¼x3¼". $15-25.

No. 1 Special - 1913-18. Kodak Anastigmat f6.3 lens. $20-25.

No. 1A - 1913-18. 2½x4¼". $20-25.
No. 1A Special - 1913-18. Kodak Anastigmat f6.3 lens. $30-40.

PREMOETTE SENIOR CAMERAS - 1915-23. Folding bed camera for filmpacks. 2½x4¼", 3¼x4¼", and 3¼x5½" sizes. (The only Premoette made in the 3¼x5½" size.) Kodak Anastigmat f7.7 or Rapid Rectilinear lens. Kodak Ball Bearing shutter. $15-25.

PREMOETTE SPECIAL CAMERAS
Versions of the Premoette No. 1 and No. 1A with better lenses and shutters. 1909-11. In 1912, the name "Special" was dropped and these lens/ shutter combinations were options on the Premoette No. 1 & No. 1A.

No. 1 - 2¼x3¼". $20-25.
No. 1A - 2½x4¼". $20-30.

PREMOGRAPH CAMERAS *Simple boxy single lens reflex cameras for 3¼x4¼" filmpacks. Not to be confused with the earlier Premo Reflecting Camera, found under the Rochester heading in this book.*
Premograph (original) - 1907-08. Single Achromatic lens. Premograph Reflecting shutter. $175-225.

Premograph No. 2 - 1908-09. Better lens. Premograph Reflecting or Compound shutter. $125-175.

Quick Focus Kodak Camera

RANCA CAMERA - 1932-34. Made by Kodak A.G. Similar to the Pupille Camera, but with dial-set Pronto shutter. Nagel Anast. f4.5 lens. 3x4cm exposures on 127 film. $175-250.

RECOMAR CAMERAS *1932-40. Kodak's entry into the crowd of popular compact folding long-extension precision view cameras. Made in Germany by the Nagel Works.*

PUPILLE - 1932-35. Made in Stuttgart, Germany by the Nagel Works. For 3x4cm exp. on 127 film. Schneider Xenon f2/45mm. Compur shutter 1-300. $200-250.

QUICK FOCUS KODAK CAMERA, No. 3B - 1906-11. Box camera for 3¼x5½" exposures on No. 125 film. Achromatic lens, rotary shutter. Original cost: $12.00. An unusual focusing box camera. Focus knob (lever on early models) on side of camera is set to proper focal distance. Upon pressing a button, the camera opens (front pops straight out) to proper distance, focused and ready. $100-150. *(illustrated top of next column)*

Model 18 - 2¼x3¼". Kodak Anastigmat f4.5/105mm in Compur shutter. $45-65.

Model 33 - 3¼x4¼". Similar, but 135mm lens. More common than the smaller model. $40-60.

REGENT CAMERA - 1935-39. Made by Nagel Works in Stuttgart, Germany. 6x9cm (2¼x3¼") on 620 film. Schneider Xenar f3.8 or f4.5, or Zeiss Tessar f4.5 lens. Compur-S or Compur Rapid shutter. Coupled rangefinder incorporated into

Kodak Regent Camera

streamlined leather covered body. $150-200.

REGENT II CAMERA - 1939. Made by Kodak A.G. in Germany. Two-format camera: 6x9cm or 4.5x6cm. Schneider Xenar f3.5 lens. Compur Rapid shutter. Coupled rangefinder in chrome housing on side of camera. Quite rare. $400-475.

REGULAR KODAK CAMERAS *"Regular" is the term used in early Kodak advertising to distinguish the No. 2, 3, and 4 "string-set" Kodak cameras from the "Junior", "Folding", "Daylight", and "Ordinary" models. The "Regular Kodak" cameras are listed at the beginning of the Eastman section, where we have called them by their simple original names: No. 2, 3, and 4 Kodak cameras.*

RETINA CAMERAS *A series of 35mm cameras made in Germany by Kodak A.G.* **Model "I"'s have no rangefinder.**

(original model- Type 117) - 1934-35. Film advance release wheel next to winding knob. Top film sprocket with short shaft. Rewind release on advance knob. Large diameter advance and rewind knobs. Black finish with nickel trim. Schneider Xenar f3.5/50mm in Compur to 1/300. $75-125. *(illustrated bottom of previous column)*

(original model, second version- Type 118) - 1935-1937. Film advance release lever at rear of top housing. Full length film sprocket shaft with top sprocket only. Rewind release on advance knob. Schneider Xenar f3.5/80mm in Compur Rapid to 1/500. $60-100

(I) (Type 119) - 1936-38. Not called "I" until 1937. Recessed exposure counter between advance knob and viewfinder. Rewind release lever to right of film advance release button. Black lacquered metal parts. Lacks accessory shoe. Reduced diameter advance and rewind knobs. Five milled rows on rewind knob. Kodak Ektar or Schneider Xenar f3.5 lens in Compur or Compur Rapid shutter. Not marketed in the USA. $50-80.

(I) (Type 126) - 1936-38. Not called "I" until 1937. Made with black or chrome trim. Accessory shoe (or 2 mounting screws)

between finder and rewind knob. Five milled rows on rewind knob. Lenses available were: Kodak Ektar f3.5 (USA market) Schneider Xenar f3.5, Zeiss Tessar f3.5, Rodenstock Ysar and Angenieux Alcor (European market). Compur Rapid shutter. $40-60.

I (Type 141) - 1937-39. Body shutter release inside edge of exposure counter disc. Seven milled rows on rewind knob. Chrome trim. Kodak Anastigmat or Schneider Xenar f3.5. Compur or Compur Rapid shutter. Only the version with the Ektar lens in Compur Rapid shutter was sold in the USA. $45-60.
I (Type 143) - 1939. Like the Type 141, but with black trim. No accessory shoe. Schneider Xenar f3.5 lens in Compur shutter. Not imported into the USA. $50-65.

I (Type 148) - 1939. Taller top housing. Body release next to exposure counter. Cable release socket next to shutter release. Double exposure prevention. Kodak Anastigmat Ektar or Schneider Xenar f3.5 lens. Compur or Compur Rapid shutter. Only the Ektar/Compur Rapid version was sold in the USA. $35-50.
I (Type 149) - 1939. Like Type 148, but black lacquered edges of body. No accessory shoe. Schneider Xenar f3.5 lens in Compur shutter. Not imported into the USA. $40-60.

Retina I, Type 010

I (Type 010) - 1946-49. Similar to Type 148. Made from pre-war and wartime parts. USA imports have EK prefix on the serial number in the inside back. f3.5 coated and uncoated Retina Xenar, Kodak Anastigmat Ektar, or Rodenstock Ysar lens. Compur Rapid shutter. Made by Kodak A.G., except for the Kodak Ektar coated lens which was made in the USA. Only theversion with Retina Xenar coated lens was sold in the USA. $25-50. *(illustrated bottom of previous column)*

I (Type 013) - 1949-54. Full top housing with integral finder. Knob film advance. Retina Xenar f2.8 or f3.5 in Compur Rapid shutter. Not imported into the USA. $30-50.

Ia (Type 015) - 1951-54. Full top housing with integral finder. Rapid film advance lever on top. Shutter cocking mechanism coupled to film transport. Retina Xenar f3.5 in Compur Rapid shutter, or Retina Xenar f2.8, Rodenstock Heligon f3.5, or Kodak Ektar f3.5 in Synchro-Compur shutter. Not imported into the USA, but is still a very common model. $35-60.

Ib (Type 018) - 1954-58. Rapid film advance lever at bottom. Body corners rounded. Rectangular strap lugs at body ends. Metal shroud covers bellows. Retina Xenar f2.8 lens in Synchro-Compur. Not imported into the USA. $40-65.

IB (Type 019) - 1957-60. Uncoupled selenium meter. Extra front window for bright frame illumination. Retina Xenar f2.8 in Synchro-Compur. Not imported into the USA. $75-100.

IBS (Type 040) - 1962-63. Retina Xenar f2.8 in Compur. Not imported into the USA. Scarce. $100-150.

IF (Type 046) - 1963-64. Rigid body. Built-in AG-1 flash on top. Recessed rewind knob. Coupled selenium meter. Prontor LK shutter distinguishes this from the IIF. Retina Xenar f2.8 in Prontor 500LK. Not imported into the USA. $75-100.

Model "II"s all have coupled rangefinders.

II (Type 122) - 1936-37. Lever film advance. Coupled rangefinder with separate eyepiece. Two round rangefinder windows. Kodak Anastigmat Ektar f3.5, Schneider Xenon f2.8 or f2.0 lens. Compur Rapid shutter. Not imported into the USA. Scarce. $85-135.

II (Type 142) - 1937-39. Knob film advance. Coupled rangefinder with separate eyepiece. Two round rangefinder windows. Kodak Anastigmat Ektar f3.5, Schneider Xenon f2.8 or f2.0 lens in Compur Rapid. The version with the Ektar lens was not sold in the USA. $50-80.

IIa (Type 016) - 1951-54. Rapid rewind lever with built-in exposure counter. Strap lugs on front viewfinder. Retina Xenon or Heligon f2.0 lens in Synchro-Compur shutter. Compur Rapid shutter also used with the Xenon. Made by Kodak A.G. Only the Xenon/Synchro-Compur version was sold in the USA. $60-80.

II (Type 011) - 1946-49. Like the IIa, Type 150. No strap lugs. Single eyepiece range/viewfinder. Viewfinder image moves when focusing. No film type indicator on top. Kodak Ektar or Retina f2.0 coated lens, or uncoated Xenon or Heligon lens. Compur Rapid shutter. Only the Xenon version was imported into the USA. $50-75.

II (Type 014) - 1949-50. Single eyepiece range/viewfinder. Film type indicator under rewind knob. Retina Xenon or Heligon lens in Compur Rapid shutter. Not imported into the USA. $50-75.

IIa (Type 150) - 1939. Coupled rangefinder with single eyepiece. Small extensible rewind knob. Strap lugs at body ends. Kodak Ektar f3.5, Schneider Xenon f2.8 or f2.0 lens. Compur Rapid shutter. Not imported into the USA. $60-85.

IIc (Type 020) - 1954-57. Viewfinder windows not equal in size. Bright frame for normal lens only. Film advance lever on bottom of body. No built-in exposure meter. MX sync. Retina Xenon-C or Heligon-C f2.8 in Synchro-Compur shutter. Interchangeable front elements change the 50mm normal lens to a 35mm wide angle or 80mm telephoto lens. Made by Kodak A.G. Only the Xenon-C version was sold in the USA. $60-80.

IIC (Type 029) - 1958. Large finder windows of equal size. Bright frames for 3 lenses. Retina Xenon-C or Heligon-C f2.8 len with interchangeable front elements available. Synchro-Compur shutter. Not imported into the USA. $60-75.

IIF (Type 047) - 1963-64. Rigid body. Built-in AG-1 flash holder. Accessory shoe recessed in top housing. Similar to the IF, but with Synchro-Compur Special shutter. Match-needle visible only in finder. Retina Xenar f2.8 lens. Not common. $50-80.

IIS (Type 024) - 1959-60. Like the IIIS, but without interchangeable lenses. Retina Xenar f2.8 lens in Synchro-Compur shutter. Not imported into the USA. Uncommon. $50-75.

IIIC (Type 028) - 1958-60. Coupled selenium meter. Equal sized finder windows. Bright frames for 3 lenses. Retina Xenon-C or Heligon-C f2.0 lens with interchangeable front elements. Synchro-Compur shutter. Only the version with the Xenon-C lens was sold in the USA. Very common. $75-140. *(These, too, are often advertised for sale at much higher prices but are nearly always available in this price range because they are so common.)*

IIIC (Type 1982) - A small quantity of IIIC cameras was assembled in 1982 using mainly original parts. These have a meter setting for up to ASA 3200 rather than 1300 as earlier. Film reminder dial is like later models such as Retina Automatic III (3 sections for Color outdoors, Color indoors, B&W) rather than various film names as earlier IIIC. No sales data.

IIIc (Type 021) - 1954-57. Like the IIc, but with coupled selenium meter. Bright frame for normal lens only. Retina Xenon-C or Heligon-C f2.8 lens with interchangeable front elements. Synchro-Compur shutter. Only the Xenon-C version was sold in the USA. Very common. $65-85. *(Although occasionally offered at much higher prices, these are very common and nearly always available in this price range.)*

IIIS (Type 027) - 1958-60. The first Retina with a non-folding body. Interchangeable lenses: Retina Xenon or Heligon f1.9, Retina Xenar or Ysarex f2.8. Synchro-Compur shutter. Only the Xenar and Xenon versions were sold in the USA. $40-75.

S1 (Type 060) - 1966-69. Rigid plastic body. Built-in flashcube socket. No meter. Manual exposure with weather symbols. Schneider Reomar f2.8 lens in Kodak 4-speed shutter with B. Not common. $35-50.

S2 (Type 061) - 1966-69. Like the S1, but with coupled selenium meter. Schneider Reomar f2.8 lens in Kodak 4-speed shutter with B. Not imported into the USA. Not common. $35-50.

RETINA AUTOMATIC CAMERAS
I (Type 038) - 1960-62. Rigid body. Coupled selenium meter. Shutter release on front. Retina Reomar f2.8. Prontormat-S shutter. Not imported into the USA. Not common. $50-60.

II (Type 032) - 1960-63. Coupled automatic meter. Shutter release on front. No rangefinder. Retina Xenar f2.8. Compur shutter. Not imported into the USA. Not common. $50-80.

(original model- Type 025) - 1956-58. Single lens reflex. Retina Xenon-C or Heligon-C f2.0 lens. Interchangeable front elements. Synchro-Compur MXV shutter. Only the Xenon-C version was sold in the USA. $50-75.

Retina Reflex III

III (Type 039) - 1960-64. Like the Automatic II, but with coupled rangefinder. Retina Xenar f2.8. Compur shutter. $40-60.

Retina Reflex IV

III (Type 041) - 1960-64. Meter needle visible in finder. Shutter release on front. Retina f1.9 Xenon or Heligon, or Retina f2.8 Xenar or Ysarex lens. Synchro-Compur MXV shutter. Made by Kodak A.G. Only the Xenar and Xenon versions were sold in the USA. $60-80. (Add $10-15 for f1.9 lens.) *(illustrated on previous page)*

IV (Type 051) - 1964-67. Small window on front of SLR prism to show settings in finder. Folding crank on rewind knob. Hot shoe. Retina f1.9 Xenon or f2.8 Xenar lens. Synchro-Compur X shutter. $70-100. (Add $10-15 for f1.9 lens.) *(illustrated on previous page)*

S (Type 034) - 1959-60. Coupled meter. Interchangeable Retina lenses:f1.9 Xenon or Heligon, or f2.8 Xenar or Ysarex. Synchro-Compur MXV shutter. Only the versions with the Xenar and Xenon lenses were sold in the USA. $50-75.

RETINETTE CAMERAS

(original model- Type 147) - 1939. Folding 35mm camera with self-erecting front. Horizontal style, not like the other folding Retina cameras. Body curved out to a flat bed. Bed hinged at bottom of camera. Kodak Anastigmat f6.3/50mm. Kodak 3-speed shutter. Not imported into the USA. $200-275.

(Type 012) - 1949-51. Horizontal body style. Bed swings to side. Half top-housing is chromed. Housing ends at viewfinder window. No accessory shoe. Separate cable release socket. Enna Ennatar or Schneider Reomar f4.5 lens in Prontor-S shutter. Not imported into the USA. $75-125.

(Type 017) - Horizontal body style. Bed swings to side. Full length top housing. Bed is deeper than Type 022. Accessory shoe. Release button threaded for cable release. Schneider Reomar or Xenar f4.5

Retinette, Type 017

lens. Prontor SV shutter. Only the Reomar version was sold in the USA. $25-45.

(Type 022) - 1954-58. Non-folding style. Rectangular front plate without the "V" design. Single finder window. Schneider Reomar f3.5 lens. Compur Rapid shutter. Not imported into the USA. $25-35.

I (Type 030) - 1958-60. Non-folding style. A continuation of the Type 022 style. Rectangular front plate with "V" design. Two windows. Schneider Reomar f3.5. Compur Rapid shutter. Not imported into the USA. $25-45. (This camera was exported to Kodak-Pathe, France as Type 030/7 and to Kodak Ltd., England as Type 030/9.)

IA (Type 035) - 1959-60. Non-folding style. "V"-shaped front plate. No zone dots on lens rim. Schneider Reomar f3.5 lens. Pronto or Vero shutter. Not imported into the USA. $25-40. (Type 035/7 was the export version for Kodak-Pathe, France.)

IA (Type 042) - 1960-63. Non-folding style.

"V"-shaped front plate. Click stops for zone focus, zones marked by dots on focus ring. Accessory shoe is not a "hot" shoe as on later Type 044. Schneider Reomar f2.8 lens. Pronto shutter. $25-35.

IA (Type 044) - 1963-67. Non-folding style. "V"-shaped front plate. Hot shoe distinguishes this model from the Type 042. Schneider Reomar f2.8 Prontor 250S or 300S shutter. $30-40.

IB (Type 037) - 1959-63. Non-folding style. "V"-shaped front plate. No hot shoe. Built-in meter. Schneider Reomar f2.8 lens. Pronto-LK shutter. Not imported into the USA. $30-55.

IB (Type 045) - 1963-66. Non-folding style. "V"-shaped front plate. Built-in meter. Hot shoe. Schneider Reomar f2.8. Pronto 500-LK shutter. Not imported into the USA. $30-55.

II (Type 160) - 1939. Folding style. Bed swings to the side. Table stand on bed. Deeper bed than on Type 147. Body not curved. Black enameled half-top housing. Ribbed front standard. Kodak Anast. f3.5 or f4.5 lens. Kodak 4-speed or Compur shutter. Not imported into the USA. $35-60.

II (Type 026) - 1958. Non-folding style. A continuation of the Type 022 style. Rectangular front plate with "V" design. Two finder windows. Shutter cross-coupled with diaphragm. Schneider Reomar f2.8. Compur Rapid shutter. Not imported into the USA. Not commonly found in the USA. $35-60.

IIA (Type 036) - 1959-60. Non-folding style. "V"-shaped front plate. Built-in meter. No hot shoe. Schneider Reomar f2.8. Prontormat shutter. Not imported into the USA. $40-60.

IIB (Type 031) - 1958-59. Non-folding style. Rectangular faceplate with "V" design. No hot shoe. Built-in meter. Schneider Reomar f2.8. Compur Rapid shutter. Not imported into the USA. $35-55.

F (Type 022/7) - 1958. Non-folding style. Same body as Type 022. Made by Kodak A.G. for export to France without lens or shutter. $50-75.

SCREEN FOCUS KODAK CAMERA *One of the first cameras to provide for the use of ground glass focus on a rollfilm camera. The rollfilm holder hinges up to allow focusing. Similar to Blair's No. 3 Combination Hawk-Eye and the earlier Focusing Weno Hawk-Eye No. 4.*

No. 4 - 1904-10. For 4x5" exposures on No. 123 film, which was introduced for this camera. Various lens/shutter combinations. $250-325.

KODAK SENIOR CAMERAS - 1937-39. Folding bed rollfilm cameras.
Six-16 - 2½x4¼". $15-30.

Signet 30

Six-20 - 2¼x3¼". $15-30.

SIGNET CAMERAS *A series of cameras with coupled rangefinders for 24x36mm exposures on 35mm film.*

Signet 40

50 - 1957-60. Styled like the Signet 30, but with built-in exposures meter. Kodak Ektanar f2.8/44mm. Kodak Synchro 250 shutter. $20-35.

35 - 1951-58. Kodak Ektar f3.5/44mm lens. Kodak Synchro 300 shutter. $18-28.

30 - 1957-59. Kodak Ektanar f2.8/44mm lens. Kodak Synchro 250 shutter 4-250. $18-28. *(illustrated in next column)*

40 - 1956-59. Kodak Ektanon f3.5/46mm lens. Kodak Synchro 400 shutter. $18-28. *(illustrated in next column)*

80 - 1958-62. Interchangeable lenses. Behind-the-lens shutter. Built-in meter. $40-55.

Signet, Signal Corps Model KE-7(1) - A version of the Signet 35, made for the U.S. Army Signal Corps. Olive drab color or U.S.A.F. black anodized model. No serial number on the body. $100-125.

SIX-THREE KODAK CAMERAS *1913-15. A variation of the Folding Pocket Kodak Cameras with f6.3 Cooke Kodak Anastigmat lens in B&L Compound shutter. (The camera itself is identified as a Folding Pocket Kodak Camera, but the official name is the Six-Three Kodak Camera.)*
No. 1A - 2½x4¼" exp. on 116 film. $20-35.
No. 3 - 3¼x4¼" exp. on 118 film. $15-25.

KODAK SIX-16 and SIX-20 CAMERAS - 1932-34. Folding bed cameras for 2½x4¼" exposures with the Six-16 or 2¼x3¼" with the Six-20. Enameled art-deco body sides. Available in black or brown. 616 and 620 films were introduced for these cameras. $15-25. *(illustrated bottom of previous column)*

KODAK SIX-16 and SIX-20 CAMERAS (IMPROVED MODELS) *Folding bed cameras. Similar to the earlier models, but improved design on the bed-support struts, recognizable by black enameling.*

Six-16 - 1934-36. 2½x4¼". $20-30.
Six-20 - 1934-37. 2¼x3¼". $20-30.
Either size with Compur shutter: $30-50.

No. 3A - 3¼x5½" exp. on 122 film. $18-25.

Kodak Six-16 Camera

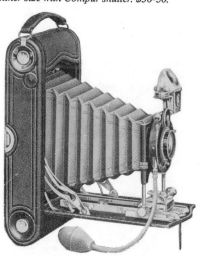

No. 3A Special Kodak Camera

SPECIAL KODAK CAMERAS *Earlier than the Kodak Special Six-16 and Six-20 Cameras listed below. These cameras are similar to the Folding Pocket Kodak cameras but with better lenses in B&L Compound shutters. They were discontinued in 1914 when the Autographic feature was introduced, and became Autographic Kodak Special Cameras.*
No. 1A - 1912-14. 2½x4¼". $20-40.
No. 3 - 1911-14. 3¼x4¼". $20-40.
No. 3A - 1910-14. 3¼x5½" (postcard size). $30-50. *(illustrated on previous page)*

KODAK SPECIAL SIX-16 and SIX-20 CAMERAS *1937-39. Folding bed cameras, similar to the Kodak Junior Series III Cameras, but with better lens and shutter.*
Six-16 - 2½x4¼". $20-40.

No. 4A - 1908-13. For 4¼x6½" exp. on No. 126 rollfilm. (No. 126 rollfilm was made from 1906-1949.) Focal plane shutter to 1000. f6.3 Dagor, Tessar, or Kodak Anastigmat or f6.5 Cooke lens. $300-325.

Six-20 - 2¼x3¼". $20-40.

SPEED KODAK CAMERAS

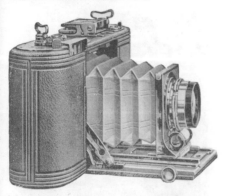

KODAK STARTECH CAMERA - c1959. Special purpose camera for close-up medical and dental photography. Body style similar to the Brownie Starflash. 1⅝x1⅝" exp. on 127 film. Full kit with flash shield, 2 close-up lenses, original box: $40-50. Camera only: $10-20.

No. 1A - April 1909-1913. For 2½x4¼" on 116 rollfilmFocal plane shutter to 1000. Kodak Anast. f6.3, Tessar f6.3 or f4.5, and Cooke f5.6 lens available. $150-175.

STEREO KODAK CAMERAS *see also Brownie Stereo and Hawk-Eye Stereo in the Eastman section.*

Stereo Kodak Model 1 Camera - 1917-25. Folding camera for 3⅛x3-3/16" pairs on No. 101 rollfilm. Kodak Anast. f7.7/5¼" lens. Earliest version has Stereo Automatic shutter, later with Stereo Ball Bearing shutter. $190-225.

No. 2 Stereo Kodak Camera - 1901-05. Kodak's only stereo box camera. 3½x6" stereo exposures on No. 101 rollfilm. Rapid Rectilinear f14/125mm lens. $300-350.

Kodak Stereo Camera, 35mm - 1954-1959. For pairs of 24x24mm exposures on standard 35mm cartridge film. Kodak Anaston f3.5/35mm lenses. Kodak Flash 200 shutter 25-200. Common. Sometimes seen at higher asking prices, but easy to find for: $70-100.

STERLING II - c1955-60. Folding camera made by Kodak Ltd. in London. Anaston f4.5/105mm lens in Pronto 25-200. $10-20.

SUPER KODAK SIX-20 - 1938-44. The first camera with coupled electric-eye for automatic exposure setting. Takes 2¼x3¼" exposures on 620 film. Kodak Anastigmat Special f3.5 lens. Built-in 8 speed shutter. $700-1000. *(illus. on front cover.)*

KODAK SUPREMA CAMERA - 1938-39. 2¼X2¼" exp. on 620 rollfilm. Schneider Xenar f3.5/80mm lens in Compur Rapid 1-400 shutter. Rare. $300-400.

KODAK TELE-EKTRA 1 & 2 CAMERAS KODAK TELE-INSTAMATIC CAMERAS KODAK TRIMLITE INSTAMATIC CAMERAS
- Late 1970's cameras for 13x17mm

exposures on 110 cartridge film. Similar to the Pocket Instamatic Cameras. Too new to establish a "collectible" value. Very common. $1-5.

TOURIST CAMERAS

Kodak Tourist Camera - 1948-51. Folding camera for 2¼x3¼" on 620 film. With Kodak Anastar f4.5 in Synchro-Rapid 800 shutter: $40-60.
With Kodak Anaston f4.5, f6.3, f8.8 or Kodet f12.5 lenses: $8-15.

Kodak Tourist II Camera - 1951-58. With Kodak Anastar f4.5 in Synchro-Rapid 800 shutter: $30-50. Other models: $8-15.

VANITY KODAK CAMERA - 1928-33. A Vest Pocket Kodak Series III Camera in color: blue, brown, green, grey, and red, with matching colored bellows. 4.5x6cm

exposures on 127 rollfilm. Camera only: $50-80. With matching satin-lined case: $100-150. *The original colored bellows were fragile and many were replaced with more durable black bellows, which reduce the collector value of the camera by 30-50%.*

*Vanity Kodak Model B Camera
from the Vanity Kodak Ensemble*
VANITY KODAK ENSEMBLE - 1928-29. Vest Pocket Kodak Model B Camera in color: beige, green and grey. With lipstick, compact, mirror, and change pocket. "Vanity Kodak Model B" on shutter face. $350-400.

Vest Pocket Kodak Camera

VEST POCKET KODAK CAMERAS *For 4.5x6cm exposures on 127 rollfilm.*
Vest Pocket Kodak Camera - 1912-14. Trellis struts. No bed. Meniscus Achromatic or Kodak Anastigmat f8 lens (1914 only). Kodak Ball Bearing shutter. $15-25. *(illustrated on previous page)*

Vest Pocket Autographic Kodak Camera - 1915-26. Trellis struts. No bed. Similar to the Vest Pocket Kodak Camera, but with the Autographic feature. Meniscus Achromatic, Rapid Rectilinear or Kodak Anastigmat f7.7 fixed focus lens. Kodak Ball Bearing shutter. Common. $15-25.

Vest Pocket Autographic Kodak Special Camera - 1915-26. Like the regular model, but with Persian morocco covering and various focusing and fixed focus lenses. $25-35.

Vest Pocket Kodak Model B Camera -

1925-34. Folding bed camera (with autographic feature until about 1930). Rotary V.P. shutter. $20-40.

Vest Pocket Kodak Series III Camera - 1926-33. Folding bed camera with autographic feature. Diomatic or Kodex shutter. f6.3 or f5.6 Kodak Anastigmat lens, or f7.9 Kodar. $20-30. *Colored models: see Vanity Kodak Camera, above.*

Vest Pocket Kodak Special Camera (early type) - 1912-14. Trellis struts. No bed. Like the V.P.K., but with Zeiss Kodak Anastigmat f6.9 lens. $40-60.

Vest Pocket Kodak Special Camera (later type) - 1926-35. Folding bed camera with autographic feature. Same

149

as the Series III, but better lens: f5.6 or f4.5 Kodak Anastigmat. $40-60.

VIEW CAMERAS *Because of the many uses of view cameras, there are really no standard lens/shutter combinations, and because they are as much a part of the general used camera market as they are "collectible", they are listed here as good second-hand cameras, the main value being their lenses. Prices given here are for cameras in Very Good condition, no lens.*

5x7" - $80-150.
6½x8½" - $50-100.
8x10" - Have increased in value in recent years. The very common model 2D is inexpensive when compared with current model 8x10 cameras, and for many purposes will perform as well. $200-275.

VIGILANT CAMERAS *Folding rollfilm cameras with folding optical finders and body release. Lenses available were Kodak Anastigmat f8.8, f6.3, f4.5, and Kodak Anastigmat Special f4.5 lens.*
Six-16 - 1939-48. 2½x4¼" on 616 film. $15-25.

Six-20 - 1939-49. 2¼x3¼" on 620 film. $12-20.

VIGILANT JUNIOR CAMERAS *Folding bed rollfilm cameras with non-optical folding frame finder. No body release. Kodet or Bimat lens.*
Six-16 - 1940-48. 2½x4¼" on 616 film. $12-18.

Six-20 - 1940-49. 2¼x3¼" on 620 film. $10-15.

VOLLENDA CAMERAS *Mfd. by Kodak A.G., formerly Nagel-Werk, in Stuttgart, Germany. See also NAGEL-WERK for earlier models.*

3x4cm size - 1932-37. Folding bed camera with self-erecting strut-supported lensboard. Radionar f3.5 or f4.5 lens. $35-60.

620 - Two different cameras: vertical style for 6x9cm, 1934-39; and horizontal style for 6x6cm, 1940-41. $18-33.

Junior 616 - 1934-37. Vertical style. 6.5x11cm. $20-35.

Junior 620 - 1933-37. Vertical style. 6x9cm. $20-35.

KODAK WINNER POCKET CAMERA - 1979-. Premium version of the Trimlite Instamatic 18 Camera. 13x17mm exp. on 110 cartridge film. $5-10.

WORLD'S FAIR FLASH CAMERA - 1964-65. Sold only at the 1964 New York World's Fair. 1⅝x1⅝". (The original box, shaped like the pentagonal Kodak pavillion, doubles the value of this camera.) Camera only: $5-10.

ZENITH KODAK CAMERAS - 1898-99. Rare box cameras made in two sizes: No. 3 for 3¼x4¼" and No. 4 for 4x5" plates. Except for the name, they are identical to the Eureka cameras of the same period. They accept standard plateholders through a side-opening door, and allow room for storage of extra holders. Made in England. Not found often. $100-150.

EBNER, Albert & Co. (Stuttgart)

Ebner - c1934-35. Folding camera for 8 exp. 6x9cm on 120 film. Streamlined bakelite body. Tessar f4.5/105mm, Radionar f4.5, or Xenar f4.5 lens. Rim-set Compur shutter 1-250. Very similar to the Pontiac, Gallus, and Nagel Regent cameras of the same vintage. (Also available in a horizontally styled model for 4.5x6cm exposures.) $100-150.

EDBAR INTERNATIONAL CORP. (Peekskill, NY)

V.P. Twin - Small plastic novelty camera for 3x4cm on 127 film. Made in England for Edbar. $4-8.

EDER PATENT CAMERA - c1933. Unusual German horizontal twin-lens (non-reflex) camera for plates or rollfilm in sizes 4.5x6cm, 6x6cm, and 6x9cm. Resembles a folding-bed stereo camera, but one lnes makes the exposure while the other is simply a viewing lens. Tessar or Xenar f4.5 taking lens, Edar Anastigmat

f4.5 viewing lens. Compur shutter to 300. Rare. Estimate: $750-1000.

EHIRA K.S.K. (Ehira Camera Works, Japan)
Ehira-Six - c1948-55. Copy of the Zeiss Super Ikonta B, complete with rotating wedge rangefinder. Tomioka f3.5/85mm lens in Ehira Rapid shutter. $75-100.

Weha Chrome Six (also Ehira Chrome Six) - A modified version of the Ehira Six design, using a telescoping tube front rather than the bed and bellows design. It retains the Ikonta-type rangefinder. $100-125.

EHO-ALTISSA (Dresden) *Founded by Emil Hofert as Eho Kamerafabrik (c1933?). The first Altiflex cameras were introduced c1937, named for Berthold Altmann. The company name changed to Amca-Camera-Werk in 1940, and after the war became VEB Altissa-Camera-Werk.*

Altiflex - c1937-49. 6x6cm TLR for 120 films. f4.5/75mm Ludwig Victar, f4.5 or 3.5 Rodenstock Trinar, or f2.8 Laack Pololyt lenses. Prontor or Compur shutter. $25-35.

Altiscop - c1937-42. Stereo camera for six pairs of 6x6cm exposures on 120 rollfilm. Ludwig Victar f4.5/75mm lenses. Vario-type shutter 25,50,100,B,T. Original price in 1942: $60. Current value: $75-85.

Altissa - c1938. Pseudo-TLR box camera for 12 exposures on 120 film. The finder on this model is like many of the cheap TLR cameras - just an oversized brilliant finder (not coupled to focusing mechanism). Rodenstock Periscop f6 lens. Simple shutter. Black hammertone finish. $25-40.

Altix, Altix IV - c1955. Low-priced 35mm camera. Body release, viewfinder, advance & rewind knobs all above the top plate. Meritar or Trioplan f2.9 lens. Synchronized. (Original price $20). $15-25.

Altix-N - c1959. Improved version of the Altix, with top housing incorporating the viewfinder. Interchangeable Trioplan f2.9/50mm lens. Lever film advance. Accessory shoe. $15-30.
Altix NB - c1960. Similar to N, but with built-in meter. $15-30.

Eho "Baby" box camera - c1932. For 3x4cm on 127 film. (Nicknamed "Baby Box" in this small size, although we have no evidence that it was ever called by that name except by collectors.) f11/50mm Duplar lens. Simple shutter, B & I. Metal body. $40-60.

Eho box, 4.5x6cm - For 16 exposures on 120 film. $15-25.

Eho Stereo Box camera - c1930's. For five stereo pairs 6x13cm or ten single 6x6cm exp. on 120. B & I shutter. f11/80mm Duplar lens. $70-95.

EIKO CO. LTD (Taiwan)
Can Cameras - c1977-83. Modeled after the original 250ml Coke Can Camera from Japan, these cameras are all shaped like a 250ml beverage can, but with different product labels: Budweiser, Coca-Cola, Mickey Mouse, Pepsi-Cola, 7-up, Snoopy. $15-35.

E.L.C. (Paris)
I'As - c1912. Folding 4.5x6cm plate camera with cross-swinging struts. Rotary disk stops in front of simple shutter. The name means "Ace". $150-200.

ELECTRONIC - Japanese subminiature of the Hit type. $10-15.

ELGIN LABORATORIES

Elgin - Unusual eye-level camera for 828 film. Stainless steel body with leatherette covering. $30-40.

Elgin Miniature - Plastic minicam for 3x4cm on 127 film. $3-7.

ELITE - Japanese novelty subminiature of Hit type. $8-12.

ELLISON KAMRA COMPANY
(Los Angeles, CA) *Michael Ellison and Edward S. McAuliffe filed for a patent in 1926 for a novel two-blade shutter, which was used in the Ellison Kamra and later in the similar, but smaller and more common QRS Kamra.*

Ellison Kamra - c1928. A long brick-shaped black bakelite camera for bulk loads of 35mm film in special cassettes. Similar in styling to the later QRS Kamra, but with a hinged bakelite door which covers the simple fixed-focus lens. The film crank, which also serves as a shutter release, is usually not broken on the Ellison model although rarely found intact on the later QRS model. $100-125.

ELMO CO. LTD. *(Originally founded by Mr. H. Sakaki in 1921 as Sakaki Shokai Co.) Although more widely recognized for their movie equipment, there were several still cameras as well.*
Elmoflex - Twin lens reflex cameras, made in several variations from the first model of 1938 through the last one introduced in 1955. $35-50.

ELOP KAMERAWERK (Flensburg, Germany) *Also associated with the Uca Werkstatten of Flensburg. Makers of ELCA cameras. ELCA = ELop CAmera.*
Elca, Elca II - c1948-51. 35mm camera with Elocar f4.5/35mm lens. Elca has simple sling shutter, while Elca II has Prontor S or Vario. Takes 50 exp. 24x24mm on standard 35mm cassette. Black painted and nickeled metal body. $60-90.

EMMERLING & RICHTER (Berlin)
Field Camera - for 13x18cm plates. Wooden body. Nickel trim. Without lens: $75-125.

EMPIRE 120 - All metal box camera for 6x9cm. $4-8.

EMPIRE BABY - Black plastic novelty camera for 16 exp. on 127. Made in Macao. $5-10.

EMSON - Japanese novelty camera of Hit type. 14x14mm exposures on 16mm paper backed rollfilm. $10-15.

ENCORE CAMERA CO. (Hollywood, CA)

Encore De Luxe Camera - c1940's-50's. An inexpensive cardboard novelty camera. Factory loaded. User returns complete camera & film to factory with $1.00 for processing. (Vaguely reminiscent of the "You push the button..." idea which made Eastman rich and famous, but it didn't work.) $15-20.

Hollywood Camera - Another novelty mail-in camera, sometimes used as an advertising premium. $15-20.

ENJALBERT (E. Enjalbert, Paris)
Colis Postal - c1886. An unusual detective camera consisting of the Alpinist folding camera disguised as a postal package tied with a cord, and with a mailing label to complete the disguise. Extremely rare. No known sales. Estimated value: $5000+

Photo Revolver de Poche - c1883. Highly unusual camera which very closely resembles a pistol. The cylinder contained a magazine mechanism for 10 plates, each 16x16mm. This camera is extremely rare and highly desirable. It is certainly a "world class" collectible, and price would be negotiable. Estimate: $10,000-20,000.

ENSIGN LTD. *The successor to Houghton-Butcher. For sake of continuity, we have listed all Ensign cameras under the Houghton heading.*

EPOCHS - Subminiature camera identical to the Vestkam and Meteor. $100-150.

E.R.A.C. SELLING CO. LTD. (London)
Erac Pistol Camera - c1938. An unusual disguised subminiature. The outer bakelite shell is shaped like a pistol, complete with trigger. Inside is a small cast metal "Merlin" camera that is coupled to the trigger, which takes the picture and winds the film. Meniscus f16 lens in single speed shutter. A few years ago, a few sold for $300-475, but that price brought them out of the woodwork, and now they are settling in at $175-285.

ERKO - 9x12cm folding plate camera. Wood body covered with black leather. H. Bauer & Sons Splendar f4.5/135 lens. Ibso shutter, T, B, 1-150. $30-40.

ERNEMANN (Heinrich Ernemann Werke Aktien Gesellschaft, Dresden, Germany) *Founded 1889 by Heinrich Ernemann. Became Heinrich Ernemann AG in 1898. Purchased the Herbst & Firl Co. of Goerlitz in 1900. Merged with Contessa-Nettel, Goerz, Ica, and Carl Zeiss Optical Co. to form Zeiss-Ikon in 1926. Some Ernemann cameras continued under the Zeiss-Ikon name.*

Bob Cameras (c1910-1920's) *Early English-language advertisements called these cameras "Ernemann's Roll Film Cameras" before the name "Bob" was used. All are folding bed style rollfilm cameras with rounded body ends. Frequently the model name is on the bed or near the handle.*

Bob O - c1913. Folding camera for ¼-plates or rollfilm. Ernemann Rapid Detective or Detective Aplanat lens in Auto shutter. $25-35.

Bob 00 - c1924-25. For 6x9cm on 120 film, or single metal plateholders. Aplanat or Anastigmat f6.8 lens. $20-35.

Bob I - c1913. Folding rollfilm or plate camera. 8x10.5cm (¼-plate) or postcard sizes. Single extension, rack & pinion focus. Aplanat f6.8 or Double Anastigmat f6. Bob, Automatic, or Auto Sector shutters. $25-35.

Bob II - c1913. 8x10.5cm or postcard size. Very similar to the Bob I, but with double extension bellows, focus scales for complete lens or rear element only. $25-35.

Bob III - c1926. 6x9cm folding bed rollfilm camera. Aluminum body. Rigid U-shaped front. Chronos shutter. $20-30.

Bob IV - c1926. Similar to Bob III, but with radial focusing and rising front. $25-35.

Bob V - c1924-26. 4.5x6cm, 6x6cm, 6x9cm, 6.5x11cm, 7.25x12.5cm, and 8x10.5cm sizes. Radial lever focusing. 4.5x6cm: $75-125. Larger sizes: $30-45.

Bob V (stereo) - c1911. Folding bed stereo camera for 45x107mm on No. 0 rollfilm. $175-250.

Bob X - 45x107mm stereo. $175-250.

Bob XV - Also a stereo 45x107mm model. $175-250.

Bobette I - c1925. Folding camera for 22x33mm format on 35mm paper-backed rollfilm. This is a strut folding type without bed. Ernoplast f4.5 lens. $75-125. *(illustrated top of next column)*

Bobette I

Bobette II - Similar to Bobette I, but with folding bed construction and radial lever focusing. Ernoplast f4.5, Ernon f3.5, or Ernostar f2 lens in Chronos shutter. With Ernostar (The first miniature camera with f2 lens): $300-500. With Ernoplast or Ernon: $75-125.

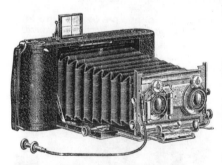

Combined ¼-plate, Postcard, Stereo, Plate & Rollfilm Camera - c1907. That is actually the name it was called in the British Journal Almanac advertment for 1907. Horizontally styled folding bed camera for 3¼x4¼" rollfilm or 3½x5½" plates. Probably a predecessor of the Stereo Bob. Shifting front allows use of both lenses for stereo or one lens for single photos. Triple extension with rack focusing. $225-300.

Combined Postcard and Stereo, Model VI - see Zwei-Verschluss-Camera

Combined Stereo and Half-Plate Focal-Plane Camera - see Heag IX.

Double Shutter Camera - see Zwei-Verschluss-Camera.

Ermanox Reflex

Ermanox - 4.5x6cm rigid-bodied model, c1924. Originally introduced as the "Ernox". Metal body covered with black leather. Focal plane shutter, 20-1000. Many were apparently supplied after the Zeiss merger with an Albada finder bearing Zeiss-Ikon identification. Ernostar f2/100mm (rarer and earlier) or f1.8/85mm lens. $800-1200.

Ermanox (collapsible bellows model) *c1926-29. Strut-folding "klapp" type camera.*

--6.5x9cm size - Ernostar f1.8 lens. $600-1000.

--9x12cm size - Ernostar f1.8/165mm lens. FP shutter 1/15-1/1500. Rare. Only one confirmed sale in October 1984 at about $3000.

Ermanox Reflex - c1926. Single lens reflex for 4.5x6cm plates. Ernostar f1.8/105mm lens in helical focusing mount. $1500-2000.
(illustrated top of next column)

Erni - Simple box camera for plates. Folding frame finder. Achromatic lens. T&I shutter. Rare in any size. 4.5x6cm: $250. 6.5x9cm or 9x12cm: $225. Stereo 45x107mm: $250.

Ernoflex Folding Reflex *Originally called "Folding Reflex" and later "Ernoflex Folding Reflex" in English-language catalogs and ads. Called Klapp-Reflex in German. Five basic types:*
Original type,
Model I (single extension),
Model II (triple extension),
Miniature Ernoflex,
Stereo Ernoflex
The latter two are listed under "Miniature" and "Stereo".

(Ernoflex) Folding Reflex (original type) - c1914. Folding SLR with drop bed and rack focus. Made in ¼-plate size only. Single or double extension models. Ernemann f6.8 or Zeiss Tessar f4.5 lens. $175-250.

Ernoflex Folding Reflex Model I -
c1924-1926. Unlike the original version, this model has no bed, but scissor-struts to support the front, and helical focus mount for the lens. Single extension only. 6.5x9cm, 3¼x4¼", or 9x12cm sizes. Ernotar f4.5, Ernon f3.5, or Zeiss Tessar f4.5. $200-300.

Ernoflex Folding Reflex Model II -
c1924-26. Triple extension. An intermediate front is supported by trellis struts and moves to infinity position upon opening the camera. For additional extension, a front bed with a double extension rack extends beyond the intermediate front. This allows for extreme close-ups with the normal lens, or long focal length lenses may be used for telephoto work. Quarter plate or 9x12cm size. $300-400.

Film K *c1917-24. Leather covered wood box camera. Meniscus f12.5 lens in T&I shutter.*
-- 6x6cm size - The rarest Ernemann box camera. $75-100.

-- 6x9cm size - The most common size. $35-50.

-- 6.5x11cm and 7.25x12.5cm sizes -
$35-50.

Film U - c1925. Box camera for 6x9cm on rollfilm. More compact than the 6x9cm Film K, because it has a collapsing front. Folding frame finder. Doublet lens in automatic shutter. $40-60.

Folding Reflex see Ernoflex Folding Reflex.

Globus - c1900. 13x18cm folding camera. Double extension bellows. Focal plane shutter. Goerz Double Anastigmat f4.6 brass-barreled lens. Polished wood body with brass trim. $350-550.

Heag *An acronym for Heinrich Ernemann Aktien Gesellschaft. Used mainly to identify a series of folding bed plate cameras. English-language advertising did not always use the name "Heag", but usually the model number was used.*

Heag O - c1918. 9x12cm plate camera. Single extension. $25-35.

Heag 00 - c1914. A cheap single-extension model in 6.5x9cm and ¼-plate sizes. T,B,I shutter. $30-40.

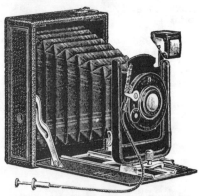

Heag I - c1914. Folding-bed camera in 6.5x9cm, ¼-plate, postcard, or ½-plate sizes. Single extension. Black imitation leathered body. Detective Aplanat f6.8. Ernemann Automat shutter. $25-35.

Heag II - c1911-1926. Similar to Heag I, but with rack focusing, genuine rather than imitation leather. 6.5x9cm, ¼-plate, postcard, and ½-plate sizes. Model I (single extension) and Model II (double extension). Aplanat f6.8 lens. $25-35.

Heag III - c1926. All metal body. U-shaped front standard. Single extension. 6.5x9cm or 8x10.5cm sizes. $25-35.

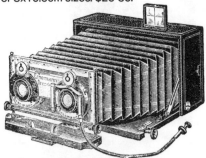

Heag IV (stereo) - c1907. Folding bed camera for stereo photos on plates. Double extension, rack focusing. Ernemann Aplanat or Anastigmat f6.8. $175-225.

Heag V - intro. 1924. A single extension camera like the Heag III, but with radial lever focus, micrometer rising front. $25-35.

Heag VI - see "Zwei-Verschluss Camera, Model VI".

Heag VII - intro. 1924. Similar to the Heag V, but also includes double extension with rack focusing. 6.5x9cm, or 9x12cm sizes. Vilar f6.8, Ernotar f4.5, or Tessar f4.5. Chronos shutter. $30-40.

Anastigmat f6.8 or f6, Aplanat f6.8. ½-plate or postcard sizes. $30-50. (See "Tropical Heag XI" for teakwood model).

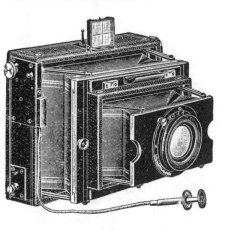

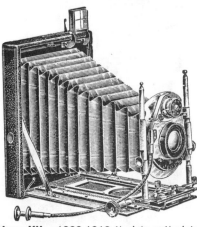

Heag XII - c1906-1913. ¼-plate or ½-plate sizes. $35-50.

Heag XII Model III (stereo) - c1925. Folding bed stereo/panorama camera for 9x18cm plates. Double extension with rack focusing. Micrometer rise, fall, cross front. $150-200.

Heag XIV - c1910. *Folding two-shutter cameras. Pneumatic front shutter plus FP 50-2500.*
-- 4.5x6 cm. - Ernemann Doppel Anastigmat f6/80mm. Front shutter 1-100. $100-150.
--9x12cm - Ernon f6.8/120mm. $75-125.

Heag IX Universal Camera - c1904-07. An interesting design for a dual-purpose strut camera. The basic design is for a stereo lensboard. To use for single photos, a separate lensboard with its own bellows & struts allows the extra extension needed for the longer focus of the single lens. In English-language ads, this was called "Combined Stereo and Half-Plate Focal-Plane Camera". With stereo or extensible lensboard: $225-275. With both lensboards: $400-450.

Heag XI - c1913-26. Leathered wood body and aluminum bed. DEB. R&P focus. Rise, fall, cross front. Swing back. Focusing scales for complete lens or rear element.

Heag XV (plate type) - c1911-14. Vertical format self-erecting folding plate camera, 4.5x6cm "vest pocket" size. Early variations have two rigid reflex finders on the front of the bed. Later models have a single folding finder. Both of these types exist in focusing and fixed focus versions. Ernemann Double Anastigmat f6.8/80mm in Automat shutter 1-100. $75-125.

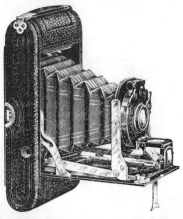

Heag XV (rollfilm type) - c1914. Self-erecting rollfilm camera, similar to the Heag XV plate model in appearance, but taller body with rounded ends for rollfilms. f6 Aplanat. Auto 3-speed, T,B shutter. $30-50.

Heag (tropical model) - listed under Ernemann Tropical cameras.

"Klapp" cameras *The word "klapp" indicates a folding camera, and came to be used primarily for folding cameras of the strut type. In the case of Ernemann, it was used for their strut-folding plate cameras with focal plane shutters. In English language advertising, these were usually called "Focal Plane Cameras". These were also available in tropical models.*

Klapp - c1905-26. Strut-folding focal plane cameras in 6.5x9cm, 3¼x4¼" or 9x12cm, 3½x5½" or 10x15cm, 4x5", and 12x16.5cm sizes. Early models had single-pleat bellows, unprotected Newton finder, and more complex shutter controls on two metal plates on side. Later models had normal pleated bellows, Newton finder, and protective clamshell cover, and two round shutter knobs on side. Ernostar f2.7, Ernotar f4.5, Tessar f4.5, or Ernon f3.5. $100-150

Liliput - c1914-26. Economy model 4.5x6cm or 6.5x9cm folding bellows vest pocket camera. Fixed-focus achromatic lens and T, I shutter. Folding frame finder. 4.5x6cm: $100-150. 6.5x9cm: $50-75
Liliput Stereo - Stereo version of the compact Liliput camera for 45x107mm. Meniscus, Guillotine shutter. $125-200.

Magazine Box - Drop-plate box camera for twelve 3¼x4¼" plates. $150-175.

Miniature Klapp, 4.5x6cm - c1925. Body style like the later "Klapp" style above, but also with front bed/door. Ernostar f2.7, Tessar f3.5, Ernotar f4.5, or Ernon f3.5. Focal plane shutter to 1000. $300-400. *(illustrated bottom of previous page)*

Miniature Ernoflex, 4.5x6cm (formerly "Folding Reflex") or **Miniature Klapp-Reflex** - c1925. Strut-type folding reflex for 4.5x6cm plates. Ernon f3.5/75 or Tessar f4.5/80mm lens. Focal plane shutter to 1000. One of the smallest folding SLR cameras ever made. $600-1000.

Reflex - c1914. Non-folding (Graflex-style) SLR with tall focus hood and flap over lens. Reversing back. FP shutter to 1/2500, T. Removable lensboard with rise and fall. Double extension, rack & pinion focus. 6.5x9cm, 3¼x4¼", 4¼x6½" sizes. Ernemann f6.8 Double Anastigmat or Zeiss Tessar f4.5. $150-200.

Rolf I - c1924-25. Folding vest pocket camera for 127 film. Leatherette covered body. Rapid Rectilinear f12/75mm lens. T,B,I shutter. $30-40.

Rolf II - c1926. Similar to Rolf I, but with genuine leather covering, Chronos precision shutter,Ernemann Double Anastigmat f6.8 or Ernoplast f4.5 lens. $30-40.

Simplex Ernoflex - c1926. Simple box-form SLR. No bellows. Helical focusing lens mount. FP shutter with 16 speeds 1/20-1/1000 sec. Cover for folding hood has front hinge on some models and rear hinge on others. 4.5x6cm size: $400-550. 6.5x9cm or 9x12cm size: $175-225.

Stereo Bob - see Bob above.

Stereo Ernoflex - c1926. A stereo version of the Miniature Ernoflex camera for 45x107mm. Scissor-struts support lensboard. Full width top door, but focus hood on one side only. FP shutter 1/10-1000. Ernotar f4.5, Ernon f3.5, or Tessar f4.5 lenses. $1000-1500.

Stereo Reflex - c1913. Rigid body stereo camera with reflex viewing. Full width viewing hood. FP to 1/2500, T. Ernemann

Anastigmat f6 or f6.8, Zeiss Tessar f6.3 or f4.5,or Goerz Dagor f6.8 lenses. $400-600.

Stereo Simplex - c1920. Non-collapsing, "jumelle" style stereo camera for 45x107mm plates. This is not a reflex model, but has only a wire frame finder. Ernemann Doppel lens f11/60. Guillotine shutter, T, B, I. $75-125.

Stereo Simplex Ernoflex - Simple reflex stereo box camera. No bellows. Ground glass focus on both sides, but reflex focus on one side only. Ernon f3.5/75mm lenses in externally coupled helical mounts. FP shutter 25-1000. $400-600.

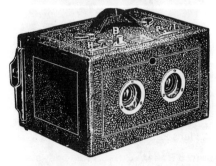

Stereoscop-Camera - c1901. Stereo box camera for 9x18cm stereo pairs. Fixed

focus meniscus lenses. B&I shutter. $200-300.

Tropical cameras *All tropical cameras, including Ernemann, are relatively uncommon. Prices increased rapidly a few years ago, and are now holding steady. There is quite a difference in price between the focal plane shutter models and inter-lens shutter types.*

Tropical Heag XI - c1920. Vertically styled 9x12cm folding-bed camera. (NOT focal plane type.) Double extension bellows. Teak body, brown bellows, brass fittings. Ernemann Vilar f6.8/135mm, Ernar f6.8, Ernoplast f4.5, or Ernotar f4.5 lens in Chronos B shutter to 1/100 or Chronos C shutter 1-300. $500-700.

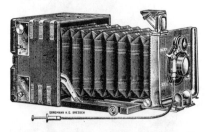

Tropical "Zwei-Verschluss-Camera" Model VI - c1914. Horizontally styled ¼-plate folding bed camera of teak with brass fittings. Triple extension, removable lensboard. FP shutter to 1/2500. Front shutter T,B,½-100. Ernemann Anastigmat f6 or Zeiss Tessar. $800-1000.

Unette - c1924-29. Miniature box camera for 22x33mm exposures on rollfilm. Overall size: 3x3½x2¼". Two speed (T&I) shutter. f12.5 meniscus lens. Revolving stops. $125-175.

Universal - c1900. 13x18cm double extension folding plate camera. Polished wood body, brass trim. Goerz Double Anastigmat f4.6 brass-barreled lens. Focal plane shutter. $350-550.

Velo Klapp - c1907-14. A low-priced focal plane camera with speeds to 1/2000 (later models to 1/2500), but without time exposure capability. Aplanat f6.8 lens. $100-150.

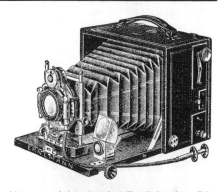

Heag model series, but English ads call it "Double Shutter Camera" and German ads call it "Zwei-Verschluss-Camera" with neither mentioning the "Heag" name. $150-250. (See "Tropical" above for teak version of this camera).

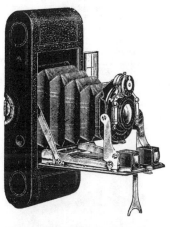

Vest Pocket Focal Plane Camera - c1911. This is a double shutter folding bed rollfilm camera with rounded body ends. The body of the camera is identical in appearance to the early Heag XV (rollfilm type) but with dual reflex finders on the bed. The important difference is that it includes a focal plane shutter to 1/2500. The front shutter is a Bob or Simple Auto. Rare. Negotiable. Estimate: $250-450.

Zwei-Verschluss-Camera, Model VI - c1907. Leather covered folding bed plate camera in 3¼x4¼" or 3½x5½" size. Focal plane shutter to 1/2000. Inter-lens shutter T,B,1-100. Double extension, rack focusing. The "Model VI" used in English-language advertising seems to fill a void in the

Zwei-Verschluss-Camera Model VI (stereo) - c1907. This is a stereo version of the "Double Shutter Camera, Model VI", available in postcard or ½-plate sizes. Focal plane and front shutters. English-language advertising called it the "Combined Postcard and Stereo, Model VI". $300-400.

ESPIONAGE CAMERA (FRENCH) - WWII vintage subminiature for 45 exposures 8x11mm. Metal FP shutter to 250. An uncommon camera, usually found without the lens: $350-400. With lens (rare): $600-700.

ESSEM - 5x7" folding camera. Rapid Rectilinear lens in B&L shutter. Mahogany interior, red bellows. $60-90.

ESSEX - Plastic minicam for half-frame on 127 rollfilm. Styled like Falcon Minicam Jr., Metro-Cam, Regal Miniature, etc. $1-5.

163

ETTELSON CORP. (Chicago)

Mickey Mouse Camera - A black bakelite box camera with red trim. Has Mickey Mouse nameplates on the front, rear, and on the advance knob. This is an uncommon camera, especially if found in its original box. Complete with original box: $100-125. Camera only: $50-75.

ETUI *A style of thin-folding plate camera c1930's. The most common model using the word Etui in its name is the KW Patent Etui.*

EULITZ (Dr. Eulitz, Harzburg)
Grisette - c1955. Bakelite camera for 35mm film. 45mm achromat lens. Simple shutter. $35-50.

EUMIG (Austria)
Eumigetta - 6x6cm rollfilm camera. Eumar f5.6/80mm lens. $20-30.

EXCO - simple box-type stereo camera, also useable for single exposures. Double anastigmat lenses. $100-125.

EXPO CAMERA CO. (New York)
Easy-Load - c1926. Small box camera for 1⅝x2½" exposures on rollfilm in special cartridges, called Expo "Easy-Load" film. Meniscus lens, rotary sector shutter. Black: $50-75. Red or Green: $75-100.

Police Camera - c1915. A tiny all-metal box camera for 12 exposures on special

cassettes. Fixed focus achromatic lens, two apertures. Cloth focal plane shutter, T & I. $165-245.

Watch Camera - Introduced c1905, produced for about 30 years. Disguised as a railroad pocket watch. Takes picture through the "winding stem", while the "winding knob" serves as a lens cap. Special cartridges. This is an interesting camera, but actually quite common since it was marketed for so long. Several variations exist. Black or blue enameled versions, rare: $550-700. Chrome camera only, complete with lens cap: $75-100. With reflex finder and original box: $100-125.

FABRIK FOTOGRAFISCHE APPARATE (Luebeck, Germany)

Fotal - c1950. Round subminiature for 8x12mm exposures on Special-Rollfilm. Optar Anastigmat f2.8/20mm lens. 1/250 shutter. Blue leather covering. $800-1200.

FALCON CAMERA CO. (Chicago) *The history of the Falcon Camera Company is somewhat unclear. The Falcon line was begun by the Utility Manufacturing Co. of New York* about 1934. One source indicates that Utility, which also made Spartus cameras, was sold to the Spartus Corp. in 1940, the new firm taking its name from the Spartus cameras. (The Utility name continued to be used at least as late as 1942, however, on price lists for Falcon cameras.)

While the ownership may have belonged to Spartus, the Falcon Camera Co. name was used in advertising in 1946, as was the Spencer Co. name. In fact, we have a camera with the Falcon Camera Co. name, but its instruction book bears the Spencer Co. name. Both of these companies operated out of a building at 711-715 W. Lake St. in Chicago, which is also the address of the Spartus Camera Co., Herold Mfg. Co., and Galter Products.

If this is not confusing enough, we should add that the founder of the original Utility Manufacturing Co., Mr. Charles Fischberg, was later prominent in the Herbert-George, Birdseye, and Imperial companies.
See also Utility Mfg. Co. for Falcon cameras.

Falcon Deluxe Miniature - Marbelized brown bakelite minicam for 3x4cm on 127 film. Folding eye-level finder. $4-8.

Falcon Miniature - Bakelite minicam for 3x4cm on 127 rollfilm. $4-8.

Falcon Minicam Senior - Another 35mm-style camera for 3x4cm on 127 film. Cast aluminum: $8-12. Bakelite: $3-7.

Falcon Rocket - Minicam for 3x4cm on 127 rollfilm. $4-8.

FALLOWFIELD (Jonathan Fallowfield Ltd., London)

Facile - c1890. Mahogany box detective magazine camera. A grooved box carries the fresh plates over a slot where they drop into a second grooved box behind the lens. A milled knob simultaneously moves the top box forward and the lower box backward so that each successive plate drops into the plane of focus in front of the previous one. An uncommon camera, which was designed to be concealed as a package wrapped in paper. Early mahogany model: $750-1000. Later black painted model: $350-450.

Miall Hand Camera - c1893. A very unusual and rare detective camera disguised as a gladstone bag. In addition to its unusual shape, it boasted the ability to be reloaded, 12 plates at a time, in broad daylight. Original advertising states that this camera was made only to order, which helps account for its rarity. Price negotiable. Estimate: $8000-10,000.

Prismotype - c1923. Direct positive street camera for 2½x3½" cards. Unusual design with reflecting turret eliminates the lateral reversal common to most direct positive cameras. $700-1000.

FED (Dzerzhinsky Commune, Kharkov, Ukraine) *Russian Leica copies. Space does not permit a complete history here, and we certainly could not compete with the excellent history of the Dzerzhinsky Commune presented by Oscar Fricke in the quarterly "History of Photography" April 1979.*

Fed - c1934-55. Copies of Leica II(D) and III cameras. Usually with FED f3.5/50mm lens. $60-100.

Fed 2 - c1955. Removable back, combined VF/RF, self-timer, sync. $35-60.
Fed 3 - lever film advance. $35-50.
Fed 4 - built-in meter. $30-40.
Note: The Fed 2, 3, and 4 are common in Europe, but not in the U.S.A., so they sell for up to 50% above these figures in the U.S.

FEDERAL MFG. & ENGINEERING CO. (Brooklyn, NY)

FED-FLASH - c1948. Low priced camera for 8 exp. 4.5x6cm on 127 film. Original prices: Camera $9.95, Case $3.95, Flash $4.51. Finally closed out in 1956 at $4.95 for the complete outfit. Current value: $5-10.

FEINAK-WERKE (Munich)
Folding plate camera - 10x15cm. Horizontal format. Double extension bellows. Schneider Xenar f4.5/165mm. Dial Compur to 150. Leather covered metal body. $75-100.

FEINMECHANISCHE WERKSTAETTEN (Karl Foitzik, Trier, Germany)
Foinix - c1955. 6x6cm folding camera, horizontal style like Ikonta B. Steiner f3.5/75mm coated lens. Pronto 25-200. $20-30.

Foinix 35mm - c1955. 35mm viewfinder camera. Foinar f2.8 or f3.5/45mm. Vario or Pronto shutter. Rapid wind lever. $25-35.

Unca - Similar to the Foinix, also for 6x6cm. f3.5 lens. Prontor-S shutter. $20-30.

FEINOPTISCHE WERKE (Goerlitz, Germany) *Successors to the Curt Bentzin Co.*
Astraflex-II - c1952. 6x6cm SLR. Astraflex was the USA name given to the camera by Sterling-Howard Corp., while the Primar Reflex II camera was distributed exclusively in the USA by Ercona Camera Corp. The two cameras are nearly identical, and prone to shutter problems. Tessar f3.5/105mm coated lens. Focal plane shutter, T, B, to 1000. Excellent working condition: $150-200.

FEINWERK TECHNIK GmbH (Lahr, Germany)

Mec-16 - ca. late 1950's. Gold-colored subminiature for 10x14mm exposures on 16mm film in cassettes. f2.8 lens. Shutter to 1000. In original presentation case: $50-65. Camera only: $30-50.

Mec-16 SB - c1960. Similar but with built-in coupled Gossen meter and f2 Rodenstock Heligon lens. The first camera with through-the-lens metering. With presentation case: $60-75. Camera only: $45-60.

FERRANIA (Milan, Italy) *Manufacturer of cameras and film. Currently owned by the 3M company.*

Condor - c1950. 35mm rangefinder camera with front leaf shutter. Some models have "Ferrania" on the top, others do not. The shutter face bears the name of "Officine Galileo" in either case, and the camera is variously attributed to both companies. This camera is often described as a Leica copy by vendors with imagination. $65-100.

Elioflex - c1950-53. Inexpensive TLR. Focusing Galileo Monog f8 in B,25-200 shutter. Non-focusing reflex finder. $25-35.

Ibis - c1950. Small cast aluminum camera for 4x6cm on rollfilm. $20-30.

Ibis 6/6 - Cast aluminum body. Gray or black imitation leather. $20-30.

Lince Rapid - c1965. Inexpensive 35mm camera for rapid cassettes. Dignar Anastigmat in 3-speed shutter. $15-25.

Rondine - c1948. Miniature all metal box camera for 4x6.5cm exposures on 127 film. Measures 3½x3½2½". Meniscus f8.8/75mm Linear (focusing) lens. Simple shutter with flash sync. Available in black, brown, tan, green, blue, & red. Fairly common. $20-30.

Tanit - c1955. Small eye-level camera for 3x4cm on 127 film. $20-30.

FERRO (Buttrio-Udine, Italy)

G.F. 81 Ring Camera - 1981. Subminature camera built into a large gold finger ring. Takes special discs of film, 25mm diameter. Variable speed guillotine shutter. Removable reflex finder doubles as screwdriver to set the controls. Originally packed in a handsome wooden case. Very limited production. $800-1000.

G.F. 82 - c1982-83. Similar to the G.F. 81, but with fixed viewfinder. $575-800.

FETTER
Photo-Eclair - c1886. A French version of the concealed vest camera, designed by

J.F. Fetter and manufactured by Dubroni in Paris. Similar to the Gray and Stirn Vest camera in outward appearance. Several variations exist, the major difference being that early models had the lens toward the top. While later models c1892 were inverted so that a waist-level finder could be used above the lens. Takes five photos 38x38mm, changed by rotating the back. $1200-1800.

FEX (France)
Elite-Fex - Dual format plastic eye-level camera for 6x9cm or 6x6cm on 120 film. Rectangular extensible front. Extinction meter. $10-20.

Rubi-Fex 4x4 - Inexpensive plastic camera for 127 film. $5-10.

Superfex - Bakelite camera, 4x6cm exposures on 127 rollfilm. Spec Fexar lens, single speed shutter. $5-15.

Ultra-Fex - Post-war camera for 6x9cm on 120 rollfilm. Plastic body, extensible front. Fexar lens. Simple shutter 25-100. $10-20.

FILMA (Milano, Italy)
Box cameras - c1936. 4.5x6cm and 6x9cm sizes. Front corners are rounded. Achromat lens, guillotine shutter. $20-28.

FINETTA WERK (P. Saraber, Goslar)
Ditto 99 - same as the Finetta 99 below.

Finetta - c1950. Basic 35mm camera without rangefinder or motor drive. Finetar f2.8/45mm interchangeable lens. Originally $30. Currently: $23-35.

Finetta 99 - c1950. Spring motor camera. 24x36mm exposures on 35mm film. Interchangeable Finetar f2.8/45mm lens. Focal-plane shutter 25-1000. Light grey. Excellent working condition: $100-150. (Deduct at least 50% for non-working example.)

Finetta Super - Finetar f2.8/45mm. Central shutter 25-100. $25-35.

Finette - f5.6/43mm Achromat Finar. Simple shutter, T, B, I. Aluminum body. $15-25.

FIPS MICROPHOT - Tiny black plastic subminiature for 13x13mm on special rollfilm. Made in Western Germany. $75-100.

FIRST CAMERA WORKS (Japan)
First Six - Copy of Zeiss Ikonta for 6x6cm on 120 film. Anastigmat f3.5. 1-400 shutter. $30-40.

Firstflex - see Tokiwa Seiki

FIVE STAR CAMERA CO.

Five Star Candid Camera - Plastic novelty minicam for 3x4cm on 127 film. $4-8.

FLASH CAMERA CO.
Candid Flash Camera - 3x4cm. $4-8.

FLEKTAR - 6x6cm TLR made in USSR occupied East Germany. Row Pololyt f3.5/75mm lens. $25-35.

FOLMER & SCHWING
Folmer & Schwing (NYC), 1887.
Folmer & Schwing Mfg. Co. (NYC), 1890.
Folmer & Schwing Mfg. Co. of N.Y., 1903.
Folmer & Schwing Co., Rochester (EKC), 1905.
Folmer & Schwing Div. of EKC, 1907.
Folmer & Schwing Dept. of EKC, 1917.
Folmer-Graflex Corp., 1926.
Graflex, Inc., 1945.

Because of the many organizational changes in this company which are outlined above, and in order to keep the continuous lines of cameras together, we have chosen to list their cameras as follows regardless of age of camera or official company name at time of manufacture:
Cirkut Cameras- see Eastman Kodak Co.
Graflex, Graphic Cameras- see Graflex

Banquet cameras - Banquet cameras are essentially view cameras with wide proportions for panoramic photographs. They were originally used to photograph entire rooms of people at banquets, and required a wide angle lens with extreme coverage. Surprisingly, these cameras are still used for the same purposes today, and maintain their value as usable equipment based on the prices of current cameras. In any case, the lens with the camera is an important consideration in determining the value. At least one filmholder should be included in the prices listed here. The film holders would be expensive if purchased separately. Common sizes are 7x17" and 12x20". With an appropriate wide angle lens: $350-650. Without a lens: $250-450.

Finger Print Camera - Portable fingerprint camera. Contains four battery operated lights. Leather covered. Kodak f6.3 lens. $50-75.

Sky Scraper Camera - A special purpose view camera incorporating an extra high rising lensboard and a back with extreme tilt to correct for architectural distortion. It was the perfect solution to the problem of taking photographs of the skyscrapers of the early 1900's. With lens & shutter: $350-500. Without lens: $200-300.

FOTAX MINI, FOTAX MINI IIa - c1948. Sweden. Bakelite camera for 25x25mm on special 35mm rollfilm. f8/35mm lens. $40-60.

FOTH (C. F. Foth & Co., Berlin)

Derby (original) - 1930-31. The only Derby for 24x36mm on 127 rollfilm. Identified by its folding Newton finder instead of an optical telescopic viewfinder. Foth Anastigmat f3.5/50, FP 1/25-1/500. Very rare. $75-125.

Derby (I) - c1931-36. 3x4cm on 127 rollfilm. Optical telescopic viewfinder. Foth Anastigmat f3.5 or f2.5/50mm, FP shutter 1/25-1/500. No self-timer. Black or brown leather covering. This model was referred to as Derby until the improved version with a self-timer was introduced. It then was

called the Derby I and the self-timer version was called the Derby II. Not often seen. $35-45.

Derby II - c1934-42. 3x4cm on 127 rollfilm. Optical telescopic viewfinder. Foth Anastigmat f3.5 or f2.5/50mm, FP 1/25-500, ST. Black or brown leather covering. There were also two rangefinder additions to this camera that were not made by Foth. The first, made in France c1937-40, had a black and chrome rangefinder that was added on to the top of the camera body. The rangefinder remains stationary on the body when the struts extend the front. A focusing knob coupled to the RF was added to the front plate. The second, c1940-42, US-made chrome RF was mounted above the front plate, not to the top of the body. When the struts are extended, the RF also moves forward. A vertical bar connects the helical lens mount to the RF. This CRF could be added to any Derby II, by returning it to the US distriburor. Advertisements in the U.S. referred to the Derby II without the added CRF as the "Standard" model or "Model I", and called the Derby II with the US added CRF simply Derby II or Derby Model II. Without CRF: $25-40.
With French CRF: $150-175.
With US CRF: $125-165.

Foth rollfilm cameras - c1933. Folding

cameras for 116 or 120 rollfilm. Foth Anastigmat lens. Waist level & eye level finders. $20-25.
-- Deluxe version - Alligator skin covering and black or colored bellows. $150-175.

Foth-Flex - c1934. TLR for 6x6cm on 120. f3.5/75mm. Foth Anastigmat. Cloth focal plane shutter 25-500, B. $65-90.

FOTOCHROME, INC. (U.S.A.)
Fotochrome Camera - c1965. "Unusual" is a kind description for this machine, designed by the film company to use a special direct-positive film loaded in special cartridges. The camel-humped body houses a mirror which reflects the image down to the bottom where the "color picture roll" passed by on its way from one cartridge to another. Made by Petri Camera in Japan. $20-30.

FOTOFEX-KAMERAS (Fritz Kaftanski, Berlin)

Minifex - c1932. Unusual looking subminiature for 36 exposures 13x18mm on 16mm film. Large Compur, Pronto, or Vario shutter dwarfs the tiny body. $325-500.

FOTOTECNICA (Turin, Italy)
Bandi - c1946. Box camera covered in brown leather, with blue front. 6x6cm on 120 rollfilm. Aplanat 75mm lens, shutter 25-100. $25-30.

Filmor - c1950. Metal box cameras for 6x6cm or 6x9cm exposures. Achromat lenses, guillotine shutter. $20-25.

Rayflex - c1946. Simple 6x9cm box camera. Duotar Optik f9 lens, guillotine shutter. $15-20.

FRANCAIS (E. Francais, Paris)
Cosmopolite - c1892. Early twin-lens reflex camera, box-shaped when closed. Side hinged front door conceals brass barrel lenses. $700-900.

Kinegraphe - c1886. Very early twin-lens reflex. Polished wood body, exterior brass barrel lens with waterhouse stops. Sold in England by London Stereoscopic Co. as "Artist's Hand Camera". $850-1200.

Franka Rolfix

FRANCYA - 14x14mm Japanese subminature of the "Hit" type. $10-15.

FRANK SIX - Folding camera for 6x6cm on 120. $30-40.

FRANKA-WERK (Beyreuth, Germany)
Rolfix - ca. WWII, pre- and post. A folding camera for 8 exp. 6x9cm or 16 exp. 4.5x6cm on 120 film. Post-war models made in U.S. occupied zone from pre- and post-war parts. $10-20. *(illustrated bottom of previous column)*

Solida - Pre- and post-war folding camera for 12 exposures, 6x6cm on 120 film. f6.3/75mm. $12-22.

Solida Jr. - $10-20.

FRANKE & HEIDECKE (Braunschweig)
Heidoscop - Three-lens stereo camera for stereo pairs on plates or cut film, in two sizes: 45x107mm and 6x13cm. Named for the designer, Reinhold Heidecke, these were the first cameras made by Franke & Heidecke. Both models have Stereo Compound shutters.

45x107mm size - 1921-41. Carl Zeiss Jena Tessar f4.5/55mm lenses. $250-300.

6x13cm size - 1925-41. Carl Zeiss Jena Tessar f4.5/75mm lenses. $275-325. (Add $100-150 for 120 rollback.)

Rollei-16 - 1963-67. (#2,700,000-2,727,999). Subminiature for 12x17mm exposures on 16mm film. Tessar f2.8/25mm. Outfit with case, flash, filter: $50-75. Camera only: $35-55.

Rollei-16S - 1966-72. (#2,728,000-2,747,882). Subminiature. Black: $50-60. Green: $100-150. Red: $100-150. Black snake: $60-90. Cream snake: $150-200.

Rollei 35 - 1967-75. (#3,000,000-on). Tessar f3.5/50mm. Model from Germany: $120-145. From Singapore: $75-100. In gold: $400-500.

Rollei 35B - 1969-78. (#3,600,000-on). Zeiss Triotar f3.5/40mm. $40-60.

Rollei 35C - intro. 1969. ($3,600,000-on). $75-100.

Rollei 35LED - 1978-80. $45-60.

Rollei 35S - intro. 1974. Prices are for Like New condition. Chrome: $85-100. Gold, in box: $500-700. Silver, in box: $130-160.

Rollei 35T - 1976-80. Black or chrome. $75-100.

Rolleicord *A series of 6x6cm TLR cameras.*

Version with bayonets on both the taking and viewing lenses sometimes referred to as the IIa. $40-55.

III - 1950-53. (#1,137,000-1,344,050). f3.5/75mm Zeiss Triotar or Schneider Xenar lens. Compur-Rapid shutter 1-500, B. X sync. $40-55.

IV - 1953-54. (#1,344,051-1,390,999). Schneider Xenar or Zeiss Triotar f3.5/75mm lens. Synchro-Compur 1-500, B. MX sync. Double exposure prevention. $45-65.

V - 1954-57. (#1,500,000-1,583,999). Schneider Xenar f3.5/75mm lens. Synchro-Compur shutter, 1-500. Self-timer. MXV sync. LVS scale. Double exposure prevention. Large focusing knob with film speed indicator on right side. $60-100.

I (nickel-plated) - 1933-36. Art-deco, nickel-plated exterior. Zeiss Triotar f4.5/75mm lens. Compur shutter 1-300, B, T. $75-100 in U.S.A. (These bring about 30% more in Europe.)

I (leather covered) - 1934-36. Black leather-covered exterior. Zeiss Triotar f3.8 lens. Compur shutter 1-300, B, T. No sync. $45-60.

Ia - 1936-47. Zeiss Triotar f4.5/75mm lens. No bayonet mounts on viewing or taking lenses. Rim-set compur shutter 1-300, B, T. No sync. Most have a frame finder in the focusing hood. Wide range of prices: $35-70.

II - 1936-50. f3.5/75mm Zeiss Triotar or Schneider Xenar lens. Compur shutter 1-300, B, T or Compur Rapid 1-500, B. No sync. Originally with no bayonet mounts, but bayonet added to the taking lens and then the viewing lens during the course of production (#612,000-1,135,999).

Va - 1957-61. (#1,584,000-1,943,999). Schneider Xenar f3.5 lens. Synchro-Compur shutter 1-500, B. Large focusing knob on left side. Non-removable focusing hood. $70-90.

Vb - 1962-70. (#2,600,000-on). Schneider Xenar f3.5 lens. Synchro-Compur 1-500 shutter. Large focusing knob on left side. Removable focusing hood. $80-135.

Rolleidoscop - 1926-41. The rollfilm version of the Heidoscop stereo camera. Actually, some of the very earliest production models of the Rolleidoscop still bore the name Heidoscop. Like the Heidoscop, this is a three-lens reflex. The center lens, for reflex viewing, is a triplet f4.2. Stereo Compound shutter 1-300.

45x107mm - Tessar f4.5/55mm lenses. Much less common than the 6x13cm size. $750-1000.

6x13cm - Tessar f4.5/75mm lenses. For B11 or 117 rollfilm. $650-850.

Rolleiflex - 6x6 TLR cameras. For 6x6cm exposures on 120 film.

I (original model) - 1929-32. (#1-199,999). The "little sister" of the already well-known Heidoscop and Rolleidoscop. Readily identified by the Rim-set Compur shutter, 1-300, B & T, and the film advance system, which, on this early model was not automatic; hence, no exposure counter. With Zeiss Tessar f4.5/ 75mm, or more often, f3.8/75mm lens.

This first model was made to take 6 exposures on No. 117 film, but some were converted to the standard 12 exposures on 120 film. Film winding knob, not lever. The earliest version of this model had no distance scale on the focus knob, and the back is not hinged, but fits into a groove. The second version has focus scale and hinge. $90-115 in the U.S.A., about 20% higher in Europe.

Rolleiflex Automat models:

Automat (1937) - 1937-39. (#563,516-805,000). Zeiss Tessar f3.5/75mm lens. Bayonet mount for accessories on taking lens only. Compur-Rapid shutter 1-500, B, T, and self-timer. Automatic film feed. No ruby window. Knurled wheels for setting lens stops and shutter speeds. No sportsfinder. $70-100.

Automat (1939) - 1939-49. (#805,000-1,099,999). Tessar or Xenar f3.5 lens. Like the 1937 model, but bayonet mounts on both the taking and the viewing lenses. $65-95.

Automat (X-sync.) - 1949-51. (Called the Automat II in Germany.) (#1,100,000-1,168,000). Tessar or Xenar f3.5/75mm lens. Synchro-Compur shutter, 1-500, B. Self-timer. X-sync. Sportsfinder. $85-110.

Automat (MX-sync.) - 1951-54. (#1,200,000-1,427,999). Tessar or Xenar f3.5/75mm lens. Synchro-Compur 1-500, B. Self-timer. Lever for selecting M or X type sync. Very common. $70-120.

Automat (MX-EVS) - 1954-56. (#1,428,000-1,739,911). Tessar or Xenar f3.5/75mm lens. Synchro-Compur shutter, 1-500, B. Self-timer. MX sync and LVS scale on shutter. $80-120.

Rolleiflex 2.8A - 1950-51. (Also known as Automat 2.8A.) (#1,101,000-1,204,000). Zeiss Tessar f2.8/80mm lens. Synchro-Compur shutter, with X or MX sync. Self-timer. Sportsfinder. $80-100.

Rolleiflex 2.8B - 1952-53. (Also known as Automat 2.8B.) (#1,204,000-1,260,000). Zeiss Biometar f2.8/80mm lens. MX sync. $100-125.

Rolleiflex 2.8C - 1953-55. (Also called Automat 2.8C.) (#1,260,350-1,475,405). f2.8/80mm Schneider Xenotar or Zeiss Planar lens. Synchro-Compur shutter with MX sync. No LVS scale. $140-165.

Rolleiflex 2.8D - 1955-56. (#1,600,000-1,620,999). f2.8/80mm Schneider Xenotar or Zeiss Planar lens. Synchro-Compur shutter with MX sync and LVS scale. $200-225.

Rolleiflex E - 1956-59. Dual-range, non-coupled exposure meter. (Original distributor's advertising referred to this camera as the model "G" when sold without the meter.) MX sync. Two variations:
2.8E - (#1,621,000-1,665,999). f2.8/80mm Zeiss Planar or Schneider Xenotar. $210-250.
3.5E - (#1,740,000-1,787,999 and #1,850,000-1,869,999). f3.5/75mm Zeiss Planar or Schneider Xenotar. $185-230.

Rolleiflex E2 - No exposure meter. Flat, removable focusing hood. Two variations:
2.8E2 - 1959-60. (#2,350,000-2,356,999). f2.8/80mm Xenotar. $245-270.
3.5E2 - 1959-62. (#1,870,000-1,872,010 and 2,480,000-2,482,999). f3.5/75mm Xenotar or Planar. $185-200.

Rolleiflex E3 - 1962-65. No exposure meter. Removable focusing hood. Planar or Xenotar lens. Two variations:
2.8E3 - (#2,360,000-2,362,024). f2.8/80mm lens. $225-250.
3.5E3 - (#2,380,000-2,385,034). f3.5/75mm lens. $175-225.

Rolleiflex Standard models:

Old Standard - 1932-38. (#200,000-

67,550). Zeiss Tessar f4.5, f3.8, or f3.5/75mm lens. Compur 1-300, B, T or Compur-Rapid 1-500, B shutter. Lens mount accepts push-on accessories; no bayonet. Single lever below lens for tensioning and releasing the shutter. Lever-crank film advance. Exposure counter. $60-80.

New Standard - 1939-41. (#805,000-927,999). Zeiss Tessar f3.5/75mm lens. Compur-Rapid, 1-500, B (no T or self-timer). Bayonet mount on viewing and taking lenses. Lens stops and shutter speeds set by levers. $60-90.

Studio - 1932-34. 9x9cm or 6x9cm. The only Rolleiflex in the 9x9cm size, this is the rarest of the Rolleiflexes. Prototypes only or possibly very limited quantities. Zeiss Tessar f4.5/105mm lens in Compur S shutter 1-1/250, T, B. Price negotiable. No known sales.

Rolleiflex T - 1958-75. (#2,100,000- on). Zeiss Tessar f3.5/75mm lens. Shutter with X or MX sync. Provision for built-in dual-range exposure meter. Available in black or grey. Grey: $200-250. Black, with meter: $200-300. Without meter: $135-160.

Tele Rolleiflex - intro. 1959. Zeiss Sonnar f4/135mm lens. Removable focusing hood. Later models allow use of 120 or 220 film. $500-650.

Wide-Angle Rolleiflex (Rolleiwide) - 1961-67. Distagon f4/55mm lens. Less than 4000 produced. $1200-1500.

Rolleiflex 4x4 Cameras *For 4x4cm exposures on 127 film. Some variations called "Baby Rolleiflex", or "Rolleiflex Sport".*

Original - 1931-38. (#135,000-523,000). Zeiss Tessar f3.5 or f2.8/60mm lens. Compur shutter 1-300, B,T or

Compur-Rapid 1-500, B,T. Earliest models (1931-33) have rim-set shutter. Later versions (1933-38) have levers for setting the lens stops and shutter speeds. Lens mount accepts push-on accessories (no bayonets). $150-225.

Sports Rolleiflex - 1938-41. (#622,000-733,000). Zeiss Tessar f2.8/60mm lens. Compur-Rapid shutter, 1-500, B,T. Bayonet mount on taking lens; some also have a bayonet mount on the finder lens. $275-425.

Grey Baby - 1957-68. (#2,000,000- on). Grey body. Xenar f3.5 lens. MXV shutter with LVS scale and self-timer. Double bayonet. Common. $100-140.

Post-War Black Baby - 1963-68. (#2,060,000-?). Black body. Zeiss Tessar or Schneider Xenar f3.5/60mm lens. Synchro-Compur MXV 1-1/500,'B shutter. Rare. $200-350.

Rolleimagic - 6x6cm TLR cameras with automatic exposure control. Xenar f3.5/75mm lens.
(I) - 1960-63. (#2,500,000-2,534,999). $70-115.
II - 1962-67. (#2,535,000-2,547,597). Manual override on the exposure control. $100-150.

FRENNET (J. Frennet, Brussels)
Stereoscopic Reflex - c1910. Graflex-style cameras for stereo exposures on 6x13cm or 7x15cm glass plates. $350-500.

FT-2 - c1955. Russian panoramic camera for 12 exposures 24x110mm on 35mm film. Industar f5/50mm lens. Shutter 100-400. $180-250.

FUJI PHOTO FILM CO. (Fuji Kogaku Seiki) *The Fuji company is a prolific manufacturer of cameras, most of which are still in use today. We are only listing a few of the early Fuji models in this collectors guide.*
Comex - Novelty subminiature for 14x14mm on rollfilm. Marked "Made in Occupied Japan". $175-225.

Fujicaflex - c1955. Twin lens reflex for 6x6cm on 120. $125-175.

Fujipet, Fujipet EE - c1954. Simple eye-level cameras for 6x6cm on 120 film. The EE model is somewhat similar in styling to the Revere Eyematic EE127. $15-22.

Lyra 4.5x6cm (Semi-Lyra) - Compact folding camera for 16 exposures 4.5x6cm on 120 rollfilm. Similar to Zeiss Ikonta A. Made before and after WWII. f3.5/75mm anastigmat. Fujiko, Noblo, or Picco shutter. $30-45.

Lyra Six, Lyra Six III - c1935-40. Horizontally styled folding cameras, 6x6cm on 120. Similar to Zeiss Ikonta B. Less common than the "semi" model. $30-50.

Lyraflex - 6x6cm TLR. Terionar f3.5/75mm lens. An uncommon "Rollei copy". $75-125.

Lyrax - c1939. 4.5x6cm on 120. Telescoping front, uncoupled rangefinder. Terionar f3.5/75mm, Fujiko shutter. $100-150.

Mini - Very small half-frame camera for 35mm film in special cartridges. f2.8/25mm lens. $65-95.

FUJITA OPT. IND. LTD. (Japan)
Classic 35 IV - c1960. Inexpensive 35mm camera imported to the USA by Peerless Camera Co., NY as one of a series of "Classic" cameras. $15-20.

FUTURA KAMERA WERK A.G., Fritz Kuhnert (Freiburg)
Futura-S - c1950's. A very well constructed 35mm RF camera. Interchangeable Kuhnert Frilon f1.5/50mm lens. Compur Rapid 1-400, B. Coupled rangefinder. $50-65.

GALILEO OPTICAL (Milan, Italy)
Associated with Ferrania, also of Milan.
Condor I - Early 1950's 35mm rangefinder camera. Similar in style to Leica, but with front shutter. $65-100.

Gami 16 - c1955's. Subminiature for exposures 12x17mm on 16mm film in cassettes. f1.9/25mm lens. Shutter 2-1000. Coupled meter, parallax correction, spring-motor wind for up to 3 rapid-fire shots. Original cost $350. These are not rare, yet are occasionally advertised at higher prices. Normal range: $250-275. Complete outfit with all accessories: f4/4x telephoto, flash, filter, 45 degree viewer, wrist strap, etc. sells for 2 to 3 times the cost of the camera & case only.

GALLUS (Usines Gallus, Courbevoie, France)
Derlux - Folding camera for 3x4cm on 127 rollfilm. Polished aluminum body. Very similar to the Foth Derby. Indeed some examples are identified as "Derby Lux" on the back. Gallus Gallix f3.5/50mm. FP shutter 25-500. $75-125.

Stereo camera - c1920's. Rigid "jumelle" style all metal camera for stereo exposures in the two popular formats: 6x13cm or the smaller 45x107mm. Simple lenses. I&B shutter. $150-250.

GALTER PRODUCTS (Chicago) *Founded in 1950 by Jack Galter, former president of Spartus Camera Co., and apparently in business for only a few years. Spartus Camera Co., meanwhile, became Herold Mfg. Co. at about the same time, having been bought by Harold Rubin, former Sales Manager for Spartus.*

Hopalong Cassidy Camera - c1950. Plastic box camera for 8 exposures 6x9cm on 120 rollfilm. Simple shutter, Meniscus lens. The front plate depicts the famous cowboy and his horse. $15-25.

Majestic, Pickwick, Pickwik, Regal - Plastic "minicam" type cameras for 3x4cm on 127 film. $3-7.

Sunbeam 120 - Black bakelite box camera without flash sync. Body style

identical to the Hopalong Cassidy camera. $4-8.

GAMMA (subminiature) - Novelty subminiature from "Occupied Japan". Shutter release on top of body. Angel f4.5 lens with rotating disc stops. $125-150.

GAMMA (Societa Gamma, Rome)
Gamma (35mm) - c1947-1950. Leica copies. Model I c1947 has bayonet-mount lens, FP shutter with speeds B,20-1000 on one dial. Model III c1950 has screw-mount lens, and shutter speeds 1-1000. Gamma or Koristka Victor f3.5 lens. Rare. Estimate: $300-500.

Pajtas - c1955. Black bakelite camera for 6x6cm on 120 rollfilm. Achromat f8/80. $15-25.

GANDOLFI (London) *The history of the Gandolfi family in the camera business is already a legend, and 1985 marks the hundredth anniversary of the founding of the business by Louis Gandolfi. It has remained a family business since that time, with sons Thomas, Frederic, and Arthur working with their father and eventually taking the reins after his death in 1932. The company has always specialized in hand-made wooden cameras. A large number of their cameras are custom-built to the specifications of clients. It would be difficult to give specific prices to such a wide range of individually crafted cameras, but as a point of departure, we can say that we have a number of recorded sales in the range of $250 to $675 and some reports of prices up to $1000. Obviously, since the cameras were made for 100 years in a traditional style, they are still very much in demand for use as well as for collections.*

GARLAND - (London, England)
Wet Plate camera - 8x10". c1865. Ross lens. $1300-1800.

GAUMONT (L. Gaumont & Cie., Paris)

Block-Notes - Compact folding plate cameras.
4.5x6cm - c1904. f6.8 Tessar, Hermagis Anastigmat, or Darlot lens. $130-160.
6.5x9cm - f6.3 Tessar lens. Less common than the smaller model. $100-150.

Gennert Montauk

Block-Notes Stereo - Compact folding cameras like the other Block-Notes models, but for stereo formats: 45x107mm and 6x13cm. f6.3 lenses, variable speed guillotine shutter. For single plateholders or magazines. $250-290.

Reporter - c1924. Heavy metal strut-folding camera for 9x12cm single plates or magazine. Flor f3.5/135mm lens. FP 1/25-1000 shutter. $200-300.

Spido - c1898. 9x12cm leather covered magazine camera. Dagor lens, pneumatic shutter. $150-200.

Stereo Spido Ordinaire - Black leather covered jumelle style stereo cameras for 6x13cm or 9x18cm stereo plates. Krauss Zeiss Protar f12.5/189mm. Decaux Stereo six speed pneumatic shutter. $150-240.

Stereo Spido Mettalique - Panoramic version with 120 rollback: $300-500. Regular 6x13cm size without rollback: $200-300.

Stereo cameras - 6x13 cm misc. or unnamed models. f6.3/85mm lenses and guillotine shutter. $250-350.

GENERAL PRODUCTS
Candex Jr. - Black plastic minicam for 127 half-frames. $3-7.

GENIE CAMERA CO. (Philadelphia, PA)
Genie - c1892. Focusing magazine-box camera for 3¼x4" plates. Push-pull action changes plates and actuates exposure counter on brass magazine. String-set shutter. $400-550.

GENNERT (G. Gennert, NYC)
Montauk - c1890. Detective style camera for plateholders which load from the side. Shutter-tensioning knob on the front next to the lens opening. Internal bellows focusing via radial focus lever on top of camera. $100-125. *(illustrated top of previous column)*

Folding Montauk - c1898. Folding plate cameras. Leather covered wood bodies. "Cycle" style. Wollensak Rapid Symmetrical, Ross Patent, or Rapid Rectilinear lens. 4x5" or 5x7". $45-85.

Long Focus Montauk - c1898. Like the Folding Montauk, but also has rear bellows extension. $60-100.

Montauk rollfilm camera - c1914. $20-30.

"Penny Picture" camera - c1890. A 5x7" studio camera with sliding back and masks to produce multiple small images on a single plate. $250-300.

Stereoscopic Montauk - c1898. Like the 5x7" Folding Montauk, but with Stereo lensboard. $250-350.

GENOS K.G. (Nurnberg. Germany)
Genos - Small bakelite eye-level camera for 25x25mm on 127 film. $30-45.

Genos Rapid - c1950. Plastic reflex camera for 12 exp. 6x6cm on 120 film. $8-15.

GEVAERT *Founded in 1890 by Lieven Gevaert to manufacture calcium paper. Merged with Agfa in 1964. Although a leader in photographic materials, the company was never a major producer of cameras.*

Gevabox: *c1950. Box cameras in several variations for 120 film:*
Gevabox 6x6 - Black bakelite camera with white trim. Looks like an overgrown "Ansco Panda". $10-15.

Gevabox 6x9 (eye level) - Metal box camera with eye-level finder above body. Shutter 1/50 and 1/100. $8-12.

Gevabox 6x9 (waist level) - Waist level brilliant finder. B & M shutter speeds. $8-12.

Ofo - Bakelite camera with helical telescoping front. Similar to the Photax camera from France. Both cameras are designed by Kaftanski, whose creations were manufactured in Germany, France, and Italy. This one, however, is made by "SIAF Industria Argentina". Black or brown. $30-50.

GEYMET & ALKER (Paris)
Jumelle de Nicour - c1867. An early binocular-styled camera for 50 exposures on 1¼x1¼" plates. A large cylindrical

magazine contained the 50 plates, which were loaded and unloaded from the camera for each exposure by gravity. (Rather like a modern slide tray.) Rare. Estimate: $7500.

GILLES-FALLER (Paris)
Studio camera - c1900. 18x24cm. Hermagis Delor f4.5/270mm lens with iris diaphragm. Finely finished light colored wood. $250-350.

GINREI CO. (Japan)
Vesta - Novelty subminiature from "Occupied Japan". Two models: one has eye-level finder, the other has both eye and waist level finders. $50-75.

GLOBAL - Japanese 16mm "Hit" type novelty camera. $10-15.

GLUNZ (S. Glunz Kamerawerk, Hannover)

Folding plate camera - c1920's. 9x12cm size. Dial Compur shutter. Goerz

Tenastigmat f6.8, or Zeiss Tessar f4.5 lens. Double extension bellows. Wood body, leather covered. $40-60.

Folding rollfilm models - f6.3 Tessar. Compur shutter. $30-40.

GNCO - Japanese novelty subminiature of the "Hit" type. $10-15.

GNOFLEX - c1956. Japanese Rolleicord copy. Horinor f3.5/75mm lens. $35-45.

GOEKER (Copenhagen, Denmark) Field camera - 18x24cm. Carl Zeiss Series II f8/140mm lens. $125-150.

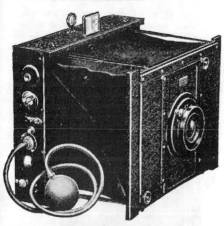

Goerz Ango

GOERZ (C. P. Goerz, Berlin, Germany) *Started in a single room in 1886, with the manufacturing of lenses as the main business. Became a major manufacturer with over 3,000 employees within the lifetime of the founder. In 1926, three years after the death of Carl Paul Goerz, the company merged with Contessa-Nettel, Ica, Ernemann, and Carl Zeiss Optical Co. to form Zeiss-Ikon. Some Goerz models were continued under the Zeiss name. In 1905, Mr. Goerz organized C.P. Goerz American Optical Co. to supply the steady demand for his products in the United States. This company is still in business, at the leading edge of space-age technology.*

Ango - (An improved version of the Anschutz camera.) Strut-type folding camera with focal plane shutter, introduced c1899 and produced for at least 30 years. Goerz Dagor f6.8, Dogmar f3.5, Syntor f6.8, Double Anastigmat f4.6, or Celor f4.8 are among the lenses you could expect to find. $75-125. *(illustrated in previous column)*

Ango Stereo - c1906. Similar to the above listing, but for stereo format. $225-275.

Anschutz - A bedless "strut" type folding focal plane camera, designed by Ottomar Anschutz, introduced c1890 and quite common with the press during the early part of the century. Most often found in the 6x9cm, 9x12cm, and 4x5" sizes. $100-125.

Anschutz Stereo - c1890-1900. A focal plane strut-folding bedless stereo camera for paired exposures on 8x17cm plates. Panoramic views are also possible by sliding one lens board to the center position. With Goerz Dagor Double Anastigmat or Goerz Wide-Angle Aplanat lenses. A relatively uncommon camera. $240-280.

Box Tengor - ca. mid-1920's. 6x9cm exp. on 120 film. Goerz Frontar f11 lens. $20-30.

Folding Reflex - c1911. A compact folding

single lens reflex camera for 4x5" plates. This camera competed for attention with the Bentzin, Goltz & Breutmann Mentor, and Ihagee Patent Klappreflex, all of which were designed to operate as an efficient full-size SLR, but be as portable as an ordinary press camera when folded. $225-275.

Folding rollfilm cameras - For 120 or 116 rollfilms. Various models with Goerz lens and Goerz or Compur shutter. $20-30.

Minicord - (C.P. Goerz, Vienna) - c1951. Subminiature TLR for 10x10mm exposures on 16mm film in special cartridges. f2/25mm Goerz Helgor lens. Metal focal plane shutter 10-400, sync. $100-125.

Minicord III - Brown leather covered. $125-150.

Roll Tengor - Vest Pocket size for 4x6.5cm on 127 film. Goerz Frontar f9/45mm lens. Shutter 25-100, T, B. $35-50.

6.5x11cm - Tenaxiar f6.8/100mm in Goerz 25-100 shutter. $20-30.

Stereo Photo Binocle - c1899. An unusual disguised detective binocular camera in the form of the common field glasses of the era. In addition to its use as a single-shot camera on 45x50mm plates, it could use plates in pairs for stereo shots, or could be used without plates as a field glass. f6.8/75mm Dagor lenses. $1500-2500.

Tenax Cameras are listed by film type. Plate models followed by rollfilm models.

9x12cm size - Goerz Dogmar f4.5/150mm. Dial Compur 1-150. $35-50.
10x15cm - Goerz Dagor f6.8/168mm, or Tenastigmat f6.3. Compound or Compur shutter. $35-50.

Coat Pocket Tenax - 6.5x9 cm on plates or film packs. Strut-type camera like the Vest Pocket Tenax. Goerz Dagor f6.8/90mm or Dogmar f4.5/100mm lens. Compound shutter 1-250, T, B. $40-60.

Vest Pocket Tenax (plate type) - c1909. Strut-folding camera for 4.5x6cm plates. A smaller version of the "Coat Pocket Tenax". Goerz Double Anastigmat Celor f4.5/75mm, or f6.8 Dagor or Syntor lens. Compound shutter 1-250, B. $60-90.

Folding Plate cameras, bed type (Tenax, Manufoc Tenax, Taro Tenax, etc.) - Plate cameras c1915-1920. Folding bed type in common square-cornered plate camera style. Double extension bellows. Ground glass back.

Roll Tenax - Bed-type folding rollfilm models similar to the American cameras of the same period.
6x9cm - Tenastigmat f6.3/100mm in Compur shutter 1-250. $20-40.
8x10.5cm - Tenastigmat f6.8/125mm. $25-45.
8x14cm - 3¼x5½" postcard size. Dogmar f4.8/165mm or Dagor f6.8 in Compur. $40-70.

Vest Pocket Rollfilm Tenax - For 4x6.5cm on 127 film. Similar to the folding vest pocket cameras of Kodak & Ansco. f6.3/ 75mm Dogmar lens in Compur shutter to 300. $50-75.

Stereo Tenax - Strut-folding stereo camera, for 45x107mm plates or packs. Goerz Syntor f6.3/60mm or f4.5/60mm Dogmar or Celor in Stereo Compur or Compound shutter. $150-200.

Tengor - see Box Tengor

GOLDAMMER (Gerhard Goldammer, Frankfurt)
Goldeck 16 - c1959. Subminiature for 10x14mm exposures on 16mm film. Interchangeable "C" mount f2.8/20mm Enna-Color Ennit lens. Behind the lens shutter. Several models exist. Standard model has fixed focus lens in Vario shutter. Model IB is similar, but with focusing mount. The Super Model has a 9-speed Prontor shutter and front cell focusing. All have rapid wind lever, bright frame finder. While classified as a subminiature because of its small film, the camera is about the same size as a compact 35mm camera. Although once considered more valuable, a number of these have surfaced in the last few years and currently sell with normal and telephoto lenses: $75-110.
With normal lens only: $50-60.

GuGo - Low priced 6x6cm camera with telescoping front. Similar to the Welta Perle Jr. 120. $10-15.

GOLDMANN (R. A. Goldmann, Vienna)
Press camera - c1900. Bedless strut-folding 9x12cm plate camera. Zeiss Tessar f6.3/135. Focal plane shutter T, B, ½-90. Black wood body, leather bellows, nickel trim & struts. $150-175. *(illustrated top of next column)*

Field camera - c1900. 13x18cm. Reversible back, Aplanat lens, mahogany body with brass trim. $125-150.

Goldmann Press Camera

GOLDSTEIN (France)
Goldy - c1947. Box camera of heavy cardboard with colored covering. Takes 6x9cm on 120 film. Built-in yellow filter. Made in blue, white, red, green, and maroon. Also available under such diverse names as Spring, Superas, Week-End, and Racing. $15-25. *(Green version illustrated on rear cover.)*

GOLTZ & BREUTMANN (Dresden, Germany) *Later Mentor Kamerawerke. All Mentor cameras are listed here, including those manufactured by the "Mentor Kamerawerk", or Rudolph Grosser, Pillnitz.*
Klein-Mentor - A relatively simple SLR for 6x9cm and 6.5x9cm formats. Fold-up viewing hood. Measures 3½x4x4¾" when closed. $75-125.

Mentor Compur Reflex - c1928. SLR box for 6.5x9cm plates. Zeiss Tessar f4.5/ 105 or f2.7/120mm lens. Compur shutter 1-250. Reflex viewing, ground glass at rear, and adjustable wire frame finder. Black metal body, partly leather covered. $100-175.

Mentor Dreivier - c1930. An eye-level camera for 16 exposures 3x4cm on 127 film. Styled much like a 35mm camera. Tessar f3.5/50mm lens in Compur shutter 1-300. Rare. $500-750.

Mentor Folding Reflex (Klappreflex) - c1915-1930. Compact folding SLR in 6x9cm, 9x12cm and 4x5" sizes. Zeiss Tessar lenses, usually f2.7 or f4.5. Focal plane shutter to 1000. $150-200.

Mentor Reflex - c1914-39. Like Graflex, basically a cube when closed. Fold-up

viewing hood, bellows focus, focal plane shutter. Various styles with or without bellows or R.B. in three common sizes: 6.5x9cm, 9x12cm, and 10x15cm. For plates or packs. Most common lenses are f4.5 Tessar, Heliar, and Xenar. $150-250.

Mentor Stereo Reflex - Bellows focusing focal plane box reflex for stereo pairs in the two common European stereo sizes: 45x107mm, with Tessar f4.5/75mm lenses, and 6x13cm with Tessar f4.5/90mm lenses. Both sizes have focal plane shutter 15-1000. $300-450.

Mentor II - c1907. A strut-folding 9x12cm plate camera (NOT a reflex). Tessar f4.5/ 120mm or Triplan f6/125mm lens. FP shutter. Wood body covered with black leather. Ground glass back. $125-175.

Mentorett - c1936. TLR for 12 exposures 6x6cm on 120 film. Mentor f3.5/75mm.

Variable speed focal plane shutter, 1/15-1/600 sec. Film transport, shutter setting and release are all controlled by a single lever. Automatic exposure counter. This is a very rare camera, as confirmed by an auction in December 1984. Against a pre-sale estimate of $480, the camera brought $850 in excellent condition with case. However, in March of 1985, another example failed to reach its $450 minimum.

GOMZ (USSR)
Sport (Cnopm) - c1935. 35mm SLR. Industar f3.5/50mm lens, shutter 1/25-500. 50 exposures 24x36mm in special 35mm cassettes. $500-800.

GOODWIN FILM & CAMERA CO. *Named for the Rev. Hannibal Goodwin, the inventor of flexible film, but taken over by Ansco. See Ansco for the listing of "Goodwin" cameras.*

G.P.M. (Giuseppi Pozzoli, Milano, Italy)
Fotonesa - c1945. Black bakelite subminiature for 20x20mm exposures. Frontar Periscop f8. $125-175.

GRAFLEX, INC. *(Also including Folmer & Schwing and Folmer Graflex products from 1887-1973 except Cirkut cameras which are listed under Eastman.)*
Founded in 1887 as a partnership between Wm. F. Folmer & Wm. E. Schwing and incorporated in 1890 as the Folmer & Schwing Manufacturing Co., it began camera manufacturing in 1897. It incorporated in 1903 as the Folmer & Schwing Manufacturing Co. of New York. George Eastman purchased the company in 1905, moving it to Rochester NY where it was called the Folmer & Schwing Co., Rochester. The company dissolved in 1907, becoming first the Folmer & Schwing Division of Eastman Kodak and then in 1917 the Folmer & Schwing Department of Eastman Kodak Co. The new Folmer-Graflex Corporation took over the reins in 1926, changing its name to Graflex Inc. in 1945. Graflex was a division of General Precision Equipment Corp. from 1956 until 1968 when it became a division of Singer Corporation. In 1973, Graflex dissolved and Singer Educational Systems was formed, the latter being bought by Telex Communications in 1982.

EXPLANATION OF SERIAL NUMBERS RELATING TO GRAFLEX CAMERAS
The numbers on the attached chart have been taken directly from the original company serial number book. The first existing page of that book starts somewhere in the year 1915. From observations of actual cameras made previous to 1915 it would be safe to assume that the serial numbers run sequentially at least back to

1905. Because of the purchase of Folmer & Schwing in 1905 by Eastman Kodak, it is not known at this time whether the serial numbering was changed because of that purchase. Furthermore, it must be kept in mind that Folmer & Schwing did not actually start manufacturing their own cameras until 1897. Before that year, the cameras that they offered under their own name were manufactured by someone else. The question is; was the serial numbering started before 1897, or only after the company began its own manufacturing? Also, whenever the serial numbering started did it begin with number 1?

The attached chart only takes the serial numbers through the end of 1947. After that year, a great deal of confusion begins, and it would take more room than the Price Guide allows to explain it all. Basically, after 1947 different camera models were assigned different serial number blocks, and the blocks do not run sequentially. In addition, several numbers were repeated within the same camera model line. The serial number list will be printed in its entirety and the confusion minimized in the forthcoming book on the history of Graflex by Roger M. Adams.

The accompanying chart should also be used only as an approximation, as it reflects only the dates that the serial numbers were entered in the book. The cameras were actually made sometime during the following 8-12 months. It should NOT be used to figure the total amount of cameras that were manufactured as some cameras were scrapped and others were never made, even though the serial numbers had already been assigned. The serial number book was never changed to show any of these variations. Actual production figures may never have existed, and if they did, have not been located as of this date.

SERIAL NUMBERS----DATES

Folmer & Schwing Division/Department
47,000- 87,976----1915-12/5/18
87,977-113,431----12/5/18-1920
113,432-122,949----1921-1922
122,950-147,606----1923-1925

Folmer-Graflex Corporation
147,607-159,488----1926-1927
159,489-175,520----1928-1930
175,521-183,297----1931-1933
183,298-229,310----1934-1937
229,311-249,179----1938-1939
249,180-351,511----1940-6/15/45

Graflex, Inc.
351,512-457,139----7/30/45-1947

GRAFLEX (cont.)

We would like to thank Roger Adams for reviewing this section and adding notes and corrections where necessary. Mr. Adams is currently working on a book on Graflex cameras, and he invites readers who are interested in Graflex to contact him at P.O. Box 184, Arcadia, CA 91006, (818)-444-5239. He is interested in everything related to the Graflex companies, including apparatus, literature, advertising, documents, records, employee papers, awards, banners, etc. He will be happy to field questions on any areas of collecting, and would like to make contact with anyone who has Graflex lore to share, especially former employees.

NOTE: To keep major lines together, we have divided this section into three parts, each in alphabetic order:
1. Graflex Single Lens Reflex Cameras.
2. Graphic cameras, including press and small format types.
3. Other cameras made by Graflex Inc.

GRAFLEX SLR CAMERAS: *All models have focal plane shutters to 1000, unless otherwise noted.*

Graflex (original) - c1902-05. (Earliest patent granted 11/5/01.) Boxy SLR with fold-up viewing hood. Stationary back. Top-hinged door covers the interchangeable lens. Focal plane shutter to 1200. Shutter controls on one piece plate. Normal lenses f4.5 to f6.8. Rare, negotiable. Estimates: 4x5" and 5x7": $250-500. 8x10": Find one first, then ask the price!

Graflex 1A - 1909-25. 2½x4¼" on 116 rollfilm. B&L Tessar f4.5 or f6.3, Zeiss Kodak Anastigmat f6.3, or Cooke f5.6 lens. Early cameras have an "accordian" style hood with struts for support. Later ones have the more typical folding hood. Autographic feature available 1915-on. $75-100. *(illustrated top of next column)*

Graflex 1A

Graflex 3A - 1907-26. 3¼x5½" "postcard" size on 122 film. Minor body changes, including the addition of the autographic feature, in 1915. Various lenses, f4.5 to f6.8. $75-125.

Early Auto Graflex with pleated hood

Auto Graflex - 1906/1907-1923. (Patented 2/5/07.) Stationary Graflex back. Extensible front with lens door hinged at top. Normal lenses f4.5 to f6.8. Design changes include: Pleated hood with front hinge, 1907-c.1910. *(illustrated bottom of previous page)* Folding hood with front hinge c.1911-15. Folding hood with rear hinge 1916-23. 3¼x4¼": $60-80. 4x5": $75-125. 5x7": $150-200. *Add $50 for early model with pleated hood.*

Auto Graflex Junior 2¼x3¼" - 1914-24. Stationary Graflex back. Top door hinges at back. Bulge at rear for reverse-wind curtain. Extensible front. Same body later used in the 2¼x3¼" series B. $90-125.

lenses f4.5 to f6.3. This camera was used as the basis for "Big Bertha". $200-250.

National Graflex - SLR for 2¼x2½" on 120 rollfilm. Focal plane shutter to 500, B. B&L Tessar f3.5/75mm. Two models:

Series I - 1933-35. Non-interchangeable lens. Mirror set lever at operator's right of hood. $100-130.

Compact Graflex - Stationary Graflex back. Top door hinged at front. Front bed. Double curtain to cap shutter.
3¼x5½" - 1915-24. $150-200.
5x7" - 1916-25. $200-250.

Home Portrait Graflex - 1912-42. 5x7". Revolving back. Focal plane shutter ½-500. Was also available as the "Special Press Model" with a high speed shutter to 1000. The focal plane shutter could be set to pass one, two, or more of the aperture slits for a single exposure, thus allowing a very broad range of "slow" speeds. Normal

Series II - 1934-41. Cable release. Mirror set lever at operator's left of hood. Ruby window cover. With normal f3.5/75mm lens: $125-200. (With additional B&L f6.3/ 140mm telephoto add $75-100.)

Naturalists' Graflex - 1907-21. One of the rarest of the Graflex cameras, it has a long body and bellows to accomodate lenses up to 26" focal length. 1907 model has a stationary viewing hood stationary, set to the rear. After that, viewing hood could be positioned to view from top or

Naturalists' Graflex

back. Recent prices have ranged widely from $1500-2800.

4x5" - 1906-41. Early models (1906-08) styled like the original Graflex. Extensible front racks out on two rails; front flap covers lens. Later styles like 3¼x4¼" size above, but with 3¾x3¾" lensboard. $125-175.

Press Graflex - 1907-23. 5x7" SLR. Stationary detachable spring back. Focal plane shutter 1/5-1500. Extensible front. No bed. Normal lenses f4.5 to f6.8. $250-350.

Reversible Back Graflex - c1902-05. Very similar to the original Graflex camera, but reversible back. 4x5" and 5x7" sizes. Focal plane shutter to 1200. Knob on the front standard to raise or lower the lensboard. $250-500. *If it says* Auto Graflex *on the nameplate it is not this rare early model. See* Revolving Back Auto Graflex, *below.*

Revolving Back Auto Graflex - Normal lenses f4.5 to f6.8.
3¼x4¼" - 1909-41. Style of 1909-16 has front door which forms bed, unlike earlier 4x5" model; front hinged top lid, 3x3" lensboard. Style of c1917-41 has unique top-front curve, rear hinged top lid, and 3¼x3¼" lensboard. $110-150.

R.B. Graflex Junior - 1915-23. 2¼x3¼". Revolving back. Fixed lenses, normally f4.5 to f6.3. Lensboard suspended from focusing rails. Similar body style later used for the R.B. Series B. Rare. $100-135.

Graflex Series B - Stationary back. Kodak Anastigmat f4.5 lens. Small front door opens allowing lens and small bellows to extend.

2¼x3¼" - 1925-26 only. Rare. $150-255.
3¼x4¼" - 1923-37. $50-80.
4x5" - 1923-37. $75-125.
5x7" - 1925-42. $150-200.

R.B. Graflex Series B - Revolving back. Kodak Anastigmat f4.5 lens.

2¼x3¼" - 1923-51. Same body style as earlier RB Graflex Junior. Small front door opens allowing lens and small bellows to extend. $75-125.
3¼x4¼" - 1923-42. Same body style as RB Tele Graflex. $60-90.
4x5" - 1923-42. Same body style as RB Tele Graflex. $75-125.

R.B. Graflex Series C - 1926-35. 3¼x4¼" only. Revolving back. Fixed Cooke Anastigmat f2.5/6½" lens. Extensible front with hood over the lens. Rare. $125-175.

R.B. Graflex Series D - Same body as the earlier RB Tele Graflex and RB Series B. Interchangeable lensboards. Extensible front with hood over the lens. Grey-painted hardware. Later 4x5" models have black hardware and chrome trim.

3¼x4¼" - 1928-41. $60-110.
4x5" - 1928-47. $125-175.

R.B. Super D Graflex - Revolving back SLR. Flash synch on focal plane shutter. Automatic stop-down diaphragm. Minor variations made during its life.

3¼x4¼" - 1941-63. Normal lenses: Kodak Anstigmat f4.5, Kodak Ektar f4.5 and f5.6. $175-225.

4x5" - 1948-58. f5.6/190mm Kodak Ektar or Graflex Optar. $300-350.

Stereo Auto Graflex

R.B. Tele Graflex - 1915-23. Revolving back. Designed with a long bellows to allow the use of lenses of various focal lengths. Same body used for RB Graflex Series B beginning in 1923. 3¼x4¼": $75-125. 4x5": 110-140.

Tourist Graflex - c1902-05. Stationary back. Extensible front. Sliding-door covers interchangeable lens. Shutter controls on one piece plate. 4x5" and 5x7" sizes. Very rare. Estimate: $300-600.

GRAPHIC CAMERAS:

Stereo Graflex - 1904-05. 5x7" stereo SLR. Stationary back. Similar to style to the original Graflex, but wider to allow for stereo exposures. Two magnifiers in the hood. Quite rare. $1500-2000.

Stereo Auto Graflex - 1906-23. 5x7" stereo SLR with only minor improvements having been made on the Stereo Graflex. Stereo prisms in the viewing hood resulted in one STEREO image on the ground glass. That has to be the ultimate composing aid for stereo photographers. Rising front. Very rare. $1000-1500. *(illustrated top of next column)*

Century Graphic - 1949-70. 2¼x3¼" press camera. Basic features of the Pacemaker Crown Graphic, but no body release, Graflock back only, and has a plastic body. Black or grey body with black or red bellows. With f4.5: $125-150. With Xenotar f2.8: $200-250.

Combat Graphic - c1942. 4x5" military camera made for the armed forces in WWII. Rigid all wood body, without bellows. Olive drab color. No tension knob on shutter. Sold as a civilian model "Graphic 45" in 1945. $175-275. *Note: the name "Combat Graphic" has been applied by collectors to other military models of conventional cameras, but we have listed those by their proper designation after the corresponding civilian*

models. See "Anniversary Speed Graphic" for KE-12(1), "Super Speed Graphic" for KE-12(2). The 70mm model KE-4(1) is in the miscellaneous models at the end of the Graflex Inc. section.

No. 0 Graphic - 1909-23. 1⅝x2½" on rollfilm. FP shutter to 500. Fixed-focus Zeiss Kodak Anastigmat f6.3 lens. $175-235.

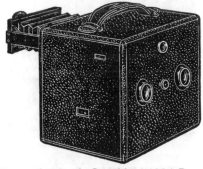

Deceptive Angle Graphic - c1904. Box camera for 3¼x4¼" exposures using

double plate holders, magazine plate holder or cartridge rollholder. The 1904 Graflex catalog calls it "in every sense of the word a detective camera, being thoroughly disguised to resemble a stereo camera and so arranged as to photograph subjects at right angles to its apparent line of vision." Quite rare. Estimate: $2000-3000.

Graphic camera - c1904. Simple plate cameras with single extension red bellows. No back movements. 4x5", 5x7", 8x10". $125-150.

Graphic 35 - c1955-58. 35mm camera made by Kowa for Graflex. Graflar f3.5 or 2.8/50mm lens in helical mount with unique push-button focus. Prontor 1-300. Coupled split-image rangefinder. $30-45.

Graphic 35 Electric - c1959. 35mm camera with electric motor built into the takeup spool. Made by Kowa. Interchangeable Ysarex f2.8 or Quinon f1.9 in Synchro Compur shutter. Coupled meter. In excellent working condition: $125-150. Often found with inoperative motor: $40-60.

Graphic 35 Jet - c1961. An unusual modification of the Graphic 35 design, incorporating an auto advance mechanism powered by CO_2 cartridges. Made by Kowa. Quite prone to problems with both the shutter and the CO_2 advance system. Completely operational, with original case, box, and a few spare cartridges: $200-250.

As normally found with the CO2 system inoperative: $75-100. With shutter also bad: $40-60. *Note: Because of the problems with the CO2 advance mechanism, a completely manual model was also made.*

Graphic Sr. - c1904. Very similar to the Graphic camera of the same era, but with swing back. Red bellows. Polished brass trim. 4x5" or 5x7". $75-150.

Pacemaker Crown Graphic - Front shutter only. No focal plane shutter. Built-in body release with cable running along bellows. Metal lensboard. Hinged-type adjustable infinity stops on bed. Wide range of current prices.
2¼x3¼" - 1947-58. $150-175.
3¼x4¼" - 1947-62. $100-140.
4x5" - 1947-73. (Top mounted Graphic rangefinder with interchangeable cams added in 1955.) Very abundant in the range of: $150-250. (Also seen advertised at higher prices for months on end.)

Reversible Back Cycle Graphic - c1900-06. "Cycle" style cameras with reversible back. Interchangeable lensboards. Black leather, triple-extension red bellows, rising front. *(illustrated top of next column)*
3¼x4¼" & 4x5" sizes - $100-125.
5x7" & 6½x8½" sizes - $100-150.

Reversible Back Cycle Graphic

Reversible Back Cycle Graphic Special - 1904-06. Similar to the original R.B. Cycle Graphic, but sturdier design. Double-swing back. Rising/falling, shifting front. Drop-bed. Front and back focusing. Black leather, triple extension black bellows. Grey-oxidized brass trim. An accessory focal plane shutter was available. 5x7" and 6½x8½" sizes. Quite rare. $150-200.

Revolving Back Cycle Graphic - 1907-22. Very similar to the Reversible Back Cycle Graphic (above), but revolving back, no back focus or rear movements. An accessory focal plane shutter was available. 4x5": $75-125. 5x7", 6½x8½", 8x10": $200-250.

SPEED GRAPHIC CAMERAS *Many modifications and improvements were made in these cameras during their exceptionally long life-span (1912-68), so they are usually sub-divided for identification purposes into the following periods: Early (or top handle), Pre-anniversary, Anniversary, and Pacemaker. All models have focal plane shutters. The Speed Graphics are listed here in essentially chronological order.*

Early Speed Graphics - Top handle. Barrel lenses. Tapered bellows, almost

double extension. Rising front. Folding optical finder with cross-hairs. Single focus knob on wooden bed.
3¼x4¼" - 1915-25. $70-115.
3¼x5½" - 1912-25. $110-150.
4x5" - 1912-27. (More compact style introduced in 1924, and called Special Speed Graphic.) $75-125.
5x7" - 1912-24. $135-185.

Miniature Speed Graphic - 1938-47. 2¼x3¼". Could almost be classified as an Anniversary model with its two focus knobs on the metal bed and chrome trim, but other features from the pre-anniversary years remain. The bed does not drop; the front does not shift. The sportsfinder is hinged, not telescoping. Earliest models with folding optical, later with tubular finder. $70-120.

Pre-anniversary Speed Graphic - Side handle. Grey trim. Larger, straight bellows to accomodate a larger lens standard and lensboard. Early versions with folding optical finder, later changed to tubular finder. Hinged, not telescoping sportsfinder. Wooden bed with single focus knob.
3¼x4¼" - 1935-39. $60-100.
4x5" - 1928-39. $85-135.
5x7" - c1932-41. $150-200.

Pacemaker Speed Graphic - Metal lensboard. Two focus knobs on the metal drop-bed. Built-in body release with cable running along the bellows. Single control on focal plane shutter. Hinged adjustable infinity stops on bed. Telescoping sportsfinder. Tubular viewfinder. Chrome trim. Prices vary widely. Most fall into the ranges listed, and there is no shortage of these cameras, but some vendors consistently advertise at higher prices.
2¼x3¼" - 1947-58. $150-195.
3¼x4¼" - 1947-63. $100-150.
4x5" - 1947-68. (Top mounted Graphic rangefinder witn interchangeable cams added in 1955.) $150-250.
Military model KE-12(1) - 4x5". Optar f4.5/127mm. Olive drab leather & enamel: $150-250. Full set KS-4A(1), with flash unit, film holders, tripod, etc. in Halliburton case. $200-300.

Anniversary Speed Graphic - 1940-47. Metal drop-bed with two focus knobs. Rising/shifting lens standard. Wooden lensboard. Telescoping sportsfinder. No body release for front shutter. All black (wartime models) or chrome trim. 3¼x4¼": $55-90. 4x5": $95-160.

Stereo Graphic (35mm) - ca. mid-1950's for stereo pairs on 35mm film. Graflar f4/35mm lenses in simple shutter, 1/50, B. $75-100.

Stereoscopic Graphic - c1902-21. Solidly built 5x7" stereo camera. Focal plane shutter. Rising front. Drop bed. Black bellows. Grey metal parts. Very rare. $1200-1500.

Longer bellows than the original model. Without lens: $150-200.

MISCELLANEOUS CAMERAS FROM GRAFLEX INC.:

Century 35 - c1961. 35mm camera made by Kowa in Japan. Several models including A, N, NE. Prominar f3.5, 2.8, or 2.0 lens. Similar to the Kallo 35. $25-35.

Ciro 35 - c1950. 35mm RF camera, formerly sold by Ciro Cameras Inc. f4.5, 3.5, or 2.8 lens. Alphax or Rapax shutter. $15-25.

Crown View - 1939-42. Wooden 4x5" view camera. 4x4" lensboards interchangeable with 4x4" Speed Graphic. Rare. $185-250.

Super Graphic - 1958-73. 4x5". All-metal press style camera. Built-in coupled rangefinder. Focusing scale for lenses from 90 to 380mm. Normal lenses include: Kodak Ektar f4.7/127, Schneider Xenar or Graflex Optar f4.7/135mm. Rise, swing, shift, tilt front movements. Revolving back. Electric shutter release. Although a few large dealers consistently advertise at higher prices, these are nearly always available in the range of: $250-350.

Super Speed Graphic - 1959-70. 4x5". Same as the Super Graphic (above), but with Graflex-1000 front shutter. No focal plane shutter. $300-400.
Military model KE-12(2) - with tripod, flash, etc. in olive drab Halliburton case: $300-400.

Graphic View - 1941-48. 4x5" monorail view camera. Without lens: $135-165.

Graphic View II - 1949-67. Improved version of the 4x5" monorail view camera.

Fingerprint Camera - 2¼x3¼". A special-purpose camera for photographing fingerprints or making 1:1 copies of other photos or documents. Pre-focused lens is recessed to the proper focal distance inside a flat-black rigid shroud. To make an exposure, camera front opening is placed directly on the surface to be photographed. Four battery-operated flashlight bulbs provide the illumination. (Two similar cameras called the Inspectograph (see listing below) and Factograph were also made. The Factograph used special positive paper film on a roll. Later models of the Factograph became very specialized using bulk loads of film, motorized advance, and special lighting and bore no resemblance to the earlier models.) $75-125.

Graflex 22 - TLR for 6x6cm on 120 film. Optar or Graftar f3.5/88mm. Century Synchromatic or Graphex shutter. Fairly common. $25-40.

Inspectograph Camera - Identical to the Fingerprint camera, but wired for 110V AC current instead of built-in batteries. Only about 500 made. $75-110.

KE-4(1) 70mm Combat Camera - c1953. Civilian black or Signal Corps Model in olive drab. For 5.5x7cm exposures on 70mm film. Designed by the late Hubert Nerwin, formerly of Zeiss Ikon, the camera resembles an overgrown Contax and is nicknamed "Gulliver's Contax". A few years ago, these were scarce and highly sought. Then Uncle Sam started disposing of them, and now they are very easy to find. Consequently, prices have dropped and they are harder to sell. Many are still advertised at higher prices, but one major dealer reported advertising an outfit with two lenses, flash, and case for 7 months at $495 before it finally sold. The f4.5/2½" Ektar wide angle is the least common lens. Camera set KS6-(1) with normal, tele, and W.A. lenses, case: $750-1000. Often found with f2.8/4" and f4/8" Ektar lenses, flash, and Halliburton case: $500-600 asking price. Camera with normal lens only: $300-400.

Norita - c1969-73. Eye-level SLR for 6x6cm on 120 or 220 film. Three models: Deluxe, Professional (with front shutter), and Super Wide. Made by Norita Kogaku K.K. in Tokyo, imported by Graflex. Originally imported as the Warner. Noritar f2/80mm lens in interchangeable breech-lock mount. Focal plane shutter 1-500. $175-275.

Photorecord - Developed around 1934, introduced to the open market in 1936. Made through the 1950's in many different forms and models, including civilian and military versions. Special purpose camera for microfilming, personnel identification, and copy work. All versions were designed around the same basic heavy cast metal camera and film magazine unit, and were offered as complete outfits including lights, stands, copy or I.D. apparatus. Designed for use with 100 ft. rolls of 35mm film, they were capable of 800 "double frame" or 1600 "single frame" exposures. Also capable of single exposures using Graflex plate or film holders. Camera with film magazine: $75-125.

GRAY (Robert D. Gray, NYC)
Vest Camera - c1885. All metal disc-shaped camera designed to be worn under a vest. Forerunner of the more common Stirn Vest Camera. Manufactured for Gray by the Western Electric Co. Takes six round exposures on an octagonal glass plate. $1300-1800.

View camera - 8x10". c1880. Periscope No. 4 lens with rotary disc stops. $175-200.

GREAT WALL SZ-1 - c1976. People's

Republic of China 35mm spring-motor camera. CRF. f2.8/45mm coated lens, rotating 1/30- 1/300 shutter. Leather covered aluminum body. $50-60.

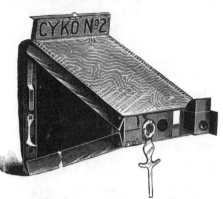

GRIFFIN (John J. Griffin & Sons, Ltd., London)
Pocket Cyko Cameras - c1902. Folding cameras of unusual book form, designed by Magnus Niell, the Swedish designer who is also responsible for the popular Expo and Ticka designs. Also sold on the continent under the name "Lopa". Several sizes and styles, including the No. 1 for 6.5x9cm plates, and the No. 2 with magazine back for 8x10.5cm plates. Despite higher prices a few years ago, more recent auction sales of the No. 1 have been in the $380-400 range, while we saw a No. 2 offered for $750 with original magazine back.

GRIFFITHS (Walter M. Griffiths & Co., Birmingham, England)
Guinea Detective Camera - c1895. Leather covered cardboard camera in the shape of a carrying case. The top hinges to one side to change plateholders, and the front conceals a guillotine shutter. $200-250.

GROSSER (Rudolph Grosser, Pillnitz)
Manufacturer of Mentor cameras during the 1950's. However, all Mentor Cameras are listed in this edition under Goltz & Breutmann.

GRUNDMANN
Leipzig Detective Camera - All wood box detective camera for 9x12cm plates. String-set shutter. $800-850.

GUERIN (E. Guerin & Cie., Paris)
Le Furet - c1923. Small, early 35mm camera for 25 exposures 24x36mm using special cassettes. This is the smallest of the pre-Leica 35mm cameras. While these sold a few years ago for $1500-1800, the current market indicates a more stable price of $800-1000.

GUILFORD - Polished walnut 5x7" English view camera with brass fittings. Brass-barreled Ross Extra Rapid lens. $150-175.

GUILLEMINOT (Guilleminot Roux & Cie., Paris)
Guilleminot Detective Camera - c1900. Polished walnut detective camera for 9x12cm plates. Brass knobs rack front panel forward and concealed viewfinders are exposed. Brass carrying handle and fittings. Aplanat f9/150mm lens. Eight speed rotary sector shutter. $800-900.

GUNDLACH OPTICAL CO., GUNDLACH MANHATTAN OPTICAL CO. (Rochester, N.Y.) *Originally founded by Ernst Gundlach for the production of optical goods, but for most of the company's history it was operated by H.H.Turner, J.C.Reich, & J. Zellweger. Gundlach Optical Co. acquired the Milburn Korona Company in 1896, which added a line of cameras to their line of lenses. Shortly thereafter, they joined with Manhattan Optical to become one of the leading sellers of dry-plate cameras well into the 1900's. The company was taken over by John E. Seebold in 1928 and the name changed to the "Seebold Invisible Camera Company."*
Korona cameras - classified here by size:

Korona 3¼x4¼ and 3¼x5½" - Folding plate cameras, including Petit. Cherry wood body, leather covered. Red bellows. $30-60.

--4x5" - Folding bed view. $65-105.

–5x7" - as above two listings. $75-125.

–5x7" Stereo - Folding plate camera for stereo exposures on standard 5x7" plates. Leather covered wood body with polished wood interior. Simple stereo shutter. $300-360.

Korona 6½x8½" view - $100-150.
Korona 8x10" view - $125-175.

Korona 7x17, 8x20, and 12x20" Panoramic View - usually called "Banquet" cameras. With holder, without lens: $200-300. Add for lens, depending on type. A good working outfit with several holders and a good lens & shutter will bring $350-650.

Long Focus Korona - $125-175.

HADDS MFG. CO.
Foto-Flex - Twin-lens box camera of unusual design. The small viewing and taking lenses are both within the round front disc which resembles a normal lens. (Design is similar to the 35mm Agfa Flexilette.) Takes 4x4cm on 127 film. One model has a cast metal body. Another has a plastic body with a cast metal faceplate. $10-15.

HADSON - Japanese novelty subminiature of the "Hit" type. $10-20.

HAKING (W. Haking, Hong Kong) *While Haking produces many cameras, most are not*

yet of collectible age. We are listing a few of the "novelty" types.

Halina 35 - c1982. Inexpensive plastic 35mm camera. Although a recent model, this is definitely a novelty camera. The same camera, of very inexpensive construction, appears under various names, often as a low-cost premium. $10-15.

Halina 35X - c1959. Inexpensive but heavy 35mm camera with cast metal body. $15-20.

Halina-Baby - Plastic novelty camera from Macau. $1-5.

Halina Prefect Senior - Fixed focus TLR-style camera, 6x6cm. $10-15.

Halina Viceroy - Twin-lens box camera for 6x6cm. $10-15.
Kinoflex Deluxe - TLR style box camera. $10-20.
Votar Flex - TLR style box camera. $10-20.

HALL CAMERA CO. (Brooklyn, NY)
Pocket Camera - Small focal plane strut camera. Goerz Celor f3.5 lens. $600-700.
(illustrated top of next column)

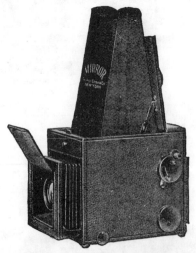

Mirror Reflex Camera - c1910. 4x5" Graflex-style SLR. f4.5/180mm lens. $75-125.

HAMAPHOT KG (Monheim, Germany)
Modell P56L - Bakelite camera with telescoping front. Takes 6x6cm on 120. Available in black or dark green. $10-15.

Hall Pocket Camera

HAMCO - Japanese 14x14mm novelty camera of Hit type. $10-15.

HANAU (Eugene Hanau, Paris)

le Marsouin - c1900. Rigid aluminum body stereo camera for 18 plates in magazine back. No. 1 size for 45x107mm plates; No. 2 size for 6x13cm plates. Tessar or Balbreck lenses. Guillotine shutter. $175-225.

Passe-Partout - c1890. Unusual brass detective camera with conical front which moves in succession to four positions on a double 6x13cm plateholder, making a 6cm round exposure at each position. Quite rare. One was offered for sale in early 1982 at $6500.

HANEEL TRI-VISION CO. (Alhambra, CA)

Tri-Vision Stereo - Plastic and aluminum stereo camera for 28x30mm pairs on 828 rollfilm. f8 meniscus lenses with 3 stops. Usually found in excellent condition with original box, stereo viewer, etc. for $30-40.

HANKEN - c1953. Subminiature camera nearly identical to the Steky, but with additional waist-level viewer. Rare. $150-300.

HANNA-BARBERA
Fred Flintstone, Huckelberry Hound, Yogi Bear (127 types) - Novelty cameras for 127 film, each featuring the image of a cartoon character printed on the side. Imitation light meter surrounds the lens. $1-5.

Fred Flintstone, Yogi Bear (126 types) - Similar small cameras, but for 126 cartridge film. On these, the front of the camera is in the shape of the character's head, with the lens in the mouth. $5-10.

HAPPY - Japanese Hit-type novelty camera. $10-15.

HARBOE, A. O. (Altona, Germany)

Wood box camera - c1870. For glass plates. Typical of the type of camera made in Germany during the 1870-1890 period. Although it pre-dated the "Kodak", it was made for the ordinary person to use. Brass barrel lens, simple shutter, ground glass back. Only one sale on record, in late 1976 at $600.

HARE (George Hare, London)
Stereo Wet-plate - c1860. For 3¼x6¾" wet collodion plates. Mahogany body with twin red bellows. Matching brass lenses with waterhouse stops. With ground glass back and wet-plate holder: $1000-1200.

Tropical Stereo Wet-plate camera - c1865. For stereo views on 5x8" wet plates. Polished teak body with brass fittings. Petzval lenses with waterhouse stops and flap shutter. $3000-3500.

Tourist camera - c1865. Half-plate. Fallowfield Rapid Doublet lens with iris diaphragm. Changing box. $350-600.

HARMONY - Inexpensive eye-level metal box camera from Japan for 6x6 on 120. Focusing lens, 3 speed shutter, PC sync. $10-15.

HARTEX - Japanese subminiature of the Hit type. $10-15.

HARUKAWA (Japan)

Septon Pen Camera - Subminiature camera combined with an oversized mechanical pencil. A rare subminiature of unusual design. Several years ago, a few new ones were discovered, complete with original box and instructions. These quickly sold for approximately $1250 each, and several recent transactions support that price. Used models, without the box and instructions have sold in the range of $600-1000.

HASSELBLAD (Victor Hasselblad Aktiebolag, Goteborg, Sweden)
Founded by Fritz Victor Hasselblad in 1841 as F.W. Hasselblad & Co., the company opened a photo department in 1887. Due to expansion in that department, a separate company, "Hasselblads Fotografiska Aktiebolag", was founded in 1908 and became the Kodak general agent in Sweden. Although the early companies sold cameras made by other manufacturers, the real beginning was when "Victor Hasselblad Aktiebolag" was established in 1941 to manufacture aerial cameras for the Royal Swedish Air Force, as well as ground reconnaissance cameras. Dr. Victor Hasselblad retained his staff after the war and began the final designing of the Hasselblad 1600F, which was introduced in 1948. To ascertain the year of production, the two letters before the serial number indicate the year, with the code "VH PICTURES" representing the digits "12 34567890".

1600F - 1948-52. The world's first 6x6cm SLR with interchangeable lenses and film magazines. It is most easily distinguished by its focal plane shutter to 1/1600. Originally supplied with Kodak Ektar f2.8/ 80mm lens and magazine back for $548.

Accessory lenses included 135mm f3.5 Ektar and 250mm f4 Zeiss Opton Sonnar. The shutter on the 1600F was not of the quality we have since grown to expect from Hasselblad, and often this model is seen for sale with an inoperative shutter for less. The prices given here are for cameras in VG-E condition, operational, with back and original lens: $450-650.

1000F - 1952-57. The second Hasselblad model, and still with a focal plane shutter, but with the top speed reduced to 1/1000 sec. This attempted to eliminate the accuracy and operational problems of the older shutter. Sold for $400 when new. Replaced the 1600F, but while supplies lasted, the 1600F continued to sell at $500. Despite the improvements, these still are often found with inoperative shutters, for less than the prices quoted here. With back and normal lens: $300-400.

Super Wide Angle - 1954-59. Also called SW and SWA. Can be easily distinguished from the normal models, since it has a short, non-reflex body. "Super Wide Angle" is inscribed on the top edge of the front. The early SWA can be distinguished from the later SWC in several ways. The most obvious is that it has a knob for film advance rather than a crank, and shutter cocking is a separate function. The shutter release is on the lower right corner of the front, while the SWC has a top release button. Zeiss Biogon f4.5/38mm lens in MX Compur to 500. The value of this camera is not as a collectible, but as a usable camera. With finder and magazine back: $675-800.

500C - 1957-70. From a technical standpoint, the 500C is an innovative camera, since it replaced the focal plane shuttered 1000F with an entirely new Compur front shutter with full aperture viewing and automatic diaphragm. From a practical standpoint, however, the value of the camera is primarily as a very usable piece of equipment, despite the advanced age of some of the earlier ones. Collectors want cosmetically clean cameras, but generally the users will outbid the collectors for a clean 500C. That's the bottom line. Because of the wide range of lenses and accessories, it would not be practical to go into detail here, but as an example, you might pick up a nice 500C with back, finder, and f2.8/80mm Planar in a $650-750 range.

HEALTHWAYS
Mako Shark - Cylindrical plastic underwater camera. The entire working mechanism including shutter, lens, and filmtransport are identical to the Brownie Hawkeye Flash Model. $30-45.

HEILAND PHOTO PRODUCTS
(Div. of Minneapolis-Honeywell, Denver, Colorado)
Premiere - c1957-59. 35mm non-RF camera made in Germany. Steinheil Cassar f2.8/45mm in Pronto to 200. $20-30.

HELIN-NOBLE INC. (Union Lake, Michigan)
Noble 126 - Miniature gold & black "snap-on" camera for 126 cartridges, with matching flash. Winding knob pivots for compactness. The world's smallest 126 cartridge camera. With tele and W.A. lenses in original plastic box: $50-75.

HELM TOY CORP. (New York City)
Bugs Bunny - c1978. Plastic camera with figure of Bugs Bunny. "Eh-Doc, Smile!". In Europe: up to $40. In the U.S.: $15-22.

Mickey Mouse - c1979. Blue plastic camera with white molded front. Mickey Mouse riding astraddle a toy train. In Europe: $20-30. U.S.A.: $15-22.

Snoopy-Matic - A modern detective camera. The camera is shaped like a dog house, with Snoopy relaxing on the roof. The chimney accepts magicubes. This camera is less common than the others from Helm, and is a more interesting design. It brings up to $100 in Europe and $50-60 in the U.S.

HENDREN ENTERPRISE

Octopus "The Weekender" - c1983. Named for its multiple functions, this device houses an AM-FM transistor radio, alarm clock with stopwatch functions, flashlight, storage compartment, and a 110 camera with electronic flash. It sold new for $70-80. This high price, coupled with quality problems, kept it from making great waves in the marketplace. $70-90.

HENSOLDT (Dr. Hans Hensoldt, Wetzlar)
Henso Reporter - c1953. 35mm RF camera produced by ISO in Italy. Dr. Hans Hensoldt Iriar f2.8/5cm lens. Folding rapid advance lever in base. Uncommon camera, so limited price data. $550-750.

Henso Standard - Similar, but knob wind rather than lever. $450-550.

HERBERT GEORGE CO. (Chicago)
Founded by Herbert Weil and George Israel c1945. Bought out in 1961 and name changed to "Imperial Camera Corp."
Davy Crockett - Black plastic box camera for 6x6cm. Metal faceplate illustrates Davy Crockett and rifles. $20-35.

Donald Duck Camera - c1946. Plastic 127 rollfilm camera for 1⅝x1⅝" exposures. Figures of the Disney ducks (Donald, Huey, Louie, and Dewey) in relief on the back. Meniscus lens, simple shutter. This was the first camera design patented by George L. Israel. The earliest models, ca. Sept 1946 were olive-drab color and without external metal back latches. This version brings about $10 more than the later ones. The body was soon changed to black plastic, and by November 1946, external back latches had been added.

Back view of Donal Duck Camera

This is the most common version. With original cardboard carton: $35-50. Camera only: $15-25.

Flick-N-Flash - Twin lens box camera. $1-5.

Happi-Time - Plastic camera for 127. Essentially the same design as the Donald Duck camera, but without the bas-relief back. $5-10.

Herco-flex 6-20 - Plastic twin-lens style. 2¼x2¼" on 620 rollfilm. $3-6.

Imperial Mark XII Flash - Plastic box camera, in colors. $1-5.

Imperial Reflex - ca. mid-1950's plastic 6x6cm TLR for 620 film. Simple lens and shutter. $1-5.

Imperial Satellite 127, Imperial Satellite Flash - $1-5.

Insta-Flash - Twin lens box camera. $1-5.

Roy Rogers & Trigger - Black plastic box camera for 620 film. Aluminum faceplate pictures Roy Rogers on Trigger. $15-20.

Savoy, Savoy Mark II, etc. - Common plastic box cameras. $1-3.

Official "Scout" cameras - Boy Scout, Brownie Scout, Cub Scout, Girl Scout. In black or in official scout colors. These cameras were based on many different "civilian" models, so quite a number of variations exist. Camera only: $5-10. In original box with flash unit: $10-15.

Stylex - An unusual design for the Herbert-George company. Plastic body with rectangular telescoping front. 6x9cm on 620 film. $5-10.

HERLANGO AG (Vienna)
Folding camera - For 7x8.5cm plates or rollfilm back. Tessar f4.5/105mm. Compur shutter 1-250. $30-40.

HERMAGIS (J. Fleury Hermagis, Paris)
Field Camera 13x18cm - Polished walnut camera with brass handle and inlaid brass fittings. Thornton-Pickard roller-blind shutter. Hermagis, naturellement, Aplanastigmat f6.8/210mm lens. Rotating maroon bellows for vertical or horizontal use. $175-250.

Velocigraphe - c1892. Detective style drop-plate magazine camera for 12 plates 9x13cm in metal sheaths. Polished wooden body built into a heavy leather covering which appears to be a case. Front and back flaps expose working parts. $600-850.

HEROLD MFG. CO. (Chicago) *The Herold name was first used in 1951 when Harold Rubin, former Sales Manager for Spartus Camera Co., purchased the Spartus company and renamed it. This was about the same time that Jack Galter, former President of Spartus, had formed Galter Products. Herold Mfg. continued to produce Spartus cameras, changing its name to Herold Products Co. Inc. in 1956, and to "Spartus Corporation" about 1960. Check under the "Spartus" heading for related cameras.*

Acro-Flash - Black bakelite minicam for 127 film. Twin sync posts above the lens barrel. One of the few minicams with flash sync. $3-7.

Da-Brite - Brown bakelite minicam for 3x4cm on 127 film. $3-7.
Flash-Master - Synchronized minicam like the Acro-Flash. 3x4cm on 127 film. $3-7.
Photo-Master - Economy model plastic minicam. "Photo Master" molded into the plastic shutter face rather than using a metal faceplate. $2-5.

Spartacord - Inexpensive 6x6cm TLR, but with focusing lenses. Nicely finished with brown covering and accessories. $10-15.

Spartus 35 - Low cost brown bakelite 35mm camera with grey plastic top. $10-15.

Spartus 35F, Spartus 35F Model 400 - Variations of the Spartus 35. $10-15.

Spartus 120 Flash Camera - Brown bakelite box camera with eye level finder on side. $4-8.

Spartus Co-Flash - Small bakelite box camera with built-in flash reflector beside the lens. 4x4cm on 127. $8-12.

Sunbeam 120 - Bakelite box camera, either brown or black. Synchronized. Several variations. $1-5.

Sunbeam 127 - Two types:
Plastic box camera for 12 square pictures 4x4cm on 127 film. Styled like the more common Spartus Vanguard. $1-3.
Streamlined brown bakelite minicam for 16 exposures 3x4cm on 127 film. $3-7.

Sunbeam Six-Twenty - Plastic TLR style box camera. Several variations. $3-7.

HERZOG (August Herzog, New York City)
Herzog Amateur Camera - c1877. Very simple 2x2½" plate camera made of wood and cardboard. Dry plate slides into the back which is mounted on a baseboard. Pyramidal front holds brass lens that slides in and out for focusing. Rare. We have seen only one offered for sale in mid-1983 for $3500 in the original box with accessories.

HESEKIEL (Dr. Adolf Hesekiel & Co., Berlin)
Pompadour - Same camera that Lancaster sold as the Ladies' Gem Camera. See Lancaster.

HESS-IVES CORP. (Philadelphia, PA)

Hicro Color Camera - c1915. Box-shaped camera for color photos 3¼x4¼" by the separation process via multiple exposures with filters. Meniscus lens. Wollensak Ultro shutter. (Made for Hess-Ives under contract by the Hawk-Eye Division of E.K.C.) $100-200.

HETHERINGTON & HIBBEN (Indianapolis)

Hetherington Magazine Camera - c1892. Magazine camera for 4x5" plates. Dark brown leather covered. Plate advancing, aperture setting, & shutter tensioning are all controlled by a key. This camera was once marketed by Montgomery Ward & Co. $450-550.

HI-FLASH - Novelty camera of Diana type. Synchronized. $1-5.

HILGER (Adam Hilger, Ltd., London)
Three-Colour Camera - Color separation camera with 2 small semi-silvered mirrors behind the lens. $700-1000.

HIT - Japanese novelty camera for 14x14mm exposures on 16mm paper backed rollfilm. Similar cameras are available under a number of other names, but usually called "Hit type" cameras by collectors. Gold models: $40-60. "Occupied Japan" model ("Made in Occupied Japan" below lens): $35-50. Normal chrome models: $10-15.

HIT TYPE CAMERAS *There are many small cameras which were made in post-WWII Japan. One class of these subminiatures is commonly called "Hit-types" because the Hit name was one of the first and most popular names found on this type of camera. Despite their overall similarity, there are many subtle differences in* construction from one camera to the next, and there is a seemingly endless number of names which graced the fronts, tops, and cases. There may never be a complete list, but this is probably the most complete one to date. If you know of others not on this list, please write to the authors. This list is intended to include only the inexpensive, lightweight "Hit" type cameras. Heavier models, such as the Corona, Mighty, Mycro, Rocket, Tacker, Tone, Vesta, Vestkam, etc. are not included on this list.

Name variations - AHI, Amerex (Occupied Japan), Arcoflex, Arrow, Astra, Astropic, Atomy, Babymax, Barco, Beica, Bell 14, Betsons, Bluestar, Charmy, Click, CMA, CMC (in chrome or gold with a variety of colored coverings), Colly, Crown, Crystar, Dale, Diplomat, Electronic, Elite, Emson, Enn Ess, Francya, Global, Globe, Hadson, Hamco, Happy, Hartex, Hit (Occupied Japan, chrome, and gold models), Homer, Homer No. 1 (gray rectangular body), I.G.B., Jay Dee, Kassin, Kent, Lenz, Lloyd's, Lucky, Marvel, Midge, Midget, Mighty Midget, Minetta, Mini Camera (Hong Kong), Miracle, Mykro Fine, Old Mexico, Pacific, Pamex, Peace, PFCA, Prince, Q.P, Real, Regent, Satellite, Shalco, Shayo, Sil-Bear, Sing 88, Speedex, Spesco, Star-Lite, Stellar, Sterling, Swallow, Tee Mee, Toyoca (note: heavier "Toyoca 16" also exists), Traveler, Vesta (this is a heavier type, but not by much!), Walklenz.

PLEASE SEND ANY ADDITIONS AND CORRECTIONS TO: Jim McKeown; Centennial Photo; Box 1125; Grantsburg, WI 54840 USA. Please send your name and address if you wish to be on our "Hit list" and to cooperate in the research and enjoyment of these little cameras.

HOEI INDUSTRIAL CO. (Japan)

Anny 35 (Howay 35) - Inexpensive 35mm novelty camera. Looks convincing from a distance, but is only a box camera. $8-12. *Perhaps Howay is a variation in the English spelling of the manufacturer's name. The Anny-35 has "Howay" stamped into the top front. The Anny-44 has "Hoei Industrial Co." on the lens rim. The two cameras are quite similar in construction.*

Anny-44 - Inexpensive metal eye-level box camera for 4x4cm on 127 film. Designed to look like a 35mm camera. $8-12.

Ebony 35 - c1950. Bakelite camera for 25x37mm exposures on 828 rollfilm. f11 meniscus lens. Simple B & I shutter. $10-15.

Ebony 35 De-Luxe - Like the Ebony 35, but metal trim on front and finder. $10-15.

Ebony Deluxe IIS - Metal front and top housing. PC sync accessory shoe. $10-20

HOFERT (Emil Hofert, EHO Kamera Fabrik, Dresden, Germany) - see EHO-ALTISSA.

HOMER 16 - Japanese novelty camera for 14x14mm exposures on 16mm film. Meniscus lens, simple shutter. Similar to Hit type cameras, but with rectangular top housing and thumb-wheel advance. Chrome top body with black covering. $15-25.

HOMER NO. 1 - see Kambayashi & Co., Ltd.

HONEYWELL
Electric Eye 35R - 35mm RF camera made by Mamiya with Honeywell name. Meter for auto diaphragm surrounds lens. $15-20.

HORIZONT - Russian 35mm panoramic camera with f2.8 pivoting lens for 120 degrees. $175-245.

HORNE & THORNTHWAITE (Newgate, G.B.)
Powell's Stereoscopic Camera - Patented in 1858 by T.H. Powell, the camera had a sliding back for two successive exposures on the same plate. The single lens camera could be positioned for the second exposure by sliding it along the tracks on the carrying case and its hinged lid. We have no recent sales recorded, but at least 2 examples sold in 1974 in the $3500-4000 range.

Wet-plate camera - c1860. Sliding box style for 12x16.5cm plates. $1000-1500.

HORSMAN (E. I. Horsman Co., N.Y.C.)

No. 3 Eclipse - c1896. Folding bed, collapsible bellows, polished cherry-wood view camera for 4½x6½" plates. Styled like the more common Scovill Waterbury camera. Brass barreled meniscus lens. Rubber-band powered shutter. $175-225.

Eclispe - c1895. An unusual box-plate camera for single exposures 4x5". Black papered wood body. Primitive meniscus lens. Wooden lens cap. $200-225.

HOUGHTON (George Houghton & Son Ltd., Houghton's Ltd.- pre-1925. Houghton-Butcher- after 1925. Ensign Ltd. after 1931.) London, England. *Established in 1834 by George Houghton six years before Daguerre's announcement of the miracle of photography. In 1840, Houghton joined forces with Antoine Claudet to introduce the Daguerreotype to England, and they secured the patent rights to the process in England. Sons and grandsons continued in the photographic business through the various changes and mergers mentioned above.*

All Distance Ensign Cameras - An euphemistic term for "fixed focus", this name was applied to box and folding model cameras for 2¼x3¼" (6x9cm) on rollfilm. Note: Colored models bring about twice the prices listed here for black ones. Box models: $5-10. Rollfilm models: $5-10. (Including Ensign Pocket Models I & II.)

Autorange 220 Ensign - c1941. Folding camera offering a choice of 12 or 16 exposures on 120 film. f4.5 Tessar in Compur 1-250. Focus by radial lever on bed. $40-60. *(illus. top of next column)*

Autorange 220 Ensign

Ensign Auto-Speed - 6x6cm format 120 rollfilm camera with FP 15-500. Film advance cocks the shutter. Aldis f4.5/4" lens. $250-350.

Ensign box cameras - Including E20, E29, 2¼A, 2¼B, etc. Black: $5-10. Colored: $15-25.

Ensign Carbine - A series of folding cameras originated by Butcher and continued after the merger. Primarily for rollfilm, but most models have a removable panel in the back which allows use with plates as well. Many models in a wide range of prices. $20-50.

Ensign Carbine (Tropical models) - Nos. 4, 6, 7, 12. Bronzed brass body, tan bellows. Tessar f4.5 lens in Compur shutter. $75-125.

Ensign Commando - Folding rollfilm camera for 6x6cm. Rangefinder coupled to the film plane. Ensar f3.5/75mm lens in Epsilon 1-300 shutter. $40-60.

Ensign Cupid - intro. 1922. Simple metal bodied camera for 4x6cm exposures on 120 film. The design is based on a 1921 prototype for a stereo camera which was never produced. Mensicus achromatic f11 lens. Available in black, blue, grey, and perhaps other colors. $35-50.

Ensign Double-8 - c1930-40. Strut-folding camera, 3x4cm on 120. Ensar Anastigmat f4.5 lens in 25-100 shutter. $50-70.

Ensign Ful-Vue - Box camera with large brilliant finder. Several major styles. Rectangular box-shaped model c1941 is less common than the oddly shaped black or red post-war model. Red: $35-45. Black: $15-30.

Ensign Greyhound - Folding bed 6x9cm rollfilm camera. Metal body with grey crackle finish. $12-18.

Ensign Mascot A3, D3 - c1910. 3¼x4¼" drop-plate magazine box cameras. $35-50.

Ensign Midget, Model 55

Ensign Midget - 1934-40. Compact folding cameras for 3.5x4.5cm exposures on E-10 film.
Model 22 - Meniscus lens, T,I shutter. Uncommon. $50-60.

Model 33 - Meniscus lens. Shutter 25-100. Most common model. $45-55.
Model 55 - Ensar Anastigmat f6.3 lens. Shutter 25-100. The most complex model. $40-50.

Silver Jubilee models - 1935. Specially finished in silver ripple enamel to memorate the silver jubilee of the King and Queen. Model S/33 has fixed focus lens; Model S/55 has Ensar f6.3 Anastigmat. These are the rarest of the Ensign Midgets. $60-80.

Ensign Multex - c1936-47. Small rangefinder camera for 14 exposures on 127. Coupled rangefinder in top housing with viewfinder above. FP shutter T, 1-1000. Ross Xpres f3.5 or f2.9 lens. $300-400.

Ensign Reflex, Popular Reflex, Popular Pressman Reflex - c1915-30. Graflex-style SLR cameras for 3¼x4¼" plates. Focal plane shutter to 1000. Various lenses. $75-125. *(illustrated top of next page)*

Ensign Rollfilm Reflex - c1920's. For 6x9cm exposures on 120 film. Several models. $75-125. Tropical: $350-450. *(illustrated on next page)*

Ensign Popular Reflex

Ensign Rollfilm Reflex

Ensign Selfix 16-20 - c1950's. For 16 exposures 4.5x6cm on 120 film. (This style of camera was often called a "semi" at that time, because it took half-size frames on 120.) f4.5/75mm Ensar or f3.8 Ross Xpress. $35-45.

Ensign Selfix 20, 220, 320, 820 - c1950's. Folding rollfilm cameras for 6x6cm or 6x9cm. Various inexpensive lenses and shutters. $10-25.

Ensign Special Reflex, Tropical - c1930's. 6.5x9cm SLR. Teak body, brassbound. Brown Russian leather bellows. FP shutter 15-1000. $400-450.

Ensign Speed Film Reflex, Tropical - c1925. 6.5x9cm SLR. Teak body, brassbound. Aldis Anastigmat f7.7/ 108mm. FP shutter 25-500. $400-450.

Vest Pocket Ensign - c1926-1930. Body design is the same as the Ensignette, but takes 1⅝x2½" exposures on 127 rollfilm. Enameled aluminum body. Achromatic f11 lens, 3 speed shutter. $40-60.

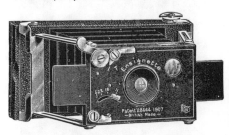

Ensignette - c1909-30. Folding rollfilm camera of the bedless strut type. Similar to the Vest Pocket Kodak camera but has extensions on both ends of the front panel which serve as table stands. Made in three sizes: No. 1 for 1½x2¼", No. 2 for 2x3", and Junior No. 2 for 2¼x3¼". Early No. 1 is brass. Later No. 1 and No. 2 are all-aluminum. Junior No. 2 is wood with metal back. Simple lens and shutter. $35-50.

**Anastigmat Ensignette,
Ensignette Deluxe -** Versions of the No. 1 and No. 2 with focusing Anastigmat lenses such as Tessar f6.8 or Cooke f5.8 and better shutters. $40-60.

Holborn Postage Stamp Camera - c1901. 9-lens copy camera. Makes 9 simultaneous stamp-sized copies of a photograph on a quarter plate. $250-300.

Klito, No. 0 - c1905. Magazine box camera, falling plate type, 3¼x4¼" size. Rapid Rectilinear lens. Rotating shutter. $50-75.

Folding Klito - For 3¼x4¼" sheet films. Double extension bellows. f6.8 Aldis Plano. $35-50.

May Fair - Metal box camera. T,I shutter. $12-18.

Sanderson cameras *Even though manufactured by Houghton, all Sanderson cameras are listed under Sanderson.*

Ticka - c1905. Pocket-watch styled camera manufactured under license from the Expo Camera Co. of New York, and identical to the Expo Watch Camera. For 25 exposures 16x22mm on special cassette film. Fixed focus f16/30mm meniscus lens. I & T shutter. $125-150.

Ticka Enlarger - to enlarge the 16x22mm Ticka negative to 6x9cm. Meniscus lens. $75-125.

Ticka, Focal plane model - With focusing lens. Rare. (Exposed works make it easy to identify.) $1000-1500. *(illus. next column)*

Focal Plane Ticka

Ticka, Watch-Face model - Hands on the face show the viewing angle. An uncommon model, and difficult to establish a price. Two sold at auctions several years ago for $70 and $460. Dealers have offered them for sale at prices from $1500-2000. Confirmed sales are $1200-1500. *(illus. on front cover)*

Triple Victo - c1890. ½-plate triple extension field camera. Mahogany body, brass trim. Taylor Hobson Cooke brass-bound lens. Thornton-Pickard roller-blind shutter. Front movements. $140-170.

Victo - c1900. Half or full plate triple extension field cameras. Polished teak, black bellows. RR or Bush lens. Thornton-Pickard roller-blind or Automat pneumatic shutter. $150-200.

HUNTER (R. F. Hunter, Ltd. London)
Gilbert - Steel box camera with brown lizard skin covering. $60-80.

Hunter 35 - Viewfinder 35. Made in Germany. Same as the Steinette. $15-20.

Purma Plus - c1951. 32x32mm on 127 rollfilm. A re-styled version of the Purma Special. Metal body. Purma Anastigmat f6.3/55mm. Metal FP shutter to 500, speeds are gravity controlled. $30-50.

Purma Special - c1930's. Bakelite & metal camera for 16 exposures 32x32mm (1¼"

sq.) on 127 film. Three speed metal focal plane shutter. Speeds controlled by gravity. Fixed focus f6.3/2¼" Beck Anastigmat (plastic) lens. One of the first cameras to use a plastic lens. $40-60.

HURLBUT MFG. CO. (Belvidere, Ill.)

Velox Magazine Camera - c1890. An unusual magazine-plate detective camera. Plates are dropped into the plane of focus and returned to storage by turning the camera over. $550-750.

HUTTIG (R. Huttig, A.G., Dresden, R. Huttig & Son, Dresden) *Claimed in 1910 advertisments to be the oldest and largest camera works in Europe. Soon became Ica, then merged to form Zeiss-Ikon in 1926.*
Atom - c1908. 4.5x6cm plates. f8/90mm lens. Compound shutter 1-250. $150-200.

Fichtner's Excelsior Detective - c1892. Polished wood body with built-in 12-plate magazine, 9x12cm. Goerz Lynkeioskop 125mm lens. 3-speed rotating shutter. 2 reflex viewfinders. $500-750.

Folding plate camera - c1906. 9x12cm plates. Red bellows. Black leathered wood body, aluminum bed. Pneumatic shutter. $30-40.

Gnom - c1900. Falling-plate magazine box camera. Holds up to 6 plates 4.5x6cm. Meniscus lens. Rotary shutter. $125-200.

Helios - 9x12cm. Strut-type folding plate camera. 185mm Anastigmat lens. Focal plane shutter 6-1000. $75-125.

Ideal - c1908. 9x12cm folding-bed plate camera. Huttig Extra Rapid Aplanat Helios f8. Automat shutter, 25-100, B, T. Aluminum standard and bed. Red bellows. $35-45.

Ideal Stereo - c1908. 6x13cm plates. Extra Rapid Aplanat Helios f8/105mm. Huttig Stereo Automat shutter 1-100, T, B. $130-170.

Lloyd, 9x12cm - Folding camera for 3¼x4¼" rollfilm or 9x12cm plates. Goerz Dagor f6.8/135mm lens. Compound shutter 1-250. Double extension red bellows. $40-60.

Lloyd, 13x18cm - Unusual in this large size. Double extension red bellows. Extra Rapid Aplanat f8 lens in Double pneumatic shutter. One example with focal plane and front shutters sold for about $200. Another with front shutter only brought $160.

Magazine cameras - c1900. 6.5x9 cm and 9x12cm drop-plate type box cameras, leather covered, including varied Monopol models. Focusing Aplanat lens and simple shutter. $50-60. (Polished wood models without leather covering $400-600.)

Record Stereo Camera - for 9x12cm plates. Hugo Meyer Aristostigmat f6.8/120mm lenses. Focal plane shutter. $250-350.

Stereolette - c1909. Small folding stereo camera for 45x107mm plates. f8/65mm Helios lens. I, B, T, shutter. $175-250.

Tropical plate camera - 6x9cm. Fine wood body with brass trim and bed. Double extension brown bellows. Steinheil Triplan f4.5/135mm lens in Compound shutter 1-150. $450-600.

HYATT (H.A. Hyatt, St. Louis, MO)

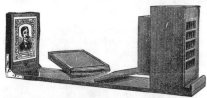

Patent Stamp Camera - c1887. 16-lens copy camera for making 16 stamp-size photos on a 4x5" plate. $500-750.

ICA A.G. (Dresden) *Formed in 1909 as a merger of Huttig, Krugener, Wunsche, and the Carl Zeiss Palmos factory. Ica became a part of Zeiss-Ikon in 1926, along with Contessa-Nettel, Goerz, Ernemann, and Carl Zeiss Optical Co. Some models were continued under the Zeiss name. See also Zeiss-Ikon.*

Atom - c1910-20. Small folding camera for 4.5x6cm plates. In two distinctly different models, both in appearance and current value:

Horizontal-format Atom (Model B) - Folding bed type with self-erecting front. Generally with f4.5/65mm Tessar or f6.8 Hekla. Compound shutter, 1-300. Unusual location of reflex brilliant finder: Viewing lens on front center of bed, but mirror and objective lens extend below the bed. $250-325.

Vertical-format Atom - (Including Models A, 50, 51.)In the more traditional folding bed style. Reflex finder is still on the front of the bed, but remains above the bed. $115-160. *(illustrated top of next column)*

Aviso - c1940. 4.5x6cm magazine box camera. Simple lens and shutter $70-90.

Bebe - Bedless strut-type folding plate camera. Bebe 40 for 4.5x6cm, Bebe 41 for 6.5x9cm. Tessar f4.5 lens in dial-set

Vertical format Atom

Compur shutter which is built into the flat front of the camera. $125-150.

Cameo Stereo - c1912. Folding bed stereo camera for 9x18cm plates. Extra Rapid Aplanat Helios lenses. Automat Stereo shutter, ½-1000, T,B. Twin tapered bellows. Black covered wood body. $150-200.

Corrida - c1910. Folding 9x12cm plate camera. Helios f8/130mm in Automat shutter. $25-35.

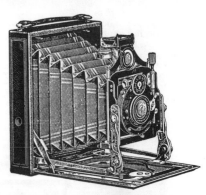

Cupido 80 - Folding bed camera for 6x9cm plates or rollfilm back. Tessar f4.5/12cm lens. Compur dial-set shutter. $25-35.

Delta - c1912. Folding 9x12cm plate camera. Double extension bellows. Hekla f6.8/135mm in Compound shutter. $35-45.

Favorit 265, 425 - c1925. Folding-bed camera, 13x18cm (5x7") plates. Square black double extension leather bellows. f6.3/210mm Tessar. Compur dial-set 1-150. An uncommon size. $100-200. *(illustrated top of next page)*

Ica Favorit

Favorit Tropical - c1927-31. Polished teakwood body. Folding 9x12cm plate or filmpack camera. Tessar f4.5 lens in Compur shutter. $450-700.

Folding plate cameras - misc. models in 6x9 & 9x12cm sizes. $25-35.

Halloh 505, 510, 511 - Folding rollfilm cameras (also for plate backs) in the 8x10.5cm (3¼x4¼") size. f4.5/12cm Tessar or f6.8/135mm Litonar. Dial Compur shutter 1-250, B, T. $30-50.

Icar 180 - c1920. Folding bed plate camera for 9x12cm. Ica Dominar f4.5/135. Compur dial-set shutter 1-200, T, B. $30-45.

Icarette - Folding bed rollfilm cameras for 120 film. Two basic styles: the horizontally styled body for 6x6cm exposures such as the Icarette A, and the vertical body style for 6x9cm such as the Icarette C, D, and L. Prices average the same for either style. $35-50. *(illustrated top of next column)*

Icarette 501, 502, 503 - 6.5x11cm image on rollfilm. Hekla f6.8/12cm or Tessar

Icarette C

f4.5/12cm in Compur, or Novar f6.8/135mm in Derval shutter. $25-40.

Ideal - c1920's. Folding-bed vertical style plate cameras. Double extension bellows. (See also Zeiss for the continuation of this line of cameras.) In three sizes:
6.5x9cm - f6.8/90mm Hekla, f6.3/90 Tessar, or f4.5/105 Litonar. Compur shutter 1-150. $35-60.
9x12cm - (Including models 245, 246.) f4.5/15cm Tessar. Compur shutter. $45-60.
13x18cm (5x7") - Model 385. f4.5/210mm Tessar in dial Compur shutter. This larger size is much less common than the others. $90-120.

Juwel (Universal Juwel) - c1925. (Also continued as a Zeiss model after 1926.) A drop-bed folding 9x12cm plate camera of standard style, except that it has square format bellows and rotating back. It also incorporates triple extension bellows, wide angle position, and all normal movements. $200-275.

Lloyd - c1910. Folding camera for 9x12cm exposures on plates or 8x10.5cm on rollfilm. Dominar f4.5/135mm, Compur 1-200. $35-45.

Lloyd Stereo - c1910. Folding stereo or panoramic camera for plates or rollfilm. 8x14cm or 9x18cm sizes. Stereo Compound shutter 1-100. f6.8 Double Anastigmat Maximar lenses. $200-250.

Maximar - Folding bed double extension precision plate camera. Although the Zeiss-Ikon Maximar is much more common, it originated as an Ica model. 9x12cm size with f4.5/135mm Novar, f6.8/135mm Hekla, f4.5/135mm Litonar, in Compound, Compur, or Rulex shutter. $40-50.

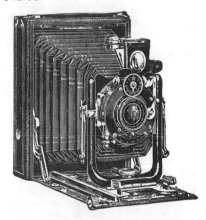

Minimal 235 - c1925. 9x12cm folding bed double extension sheetfilm camera. f6.8/135mm Hekla, or f6.8/120mm Goerz Dagor lens. Ica Automat or Compound shutter. Leather covered wood body. $35-45.

Minimum Palmos - c1925. Compact vertical format folding bed plate camera. Most unusual feature is the focal plane shutter, T, B, 50-1000. The 4.5x6cm size is Ica's smallest focal plane camera. Tessar

f2.7 lens. 4.5x6cm: $250-300. 6.5x9cm: $175-250. 9x12cm (456): $100-150.

Nelson 225 - c1915. Folding bed double extension plate camera for 9x12cm. Tessar f4.5/150mm. Dial Compur T,B,1-150. $35-45.

Nero - c1905. Magazine box camera for 9x12cm plates. Guillotine T,I shutter. $40-60.

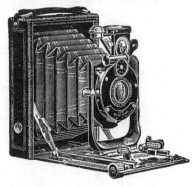

Niklas 109 - c1920's. Folding bed plate cameras in 6.5x9 and 9x12cm sizes. f4.5

Litonar or Tessar lens in Compur shutter. $30-40.

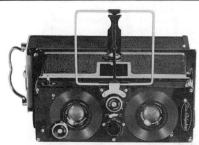

Nixe 555, 595 - c1920's. Folding bed camera. 9x12cm: $40-60. 9x14cm plates or 122 rollfilm. $40-70.

Palmos Klapp-Stereo - c1911-26. (Originally from Zeiss Palmos Werk c1905.) Folding-bed stereo camera for 9x12cm plates. Aluminum body and bed, covered with leather. Focal plane shutter. Zeiss Tessar f6.3 or f4.5/9cm lenses. Some Zeiss and Ica models have the Dr. W. Scheffer inter-lens adjusting system. The two lenses are drawn closer together by stylus-type rods running in converging tracks on the camera bed. This allows for close-up work with automatic adjustment. This rare accessory dates from c1908-14. With close focus system: $450-550. Normal models: $300-475.

Periscop - 9x12cm plate camera. Alpha lens. $30-40.

Plaskop - c1925. Rigid-bodied stereo camera for 6x13cm plates or packfilm. Ica Novar Anastigmat f6.8/75mm lens in guillotine shutter, T,I. Black leather covered wood body with black painted metal parts. Reflex & wire frame finders. $100-150. 45x107mm: $80-120.

Polyscop (rigid body) - c1910-25. Rigid-bodied stereo camera in two common formats: 45x107mm and 6x13cm. Some models had plate backs; some had magazine backs. Could also be used as panoramic cameras by using one lens in the center position and removing the septum. Tessar f4.5 or 6.3 lenses. 45x107mm: $150-200. 6x13cm: $140-240.

Polyscop (folding model) - For 45x107mm plates. Less common than the rigid models. $175-225.

Reflex 748, 750, 756, 756/1 - c1910-25. Graflex style SLR's, such as the Artists Reflex for 6x9cm, 8.5x11cm, or 9x12cm plates. Tessar f4.5 or Maximar f6.8 lens. Focal plane shutter to 1000. $150-175.

Folding Reflex - a very compact SLR which folds to about one-third the size of the box model. f4.5 Tessar or Dominar. $175-225.

Reporter (Record) - Strut-folding 9x12cm plate camera. Tessar f4.5/150mm. FP shutter to 1000. $100-150.

Sirene - Folding plate cameras, 6x9 or 9x12cm sizes. Economy models with f11 Periskop or f6.8 Eurynar lens. Ibso shutter. Most common is Model 135 in 9x12cm. $20-25.

Stereo Ideal (Type 650) - Folding stereo camera for 9x18cm plates. Twin f6.3 Tessar lenses. Compound shutter to 150. Twin black bellows. $150-250.

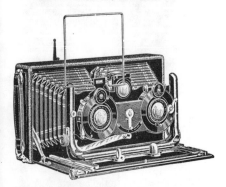

Stereo Ideal (651) - c1910. Folding bed stereo camera for 6x13cm plates. 90mm lenses (f4.5 or 6.3 Tessar or f6.8 Double Anastigmat) in Stereo Compound shutter. Magazine back. $150-250.

Stereo Reicka - c1910-14. Folding bed stereo camera for 10x15cm plates. Various lenses in Stereo Compound shutter. $350-400.

Stereo Toska - c1912. Folding-bed stereo for 10x15cm plates. Hekla f6.8/135mm. Compound shutter to 100. $150-200.

Stereolette 610 - c1912-26. Compact folding-bed type stereo camera for 45x107mm plates. Variety of available lens/shutter combinations. $125-175.

Stereolette Cupido (620) - c1912. Folding 45x107mm stereo. Hekla f6.8 or Tessar f4.5 lenses. Stereo Compound or Compur shutter. $125-175.

Stereofix - Simple rigid-body jumelle-style stereo camera for 45x107mm plates. Novar Anastigmat f6.8 in Ica Automatic shutter, T,B, 25-100. $150-175.

Teddy - 9x12cm folding plate camera. f8/130mm Extra Rapid Aplanat Helios or f6.8/135 Double Anastigmat Heklar. Automat shutter. $20-30.

Toska - 9x12cm folding plate camera. Zeiss Double Amatar f6.8/135mm or Rapid Aplanat Helios f8/130mm. Ica Automat or Compound shutter. $25-40.

Trilby 18 - c1912. Magazine box camera for 6 plates 9x12cm or 12 exposures on sheet film. Ica Achromat lens. Guillotine shutter, T & I. Automatic exposure counter. $100-150.

Trix - c1915. For cut film. 4.5x6cm: $100-125. 9x12cm: $35-45. 10x15cm: $40-60.

Trona - 6x9 or 9x12cm double extension plate/rollfilm cameras. f4.5 Tessar. Compur shutter. $35-55.

Tropica 285 - Tropical model folding-bed 9x12cm plate camera. Square back style. Double extension bellows, finely finished wood body with brass trim. $400-600.

Tudor Reflex - 9x12 SLR. Dominar f4.5/105mm or Tessar 150mm lens. FP shutter. $130-195.

Victrix - c1912-25. Folding bed camera for 4.5x6cm plates. Ica Dominar f4.5/75mm or Hekla f6.8/75mm. Automat or Compur shutter. Focus by radial lever on bed. $100-150.

Volta 125, 146 - c1914. Folding-bed 9x12cm plate camera. Novar Anastigmat f6.8/105mm. Shutter 25-100, T,B. $20-35.

IDAM (Societe d'Appareils Mecaniques IDAM, Colombes, France)
Belco - Cast metal camera for 36x36mm exposures on 127 rollfilm. Similar to the Clic camera, but with extinction meter incorporated in finder housing. Since the camera is not adjustable, the meter serves only to let the user know if it is practical to take a picture. The same camera was also sold with the name Roc. $40-50.

Clic - Cast metal camera for 3x3cm on special film similar to Kodak 828. Single speed shutter. Bilux f8 lens. $40-50.

Roc - Specifications and prices as Belco, above.

IDEAL TOY CORP. (Hollis, NY)
Kookie Kamera - c1968. Certainly in the running for the most unusual camera design of all time, from the plumbing pipes to the soup can. It looks like a modern junk sculpture, but takes 1¾x1¾" photos on direct positive paper for in-camera processing. With colorful original box, instructions, disguises etc. : $85-125. Camera only: $60-90.

I.G.B. Camera - Japanese novelty subminiature of the Hit type. $10-15.

IHAGEE KAMERAWERK,(Steenbergen & Co., Dresden, Germany) *(The name derives from the German pronunciation of the initials "IHG" from the full company name "Industrie und Handels Gesellschaft" which means Industry and Trading Company.*

Duplex cameras - Ihagee used the name "Duplex" for two distinctly different cameras:
Two-shuttered Duplex - c1920's. Folding bed plate camera. Square body. Focal plane shutter in addition to the front inter-lens shutter. This was the camera which inspired the name. 6x9cm and 9x12cm sizes. $100-150.

Vertical format Duplex - c1940's. Folding bed plate camera. f3.5 or 4.5 Steinheil lens, Compur shutter. Double extension bellows. $30-40.

Exa - 35mm focal plane SLR. Models I, Ia, II, IIa, IIb. Normal lenses: Meritar f2.8 or Domiplan f2.9. $25-40. (Usually offered for under $35, with lens.)

Exakta (original) - (A) - intro. 1933. The first small focal plane SLR. For 8 exposures 4x6.5cm on 127 rollflm. f3.5 Exaktar or Tessar. Focal plane shutter 25-1000. Black finish. Some models with slow speeds to 12 sec; some models not synched. $100-150.

Exakta B - c1935. Similar to the model (A) above. Main body still black leather covered, but some models have chrome finish on metal parts. Focal plane shutter 25-1000, and slow speeds to 12 sec. Self-timer. f2.8 or f3.5 Tessar or Xenar normal lens. $125-165.

Exakta C - c1935. Much less common than the A & B. Accepts plate back adapter with ground glass for using plates or cut film. $150-200.

Exakta Jr. - c1936. Similar to the model B, but speeds only 25-500. "Exakta Jr" on the front. Non-interchangeable lens. No self-timer. $100-150.

Night Exakta - Similar to the model B, but wider lens flange size for special fast lenses. Not a common model, probably because of a non-standard lens mount. It was available in all-black or in black and nickel. Biotar f2.0/80mm or Xenon lens. $250-325. *The easiest way to make a quick identification is that the serial number is on the viewing hood and not on the lens flange.*

Kine Exakta I (original type) - Identifiable by the round magnifier in the non-removable hood. The world's first single lens reflex for 35mm film. Similar in appearance to the larger "VP" model from which it was derived. FP shutter 12 to 1/1000. Bayonet mount interchangeable lenses include Exaktar f3.5/50, Primotar f3.5/50, Tessar f3.5/50, Tessar f2.8/50, Primoplan f1.9/50, and Biotar f2/58mm. Historically important and rare. $400-500.

Kine Exakta I (rectangular magnifier) -

c1937-46. Like the original type, but with a rectangular focusing magnifier. No cover on the magnifier. Non-removeable finder. Most say "Exacta", not "Exakta". $75-100.

Exakta II - c1949-50. 35mm SLR. Rectangular focus magnifier with hinged protective door. Most say "Exakta", some "Exacta". Interchangeable bayonet-mount lenses: f2.8 or 3.5/50mm Tessar, f2.8/50 Westar, f2/50 Schneider Xenon. $50-90.

Exakta V - c1950. 35mm. Normal lenses as listed above. $65-90.

Exakta VX (Varex) - c1950's. 35mm. Same normal lenses as Exakta II. Common. With normal lens: $65-85. Body only: $40-55.

Exakta VX IIA - Also very common. With normal lens and prism finder in Excellent condition: $60-100. Body only: $45-60.

Exakta 66 - Single lens reflex for 12 exposures 6x6cm on 120 rollfilm. f2.8 Tessar or Xenar. Two distinct body styles:

Pre-war model - c1938. Horizontal body sytle and film transport (like an overgrown Exakta A, B or C). Focal plane shutter, 12 sec to 1/1000. $400-600.
Post-war style - Vertical style, much like the twin-lens reflex shape, but with only one lens. $300-475.

Ihagee folding plate cameras - 6x9cm size with f4.5/105mm Tessar in Compur shutter: $30-40. Larger 9x12cm size with

similar lens/shutter: $30-40.

Ihagee folding rollfilm cameras - For 8 exposures 6x9cm on 120 film. f4.5 Anastigmat lens in Compur or Prontor shutter. $20-30.

Newgold - c1927. Tropical folding plate camera. 6x9cm or 9x12cm sizes. Polished teak, brass fittings. Brown leather bellows. U-shaped brass front standard. Rising/falling, cross front. Huttig f8 or Tessar f5.6 lens in Compur shutter. $400-600.

Paff - c1920's. SLR box camera for 120 film. Simple meniscus lens, single speed shutter. $75-100.

Parvola - c1930's. For 127 rollfilm, plates or packs. Telescoping front. Three models: 3x4cm, 4x6.5cm, and the twin or "two-format" model for either size. $65-95.

Patent Klapp Reflex - c1920's. Compact folding SLR for 6.5x9 or 9x12cm. Focal plane shutter to 1000. f4.5 Dogmar, Tessar or Xenar. $250-300.

Stereo camera - Folding bed style for 6x13cm plates. Meyer Trioplan f6.3/80mm lens. Stereo Prontor shutter. $175-250.

Ultrix (Auto) - c1930. Folding bed camera. Small size for 4x6.5cm on 127 rollfilm. Larger size for 6x9cm on 120 film. $30-45.

Ultrix (Cameo, Weeny) - Models with telescoping screw-out lens mount like the Parvola, above. $50-75.

Ultrix Stereo - c1925-37. Folding bed rollfilm camera for 7x13cm stereo exposures. Doppel-Anastigmat f4.5/80mm. Compur shutter 1-300. Leather covered. Black enamelled baseboard. Brass and nickeled parts. $175-250.

IKKO SHA CO. LTD. (Japan)
Start 35 - A simple bakelite eye-level camera for 35mm wide Bolta-size rollfilm. "Start 35" molded into top. Top removes to load film. This model is much less common than the later ones. $35-50.
Start 35 K - Similar, but with hinged back. $20-25.

Start 35 K-II - c1958. A deluxe version

with metal top housing and front trim plate. PC sync post on front. "Start 35 K-II" on top. An attractive camera. $30-40.

ILFORD LTD. (England)
Advocate - c1953. Cast metal 35mm. Ivory enameled finish. Dallmeyer Anastigmat f3.5/35mm. Shutter 25-200. $75-95.

Sportsman - Viewfinder 35mm. Made for Ilford by Dacora. Like the Super Dignette. Dignar f2.8/45mm. Pronto LK 15-500 shutter. $10-20.

Sprite - 4x4cm gray plastic eye-level box camera. $4-8.

Witness - c1951. 35mm, coupled rangefinder. Dallmeyer Super-Six f1.9/2" lens in interrupted screw-thread mount. FP shutter 1-1000. It is rumored that only about 500 were made. Uncommon. $500-700.

IMPERIAL
Plastic 4x4cm cameras - Such as: Cinex, Cubex IV, Delta, Deltex, Lark, Mark 27, Matey 127 Flash, Mercury Satellite 127, Nor-Flash 127, Satellite II. $1-5.

Plastic 6x6cm cameras - Such as: Debonair, Mark XII Flash,Reflex, Savoy, Six-twenty, Six-Twenty Reflex. $1-5.

Special models - Scout cameras, Rambler Flash Camera (AMC preminum), etc. $5-10.

IMPERIAL CAMERA & MFG. CO. (LaCrosse, WI)
Magazine camera - Falling-plate magazine box camera for twelve 4x5" plates. $30-45.

INDUSTRIES BRASILEIRA (Brazil)
Plik - 127 plastic box camera. Similar in style to the Bilora Boy. $35-45. *(illustrated top of next page)*

INGERSOLL (Robert Ingersoll Brothers, New York City)
Shure-Shot - Tiny all-wood box plate camera for single exposures 2½x2½" on glass plates. Simple rotary shutter. $150-225. *Note: This is not to be confused with the later model "Shur-Shot" box cameras by Agfa and Ansco for rollfilms.*

INTERNATIONAL METAL & FERROTYPE CO. (Chicago, Ill)

Diamond Gun Ferrotype - Large nickel cannon-shaped street camera. $800-1200.

IRWIN (U.S.A.)

Cheap 3x4cm cameras - Such as: Dual Reflex, Irwin Reflex, Irwin Kandor, Kandor Komet. Metal sardine-can shaped novelty cameras. $10-20.

ISGOTOWLENO: *Translates as "Made in the U.S.S.R."*

ISING
Isoflex I - Heavy cast metal reflex box, 6x6cm. Focusing lens. Large brilliant finder. $10-20.

Puck - c1948. Telescoping 3x4cm rollfilm camera. Cassar f2.8/50mm in Prontor II. $15-25.

Industria Brasileira Plik

ISO (Milan, Italy)
Duplex, Super Duplex 120 - c1950. Stereo camera for 24 pairs of 24x24mm exposures on 120 film. The 24x24 format was the common format for 35mm stereo, but putting the images side-by-side on 120 film advanced vertically was a novel idea. $125-150.

Standard - c1953. Rangefinder 35mm. ladar f3.5/50mm. FP shutter 20-1000. Quite similar to the Hensoldt "Standard", a knob-advance version of the more interesting Henso Reporter. $450-550.

ISOPLAST GmbH (Germany)
Filius-Kamera - c1954. Black plastic novelty camera for 32x40mm on 828 film. $15-25.

IVES (F.E. Ives, Philadelphia, Penn.)
Kromskop Triple Camera - c1899. First American camera making tri-color separation negatives in a single exposure. Three plates exposed simultaneously through 3 colored filters, by the use of prisms. Plates were arranged vertically in the camera body. Rare. Price negotiable. Estimate: $3000-5000 or more.

JAK-PAK
Kiddie Camera - Novelty camera for 126 cartridges. A boy's or girl's face covers the camera front. $1-5.

JAPY & CIE. (France)
le Pascal - c1898. Box camera with spring-motor transport. 12 exposures, 40x55mm on rollfilm. Meniscus lens, 3 stops. 2-speed shutter, B. Leather covered wood and metal body with brass trim. The first motorized rollfilm camera. $500-650.

JAY DEE - "Hit" type Japanese novelty subminiature. $10-15.

JEANNERET & CIE. (Paris)

Monobloc - c1915-25. Stereo camera for 6x13cm plates. f4.5 Boyer Sapphir or f6.3 Roussel Stylor 85mm lenses. Built-in magazine. Pneumatic shutter. Metal body, partly leather covered. $150-175.

JEM (J. E. Mergott Co., Newark, N.J.)
Jem Jr. 120 - c1940's. All metal box camera. Simple lens and shutter. $4-8.

Jem Jr. 120, Girl Scout - All metal, green-enameled box camera. The Girl Scout emblem is on the front below the lens. $8-12.

JEWELL 16 - Plastic camera for half-frame exposures on 127 rollfilm. $5-10.

JONTE (F. Jonte, Paris, France)
Field camera - c1900. 5x7" mahogany camera with brass binding. Rotating bellows for vertical or horizontal use. $200-300.

JOS-PE GmbH (Hamburg & Munich)
The company name comes from one of the owners, JOSef PEter Welker, a banker. The other owners were photographer Koppmann and engineer Gauderer.

Tri-Color Camera - c1925. All-metal camera for single-shot 3-color separation negatives. 4.5x6 and 9x12cm sizes. Scarce. A 4.5x6cm size example sold for about $3500. Estimated current value of 9x12cm size: $2000-2500.

JOUGLA (J. Jougla, Paris, France)
Sinnox - c1901-06. Magazine-box camera with tapered body. Magazine holds six plates, 9x12cm. Rapid Rectilinear lens in Wollensak pneumatic shutter. $150-175.

JOUX (L. Joux & Cie. Paris, France)
Alethoscope - 1905. All-metal stereo plate camera. Rectilinear Balbreck lenses. 5-speed guillotine shutter. Newton finder. 45x107mm or 6x13cm sizes. $150-200.

Ortho Jumelle Duplex - c1895. Rigid-bodied "jumelle" style camera. Magazine holds 6x9cm plates. f8/110 Zeiss Krauss Anastigmat. Five speed guillotine shutter. An uncommon camera. $150-200.

Steno-Jumelle - c1895. Rigid, tapered body, magazine camera for 18 plates 6.5x9cm or 12 plates 9x12cm plates. The magazine is built into the camera body, and is loaded through a panel on top. Raising the hinged top when the lens is pointed upward moves the push-pull plate-changing mechanism. $300-375.

Steno-Jumelle Stereo - c1898. Similar design to the Steno-Jumelle, but with two lenses for 8x17cm stereo exposures. 12 plate magazine. $300-375.

JUMEAU & JANNIN (France)
Le Cristallos - c1890. Folding bed camera for darkroom-loaded rollfilm. 9x12cm or 6x9cm size. Black leather with gold outlines. Lens has external wheel stops. $200-250.

JUMELLE *The French word for "twins", also meaning binoculars. Commonly used to describe stereo cameras of the European rigid-body style, as well as other "binocular-styled" cameras where one of the two lenses is a viewing lens and the other takes single exposures. See French manufacturers such as: Bellieni, Carpentier, Gaumont, Joux, Richard.*

JUNKA-WERKE

Junka - c1938. 3x4cm exposures on

special paper-backed rollfilm. Achromat f8/45mm lens in single speed shutter. $50-75. *The same basic camera was sold by Adox adter WWII and was named Juka.*

JURNICK (Max Jurnick, Jersey City, New Jersey)

Ford's Tom Thumb Camera - c1889. Similar body style to the Photosphere camera. All metal. Camera is concealed in a wooden carrying case for "detective" exposures. Later models are called the Tom Thumb camera, dropping Ford's name from the camera name. With original wooden case: $2500-3500.

JUSTEN PRODUCTS
Justen - Plastic novelty camera of the "Diana" type. $1-5.

KAFTANSKI (Fritz Kaftanski)
Banco Perfect - Plastic bodied rollfilm camera with telescoping front. 2¼x3¼" exposures. Focusing lens, built-in yellow filter. $10-15.

Sida - c1930. Small eye-level camera, 24x24mm exposures. Variations include early black cast metal body, later version made in France with black plastic body, and Italian version in red marbelized plastic. $20-40.

Sida Extra - c1935. Small eye-level camera making, 24x24mm exposures. Dark brown/black plastic body. Similar to the Sida, but the name "Extra" is molded into the body above the lens. $30-50.

Sidax - Small black bakelite camera similar to the Sida and Extra. Made in France. Uses Lumiere #1 rollfilm for 25x25mm exposures. $40-60.

KALART CO. (New York City)

Kalart Press camera - 1948-53. 3¼x4¼". Dual rangefinder windows to allow for use with either eye. f4.5/127mm Wollensak Raptar in Rapax 1-400 shutter. Dual shutter release triggers controlled by Electric Brain. $140-160.

KALIMAR (Japan)

Kalimar A - c1950's. Non-rangefinder

35mm camera. f3.5/45mm Terionar lens. Between-the-lens synchro shutter to 250. $15-25.

Colt 44 - c1960. 4x4cm on 127 rollfilm. Kaligar f8/60mm lens. $15-25.

Kali-flex - c1966. Simple, plastic, TLR style camera. Kalimar f8 to f22 lens. Between-the-lens shutter. 6x6cm exposures on 120 film. $8-12.

Kalimar Reflex - c1957-62. SLR made for Kalimar by Fujita Optical Ind. Kaligar interchangeable f3.5/50mm lens, focuses to 3½". FP shutter 5-500, B, X sync. Instant return mirror. With normal lens: $60-90.

KAMBAYASHI & CO. LTD. (Japan)

Homer No. 1 - c1960. 16mm novelty subminiature. Construction similar to "Hit" type cameras, but style is different. Grey metal exterior, black plastic interior. 14x14mm exposures on rollfilm. Meniscus lens. Single speed shutter. $60-80.

KAMERAWERKE (Germany)
Vitaflex - c1940. TLR-style, 6x6cm on 120 film. f4.5 lens. $25-40.

KAMERETTE No. 1, No. 2 - Small Japanese "Yen" box camera with ground glass back. Uses sheet film in paper holders. $10-15.

KAMERETTE JUNIOR No. 1, No. 2, No. 4 - c1930. Japanese "Yen" box camera for 1¼x2" cut film. $10-15.

KAMERETTE SPECIAL - Japanese folding "Yen" camera for single sheet films in paper holders. Wood body, ground glass back. $15-20.

KASSIN - Japanese novelty subminiature of the Hit type. $10-15.

Keith Portrait camera

KEITH CAMERA CO.
Keith Portrait Camera - c1947. 5x7"
wooden studio camera. Silver hammertone
finish. 17" bellows extension. Swing back.
$150-200. *(illustrated bottom of
previous page)*

KEMPER (Alfred C. Kemper, Chicago)

Kombi - intro. 1892. The mini-marvel of the
decade. A 4 oz. seamless metal miniature
box camera with oxidized silver finish.
Made to take 25 exposures 1⅛" square or
round on rollfilm, then double as a
transparency viewer. (From whence the
name "Kombi".) Sold for $3.00 new, and
Kemper's ads proclaimed "50,000 sold in
one year". Although not rare, they are a
prized collector's item. $150-175. (Add
$25 for original box, often found with the
camera.)

KENFLEX - Japanese 6x6cm TLR. F3.5
First lens. $15-25.

**KENNEDY INDUSTRIES (London,
England)**
K.I. Monobar - c1950. 35mm monorail
camera, with full movements. 24x36mm
exposures on cut film. $600-900.

KENNGOTT (W. Kengott, Stuttgart)
6x9cm plate camera - c1920's. Folding-
bed style. Double extension bellows. f4.8/
105mm Leitmeyr Sytar lens in Ibsor
1-125 shutter. $25-35.

10x15cm plate camera - Leather
covered wood body. Revolving back. Triple
extension bellows. Kengott (Paris) Double
Anastigmat f6.8/180mm lens in Koilos
shutter 1-300. $50-75.

10x15cm plate camera, Tropical model
- Lemonwood body. Gold-plated brass
trim. Light brown leather bellows.
Steinheil Unifocal f4.5/150 lens in
Kengott Koilos 1-100, T, B shutter. $500-
750.

Matador - c1930. 6.5x9cm folding plate
camera. Self-erecting front. $20-30.

Phoenix - c1924. Tropical camera with
gold-plated metal parts. Brown bellows.
Sizes: 6x9cm, 9x12cm, or 9x14cm.
$500-750.

KENT - Japanese novelty camera of the
"Hit" type. 14x14mm. $10-15.

KERN (Aarau, Switzerland)
Bijou - c1925. Aluminum-bodied hand
and stand camera. Inlaid leather panels on
sides. Rounded corners. Kern Anastigmat
f4.5 lens in Compur 1-200 shutter. 6.5x9
or 9x12cm size. $300-400.

Stereo Kern SS - 1930-35. Early 35mm
stereo camera, 20x20mm exposures. Kern
Anastigmat f3.5/35mm lenses, with 64mm
inter-lens separation (larger than the
Homeos). All controls are located on the
top of the camera. Leica-style viewfinder.
$800-1000. (A complete outfit with camera,
case, transposing table viewer, etc. could
nearly double this price.)

KERSHAW (London) *A. Kershaw & Sons,
Ltd. through, 1946, Kershaw-Soho Sales, Ltd.
beginning 1947.*

Eight-20 Penguin - c1952. 6x9cm rollfilm
camera. $10-20.

Kershaw Patent Reflex - c1920. Graflex-
style single lens reflex. Revolving back.
6x9cm exposures. $100-150. *(illustrated
top of next page)*

KEYS STEREO PRODUCTS (U.S.A.)
Trivision Camera - c1950's. For 6 stereo
pairs or 12 single shots on 828 film. Fixed
focus f8 lenses. Single speed shutter.
$20-30.

Kershaw Patent Reflex

KEYSTONE (Berkey Keystone, Division of Berkey Photo, Inc.)
Wizard XF1000 - c1978. Rigid-bodied instant camera for Polaroid SX-70 film. f8.8/115mm lens. Electronic shutter. Production of this camera resulted in a legal confrontation between Keystone and Polaroid. $10-15.

KEYSTONE FERROTYPE CAMERA CO. (Philadelphia, PA)

Street camera - Suitcase style direct-positive street camera with ceramic tank inside. Various masks allow for taking different sized pictures. $125-175.

KIKO 6 - Japanese 120 rollfilm camera. $15-25.

KILFITT (Heinz Kilfitt, Munich, Germany; Heinz Kilfitt Kamerabau, Vaduz, Liechtenstein; Metz Apparatebau, Nuernberg, Germany)
Mecaflex - A well-made 35mm SLR in an odd 24x24mm format for 50 exposures on regular 35mm cartridge film. Interchangeable bayonet mount lenses, f3.5 or 2.8/40mm Kilar. Prontor-Reflex behind-the-lens shutter. Entire top cover of camera hinges forward to reveal the

waist-level reflex finder, rapid-wind lever, exposure counter, etc. When closed, the matte-chromed cast metal body with its grey leatherette covering looks somewhat like a sleek, knobless Exakta. Not too many were made, and it was never officially imported into the United States. $250-375.

KINDER

Kin-Dar Stereo camera - 35mm film in standard cartridges. f3.5 Steinheil Cassar lenses. $65-95.

KING (Germany)

Regula IA above, Regula Gypsy below

Regula - 35mm cameras, various models: IA through IF, IP, IPa; IIIa, b, bk, c, d; Cita III, IIId; Gypsy; KG, PD, RM, etc. f2.8 Cassar, Gotar, Ennit, or Tessar lens. $10-20.

KING SALES CO. (Chicago, Illinois)
Cinex Candid Camera - Bakelite minicam for half-frame 127. Identical to the Rolls Camera Mfg. Co.'s Rolls camera. $3-7.

KING CAMERA - Japanese miniature cardboard "Yen" box camera for single sheet film in paper holder. Single speed shutter. Ground glass back. $10-15.

KING'S CAMERA - Plastic novelty camera for half-127. Made in Hong Kong. $5-10.

KINN (France)
Kinax - Folding camera. 8 exposures on 120 film. f4.5/105 Berthiot lens. $15-20.

Kinax II - c1950. Folding camera for 120 rollfilm, 6x9cm. Variations include: black or grey leather with black or grey bellows, red metal with red leather bellows. f4.5/105 Som Berthiot or Major Kinn lens in Kinax shutter. Red or grey: $25-40. Black: $15-25.

Kinax Alsace - Folding rollfilm camera for 6x9cm on 620 film. Berthiot f6.3/100mm lens. Kinax shutter 25-100. Burgundy: $25-40. Black: $15-25.

KINO-44 - Baby Rollei-style TLR for 4x4cm on 127. Kinokkor f3.5/60mm in Citizen MXV 1-500 shutter. $35-50.

KIRK Stereo camera, Model 33 - Brown bakelite body. Same body style as Haneel Tri-Vision. Takes six stereo pairs on 828 film. $35-50.

KIYABASHI KOGAKU (Japan)
Autoflex - 6x6cm TLR for 120 film. f3.5 Tri-Lausar lens. $30-40.

K.K. - *Found after the name of many Japanese camera companies, the initials K.K. stand for "Kabushiki Kaisha" meaning "Joint Stock Co."*

KLAPP - *Included in the name of many German cameras, it simply means "folding". Look for another key reference word in the name of the camera.*

KLEER-VU FEATHER-WEIGHT - Plastic novelty camera made in Hong Kong. Half-frame on 127. $1-5.

KLEFFEL (L. G. Kleffel & Sohn, Berlin)
Field camera - c1890. 13x18cm horizontal format. Brown square-cornered bellows. Wood body with brass trim. Brass barrel lens. $150-200.

KOCH (Paris, France)
Stereo wet-plate camera - c1860. Wooden stereo box camera for 9x21cm wet-plates. Jamin f11/125mm lenses mounted on a tamboured panel for adjustment of lens separation. Rare. $3000-4000.

KOCHMANN (Franz Kochmann, Dresden)

Enolde - c1931. Folding 6x9cm self-erecting rollfilm camera with an unusual detachable telescope-viewer which mounts on the side. The front of the telescopic finder attaches to the lens standard while the rear portion is fixed to the camera body. It serves for focusing and as a viewfinder, especially for close-ups. Rack & pinion focusing to 3 feet. f4.5 Enolde Anastigmat in 3-speed shutter or f4.5 Zeiss Tessar in Compur. $200-250.

Korelle cameras - *There are several basic types of Korelle cameras which appear regularly on today's market. The most common of these by far is the reflex. All types, even if not identified by model name or number on the camera, are easily distinguished by size and style. For this reason, we have listed the Korelle cameras here in order of increasing size.*

18x24mm (Korelle K) - Compact 35mm half-frame camera in vertical format. Thermoplastic body is neither folding nor collapsing type. Shutter/lens assembly is a fixed part of the body. Front lens focusing. Trioplan f2.8/35mm in Compur 1-300 shutter. $175-225.

3x4cm (style similar to the model K, or like a Wirgin Klein-Edinex) - For 16 exposures on 127 film. This model has telescoping front like the Edinex. Schneider Radionar f2.9/50mm. Compur 1- 300, T, B. $50-75.

3x4cm (strut-folding type) - For 16 exposures on 127 film. E. Ludwig Vidar f4.5/50mm lens in Vario or Compur shutter. $50-75.

4x6.5cm (strut-folding rollfilm type) - c1930. For 8 exposures on 127 film. Schneider Radionar f3.5/75mm or Xenar f2.8/75mm. Compur or Compur Rapid shutter. Basically the same as the Korelle "P" below, but with rounded ends added to the length of the body to house the film rolls. $50-75.

4.5x6cm (Korelle P) - Strut-folding type for plates, similar to the above rollfilm model, but shorter and with square ends. A fine quality vest-pocket plate camera. Tessar f2.8/75mm or f2.9 Xenar. Compur shutter 1-250. Leather covered metal body. Uncommon. $200-400.

Reflex Korelle (also called Meister Korelle and Master Reflex) - Introduced c1934. Single lens reflex for 12 exposures 6x6cm on 120 film. (Probably the earliest 6x6cm SLR.) The first model is identifiable by the focal plane shutter 1/25 to 1/500 only, & B. Later models (Models II, IIa, III) with self-timer and shutter speeds extended from 2 secs to 1000. $50-85. *(illustrated top of next column)*

Reflex Korelle

KOEDA (Japan)
Colly - "Hit" type subminiature for 14x14mm exposures. Meniscus lens. $10-15.

KOGAKU - *Japanese for "Optical". This term is found in the name of many Japanese firms, usually preceded by the key name of the manufacturer. (However, if you are reading the name from a lens, it may only be the maker of the lens and not the camera.)*

KOLAR (V. Kolar, Czechoslovakia)
Kola - c1936. An unusual camera for various formats on either of two film types. Takes 4x4cm or 3x4cm exposures on 127 film, or takes 24x36mm exposures on 35mm film with different masks. Zeiss f2.8/60mm Tessar or f2.9/ 50mm Xenar. Compur shutter. Early model has folding optical finder; later model has tubular finder. Quite uncommon. $350-400.

KOMLOSY - Metal-bodied 70mm camera. Rapid advance. $75-125.

KONISHIROKU KOGAKU (Japan)

Konica - c1948-54. 35mm RF. Hexar or Hexanon f2.8 or 3.5 lens in Koni-Rapid or Koni-Rapid S 1-500 shutter. Earliest models were made in Occupied Japan, and were not synched. No double exposure prevention. $35-50.

Konica IIIA

Konica II - 1951-58. 35mm RF. Hexanon f2.8/50mm lens in Konirapid-MFX 1-500 shutter. Double exposure prevention. $30-40.

Konica IIIM - 1959-60. 35mm RF with meter (usually not working). Hexanon f1.8/50mm lens in Seikosha SLV 1-500 shutter. Takes full or half frame exposures. $75-125.

Konica III - 1956-59. 35mm RF. Hexanon f2/48mm lens in Konirapid-MFX 1-500 shutter. $35-50.

Konica IIIA - 1958-61. Similar to the Konica III, but large center viewfinder window and larger rangefinder windows. Hexanon f1.8/50mm lens. $40-55. *(illustrated top of next column)*

Konilette 35 - c1960. 35mm viewfinder camera. Konitor f3.5/45mm lens. Shutter to 1/200, B, sync. $15-25.

Pearl (Baby) - c1935. Folding camera for 16 exposures on 127 film. f4.5/50mm Optar lens. $75-125.

Pearl II (6x9cm) - c1920's. Typical folding bed rollfilm camera for 120 film. $30-45.

Pearl II (4.5x6cm) - c1950. Folding 120 rollfilm camera for "semi" or half-size frames. f4.5/75mm Hexar. Rangefinder, coupled on some models. $40-60.

Pearlette - c1920's-1930's. Trellis-strut folding camera for 4x6.5cm exposures on

127 film. Rokuohsha Optar f6.3/75mm in Echo shutter 25-100. $60-80.

Semi-Pearl - c1930's-1950's. Folding bed camera for 16 exposures, 4.5x6cm, on 120 film. Some post-war models with rangefinder. Hexar f4.5/75mm lens. $30-45.

Snappy with telephoto lens

Snappy - Subminiature camera for 14x14mm exposures. Interchangeable Optar f3.5/25mm lens. Guillotine shutter behind the lens: B, 25, 50, 100. Made in Occupied Japan. With normal lens: $100-150. With f5.6/40mm Cherry Tele lens add: $50-75.

KORSTEN (Paris)
La Litote - 1902-04. Rigid-bodied jumelle style stereo for plates. 4.5x10.7cm or 6x13cm sizes. Aplanat or Krauss lenses. 3-speed guillotine shutter. Newton finder. $75-150.

Kowa Kalloflex

KOSSATZ (Konstantin Kossatz, Berlin, Germany)
Spiegel-Reflex - c1920. Single lens reflex of the Graflex style. Leather covered body with nickel-plated metal parts. 13x18cm exposures on plates. Goerz Dogmar f4.5/240mm lens. Focal plane shutter. $350-375.

KOWA OPTICAL
Kallo - Rangefinder 35. Uncoupled meter. $20-30.

Kalloflex - c1956. 6x6cm TLR, 120 film. Prominar f3.5/75mm lens in Seikosha-MX 1-500 shutter. $60-90. *(illustrated bottom of previous page)*

Komaflex-S - c1960's. One of the very few 4x4cm SLR's ever made. 127 film. Die-cast body. Gray anodized finish. Gray covering. Kowa Prominar f2.8/65mm. Seikosha SLV between the lens shutter, 1-500, B. $75-125.

Kowa E - 1962-66. 35mm SLR. Coupled selenium meter. Prominar f2/50mm non-interchangeable lens (with telephoto and wide-angle attachments available). Seikosha SLV shutter, 1-500, B. $20-35.

Kowa H - 1963-67. 35mm SLR. Coupled selenium, automatic, shutter preferred. Kowa f2.8/48mm lens in Seikosha 30-300 shutter. $25-40.

Ramera - intro. 1959. Plastic six-transistor radio with 16mm sub-miniature camera. 10x14mm exposures. Prominar f3.5/23mm. 3-speed shutter, 50-200, B. Available in: black, blue, red, white. $55-95.

Super Lark Zen-99 - Gray 127 camera with imitation light meter and rangefinder windows. $10-20.

Zen-99 - Inexpensive eye-level camera for 8 or 12 exposures on 127 film. Dark grey enamel with light grey covering. $10-20.

KOZY CAMERA CO.
Pocket Kozy - c1895. Flat-folding bellows camera. Bellows open like the pages of a book. This early model has a flat front, not rounded as the on later model. 3½x3½" exposures on rollfilm. Meniscus f2.0/5" lens. Single speed shutter, T. Waist-level viewfinder. $1200-1500.

Pocket Kozy, Improved - c1898. Similar to the first model, but front end with lens is rounded, not flat. $600-750.

KRANZ (L.W. Kranz)
Sliding-box Daguerreotype Camera - c1856. Wood body. 9x12cm. $5000+

KRAUSS (G. A. Krauss, Stuttgart; E. Krauss, Paris)

Eka - (Paris, c1924). For 100 exposures, 35x45mm on 35mm unperforated film. Krauss Zeiss Tessar f3.5/50mm lens in Compur 1-300 shutter. $800-1200.

Peggy I - (Stuttgart, c1934). 35mm strut-folding camera. Tessar f3.5/50mm lens. Compur shutter 1-300. $350-600.

Peggy II - (Stuttgart, c1934). Basically the same as Peggy I, but with coupled rangefinder. Early model automatically cocked the shutter by pushing in the front and releasing it, but this meant that the camera was stored with the shutter tensioned. Later model (scarcer) had manual cocking lever. Often with f2 Xenon or f2.8 Tessar. $350-600.

Photo-Revolver - c1920's. For 18x35mm exposures on 48 plates in magazine or

special rollfilm back. Krauss Tessar f4/40mm lens. 3-speed shutter, 25-100, T. $1800-2200.

Polyscop - c1910. Stereo camera for 45x107mm plates in magazine back. $150-200.

Rollette - c1920's. Folding rollfilm cameras, with Krauss Rollar f6.3/90mm lens in Pronto 25-100 shutter. Focus by radial lever on bed. $40-70.

Stereoplast - c1921. All-metal rigid body stereo, similar to the Polyscop. 45x107mm exposures. f4.5/55mm lenses. Stereo-Spezial shutter to 300. Magazine back for glass plates. $150-200.

Takyr - (Paris, c1906). Strut-folding camera for 9x12cm plates. Krauss Zeiss Tessar f6.3/136mm lens. Focal plane shutter. $125-175.

KRUGENER (Dr. Rudolf Krugener, Bockheim/Frankfurt, Germany)

Delta - c1895-1905. Folding plate camera, 9x12cm. Black leather covered wood body. Aluminum standard, nickel trim. f6.8/120mm Dagor or Euryscop Anastigmat lens. Delta shutter 25-100. $75-125.

Delta Magazine Camera - c1892. For 12 exposures 9x12cm on plates which are changed by pulling out a rod at the front of the camera. Achromat lens in simple spring shutter. $400-500.

Delta Periskop - c1900. Folding bed camera for 9x12cm plates. Leather covered wood body. Red bellows. Krugener Rapid Delta Periscop f12 lens in Delta shutter 25-100. $75-100.

Delta Stereo - c1898. Folding bed stereo camera for 9x18cm exposures on plates or rollfilm. Earliest models with wooden lensboard, later made of metal. Periplanat or Extra-Rapid Aplanat lenses. Red bellows. Polished wood interior. $175-275.

Detective - c1890. Small polished mahogany box camera. Leather changing bag for 12 plates, 6x8cm. Shutter cocked and released by pulling on 2 strings on top of the camera. $800-1200.

Electus - c1889. Non-focusing TLR-style magazine box camera. Similar to the Simplex Magazine camera, but only holds 18 plates. Steinheil lens. Single speed shutter. $800-1200.

Jumelle-style magazine camera - For 18 plates 6x10.7cm. Brass-barrel Periscop lens, leather covered wood body. Built-in changing magazine. $175-250.

Million - c1903. Leather covered stereo. Looks like a box camera, but has a short bellows extension. Red bellows. 9x18cm on rollfilm, single or stereo exposures. Periskop lenses. Guillotine shutter. $150-200.

Normal Simplex - c1892. Polished mahogany magazine camera for 12 plates, 9x12cm. Small box with waist-level viewfinder retracts into the top of the camera body when not in use. Antiplanat lens, 3 diaphragm stops. $1200-1600.

Plastoscop - c1907. Strut-folding stereo camera for 45x107mm plates. $125-175.

Simplex Magazine - c1889. Non-focusing TLR-style with changing mechanism for 24 plates, 6x8cm. Polished mahogany. Steinheil or Periscop f10/100mm lens. Single speed sector shutter. $1200-1400.

Taschenbuch-Camera - c1889-1892. Leather covered camera, disguised as a book. Achromatic f12/65mm lens is in the "spine" of the book. Guillotine shutter, T,I. Shutter is cocked and released by pulling on 2 strings. Internal magazine holds 24 plates for 40x40mm exposures. $2300-2700.

K.S.K.
Corona - Subminiature made in Occupied Japan. 14x14mm exposures. Rim-set leaf shutter, iris diaphragm. Red leather covering with gold-colored metal parts. $200-250.

KUGLER (Earl Kugler, U.S.A.)
Close Focus Camera - Unusual vertically styled polished wood folding bed camera

229

for 2½x4¼" exposures on rollfilm. Rack and pinion focusing to 12". Symmetrical 4x5 lens in Unicum shutter. Rigid wood handle on top. $100-150.

KULLENBERG, O. (Essen, Germany)
Field camera - 5x7". Vertical format field camera with red tapered bellows, brass-barreled Universal Aplanat f8 lens with iris diaphragm. Rouleau shutter. $175-225.

KUNIK, Walter KG. (Frankfurt)
Foto-Fueller, Luxus - The German version of the French Stylophot, designed by Fritz Kaftanski. This luxus version has a crudely applied covering of imitation snakeskin. Hardly in competition with the Luxus Leica, but still not often found. $200-250. *(illustrated top of next column)*

Kunick Luxus Foto-Fueller

Gray crinkle finish enamel with gold-colored trim: $75-100. Black with silver parts: $20-40 in Europe; $30-50 in USA.

Petie Lighter - Petie camera in a special housing which also incorporates a cigarette lighter. Art-deco enamel finish or leather covered. $450-500.

Mickey Mouse Camera - c1958. Subminiature, like the Ompex, but with the Mickey Mouse name on the faceplate. 14x14mm exposures on 16mm Tuxi film. Red hammer-tone body. Meniscus lens, single speed shutter. $75-100.

Ompex 16 - c1960. Subminiature similar to the Tuxi. Black body. Meniscus lens, single speed shutter. $30-40 up in Europe; up to $50 in the USA.

Petie Vanity - Petie camera housed in a make-up compact. Front door opens to reveal mirror and powder. One top knob contains a lipstick, another provides storage for an extra roll of film. Art deco enameled finish in red, green, or blue. $450-500.
(illus. on front cover)

Petie with gold trim

Petie - c1958. Subminiature for 16 exposures 14x14mm on 16mm film. Meniscus f11/25mm lens in simple shutter.

Petitax - c1962. Novelty camera for 14x14mm exposures on rollfilm. f11/25mm lens. Simple shutter. $30-50 in USA; $20-30 in Europe.

Tuxi - c1960. For 14x14mm on 16mm film. Achromat Roeschlein f7.7/25mm lens in synched shutter, B, M. $30-50 in USA; $20-40 in Europe.

Tuximat - c1959. 14x14mm on 16mm film. Meniscus lens f7.7/25mm. Synched shutter. Simple built-in meter. $90-120 in USA.

KURBI & NIGGELOH - see Bilora

KURIBAYASHI CAMERA INDUSTRY *For Petri cameras, see Petri.*
Karoron - Japanese Super Ikonta A copy, 4.5x6cm on 120 rollfilm. Orikor f3.5/75mm lens. Carperu shutter to 200. Built-in rangefinder. $35-50.

K.W. (Kamera Werkstatten A.G., Dresden, Germany) *After WWII, KW became part of the "V.E.B. Pentacon" group, but cameras continued to bear the KW trademark.*

Happy - c1931. Folding 6.5x9cm plate camera. Similar to the Patent Etui. Black leather covered metal body. Schneider Radionar f6.3/105mm lens in Vario shutter. $50-75.

Jolly - c1950. Subminiature for 10x15mm exposures. T & I shutter. Rare. One of the first post-war subminiatures from Germany, and the only one from K.W. $200-250.

Kawee - *The name used in the U.S.A. for the "Patent Etui". See the next four entires.*

Patent Etui, 4.5x6cm - c1930's. As the name Etui denotes, this is an extremely flat folding plate camera. Folding bed style with double extension bellows; it all folds to a thickness of about an inch. $40-60.

Patent Etui, 6x9cm size - Tessar f4.5/or Radionar f6.3/105mm lens. Focus knob on bed. Vario, Ibsor or Compur shutter. Black leather and bellows. $40-60.

Patent Etui, 6x9cm Deluxe Model - Tastefully finished in brown leather with light brown bellows. $175-225.

Patent Etui, 9x12cm size - The most common size. f4.5 or f6.3 Rodenstock Eurynar, Schneider Radionar, Isconar, Erkos Fotar, or Zeiss Tessar or Trioplan. Shutter:Ibsor, Vario, or Compur. $35-50.

Pilot 6 - 1937-40. SLR for 12 exposures 6x6cm on 127 film. Laack Pololyt f3.5/75mm or 80mm, or KW Anastigmat f6.3/75mm. Metal guillotine shutter 20-200, B. $40-60.

K.W. Prakti

Pilot Reflex - 1932-37. TLR for 16 exposures 3x4cm on 127 film. With f2.0 Biotar: $400-500. With Xenar f2.9 or Tessar f2.8: $150-200.

Pilot Super - 1939-41. SLR for 12 exposures 6x6cm on 120 film. Could also take 16 exposures 4.5x6cm with mask.

Built on the same chassis as the Pilot 6, but easily distinguished by the addition of a small extinction meter attached to the viewing hood. Interchangeable lens, such as: Ennastar, Pilotar, or Laack, f2.9, 3.5, or 4.5. Shutter 20-200,T,B. $60-90.

Prakti - c1960. 35mm with automatic electric drive. Domitron or Meyer lens. $30-40. *(illustrated top of previous column)*

Praktica - c1952. 35mm SLR. Waist-level viewing. Interchangeable lens: f2.8 or 3.5. Focal plane shutter 2-500, B. $25-50.

Praktica FX - 1952-57. 35mm SLR. Westanar or Tessar f2.8 or 3.5 lens. Focal plane shutter 2-500. $30-50.

Praktica Nova - c1965. 35mm eye-level SLR. Domiplan f2.8 lens. Focal plane shutter 2-500. $20-40.

Praktiflex - c1938. 35mm waist-level SLR. Victor f2.9/50mm, Tessar f3.5 , or Biotar f2.0 lens. Focal plane shutter 20-500. $30-50.

Praktiflex II - c1940. Victor f2.9/50mm lens. $25-40.

Praktiflex FX - c1955. Tessar f2.8 or Primoplan f1.9 lens. $25-40.

Praktina FX - c1956-66. 35mm SLR. Interchangeable Biotar f2/58mm lens. FP shutter 1-1000, B. Interchangeable penta-prism. $50-80.

Praktina IIa - c1959-74. 35mm SLR. Jena T 2.8/50mm. Focal plane shutter to 1000. With spring motor drive: $125-175. Without motor: $30-50.

Praktisix, Praktisix II - c1957-62. 6x6cm SLR, also known as Pentacon Six. Bayonet mount Meyer Primotar f3.5/80mm. Focal plane shutter 1-1000. Changeable waist-level or prism finders. $125-175.

Reflex-Box - c1933. Boxy SLR for 8 horizontal exposures 6x9cm on 120 rollfilm.

KW Anastigmat f6.3/105mm, or Steinheil f4.5/105mm. Three speed shutter 25-100, B. Folding top viewing hood. $100-125.

Rival Reflex - 35mm SLR made in USSR occupied Germany. Praktica body with crude name change. Wetzlar Vastar f2.8/50mm lens. Focal plane shutter, sync. $30-45.

LA CROSSE CAMERA CO. (LaCrosse, Wisc.)

Snapshot - c1898. Miniature cardboard and brass box camera. 28x28mm exposures. (Identical to the Comet Camera made by Aiken-Gleason Co. of LaCrosse.) $350-450.

LA ROSE (Raymond R. La Rose & Sons, Culver City, USA)
Rapitake - c1948. Unusually designed 35mm for 18x24mm exposures. Metal body. Tubular viewfinder. Fixed focus f7.5/35 lens. Single speed shutter. Plunger at back is the shutter release and also advances the film. $200-300.

LAACK (Julius Laack & Sons, Rathenow)
Ferrotype camera - c1895. Metal "cannon" camera for 25mm dia. ferrotypes. f3.5/60mm lens. $700-900.

Padie - 9x12cm folding plate camera. Laack Pololyt f6.8/135mm. Rulex 1-300 shutter. $25-35.

Tropical camera - Folding plate camera, 9x12cm. Wood exterior, brown bellows, gold-plated lens standard. Laack Pololyt f4.5/135 lens in Ibsor shutter. $500-600.

Wanderer - 6.5x9cm plate camera. $25-40.

LACON CAMERA CO., INC. (Shinano Camera Works, Japan)

Lacon C - 35mm viewfinder camera. f3.5 S-Lacor lens, shutter to 300. $15-20.

LAMPERTI & GARBAGNATI (Milan)
Detective camera - c1890. 9x12cm. Polished wood body. Leather changing sack. $250-350.

Wet-plate camera - c1870. Polished walnut body, square blue bellows. 18x18cm. Tilting back. Brass barrel Darlot Petzval lens, waterhouse stops. $1500-2000.

LANCART (Etablissements Lancart, Paris)

Xyz - c1935. Nickel-plated subminiature. Roussel Xyzor f7/22mm lens. Shutter: 25,B,I. 12x15mm exposures. $500-650.

LANCASTER, (J. Lancaster, Birmingham, England)
Brass Bound Instantograph - c1908. Mahogany view, with brass binding. Lancaster lens and shutter. $175-250.

Gem Apparatus - c1880. 12-lens camera, taking 12 exposures on a 9x12cm ferrotype plate. Polished mahogany body. Front panel is slid sideways to uncover the lenses and back again to end the exposure. $1000-1500.

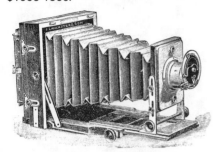

Instantograph ¼-plate view -c1886-1910. Brass barrel Lancaster f8 or f10 lens in Lancaster rotary shutter. Iris diaphragm. Tapered red bellows. Wood body. $150-225.

Instantograph ½-plate view - c1886-1910. Wood body. Brass-barrel Lancaster lens. $150-225.

Kamrex - c1900. ¼-plate. Mahogany with brass trim. Red leather bellows. R.R. lens. $125-175.

Ladies Cameras: Note there are several cameras with similar names.

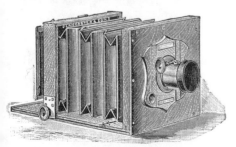

Ladies Camera - c1880's. Folding tailboard style view camera of polished mahogany. Not to be confused with the handbag style "Ladies" cameras. $150-250.

Lancaster Le Meritoire

Ladies Camera - c1890's. ½-plate reversible-back camera. Achromatic lens, iris diaphragm. Single speed pneumatic shutter. When closed, the case resembles a lady's purse with tapered sides. In the early variation, c1894, the front door hinges 270 degrees to lay flat under the body. The rear door forms a tailboard for rearward extension of the back. Later models use the front door for a bed on which to extend the front with tapered bellows. $1000-1500.

Ladies Gem Camera - c1900. Lyre-shaped body covered in alligator skin. (Same camera as the Certo Damen-Kamera.) Looks like a stylish woman's handbag when closed. ¼-plate size. Rare. Negotiable. Estimate: $7500+. (One reported sale for about $18,000.)

Le Meritoire - c1882. Wooden view. Brass trim. Brown or blue double extension bellows. Lancaster lens. Sizes from ¼-plate to 10x12". $175-250. *(illustrated on previous page)*

Le Merveilleux - c1890's. ¼-plate field camera. Aplanat lens. $125-150.

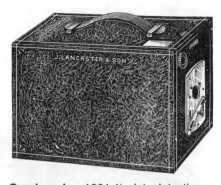

Omnigraph - c1891. ¼-plate detective box camera. Achromatic lens. See-Saw shutter. $350-500.

Postage Stamp Cameras - c1896. Wood box cameras of various designs, having four or six lenses, for "gem" exposures. $1000-2000.

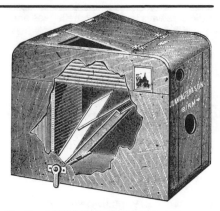

Rover - c1891. Detective box camera, holding 12 plates. Rectilinear lens See-Saw shutter. $450-650.

Special Brass Bound Instantograph - c1891. Folding tailboard camera, double swing. Brass bound. Red or black square leather bellows. Rectigraph or Lancaster lens. Patent See-Saw shutter. ¼ and ½-plate sizes. $250-300.

Stereo Instantograph - c1891. Folding 8x17cm stereo. Red bellows. Rectograph lenses. $325-375.

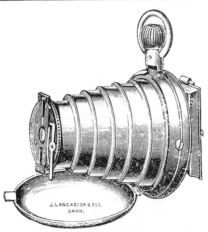

Watch Camera - c1890's. Camera designed like a pocket watch. Self-erecting design consists of six spring-loaded telescoping tubes. Men's size (1½x2" plates) or Ladies' size (1x1½" plates). Rare. Price negotiable. Estimate: Men's: $13,000. Ladies': $15,000. Beginning about 1982, reproductions of this rare camera have been offered for sale. Recent auction sales have been in the range of $1100-1200.

LAURIE IMPORT LTD. (Hong Kong)

Miniature Novelty Camera - c1974. Small plastic novelty for 14x14mm exposures on 16mm unperforated rollfilm. Originally could be obtained for ten Bazooka gum wrappers. $1-3.

LAVA-SIMPLEX INTERNATIONALE
Simplex Snapper - c1970. Novelty camera for 126 cartridge. The film cartridge becomes the back of the camera. 28x28mm exposures. $5-10.

LAWLEY (London)
Wet-plate camera - c1860. Bellows-type wet-plate camera for plates up to 13x13cm. Brass Petzval lens, waterhouse stops. $1000-1500.

LE DOCTE (Armand Le Docte, Brussels, Belgium)
Excell - 1890. Twin-lens reflex style box camera. Teak body, brass fittings. Rapid Rectilinear f8 lenses are on a recessed board, behind the front door. Bag-type plate changer. Magazine holds 20 plates, 8x10.5cm. Mirror system allows for either horizontal or vertical viewing. $900-1200.

LEE INDUSTRIES (Chicago, IL)
Leecrest - Bakelite minicam, 3x4cm on 127 rollfilm. $6-10.

LEHMANN (A. Lehmann, Berlin)

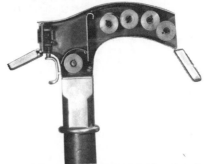

Ben Akiba - c1903. Cane handle camera. Obviously, a rare camera like this cannot be shackled with an "average" price. Two known sales were for $5,000 and $8,000.

LEIDOLF (Wetzlar)
Leidox II - c1951. 4x4cm. Triplet f3.8/50mm lens in Prontor-S shutter to 300. $35-50.

Lordomat, Lordomatic - 35mm cameras with interchangeable f2.8/50mm Lordonar. Prontor-SVS shutter. CRF. Built-in meter. Two-stroke film advance. Early models: $30-40. With meter and multi-lens viewfinder: $60-100.

Lordox - Compact 35mm. f2.8 or 3.8/50mm lens. Pronto shutter. Body release. $30-40.

LEITz

LEITZ (Ernst Leitz GmbH, Wetzlar) *The history of Ernst Leitz in the optical industry began in 1849, only a decade after Daguerre's public announcement of his process. It was not until 75 years later that the first Leica camera was put on the market. If that seems like a long time for research and development it must be pointed out that the Leica was not the raison d'etre of the company. In 1849, Ernst Leitz began working in the small optical shop of C. Kellner at Wetzlar, whose primary business was the manufacturing of microscopes and telescopes. After Kellner's death, Ernst Leitz took over the company in 1869, and the operation continued to grow, becoming one of the world's major manufacturers of microscopes. Oskar Barnack, who worked for Zeiss from 1902-1910, joined the Leitz firm in 1911 and built the first Leica model in 1913. (Some historians indicate that he had proposed a similar camera to his former employer before joining the Leitz firm.) This first prototype had a fixed speed of 1/40 second, the same as movie cameras. Several 35mm still cameras were marketed at about this time by other companies, but without great success. At any rate, the "Leica" was mothballed for 10 years before finally being placed on the market in 1925. The immediate popularity of the camera coupled with continued quality of production and service catapulted the Leitz company into a strong position in the camera industry which continues to this day.*

LEICA COLLECTING - Leica collecting is a fascinating field which has attracted collectors of all ages, from those who used the Leica cameras when they were youngsters to those who have just acquired their first camera within the last few years. Hence, there is an international demand worldwide for cameras of all ages, from the first Leica I with fixed lens to the latest limited edition of the Leica M4P.

During the late 1970's, the prices of rare or unusual Leica cameras had increased to such an extent that speculators joined the bandwagon and the ensuing unselective buying sent the prices sky high for even the most mundane items. Fortunately, the speculators have now left the field of collecting and the price structure is now a more adequate reflection of demand.

TWO GOLDEN RULES that apply to Leica Collecting are:
1. That all items in excellent or like-new condition should be acquired.
2. That items of extreme rarity be acquired regardless of condition.
Thus, common items in less than excellent condition should be acquired only for use or for parts. For some of the more specialist items such as the Leica M Anniversary cameras, it is now essential for them to

have their certificates, as of late some forgeries have been circulating. On the whole, the price structure has not changed, although rarer items have seen their values increase disproportionately to common ones. The five most desirable Leica cameras are the following: The Leica I with Elmax, the Leica Compur, the Leica 250, the Leica 72, and the Leica MP. These items will always demand very high prices, and the condition is important but not essential. More important is the authenticity and the originality of these cameras. It is better to have a camera in lesser but all original condition than a like-new specimen that has been renovated at great cost.

Leica cameras - *All models listed are for full-frame (24x36mm) exposures, and all are listed in chronological order by date of introduction. Although we have included a few basic identification features for each camera, these are meant only for quick reference. For more complete descriptions, or history of each model, we would suggest that you refer to a specialty book on Leica cameras. There are a number of good references, among which are: "Leica, The First Fifty Years" by G. Rogliatti, published by Hove Camera Foto Books in England; "Leica Illustrated Guide" by James L. Lager, published by Morgan & Morgan in New York; or "Leica, A History Illustrating Every Model and Accessory" by Paul-Henry van Hasbroeck, published by Sotheby Publications in London.*

SERIAL NUMBERS: *In most cases, concurrent camera models shared the same group of serial numbers. Therefore, where a serial number range is listed for a particular model, it does not belong exclusively to that model.*

This guide presents the basic information to help a novice collector to determine the probable value range of most common Leica cameras. It is not intended to be complete or extensive. That would require much more space than our format will allow. Our intention with this guide is not to give Leica specialists a price list, but rather to report to our more general audience the current price ranges which are being established by those specialists. There are many specialists in Leica cameras. Three of them have been especially helpful in reviewing all of the prices in this section. A "blind" survey comparing their separate price estimates with our data proved to be surprisingly close on most items. We should caution, however, that the Leica market fluctuates more than many of the other areas of collecting, and you should consult with several respected authorities before making any major decisions about which you are unsure. Our two primary

Leica consultants in the United States are both well-known dealers in the field, and either could help you with questions on important cameras. Of course, they would also be interested in hearing about Leica cameras you have for sale. Contact: Don Chatterton, 1126 Crestline Drive, Santa Barbara, CA 93105 (805-682-3540); or Bob Sperling, 52 Brower Ave., Woodmere, NY 11598 (516-295-3256). From England, we have had help from Paul-Henry van Hasbroeck, one of the world's leading Leica historians. He would be particularly interested to hear of unusual Leica items, and he may be contacted at 34 Bury Walk, London SW3 6QB, England (01-352 8494).

CONDITION OF LEICA CAMERAS:

Leica collectors are generally extremely conscious of condition. The spread of values is quite great as condition changes from MINT to EXC to VG (Range 2 to 6). With the exception of some of the very early and rare Leicas which are collectible regardless of condition, it would be wise to assume that EXCELLENT CONDITION (5) should be considered the MINIMUM condition which collectors seek. Therefore we are using figures in this section of the book only which represent cameras in at least EXCELLENT but not quite MINT condition (Range 3-4). Cameras which are truly MINT or NEW (Range 0-2) would bring higher prices and be easier to sell. Cameras in less than excellent condition (Range 6-9) are difficult to sell and often must be discounted considerably below these figures. Even the rare models, where less than perfect condition is tolerated, must be complete and in the ORIGINAL state.
For further information, or if in doubt about authenticity of rare models, contact: Leica Historical Society of America % James Munro, 3327 So. Hametown Rd., Norton, OH 44203. (216)-825-7364. Memberships $20.00/yr.

Except where noted, prices are given for body only. A separate list of add-on prices for normal lenses is at the end of the Leica section.

Ur-Leica Replica
A reproduction of the original
1913 prototype

Ur-Leica (Replica) - Non-functional display model of Oscar Barnack's original 1913 prototype, reproduced by Leitz for museums, etc. Cosmetic condition is the important consideration, since these are inoperative cameras. $500-750. *(illustrated bottom of previous column)*

Leica O-Series - Preproduction series of 31 cameras, Serial #100-130, hand-made in 1923 & 1924. Since the focal plane shutter was not self-capping on the first seven examples, they required the use of a lens cap which was attached with a cord to a small bracket on the camera body. This feature was retained on the second batch even though they had a self-capping shutter. The viewfinder (either folding or telescope type) is located directly above the lens. Leitz Anastigmat f3.5/50mm lens in collapsing mount. Extremely rare and highly desirable. $15,000-25,000.

Leica I (A) - 1925-1930. The first commercially produced Leica model, and the first mass produced 35mm camera of high quality. These facts make the Leica I a highly sought camera among not only Leica collectors, but general camera collectors also. Black enameled body. Non-interchangeable lenses, all 50mm f3.5 in collapsible mount with helical focus. "Hockey stick" lens lock on the front of the body is the most obvious identification feature. Body serial numbers listed are approximate and may overlap between the variations. Value depends on lens and serial number:

- Anastigmat f3.5/50mm (1925) - The earliest and rarest. Perhaps 100-150 made. (#130-260?) Shutter speed 1/25-1/500. $10,000-15,000.

- Elmax f3.5/50mm (1925-1926) - (#260?-1300?) $4,000-6,000. Originality and completeness of original fittings is an important consideration with this camera. There are lots of fakes, perhaps as many as the real ones. Current value opinions differ widely on this, from about $4,000 to $6,000 as the TOP price for a very nice one.

- Elmar f3.5/50mm (1926-1930) -
(#1300?-60000) Priced by Serial #.
4-digit: $400-600. 5-digit: $300-500. Most
examples found are in less than excellent
condition and would bring $200-300, while
a truly mint example could reach $1000.
The close focusing model (to 20" rather
than 1m.) used to add $25-50 to above
prices, but that price distinction generally
has disappeared.

- Hektor f2.5/50mm (1930) - (#40000-
60000) Relatively rare, but not as
appealing to some collectors as the other
early Leicas. In Exc+ condition: $1300.

I Luxus - Gold-plated A-Elmar camera with
lizard skin covering. Only about 95 were
made by the factory, but many imitations
abound. Authentic models have serial
numbers between 28,692 and 68,834.
Check with a specialist for exact numbers.
Only a handful of original authentic
specimens have been recorded. Authentic,
with verified serial number, not modified:
Prices of $15,000 are asked, but probably
not achieved. Realistically, they have
been known to bring $12,000. With original
crocodile case, add $1000-2000.

Luxus Replica - A gold-plated model
which is not factory original. A number of
replicas or "counterfeit" Luxus models
have been made from other Leica I
cameras, and while these resemble the
real thing for purposes of display, they are
not historically authentic. High quality
conversions (some of the best conversions
are being imported from Korea), if
beautifully Mint condition have sold for
$1,000-$1,500. Many replicas are offered
in lesser condition for $1000, most of
which are only worth half that amount.
While they serve a good purpose for
decoration, they are not necessarily
considered to be a good investment item.

Leica Mifilmca - c1927. Microscope
camera with permanently attached
microscope adapter tube with a Mikas
beam splitter and an Ibsor shutter. Body
design is like the Compur Leica (B) but
without a viewfinder or accessory shoe.

The design was modified about 1932 to
accomodate the standard lens flange
fittings. Early Mifilmca camera with fixed
tube is quite rare, but not as highly sought
as non-technical models, so despite rarity,
when encountered they sell for: $2000-
3000. The later models with detachable
tube might bring $1600-1800.

Leica I (B) - 1926-1930. The "Compur"
Leica. Approximately 1500 were made in
two variations, both with Elmar f3.5/50mm
lenses:

- Dial-set Compur - (1926-1929) is
extraordinarily rare, especially if in good
condition. About $5500.

- Rim-set Compur - (1929-1930). Although
not as rare as the dial-set version, this is
still a highly sought camera. $3500-4000.

Leica I (C) - 1930-1931. First Leica with
interchangeable lenses. Two variations:
- Non-Standardized lens mount - Lenses
were custom fitted to each camera because

the distance from the lens flange to the film plane was not standard. The lens flange is not engraved, but each lens is numbered with the last three digits of the body serial number. With matching engraved Elmar lens: $900-1000 if very clean. A very few (first couple hundred made) had the full serial number on the lens. These bring an extra $100. Most which do not have a swing-down viewfinder mask were fitted with Hektor lenses: $1200-1400. It is difficult to locate an outfit with two lenses, let alone three lenses. With swing-down mask and 35mm, 50mm, and 135mm lenses, all with matching number; full set: $2000.

- Standardized lens mount - The lens mount on the body has a small "o" engraved at the top of the body flange. Lenses now standardized and interchangeable from one body to another. With f3.5/50mm: $250-300 maximum.

Leica Standard (E) - 1932-1948. Similar to the standardized "C", but with smaller (12mm dia.) rewind knob, which pulls out to make rewinding easier. A rare camera, especially if found in black and nickel finish, complete with rotating range finder and nice nickel lens. Such a set would be expected to bring $300-500. A similar set in chrome with Elmar lens, excellent condition: $200. Black body: $250-350.

Leica II (D) - 1932-1948. The first Leica with built-in coupled rangefinder. This is a desirable camera, but only if in exceptional condition. Several variations:

- Black body - Quantity-wise, there are more black ones, but condition is harder to maintain on black. If exceptionally fine condition: $100-150.

- Chrome body - Not as commonly available as black, but retails for less. $75.

- Body & lens - Together with a matching lens in the correct serial number range, the set will bring a slight premium. Serial numbers for lenses up through the early post-war models should be approximately 50% above the serial number of the body. This is because about three lenses were made for every two bodies. So a nice clean outfit with a black body and a nickel Elmar lens would bring $250-350. A chrome body lens in similar condition: $150.

Leica III (F) - 1933-1939. The first model with slow-speed dial, carrying strap eyelets, and diopter adjustment on rangefinder eyepiece. Shutter to 500. Black body with lens: $225. Chrome body & lens: $100-135. (As with most Leica cameras, one in exceptionally fine condition could bring twice the prices listed, which are for cameras between excellent and mint.)

Leica 250 Reporter - 1934-1943 - The early model (FF) is like Model F, but body ends extended and enlarged to hold 10 meters of 35mm film for 250 exposures. Only about 950 were made. Later model (GG) is built on a model G body and has shutter speed to 1000. These were designed for heavy use, and most were

used accordingly, so there are not many which are very clean. They are difficult to sell if restored. Very clean, original examples would sell in these ranges -- FF: up to $4500, GG: up to $3500. More commonly available in lesser condition for $2500-3000. Probably the rarest but not the most expensive is the chrome version of the 250. A motorized version camera would probably bring twice as much.

Leica IIIa (G) - 1935-1950. Basically like the "F", but with the addition of 1/1000 sec. shutter speed. Chrome only. (There are rumors of a small number of black finished IIIa's, but to date none with any sort of pedigree have appeared.) The IIIa was the most produced of all pre-war Leicas, and therefore is not highly rated as a collectible. However, an early example in mint condition might prove to be a wise purchase, since they can be bought with Elmar lens in nice condition for $75.

Leica IIIa "Monte en Sarre" - Assembled after WWII (between 1950 and 1955) in the French occupied German state of Saarland, from pre- and post-war parts. Very few were made. The top of the body is engraved "Monte en Sarre" below the normal "Ernst Leitz, Wetzlar" engraving. Down considerably from earlier sales figures. Hopeful sellers are still asking $2000, but there is little enthusiasm on the part of buyers. Realistically: $800-1000, and even this price may not hold.

Leica IIIb (G) - 1938-1946. Similar to the IIIa, but rangefinder and viewfinder eyepieces are next to each other. Diopter adjustments lever below rewind knob. Hard to find in excellent condition, but worth: $125-175. This was the last pre-war camera

produced by Leitz, and the first to have batches allocated to the military. Luftwaffen Eigentum specimens would fetch about two or three times the price of a normal civilian model.

Leica IIIc - 1940-1946. Die-cast body is ⅛" longer than earlier models. One-piece top cover with small "platform" for advance-rewind lever. This is a difficult camera to locate in fine condition, due to the poor quality of the chrome during wartime Germany. An exceptionally clean example would be worth $200. Early model with red curtain (one curtain has red side facing forward): $200-250. A regular body in excellent condition: $90-125. Less than excellent: $50-60.

Leica IIIc "K-Model" - The letter K at the end of the serial number and on the front of the shutter curtain stands for "kugellager" (ball-bearing), or perhaps "kaltefest" (cold weather prepared). The ball-bearing shutter was produced during the war years, primarily for the military. Chrome model: $650. Often blue-grey painted: $450-650, depending on condition.

Leica IIIc Luftwaffe & Wehrmacht models - Engraved with "Luftwaffen Eigentum", "W.H.", eagle, or other military designations. Most have "K" shutter. The most interesting military markings are worth more. Grey or chrome body: $500-650. Up to $1000 for truly MINT condition.

Leica IIId - 1940-42. Similar to the IIIc, but with the addition of an internal self-timer. This was the first Leica to include the self-timer. Factory and other conversions exist, and considering the elevated price of this camera, it would be wise to verify authenticity before paying the going rate of: $3000-3500.

Leica 72 - 1954-57. Similar to the IIIa but for 18x24mm format. Identifiable by exposure counter for 75 exposures, half-frame masks on viewfinder and at film plane. Most were made in Midland, Ontario. $4500-6000. A very small quantity was made in Wetzlar. A Wetzlar model with verified serial number: $5000-7000. There have been fakes of the Wetzlar model.

Leica IIc - 1948-1951. Like the IIIc, but no slow speeds. Top shutter speed 500. Not a hot selling camera. Body only, MINT: $125-150.

Leica Ic - 1949-1951. No slow speeds. No built-in finders. Two accessory shoes for mounting separate view and range finders. Difficult to find in Mint condition, but will bring: $200-250.

Leica IIIf - 1950-1956. Has MX sync. Three variations, all common, so prices are for MINT.

- "Black-dial" - shutter speed dial lettered in black, with speeds 30, 40, 60. $100-140.

- "Red-dial" - shutter speed dial lettered in red, with speeds 25, 50, 75. $100-140.
- "Red-dial" with self-timer. $175-225.

Leica IIIf (Swedish Army) - An all black version, made for the Swedish Army, if complete with matching black lens: $3,500-4,500.

Leica IIf - 1951-1956. Like the IIIf, but no slow speeds. Black dial and red dial models. Body only: $100-135 if Mint; $50 if Excellent.

Leica If - 1952-1956. No slow speed dial nor finders. Separate finders fit accessory shoes. Flash contact in slow speed dial location. Black dial body is rare,and used to bring much higher prices. Even though difficult to find in really clean condition, they sell currently for $300-350. Red dial body: $200-250.

Leica If Swedish 3 crown - Chrome body. Actually engraved by Swedish military,not Leitz. Not a legitimate Leica model.

Leica IIIg - 1956-1960. The last of the screw-mount Leicas. Bright-line finder and small window next to viewfinder window which provides light for finder illumination. MINT condition could sell in $400 range. EXC or less sells with difficulty for $200-250.

Leica IIlg Swedish Crown Model - 1960. A batch of 125 black-finished cameras for the Swedish Armed Forces were among the very last IIlg cameras produced. On the back side of the camera and on the lens are engraved three crowns (the Swedish coat-of-arms). With lens: $4000-4500.

Leica Ig - 1957-1960. Like the IIlg, but no finders or self-timer. Two accessory shoes accept separate range & view finders. Top plate surrounds the rewind knob, covering the lower part when not extended. Only 6,300 were made. Body only: $500.

Leica Single-Shot - ca. 1936. Ground glass focus. Single metal film holder. Ibsor shutter. Should be complete with lens, shutter, film holder, and ground glass for $600-700. Add $250 for rare viewfinder.

Leica MP, black

Leica MP, chrome

Leica MP - 1956-57. A variation of the M3. Normally identifiable by the MP serial number, but authenticity should be verified as counterfeit examples have reached the market. Chrome: $4000-4500. Black: $5000-5500. *The Leica MP must not be confused with the Leica MP2 which is a motorized Leica M3. This motorized Leica MP2 is extremely rare.*

Leica M3 - 1954-1966. This is a classic Leica in itself and much sought after, being one of the leading cameras of the 1950's. Fine specimens will reach good prices especially if boxed and in Mint condition. Two variations in film advance:

- **Single-stroke advance** - There is a price differential based on serial number ranges. Prices listed are for body only. Serials below 1,000,000: $300-325. Serials 1,000,000 to 1,100,000: $400-450. Serials above 1,100,000: $500-600.

- **Double-stroke advance** - Body only: $175-225.

Leica M2 - 1957-1967. Like the single-stroke M3, but with external exposure counter. Finder has frame lines for 35, 50, & 90mm lenses. All early models and some later ones were made without self-timer. (Existence of self-timer does not affect price). Body only. Button rewind: $250. Lever rewind, serials under 1,100,000: $325. Serials over 1,100,000: $375.

Leica M2, Grey finish - Much rarer than green M3 or M1. $3000-4500.

Leica M2, Motorized, M2M - $1500-2000.

Leica M1 - 1959-64. Simplified camera for scientific use, based on the M2. Lacks rangefinder, but has automatic parallax correcting viewfinder. $300-350.
Leica M1 Military Green - $4000-5000.

Leica MD - 1965-66. Replaced the M1, and further simplified. Based on the M3 body, but has no rangefinder or viewfinder. Allows insertion of identification strips to be printed on film during exposure. $350-375.

Leica MDa - 1966-75. Similar to the MD in features, but based on the M4 body (slanted rewind knob). $250-350.

Leica M4 - 1967-73 (plus a later batch in

1974-75 in black chrome). Similar to M2 and M3, but slanted rewind knob with folding crank. Frames for 35, 50, 90, and 135mm lenses.
- Silver Chrome - Excellent: $525. Mint to $1000.
- Black Chrome - Excellent condition. Canadian: $550. Wetzlar: $625. *These can be identified by the wax seal in a small hole at 12 o'clock on the lens mounting flange. New cameras have excised letters: "C" for Canada or "L" for Wetzlar. Factory serviced cameras have incised letters: "Y" for Rockleigh, "51" for Vancouver, "T" for Toronto, "L" for Wetzlar.*

- Black Enamel - $700.
- Fiftieth Anniversary model - Must be NEW in box with warranty cards. These have dropped in price in the last few years. Wetzlar model: $1250. Midland: $1450.

Leica M4M, M4 Mot - Should be complete with electric motors, and MINT condition. M4M: $3,500. M4 Mot: $3000. In Exc+ condition: $1800-2000.

Leica KE-7A - A special rendition of the M4, made for the U.S. Millitary and using their designation "KE-7A Camera, Still Picture". With Elcan f2/50mm lens. Military version with federal stock number, or "Civilian" model without back engraving: $2000-$3000.

Leica M5, black

Leica M5 - 1971-85. Rangefinder camera with TTL metering. Price is currently down because of the M6, but expected to rebound. Probably a good investment at current prices. Black: $550-600. Chrome: $600-900 MINT. *If absolutely like new, in box with cards, the silver chrome model will bring more than the anniversary model, because most*

Leica M5, chrome

Leicaflex, black

were used and fewer remain in truly mint condition. On any M-camera, the condition of the strap lugs is often an indicator of the amount a camera has been used. Any scratch can knock the price down by 50%.
- Fiftieth Anniversary model - Must be NEW. Black chrome: $1250.
Silver chrome: $1450.

Leicaflex - Original model introduced 1964. A landmark in the development of reflex cameras, due to its very bright prism system. Chrome: $150 if MINT. Black: $500-600 normally, but up to $850 MINT.

Leica CL, 50th Anniversary

Leicaflex SL, chrome

Leica CL - 1973-75. Designed by Leitz Wetzlar, but made in Japan by Minolta. $200-300.
- Fiftieth Anniversary model - $700-800.

Leicaflex, chrome

Leicaflex SL, black

Leicaflex SL - Chrome: $200. Black Enamel: $200 if used, up to $400 MINT. Black Chrome: $250. Olympic, new in box with cards: $400-600.

Leicaflex SL Mot - With motor, nice condition: $700-750.

Leicaflex SL2 - Important in that it is the last mechanical Leitz reflex camera and sought after by both collectors and users. This accounts for the high prices. Black or Chrome: $750.

- Anniversary Model (50 Jahre) - Only collectible if NEW. Black: $1250. Chrome: $1450.

Leicaflex SL2 Mot - With motor: $1500-1800.

Leica R3 - Black: $200. Chrome: $400 if MINT. *This camera was produced in Portugal. A small number have German baseplates as though made in Germany and not Portugal. One source indicates that this may have been done to avoid problems with customs for Photokina. At any rate, the "German" models in either black or chrome bring about the same price as the normal chrome model or perhaps just slightly more.*

Leica R3 Mot - With winder: $400.

Leica R4 - Although people collect them, these are primarily usable cameras, and an important word of warning comes from one of our consultants. Due to the high cost of repairs, Leitz only repairs the R4 under its "Signature Service" which costs $235. There are four generations of R4 cameras, the first three of which were subject to electronic problems. Try to avoid a used R4 which is out of warranty or with serial number below 1,600,000. Black or Chrome: $300-350.
R4 Mot (incorrectly engraved) - Over 1000 were made, and they are not rare, but they may bring slightly more than the normal ones.

Leica R4S - A limited version of the R4. Same warnings apply, and not much different in price.

SCREWMOUNT LENSES - The following lens prices are "add-on" values to the body prices previously listed. Condition is extremely important in buying a used Leica lens. Because of the age of these lenses, and the type of balsam glue used to cement the elements together, a large number of these lenses are showing signs of separation, crazing, or cloudiness. They should be carefully checked by shining a flashlight through from the rear of the lens and examining closely. If the lens shows signs of deterioration, forget it. Not only would it be costly to repair, but it would be virtually impossible to match the original optical quality.

- 15mm f8 Zeiss Hologon: $1800, MINT with filter and finder.
- 21mm f4 Super Angulon: $250.
- 28mm f6.3 Hektor: $100.
- 28mm f5.6 Summaron: $225.

- 33mm f3.5 Stemar: $1300-1400 with viewfinder and beamsplitter in case.
- 35mm f3.5 Elmar: $35.
- 35mm f3.5 Summaron: $50.
- 35mm f2.8 Summaron: $150.
- 35mm f2 Summicron: $350-400.
- 50mm f3.5 Elmar, pre-war uncoated: $20.
- 50mm f3.5 Elmar, postwar, coated: Black scale: $20. Red scale: $120.
- 50mm f3.5 Wollensak Velostigmat: $50

- 50mm f2.8 Elmar: $100.
- 50mm f2.5 Hektor: $100.
- 50mm f2 Summar (collapsible mount): $10.
- 50mm f2 Summar (rigid mount): $750.
- 50mm f2 Summicron (collapsible mount) - Inspect carefully. About 90% have scratches on front element. They are also subject to crystallization and haze. Unscratched & crystal clear: $125.
- 50mm f2 Summicron (rigid mount): $500.

- 50mm f2 Summicron (in Compur shutter): $1500-2500 with arm.
- 50mm f2 Summitar: $18.
- 50mm f1.5 Summarit: $50.
- 50mm f1.5 Xenon: $50.
- 50mm f1.4 Summilux: $700.
- 65mm f3.5 Elmar: $125.
- 73mm f1.9 Hektor: $125.
- 85mm f1.5 Summarex (black): $650.

- 85mm f1.5 Summarex (chrome): $350.
- 90mm f4.5 Wollensak Velostigmat: $85.
- 90mm f4 Elmar: $60.
- 90mm f2.8 Elmarit: $300.
- 90mm f2.2 Thambar (with shade & caps): $800-1000.
- 90mm f2 Summicron: $375.
- 105mm f6.3 Elmar ("Mountain" Elmar): $375-475.
- 125mm f2.5 Hektor: $225.
- 127mm f4.5 Wollensak Velostigmat: $75.

- 135mm f4.5 Hektor: $60.
- 135mm f4 Elmar: $200.
- 180mm f2.8 Elmarit (for Visoflex): $350.
- 200mm f4.5 Telyt (for Visoflex): $90.
- 200mm f4 Telyt (for Visoflex): $170.
- 280mm f4.8 Telyt (for Visoflex): $200.
  (New in box: $300.)
- 400mm f5 Telyt (attached shade): $450.
- 400mm f5 Telyt (removable shade):
  $550.

LENINGRAD - c1950. Russian 35mm RF Leica copy. f3.5/50mm lens in Leica mount. FP shutter, 1-1000. Motor drive. $275-325.

LENNOR ENGINEERING CO. (Illinois)
Delta Stereo - c1955. 35mm stereo camera, 23x25mm pairs. Blue enamel and leatherette covered. La Croix f6.3 lens in guillotine shutter 25-100, B. Scale focus 5, 8, 10, 12' to infinity. Camera and case only: $40-60. With matching viewer: $90-100.

LENZ - "Hit" type novelty camera for 16mm film. $10-15.

LEONAR KAMERAWERK (Hamburg)

Leonar, 9x12cm - Folding plate camera. Leonar Aplanat f8/140mm or Periscop Aplanat f11/140mm. Shutter 25-100. $25-35.

Leonar, 10x15cm - Similar to the smaller size, but with Leonar Anastigmat f8/140 or f6.8/170 lens. Dial Compur 1-200 shutter. $30-40.

LEREBOURS (Paris)
Gaudin Daguerreotype - c1841. Cylindrical all-metal daguerreotype camera. Fixed-focus. Rotating diaphragm. One recorded sale, Oct. 1982: $8350.

LEROY (Lucien LeRoy, Paris)
Minimus - rigid body stereo. $175-225.

Stereo Panoramique - 1905-11. Black, all-metal camera for 6x13cm plates in stereo or, by rotating one lens to center position, panoramic views. Krauss Protar f9/82mm or Goerz Doppel Anastigmat f8.5/80mm. Five speed shutter. $175-225.

LESUEUR & DUCOS du HAURON
Melanochromoscope - c1900. Color separation camera. Three exposures on one plate. Could also be used as a chromsoscope, for viewing the pictures. Despite considerably higher estimates, one failed to attract bids over $1800 at a November 1982 auction, and remained unsold.

LEULLIER (Louis Leullier, Paris)

Summum - c1925. Roussel Stylor f4.5/75mm fixed focus lenses. Stereo shutter 25-100. Rising front. Changing magazine for six 6x13cm stereo plates. $150-200.

Summum Sterechrome - c1940. 24x30mm stereo exposures on 35mm film. Berthiot Flor f3.5/40mm lens. Shutter to 300. $300-400.

LEVI (S.J. Levi, London, England)
Pullman Detective - c1896. Satchel style detective, 5x7" plates. The bottom becomes the bed of the camera, when the leather case is placed on its back. Single or stereo lensboards were available. Archer & Sons lens. Roller blind shutter. $1200-1800.

LEVY-ROTH (Berlin)

Minnigraph - c1915. 18x24mm exposures on 35mm film in special cassettes. The first European still camera to use cine film. f3.5/54mm Minnigraph Anastigmat lens. Single speed flap shutter. Despite earlier high prices, these seem to be settling at about $1100-1300.

LEWIS (W. & W.H. Lewis, New York)
Daguerreotype camera - c1852. Initiated the so-called "Lewis-style" daguerreotype cameras later made by Palmer & Longking. Collapsible bellows daguerreotype camera for ½-plates. Ground glass focusing. $6000-6500.

Wet Plate camera - c1862. Large size,

for plates up to 12x12". Folding leather bellows. Plates and ground glass load from side. A rare camera. $900-1100.

L.F.G. & CO. (Paris, France)

Franceville - c1908. Simple black box camera made of plastic or cardboard. Takes 4x4cm exposures on plates. Meniscus lens, guillotine shutter. $135-185.

LIEBE (V. Liebe, Paris)
Monobloc - c1920. For 6x13cm stereo plates. Boyer Saphir f4.5/85mm lenses in pneumatic spring shutter. Metal body is partly leather covered. $150-175. *See also Jeanneret Monobloc.*

LIFE-O-RAMA CORP.
Life-O-Rama III - German 6x6cm on 120 film. f5.6/75 or f3.5 Ennar lens. Vario shutter, sync. $15-20.

Light Industrial Products Seagull 4

LIFETIME
Lifetime 120 Synchro Flash - All metal box camera identical to the Vagabond 120. $1-5.

LIGHT - c1934. Japanese Maximar copy. 6.5x9cm. Heliostar f4.5/105mm lens in Neuheil rim-set 25-150 shutter. $45-60.

LIGHT INDUSTRIAL PRODUCTS (China)
Seagull 4 - c1960. TLR for 6x6cm on 120 rollfilm. f3.5/75mm lens. 1-300 shutter, x-synch. Collectible because few Chinese cameras are imported to the U.S.A. $50-60. *(illustrated bottom of previous page)*

Seagull No. 203 - 6x6cm folding bed camera. Copy of Zeiss Ikonta IV. Takes 12 or 16 exposures on 120 film. f3.5/75mm lens. $50-75.

LINA, LINA-S - 4x4cm plastic novelty cameras of the "Diana" type. $1-5.

LINDEN (Friedrich Linden)
Lindar - c1953. Metal box camera, leatherette covering. 6x6cm on 120. Meniscus f9.5/80 lens. T, I shutter. Large waist-level brilliant finder. $5-10.

LINHOF PRAZISIONS KAMERAWERK (V. Linhof, Munich) *While we are presenting here a selection of cameras which could be considered "collectible", generally the Linhof line tends to be a family of cameras which fall more into the category of usable equipment.*

(Early folding cameras) - c1910-1930. (pre-"Technika" models.) Folding plate cameras in standard sizes, 6.5x9cm to 13x18cm. Front and back extensions. Ground glass focus. $75-150.

Multi-Speed Precision Camera - c1925. Folding bed camera for 9x14cm plates. Spring-loaded back accepts single metal holders in front of ground glass. Emil Busch Multi-Speed Leukar f6.8/6½" lens in General T,B, 5-100 shutter. $60-90.

Precision View - c1930. Triple extension hand camera. Rise/cross front. Tessar f4.5/135mm in Compur. $150-200.

Stereo Panorama - c1920. For 6x13cm exposures (stereo or panoramic). Two Reitzschel Sextar f6.8/120mm lenses and one Reitzschel Linar f5.5/150mm lens. Compound shutter. Metal body, leather covered. $250-300.

Technika I - c1930. With Tessar f4.5 in Compound or Compur shutter. 6.5x9cm: $425-525. 5x7": $400-600.

Technika III - 1946-1950. Despite the fact that these are old enough to be considered collectible, their primary value lies in their usability. Price dependent on lens and shutter accessories. Commonly found with f4.5 Xenar. 2¼x3¼" or 4x5": $300-450. 5x7": $400-550.

Technika Press 23 - 1958-1963. Press camera for 6x9cm exposures. Accepts cut film, film packs and rollfilm. Interchangeable lenses. Compur shutter to 400. The high prices are due to usability, not rarity. $325-425. *(illustrated top of next page)*

Linhof Technika Press 23

LIONEL MFG. CO. *(The train people)*
Linex - ca. late 1940's. Cast metal subminiature for stereo pairs of 16x20mm exposures on rollfilm. f8/30mm lenses. Guillotine shutter, synched. Camera only: $40-60. Outfit with case, flash, viewer: $60-85.

LIPPISCHE CAMERAFABRIK (Barntrup)

Flexo - c1950. Twin lens reflex for 6x6cm on 120 film. Helical focus operated by lever below lens. Identical taking and viewing lenses include Ennar f3.5 or f4.5 and Ennagon f3.5. Prontor-S, Pronto-S, Prontor II, or Vario shutter. $35-50.

Flexora - c1953. 6x6cm TLR. Ennar f3.5 or 4.5/75mm or Ennagon f3.5/75mm lens. Vario, Pronto-S, or Prontor-SV shutter. $35-50.

Rollop - c1954. TLR for 6x6cm on 120 film. Ennagonf3.5/75mm lens. Prontor-SVS shutter 1-300. $50-80.

Rollop Automatic - c1956. TLR for 6x6cm on 120. Ennit f2.8/80mm lens. Prontor SVS 1-300 shutter. $70-100.

LITTLE WONDER (cardboard) - c1900. Miniature box camera for 2x2" plates. Made of two cardboard boxes sliding into one another. Almost identical to the Yale and Zar cameras. $60-90.

LITTLE WONDER (metal) - c1932. All metal box camera for 40x64mm on 127 rollfilm. Folding frame finder, external T & I shutter. Lens housing extends via helix. Meniscus lens. Sold by L. Trapp & Co., London, but made in Germany. Similar to Ruberg.$40-60.

LIZARS (J. Lizars, Glasgow)
Challenge - c1905. 3¼x4¼" plates. Leather covered mahogany construction. f6 or f8 Aldis or Beck lens, or f6.8 Goerz. $150-175.

Challenge Dayspool, 3¼x4¼" - c1905. For rollfilm. Leather covered mahogany construction. f6 or f8 Aldis or Beck lens, or f6.8 Goerz. $150-175.

Challenge Dayspool Tropical - Similar to the above model, but with polished Spanish mahogany body. Red leather bellows. $400-550

Challenge Dayspool, 4¼x6½" - c1900. For rollfilm. Leather covered. Red bellows. Beck Symmetrical lens. $175-225.

Challenge Dayspool Stereoscopic Tropical - c1905. Mahogany camera for 2¼x6¾" plates or rollfilm. $650-900.

Challenge Magazine Camera - c1903-1907. Box camera for 12 plates or 24 films, 3¼x4¼". Beck Symmetrical lens. Unicum shutter. $50-75.

Challenge Stereo Camera, Model B - c1905. 3¼x6-3/4" plates. Leather covered wood body. B&L RR or Aldis Anastigmat lenses in B&L Stereo shutter.

Lizars Challenge Stereo, Model B

$450-500. Wooden "Tropical" model, teak with brass trim. $750-900.

LLOYD, Andrew J. & Co. (Boston)
Box camera - 4x5" glass plates. $40-60.

LLOYD (Fred V.A. Lloyd, Liverpool, England)
Field camera - c1910. Half-plate folding camera. $100-150.

LOEBER (Eugene Loeber, Dresden)
Klapp camera - c1915. Strut-folding camera, 9x12cm plates. Anastigmat f6.8/135mm lens. $75-125.

Magazine Camera - c1905. Leather covered box camera, holding 12 plates, 9x12cm. f8 lens, 3-speed shutter. Rapid wind lever. Two large brilliant finders. $75-125.

LOEBER BROTHERS (New York) *The Loeber Brothers manufactured and imported cameras c1880's-1890's.*
Folding bed plate camera - British full-plate camera. Fine polished wood, black bellows, brass trim. Brass-barreled lens with waterhouse stops. $150-200.

Logix Logikit

LOGIX ENTERPRISES (Montreal, Canada & Plattsburgh, NY)
Kosmos Optics Kit - 35mm SLR with interchangeable lenses in an optical experiment kit. $15-20.

Logikit - Kit of plastic parts to build your own 35mm SLR. $15-20.

LOMAN & CO. (Amsterdam)
Loman's Reflex - c1892. Box-style SLR. Polished wood, brass fittings. Loman Aplanat f8/140mm lens. FP shutter 3-200. Made in sizes ¼ to ½ plate. $600-900.

LOMO (Leningrad)
135 BC - Spring-wound 35mm. f2.8 lens, shutter to 250. $35-50.

LONDON STEREOSCOPIC & PHOTO CO. *This company imported and sold under their own name many cameras which were manufactured by leading companies at home and abroad.*

Artist Hand Camera - c1889. Twin lens reflex style box camera. Mahogany body, brass lens. Identical to the Francais Kinegraphe. 9x12cm plates. $900-1400.

Artist Reflex, Tropical - c1910. SLR for ¼-plates. Very similar to the Marion Soho Tropical. Mahogany or teak body, green or red leather hood and bellows. Brass trim. Heliar f4.5/150 lens. FP shutter to 1000. $1500-1800.

Binocular camera - c1898. Rigid-bodied, jumelle style stereo. Two sizes:6x9cm, 18-plate magazine; 5x7", 12-plate magazine. Krauss-Zeiss Anastigmat f6.3 or f8/110mm lens. Guillotine shutter. $200-250.

Carlton - c1895. Box-TLR for 12 plates or 12 films. Sizes: ¼-plate, 4x5", ½-plate. Euryscope f5.6 or Rapid Rectilinear or Ross Goerz Double Anastigmat f7.7. Shutter 1-100, T,I. $325-350.

Dispatch Detective - c1888. Wooden-box style detective camera covered in dark green leather. Camera is in the front half of the box, the 9x12cm plates store in the back half. Side-hinged lid. $600-800.

Field camera - c1885. Mahogany body, brass trim, red double extension bellows. RR f8 lens. Full and half plate sizes. $175-250.

King's Own Tropical - c1905. Folding bed camera for 2½x4¼" plates or rollfilm. Teak with brass fittings. Goerz Dagor f6.8/120mm lens in Koilos pneumatic shuter, 1-300. $700-1000.
--same, but 4¼x6½'' - Goerz Doppel Anastigmat f9/180mm in B&L shutter. $800-1200.

Tailboard stereo - c1885. 3½x6¼" plate. Swift & Son 4" lenses. Side board panel. Thornton rollerblind shutter. Dark maroon bellows. $450-550.

Twin Lens Artist Hand Camera - c1889. Large twin lens reflex. Front door covers the recessed lenses. Leather covered. 9x12cm, 4x5", ½-plate sizes. Magazine holds 24 sheets or 12 plates. $350-450.

Wet plate camera - c1855. 4x5" sliding box style. Light colored wood body (7x7½x6¼" overall) which extends to 10". London Stereoscopic Petzval-type lens in brass barrel. $1800-2000.

LOVELY - c1948. Rare Japanese subminiature made by Kyoto Seiko Co. Takes 14x14mm exposures on paper-backed rollfilm. $500+.

LUBITEL, LUBITEL 2 - c1949. TLR, 12 exposures, 6x6cm on 120 film. Copy of Voigtlander Brillant. f4.5/75mm T-22 lens. Variable speed shutter, 10-200. $20-30.

LUCKY - Japanese novelty subminiature of the Hit type. $10-15.

LUETTKE (Dr. Luettke & Arndt, Wandsbek, Hamburg, & Berlin, Germany)
Folding rollfilm camera - 8x10cm. Black leathered body with red cloth bellows. Nickel trim. Luettke Periplanat lens. $40-50.

Folding bed plate camera - Black leathered wood body. 9x12cm horizontal format. Red-brown bellows. Luettke

Periscop lens with rotary stops. Brass shutter. $50-75.

Linos - c1898. 9x12cm folding plate camera. Walnut body, brass trim. Aplanat f8/165mm, pneumatic shutter. $400-450.

LUMIERE & CIE. (Lyon, France)

Box camera - Simple lens and shutter, 127 rollfilm. $10-15.

Box camera, No. 49 - 122 film. $10-15.

Eljy, Super Eljy - c1937-48. 24x36mm exposures on special 30mm wide paper-backed rollfilm. Lypar f3.5/50mm lens in Eljy shutter. Fairly common. $50-75.

Eljy Club - c1951. 24x36mm exposures on special 35mm film. Lypar f3.5/40mm.

Synchro shutter 1-300. Chrome top housing incorporates optical finder and extinction meter. (Last model is without extinction meter.) $100-125.

Lumix F - simple folding 6x9cm rollfilm camera. Meniscus lens. $15-25.

Scout-Box - c1935. Painted metal box camera. 6x9cm on 120 rollfilm. $5-10.

Sinox - 6x9cm folding rollfilm. Nacor Anastigmat f6.3/105mm lens. Central shutter 25-100. $15-25.

Sterelux - c1920-37. Folding stereo camera for 116 rollfilm, 6x13cm. Spector Anastigmat f4.5/80mm. Shutter 1/25-1/100, later models have 1-100. $180-230.

LUNDELIUS MFG. CO. (Port Jervis, N.Y.)
Magazine camera - c1895. For 12 plates in vertical format. Leather covered wood body. Measures 10x8x4½ overall. $100-150.

LURE - c1973. Plastic 110 cartridge camera. Camera was sent in for processing of film, pictures and a new camera were mailed back. $1-5.

MACKENSTEIN (H. Mackenstein, Paris)

Folding camera - c1890. Hinged mahogany hinged panels with round cutout support front standard, like the Shew Eclipse. Maroon bellows. Brass Aplanat f9/150mm lens. $250-275.

Francia - c1906. Strut-folding stereo cameras for 45x107mm or 6x13cm plates. Max Balbreck or Sumo Aplanat lenses, guillotine shutter with variable speeds. Red leather bellows. $175-200.

Photo Livre - c1890. The French edition of the popular Krugener Taschenbuch-Camera. A leather-covered camera disguised as a book. Achromatic f12/65mm lens is in the "spine" of the book. Guillotine shutter. Internal magazine holds 24 plates for 4x4cm exposures. $2300-2700.

Pinhole camera - c1900. Polished walnut ¼-plate tailboard camera. Maroon bellows. Six "pinhole" openings on the lenboard, take six exposures per plate. One offered in Nov. 1982 for $750.

Stereo Jumelle - c1893. For 18 plates 9x18cm in magazine. Goerz Double Anastigmat 110mm lens, variable speed guillotine shutter. $150-200.

MACRIS-BOUCHER (Paris)

Nil Melior Stereo - c1920. A wide-angle stereo camera, based on the theroy that short focus wide angle lenses gave more natural stereo vision and allowed 6x13cm exposures in a camera just slightly longer than most 45x107mm stereos. Boyer Sapphir or E. Krauss Tessar f4.5/85mm lens in seven-speed spring shutter. Large newton finder. 12-plate magazine for 6x13cm plates. $175-225.

MACVAN MFG. CO.
Macvan Reflex 5-7 Studio camera - c1948. A large studio-style TLR. Revolving, shifting back. Parallax correction. Uses 5x7" plates or cut film. Ilex Paragon f4.5/8½" lens in Ilex #4

Universal shutter. Reflex or ground glass viewing. $225-275.

MACY ASSOCIATES
Flash 120 - Metal box camera, 6x9cm. Black crinkle enamel finish. Art-deco faceplate. $5-10.

MADER (H. Mader, Isny, Wuerttemberg)
Invincibel - c1889. All-metal folding bed camera for 5x7" plates. Aplanat f6/180mm lens. Iris diaphragm. $600-700.

MADISON I - Folding camera for 6x6cm on 620 film. f4.5 lens. Shutter to 200. $15-25.

MAGIC INTRODUCTION CO. (N.Y.)

Photoret Watch Camera - c1894. For 6 exposures ½x½" (12x12mm) on round sheet film. Meniscus lens. Rotating shutter. $300-450. (Original box and film tin would add to this price.)

Mamiya 16 Super

Presto - c1896. All-metal, oval-shaped camera, invented by Herman Casler. 28x28mm exposures on rollfilm or glass plates. Meniscus lens with rotating front stops. Single speed shutter. $350-550.

MAGNACAM CORP. (New Jersey)

Wristamatic Model 30 - c1981. Short-lived plastic wrist camera. Six circular exposures on 9mm dia. film. Fixed focus. $40-50.

MAL-IT CAMERA MFG. CO. INC. (Dallas, TX)
Mal-It Camera - Factory-loaded disposable cardboard camera, pre-addressed to the processing lab. The original price of the camera included processing and printing of 8 Jumbo pictures. $25-35.

MAMIYA CAMERA CO. (Tokyo)
Mamiya 6 - c1950's. Basically a folding-bed camera for 12 square exposures 6x6cm on 120. Some models featured the option of 16 vertical exposures 4.5x6cm as well. Camera body is in horizontal style. f3.5/75mm Zuiko lens in Copal or Seikosha shutter. Coupled rangefinder. Unusual feature: Knurled focusing wheel just above the back door of the camera moves the film plane to focus while the lens remains stationary. $50-75.

Mamiya-16 - c1950's. Subminiature for 20 exposures 10x14mm on 16mm film.

Various models including: Original model, Deluxe (with plain, smooth body), Super (like original but with sliding filter), Automatic (built-in meter). No significant price difference among these models. $25-35.

Mamiya-16 Police Model - c1949. This was the first Mamiya 16 camera, made in black finish. Has no serial number. Shutter B,25,50,100 only. No built-in filter. Detachable waist-level brilliant finder. $350-375.

Mamiya Magazine 35 - c1957. 35mm rangefinder camera. Non-interchangeable Mamyia/Sekor f2.8/50mm lens. Interchangeable film magazines. $60-90.

Mammy - c1953. Small bakelite camera for 24x28mm exposures on 828 film. Cute Anastigmat f3.5/45mm lens. Shutter 25-100. Unusual design. $60-85.
(illustrated top of next page)

Pistol camera - c1959. Half-frame 35mm camera, shaped like a pistol. Single speed shutter. Only 250 believed to have been made for police training. $1000-1200.

Mamiya Mammy

MANHATTAN OPTICAL CO. (New York)
(See also Gundlach-Manhattan)

Bo-Peep, Model B, 4x5" - ca. late 1890's. Folding plate camera. Red bellows, brass shutter. (Similar to other brands of the same period.) $50-75.

Bo-Peep, Model B, 5x7" - Double extension bellows. Brass lens with rotating stops. $60-90.

Night-Hawk Detective - c1895. For 4x5" plates. Polished oak body, or leather covered. String-set shutter, T & I. Ground glass or scale focus. Rapid Achromatic lens. All wood: $300-350. Leather covered: $200-275.

Wizard Duplex No. 1, No. 2 - c1902. Folding bed rollfilm camera for 3¼x4¼" exposures. Focusing similar to the Screen Focus Kodak: ground glass focusing where back is removed. Dark slide on back prevents exposures of film. $250-300.

Wizard folding plate cameras:
4x5" size - Including Baby, Cycle, Wide Angle, Senior, Junior, A, and B models. $45-65.
5x7" size - Including Cycle, B, and Senior models. $60-85.

Long-Focus Wizard - 5x7". Including Cycle and Senior models. Triple extension maroon bellows, RR lens, Unicum shutter. $100-140.

MANSFIELD HOLIDAY
Skylark - c1962. 35mm camera with coupled meter. Luminor Anastigmat fixed focus lens. Shutter 10-200, X-sync. $15-20.

MAR-CREST MFG. CORP.

Mar-Crest - Bakelite novelty camera for half-frame 127. $3-7.

MARION & CO., LTD. (London)
Academy - c1885. TLR-style camera. Eye-level viewfinder. 4 sizes: 1¼x1¼" to 3¼x4¼". Magazine holds 12 plates. Petzval-type lens. Rotary shutter, T,I. Finished wood, brass fittings. Rack and pinion positioning of plates for exposure. In 1887, a mirror was added to the finder of the larger models to make it usable as a waist-level camera. This improved version was called the "New Academy". Estimate: $2000-3000.

Metal Miniature - c1884. Tiny, all-metal plate camera. Back moved into focus by a rack-and-pinion. Petzval-type f5.6/55mm. Guillotine shutter. 3x3cm plates. Later versions were more streamlined, with a sliding lens tube for focusing. Made in 5 sizes from 3x3cm to half-plate. Despite higher prices a few years ago, more recent auction sales indicate a range of $1250-1500.

Parcel Detective - 1885. A box detective camera, neatly covered with brown linen-lined paper and tied with string to look like an ordinary parcel. Fixed focus lens. It used standard 3¼x4¼" plates which could be loaded into the camera in daylight from flexible India-Rubber plateholders. No known sales. Estimated value: $5000+.

Perfection - c1890. Folding field camera, full plate or 10x12" size. Find polished wood. Dallmeyer f8 RR lens in brass barrel with iris diaphragm. $175-225.

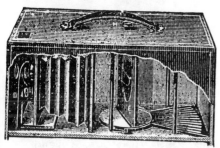

Radial Hand camera - c1890. Mahogany magazine camera for 12 ¼-plates. Plates were held in radial groves to be moved into position for exposure and then moved back again. Guillotine shutter. $700-900.

Soho Pilot - c1932. Bakelite folding rollfilm camera. $10-20.

Soho Reflex - Graflex-type SLR for 2¼x3¼". f4.5/120mm Tessar. Focal plane shutter. $200-250.

Soho Reflex - 3¼x4¼". Ross Xpres f3.5/5½" lens. $200-250.

Soho Stereo Reflex - c1909. Similar to the Soho Reflex, but for stereo exposures. Goerz lenses. FP shutter. 9x14cm plates. $500-750.

Soho Tropical Reflex - 3¼x4¼". Dallmeyer f3.5/150mm Dalmac, or Ross Xpres f3.5/6½" lens. Revolving back. Fine polished wood. Red bellows and viewing hood. Brass trim. A beautiful tropical camera. Recent prices softening somewhat. $1200-1600.

MARKS (Bernard Marks & Co., Ltd., Canada)
Marksman Six-20 - Metal box camera, 6x9cm. $5-10.

MARLOW BROS. (Birmingham, England)
MB, No.4 - c1900. Mahogany field camera, with brass fittings. Various sizes 3¼x4¼" to 10x12". $400-500 with appropriate lens.

MARTAIN (H. Martain, Paris)
View Camera - 13x18cm size. Bellows and back swivel for vertical or horizontal format. Sliding lensboard. With Darlot lens: $175-200.

MARVEL - Half-127 camera similar to the Detrola. Extinction meter and uncoupled rangefinder in top housing. $12-18.

MASHPRIBORINTORG (Moscow)

Kiev 30, Kiev-Vega 2, Kiev-Vega

Bera - see Kiev-Vega below.

Kiev - c1945-1970's. 35mm RF cameras, including Models 2, III, 4, 4A. Contax copies. f2/50mm Jupiter lens. $60-80.

Kiev 30 - c1960. Subminiature for 13x17mm exposures on 16mm film. Third in the series, following Kiev-Vega, Kiev-Vega 2. All black body. $30-50.

Kiev-Vega, Kiev-Vega 2 ("Bera" in cyrillic lettering) - Subminiature for 20 exposures on 16mm. Copies of Minolta-16, but with focusing lenses. Industar f3.5/23mm. Shutter 30-200. $75-125.

Kneb - see Kiev on previous page.

Narciss - c1960. Subminiature SLR for 14x21mm on 16mm unperforated film. White or black leather covering. Industar-60 f2.8/35mm lens. Previously peaked at $750-1000, but now stabilized at $450-550.

Smena - c1952. Letters on camera look like Cmeha. Black plastic 35mm cameras, models 1 to 4. F4.5/40mm lens. Shutter 10-200, T. $15-25.

Smena Symbol - $12-18.

MASON (Perry Mason & Co., Boston)

Argus Repeating Camera - c1890. Metal bodied camera in leather case giving the appearance of a handbag. Vertical style. 12-plate magazine. 3" dia. image on 3¼x4¼" plates which drop into plane of focus when lenstube assembly is turned. $1500-2000.

Companion - c1886. 4x5" polished mahogany tailboard view. Brass Achromatic lens, rotating disc stops. $100-150.

Harvard camera - c1890. For 2½x3½" plates. Meniscus lens. All metal. Black with gold pin-striping. A few years ago these

sold in the $150 range, but recent trends put it at $60-90.

MASTER REFLEX - The anglo version of the pre-war Meister-Korelle. *See Kochmann.*

MAWSON (John Mawson, Newcastle, England)
Wet-plate camera - c1860. Sliding-box style. Petzval type lens. $1000-1500.

Wet-plate stereo camera - c1865. Bellows style for 3¼x6½" stereo exposures on wet-plates. Ross Achromatic lenses. $1000-1500.

MAY, ROBERTS & CO. (London, England)
Sandringham - c1900. 8x10.5cm field camera. Wood body, brass fittings, black bellows. Wray 5" lens. $125-150.

MAZO - (E. Mazo, Paris)
Field & Studio camera - c1900. For 13x18cm on plates. Fine wood body, GG back, double extension bellows. Horizontal format. Mazo & Magenta Orthoscope Rapid f8 lens. Thornton-Picard shutter. $175-225.

Stereo camera - Polished mahogany tailboard stereo. Brass-barrel Mazo lenses in Thornton-Pickard shutter. Red leather bellows. $400-600.

McBEAN (Edinburgh)

Stereo Tourist - 9x18cm. Steinheil Antiplanat lens. Thornton-Picard shutter 1-225. $350-450.

McCROSSAN (Glasgow, Scotland)
Wet-plate camera - Sliding-box style. Petzval-type lens. $600-800.

McGHIE and Co. (Glasgow, Scotland)
Studio View - c1890. Polished mahogany, folding bed camera. Square bellows. Brass barrel lens, focused by rack and pinion. Swing/tilt back. GG back. Pneumatic shutter. $200-250.

McKELLEN (S.D. McKellen, England)
Treble Patent Camera - c1884. Mahogany field camera. First folding field camera to feature the double-stay lensboard support system which was later

improved by Sanderson. Also the first with built-in tripod head in the base of the camera, which became a common feature of the English cameras. Dallmeyer R.R. lens with waterhouse. Full plate size. $200-250.

MEAGHER (London, England)
Stereo camera - c1870. 9x18cm polished mahogany tailboard stereo. Brass-barrel Dallmeyer or Ruby f6 lenses. Thornton-Pickard shutter. $350-500.

Wet-plate bellows camera - c1860. Made in front bed and tailboard styles. Half or full plate size. Polished mahogany, maroon bellows. Dallmeyer, Wollensak, or Ross lens. Waterhouse stops. $250-400.

Wet-plate sliding-box camera - c1860. Polished mahogany. Sliding box moves by rack and pinion. Made in sizes ¼-plate to 5½x7½" sizes. Petzval-type brass barrel lens. $1300-1800.

MECUM - c1910. Stereo box camera for 9x12cm plates. Leather covered. Meniscus lenses. T,B,I shutter. Either lens can be capped for single exposures. Ground glass or waist-level viewing. $70-120.

MEGO MATIC - Blue and black plastic camera of the "Diana" type. $1-5.

MEGURO KOGAKU KOGYO CO. LTD. (Japan)
Melcon - 35mm Leica-copy. Collapsible Hexar f3.5/50mm lens. $400-600. (illustrated top of next column)

MENDEL (Georges Mendel, Paris)
Detective camera - for 12 plates 3¼x4¼". RR lens, rotating shutter, iris diaphragm. $150-175.

MEOPTA (Prague, Czechoslovakia)

Flexaret - 6x6cm TLR. Models (I), II, III, IV. Mirar or Belar f3.5/80mm in Prontor II

Meguro Optical Melcon

shutter. Crank advance on early models, changed to knob advance in model IV. $20-40.

Mikroma - c1949. 16mm subminiature. Mirar f3.5/20mm lens. Three-speed shutter 25-200. Rapid-wind slide. $60-100.

Mikroma II - c1964. Similar to the above, but with 7-speed shutter, 1/5-1/400. $60-100.

Opema - c1951. Leica copy. Opemar f2 or Belar f2.8 lens. Rare. $200-250.

Stereo Mikroma (I) - For stereo exposures on 16mm film. Mirar f3.5/25mm lenses. Shutter 1/5-1000. Sliding bar cocks shutter. $125-175.

Stereo Mikroma II - Similar to the Stereo Mikroma, but advancing film automatically cocks shutter. Grey or black leather. $125-175.

Stereo 35 - c1960's. 12x13mm stereo exposures on 35mm film. Mirar f3.5/25mm fixed focus in Special shutter 1/60, B. Stereo slides fit into View-Master type reels. Diagonal film path allows 80 stereo pairs to be exposed in two diagonal rows on a single pass of the film. MX sync. Plastic and metal. Camera only: $125-175. Add $100-125 for cutter and viewer.

MERIDIAN INSTRUMENT CORP.

Meridian - 4x5" press/view. Linhof copy. f4.5/135mm lens. $150-250.

MERIT - Plastic Hong Kong novelty camera of the "Diana" type. 4x4cm on 20 rollfilm. $1-5.

MERTEN (Germany)
Merit Box - c1935. Brown or red and black bakelite box for 4x6.5cm on 127 film. f11/75mm Rodenstock lens. T, I shutter. $20-30.

METASCOFLEX - 6x6cm Rolleicord copy. Metar f3.5/80mm lens. $40-60.

METRO MFG. CO. (New Jersey)
Metro Flash No. 1 Deluxe - Self-erecting, rollfilm camera with art-deco covering. 6x9cm. $20-30.

METROPOLITAN INDUSTRIES (Chicago, IL)
Clix 120 - All metal box camera, 6x9cm on 120. $1-5.

Clix Deluxe, Clix-Master, Metro-Cam - Black plastic minicams for half-127. $3-7.

Clix Miniature - Black plastic minicam for 828 film. $3-7.

Clix-O-Flex, Metro-Flex - c1947. Reflex style plastic novelty cameras. Half-frame 127. $5-10.

METROPOLITAN SUPPLY CO. (Chicago, IL)
King Camera - Small 2x2x3½" cardboard camera for glass plates. Back fits on like a shoe-box cover, similar to Yale and Zar. Not to be confused with the Japanese King Camera of the WWII era. $75-100.

MEYER (Hugo Meyer & Co., Goerlitz)

Megor - c1931. Strut-folding 3x4cm rollfilm camera, similar to the Steinheil and Korelle models. Leather covered aluminum body. Trioplan f3.5/50mm lens. Compur 1-300, T,B shutter. $75-100.

Silar - For 10x15cm plates. Triple extension bellows. Meyer Aristostigmat f5.5/180mm lens in Compound shutter 1-150. $75-125.

MF Stereo Camera - 45x107mm plates. f6.8 Luminor lenses. $125-175.

MICRO PRECISION PRODUCTS (England)
Microcord - c1952. 6x6cm Rolleicord copy. Ross Xpres f3.5/75mm lens. Prontor SVS 1-300 shutter. $50-75. *(illustrated top of next page)*

Microflex - c1959. 6x6cm Rolleiflex copy. F3.5/77mm lens in Prontor SVS shutter. $50-75.

MIDGET - Japanese novelty subminiature camera of the "Hit" type. $10-15.

Micro Precision Microcord

MIGHTY MIDGET - Japanese Hit-type novelty camera. Red leather covering. $15-25.

MIKADO - 6x6cm copy of Kodak Duo 620. Westar Anastigmat f3.5/75mm lens. Northter Model II shutter to 200. $30-45.

MIKUT COLOR CAMERA - c1937. For three color-separation negatives 4x4cm on a single plate 4.5x13cm. Mikutar f3.5/130mm lens. Compur shutter 1-200. $2500-3000.

MILBRO - c1938. Simple Japanese folding bed "Yen" camera for 3x5cm sheet film. Meniscus lens, simple shutter. $15-25.

MIMOSA AG (Dresden)
Mimosa I - c1947. Compact 35mm. Meyer Triplan f2.9/50mm lens. Compur Rapid shutter. Unusual boxy style for 35mm camera. $50-75. *There were isolated earlier sales for higher prices, but recent confirmed sales have all been in the $40-80 range.*

Mimosa II - f2.9 Trioplan lens. Velax shutter 10-200. $50-75. *see note above.*

MINETTA - "Hit" type Japanese 16mm rollfilm novelty camera. A relatively late and common model. $5-10.

MINI-CAMERA - Common "Hit" type novelty camera from Hong Kong. Much poorer quality than the earlier Japanese types. $3-6.

MINOLTA (Osaka, Japan) *The Minolta Camera Company was established by Mr. Kazuo Tashima in 1928 under the name of "Nichi-Doku Shashinki Shokai" (Japan-Germany Camera Company). The company's history is more easily followed by breaking it into five distinct periods. The brand names of the cameras made during each period follow in parentheses.*

1928-31 Nichi-Doku Shashinki Shokai (Nifca cameras)
1931-37 Molta Goshi Kaisha Company (Minolta cameras)
1937-62 Chiyoda Kogaku Seiko K.K. (Minolta, Konan, and Sonocon cameras)
1962-82 Minolta Camera Co. Ltd. (Minolta cameras)
1982- Minolta Camera Co. Ltd. (Minolta cameras)

The Nifca Period - 1928-31. The newly formed company produced cameras which were of the latest designs of their day, using Japanese made bodies and German made lenses and shutters. NIFCA = *(NI)ppon (F)oto (CA)meras.*

The Molta Period - 1931-37. As the company grew it was reorganized as a joint stock firm under the name Molta Goshi Kaisha. It was during the early years of this period that the name Minolta was adopted as a trade name on the cameras. MOLTA = *(M)echanismus (O)ptik und (L)insen von (TA)shima.*

The Chiyoda Period - 1937-62. As expansion and progress continued the company went through another reorganization and emerged as Chiyoda Kogaku Seiko, K.K. This expansion saw Chiyoda become the first Japanese camera company to manufacture every part of their own cameras.

The Minolta Period - 1962-82. Began with a change of the company name to The Minolta Camera Company, Ltd. Marketing areas were expanded; so were the products that were manufactured. It was during this period that Minolta entered the fields of office copy machines, planeteria, and manufacturing for other companies.

The Modern Minolta Period - 1982-. Signified by the new Minolta logo. To date, Minolta has produced in excess of 38 million cameras. The 40 million mark is anticipated prior to the end of 1985.

Many arguments exist regarding which of Minolta's many "firsts" was most significant to photography. My nomination is Minolta's founder, Mr. Kazuo Tashima, who remained at the head of his company from 1928-76. "The first founder of any camera company to remain its president for 54 years." (His son, Hideo Tashima, became Minolta's president at that time, and Kazuo Tashima stepped into the role of "Chairman of the Board" of the Minolta Camera Co.)

Most of the information and photographs in this section have been provided by Jack and Debbie Quigley of Quigley Photographic Services. Both are particularly fond of Minolta equipment, which led them to study Minolta cameras and history. If you have any questions on Minolta, Nifca, or Molta cameras, particularly rare or unusual models, the Quigleys will be happy to help. Contact them in care of Quigley Photographic Services, 1120 NE 155 St., N. Miami Beach, FL 33162. You may also wish to have a free copy of their newsletter. See details in their display ad in the back of this book.

Prices are as estimated by the Quigleys in consultation with Minolta collectors worldwide. Many of the early cameras are not often seen for sale, so estimates of experts are our best guide. For the cameras which are common, we used price statistics from our data base.

The cameras in the Minolta section have been arranged in a somewhat unusual manner. Generally we have followed a chronological order, but usually we have listed second and third generation models immediately after their predecessor to aid collectors in identification and comparing of features. For the same reason, we have listed all of the twin-lens reflex models together, and likewise the subminiatures. These two groups are toward the end of the Minolta section.

Nifcalette - 1929. Folding camera for 4x6.5cm on 127 film. Hellostar Anastigmat

f6.3/75mm. Koilos 25-100,T,B shutter. There were five models of Nifcalette A, four models of Nifcalette B and two models of Nifcalette D. Some have Compur 1-300, T,B shutters with Zeiss Anastigmat lenses. Others had Vario shutters with Wekar lenses. The camera itself was marked Nifca Photo. New price: 39 Yen. Current value: $350+.

Nifca-Klapp - 1930. 6.5x9cm folding plate camera. f6.3/105mm Zeiss Anastigmat or Wekar Anastigmat. Vario 25,50,100,T,B or Compur 25-200 shutter. New price: 39 Yen. Current value: $225+.

Nifca-Sports - 1930. 6.5x9cm folding plate camera. Wekar Anastigmat f4.5/105, Compur 1-200,T,B. There were three models of this camera. Some had Vario and Koilos shutters with Zeiss Anastigmat lenses. New price: 85 Yen. Current value: $225+.

Nifca Dox - 1930. 6.5x9cm strut folding camera. Two models were made. One had Nifca Anastigmat f6.8/105mm in Koilos 25-100,T,B. The other had a f6.3/105 lens,

Happy (Molta Co.) - 1931. 6.5x9cm folding plate camera. Earliest models were equipped with Zeiss and Wekar Anastigmat f4.5 lenses in a Compur shutter 1-200. Later models had Coronar Anastigmat f4.5/105mm, Crown 5-200, T, B. New price: 40 Yen. Current value: $175+. *(illustrated previous column)*

Semi-Minolta I - 1932. Folding camera for 4.5x6cm on 120 rollfilm. Coronar Anastigmat f4.5/75mm in Crown 5-200,T ,B shutter. New price: 15 Yen. Current value: $125. *(illustrated previous column)*

details uncertain. New price: 29 Yen. Current value: $500+.

Semi Minolta II - 1937. Folding camera, for 16 exposures, 4.5x6cm on 120 rollfilm. Coronar Anastigmat f3.5/75mm in Crown 5-200,T,B. New price: 120 Yen. Current value: $45-55.

Minolta Happy

Semi-Minolta I

Auto Semi Minolta - 1937. Folding camera for 6x4.5cm on 120 rollfilm. Promar Anastigmat f3.5/75mm in Crown II-Tiyoko 1-400,T,B. CRF. Self-stop film counter and advance. The body is almost identical to the Welta Weltur. New price: 248 Yen. Current value: $100-150.

Minolta - 1933. (Note: This was the first use of the Minolta name.) 6.5x9cm strut folding camera. Coronar Anastigmat f4.5/105mm, Crown 1-200,T,B. Featured a built-in footage scale. New price: 97 Yen. Current value: $175.

9.5 Yen. Current value: $60-75.

Minolta Best (Also called Vest and Marble; Best is the official name.) - 1934. Collapsing dual format 127 rollfilm camera. Formats 4x6.5cm and 4x3cm obtained by inserting a plate at the film plane. The Minolta name was embossed in the leather. There were three different models. Model I: f8/75mm fixed focus. Model II: f5.6/75mm front element focus. Model III: f4.5/80mm front element focus. All were Coronar Anastigmat lenses in Marble 25-100 shutters. The body and back door were made of a plastic which was not widely known at that time. It was only in the experimental stage in Germany. The telescoping plastic sections were reinforced with bright stainless steel. New prices: Model I- 19.5 Yen; Model II-28.5 Yen; Model III- 37.5 Yen. Current value: $65-80.

Baby Minolta - 1935. Bakelite 127 rollfilm camera; 4x6.5cm or 4x3cm formats were changed by a removable plate at the film plane. Coronar Anastigmat f8/80mm fixed focus, fixed f-stop, pull-out lens in bakelite housing. Japanese-made Vario-type 25-100,T,B shutter. New price:

Minolta Six - 1935. Collapsible folding camera for 6x6cm on 120 follfilm. Horizontally styled bakelite body without bed or struts. Front standard pulls out with telescoping stainless steel snap-lock frames around bellows. Coronar Anastigmat f5.6/80mm. Crown 25-150,T,B. New price: 50 Yen. Current value: $85.

Auto Minolta - 1935. 6.5x9cm strut folding

plate camera. Actiplan Anastigmat f4.5/105mm, Crown 1-200,T,B. Top mounted CRF. Footage scale on the face of the camera. New price: 135 Yen. Current value: $225.

Minolta Auto Press - 1937. 6.5x9cm strut folding plate camera, similar in style to the Plaubel Makina. Promar Anastigmat f3.5/105. Crown Rapid 1-400,T,B, synched at all speeds. CRF on the top aligns with a folding optical finder on the camera face. Coupled automatic parallax correction. Footage scale on the face. This camera has commonly been referred to as a Plaubel Makina copy; however, it had features not found in Plaubel Makina until many years later. Complete outfit includes ground glass focusing panel, three single metal plate holders, flashgun, and FPA. New price for body and flashgun: 310 Yen. Current value for complete outfit: $275-325. Camera only: $150-200.

Aerial camera - 1939. Designed for military use. Never commercially sold. 11.5x16cm format. Unmarked Minolta f4.5/200mm lens with f4.5, f5.6 settings. Shutter speeds 200, 300, 400. Current value: $375.

Minolta 35 (I) - 35mm rangefinder camera, styled like Leica.

Minolta 35 (I), Early Type D

Interchangeable (Leica thread) Super Rokkor f2.8/45mm lens. Horizontal cloth focal plane shutter 1-500,T,B, ST. This was Minolta's first 35mm camera. It went through six minor model changes:
- (Type A): 2/48. Serial #0001-4000. Image size of 24x32mm. "Chiyoda Kogaku Osaka" on top.
- (Type B): 8/48. Serials to about 4800. Image size 24x33.5mm, otherwise like the Type A.
- (Type C): 2/49. Serial range uncertain. "C.K.S." stamped on top. Image size 24x34mm.
- (Type D): 8/49. Begins with serial #9001. Front grooved for focusing tab. Has strap lugs. Rewind lever repositioned concentric with wind knob. (Early Type D may still have early rewind lever.)
- Model E: 2/51. Begins with serial #10,001. "Model-E" engraved on front.
- Model F: 2/52. Begins with serial #20,000. "Model-F" on front.
None of these cameras were exported, although some were brought back by soldiers. New price: 35,000 Yen. Current values: Type A: $100-125. Later types: $70-80.

Minolta Memo - 1949. 35mm viewfinder camera. Rokkor f4.5/50mm lens. Between-the-lens 25-100,B shutter. Helical lever focusing. Rapid advance lever. This was Minolta's low priced 35mm camera of the day. Steel body and basic mechanism, bakelite top and bottom plates. New price: 8,000 Yen. Current value: $95-125.

Minolta 35 Model II - 1953. 35mm rangefinder camera. Interchangeable Super Rokkor f2.8/45mm or optional f2.0/50mm lens. Horizontal cloth focal plane shutter, 1-500,T,B, ST. New price: 47,200 Yen. Current value: with f2.0, $125; with f2.8, $100.

Minolta A - 1955-57. 24x36mm rangefinder. Early models had Optiper MX, Chiyoda Kogaku, and Citizen MV between-the-lens shutters set by wheel on camera top. Non-interchangeable Chiyoko Rokkor f3.5/45mm lens. New price 14,800 Yen. Current value: $35-40.

Minolta A2 - 1955-58. 35mm rangefinder. Non-interchangeable Chiyoko Rokkor f3.5 or f2.8/45mm lens. Between-the-lens shutter set by wheel on camera top. Citizen in 1955-56, Citizen MV and MVL in 1957, and Optiper MXV in 1958. New price: 17,900 Yen with f3.5, 20,100 with f2.8. Current value: $35-40.

Minolta A3 - 1959. 35mm rangefinder. Non-interchangeable Minolta Rokkor f2.8/45mm lens. Shutter 1-500, B. $25-35.

Minolta A5 - 1960. 35mm rangefinder camera. Rokkor fixed mount lens in Citizen MVL shutter.
- Two Japanese models: f2.8/45mm or f2.0/45mm lens. Both have shutter 1-1000, B. New price: 14,000 and 17,500 Yen. Current value: $60.00.
- U.S.A. model: f2.8/45mm lens, shutter 1-500, B. New price: $69.50. Current value: $15-30.

Minolta Sky - 35mm rangefinder camera designed by Minolta for release in 1957 but was never introduced into the public marketplace. About 100 made. Built-in bright-line viewfinder, auto parallax correction. Used interchangeable Minolta M-mount lenses. It could also use screw mount lenses from the Minolta 35 and 35 Model II by use of an M-mount/SM adapter. New price was to be about $325 with Rokkor f1.8/50mm. Current value estimate: $8,000-10,000.

Minolta Super A - 1957. 35mm rangefinder camera. Seikosha-MX 1-400,B between-the-lens shutter. Single stroke lever advance. Most commonly found with Super Rokkor f1.8/50mm lens. (New price: 36,500 Yen.) Other normal lenses were f2.0/50mm (New: 34,500 Yen) and f2.8/50mm (New: 31,300 Yen). Current value of the body with 1 normal lens: $45-70. Current values on other Super Rokkor lenses:
- 35mm/f3.5: $40. - Lenses with auxillary finders and case:

- 85mm/f2.8: $65.
- 100mm/f3.8: $65.
- 135mm/f4.5: $50.
- Coupled selenium meter: $20-25. (The meter clipped into the accessory shoe and coupled to the shutter speed control.)

Minolta SR-1, early style

Minolta. New price: 36,000 Yen. Current value of any of the five models, with lens: $70-90.

Minolta Auto Wide - 1958. 35mm rangefinder camera, similar to the Super A, but with Rokkor fixed mount f2.8/35mm lens. Between-the-lens Optiper MVL 1-500, B,ST shutter. Film advance and rewind on the bottom of the camera. CdS match needle metering. New price: 21,000 Yen. Current value: $40-60.

Minolta SR-1, new style - 1964. Same features as the early SR-1 of 1962, but body styling is more squared in appearance around the top cover edges. Viewfinder eyepiece was squared rather than rounded as on the early model. A new set of accessories were introduced with this model such as a slip on CdS meter. $70-90.

Minolta SR-2 - 1958. 35mm SLR. Quick return mirror, auto diaphragm. Horizontal cloth FP shutter 1-1000, B. Minolta bayonet lens mount. Most common lens is the f1.8/55mm Minolta Rokkor PF. New price: 51,500 Yen with lens. Current value: $90-110.

Minolta SR-1, early style - 1959. 35mm SLR. Minolta bayonet lens mount. Most common lens is the Minolta Rokkor PF f2.0/55mm. Horizontal cloth focal plane shutter, 1-500, B. There were five different models of the first style SR-1. The first three models, 1959-61, did not have the bracket for the coupled meter. The bracket was added in 1962. Other changes include the addition of depth of field preview button. On very early models the name "SR-1" was placed to the left of the word

Minolta SR-1S - 1964. Same features as the SR-1 of 1964, but top shutter speed now 1000, not 500. $70-90.

Minolta Uniomat

Minolta SR-3 - 1960. 35mm SLR. Minolta bayonet lens mount. Most common lens is the Minolta Auto Rokkor PF f1.8/55mm. Horizontal cloth focal plane shutter 1-1000, B. Detachable coupled CdS exposure meter. New price: 41,500 Yen with lens. Current value: $75-100.

Minolta V2 - 1958. 35mm rangefinder camera. Rokkor f2.8/45mm, between-the-lens Optiper HS (High Speed) 1-2000, B shutter. New price 23,000 Yen. Current value: $85. *Note: Usually found with loose lens and shutter assembly due to the loosening of screws. They should be replaced, not just tightened, to be worth the value shown.*

Uniomat III - 1964. 35mm rangefinder. Built-in meter on the lens front. The camera says "Uniomat" not "Uniomat III". Non-interchangeable Rokkor f2.8/45mm. Shutter automatically controlled by the meter and ASA settings. New price: 14,000 Yen. Current value: $30-50.

Minolta V3 - 1960. Like the V2, but with selenium metering. Rokkor f1.8/45mm lens, Optiper HS 1-3000,B shutter. New price: 23,000 Yen. Current value: $115. *Note: These also are usually found with a loose lens and shutter assembly. The screws should be replaced, not just tightened, to be worth the value shown. It costs about $40 to have this done professionally.*

Minolta AL - 1961-65. 35mm rangefinder. Built-in selenium meter. Non-interchangeable f2.0/45mm Rokkor PF lens. Citizen shutter 1-1000, B, MX sync, ST. New price: 19,500 Yen. Current value: $30-40.

Uniomat - 1960. 35mm rangefinder with coupled built-in selenium meter. Minolta Rokkor f2.8 lens. Shutter speeds automatically determined by the light readings. New price: 16,000 Yen. Current value: $45. *(illustrated top of next column)*

Minolta AL-2 - 1963. 35mm rangefinder. Built-in CdS meter. Non-interchangeable Rokkor f1.8/45mm lens. Shutter 1-500, B. New price: 21,800 Yen. Current value: $65.

Minolta AL-S - 1965. 35mm rangefinder with meter. Non-interchangeable Rokkor QF f1.8/40mm. Shutter 1-500, B. Made for the USA market. New price: $92,90. Current value: $40.

Minolta AL-F - c1968. 35mm rangefinder camera. Automatic, CdS controlled, shutter-priority metering. Shutter 30-500. Rokkor f2.7/38mm lens. $35.

Minolta SR-7, early style - 1962. First 35mm SLR with built-in CdS meter and scale. Minolta bayonet lens mount. Most common lens is the Rokkor PF f1.4/58mm. Horizontal cloth focal plane shutter, 1-1000, B. ASA dial settings from 6 to 3200. New price: 28,500 Yen with lens. Current value: $75-100.

Minolta SR-7, new style - 1964. Same features as the early SR-7, but with squared off body styling. $75-100.

Minolta Repo - 1962. Half-frame 35mm rangefinder. Built-in meter automatically sets shutter speeds on Citizen L shutter. MX sync. Non-interchangeable Rokkor f2.8/30mm lens. New price: 10,300 Yen. Current value: $30. *(illustrated top of next column)*

Minolta Repo-S - 1964. Half-frame 35mm rangefinder. Built-in match needle metering. Rokkor PF f1.8/32mm. Shutter ⅛-500, B. New price: 14,500. Current value: $50-70. *(illustrated in next column)*

Minolta Repo

Minolta Repo-S

Minolta Hi-Matic - 1962. 35mm rangefinder camera with built-in selenium meter. Rokkor PF f2.0/45mm lens in Citizen shutter to 500, ST, sync. New price: 19,800 Yen. Current value: $35.

Variation: Ansco Autoset - 1962. Made

by Minolta for Ansco in the USA. Identical to the Hi-Matic but has Rokkor f2.8/45mm lens, and auto metering is slightly different. New price: $90. Current value: $20-35.

Minolta Hi-Matic 7 - 1963. 35mm RF. Built-in meter. Non-interchangeable Rokkor PF f1.8/45mm. Shutter has manual speeds ¼-500, B. Could also be used on auto. New price: 22,900 Yen. Current value: $30-50.

Minolta ER - 1963. 35mm SLR. Fixed mount Rokkor f2.8/45mm lens in 30-500, B shutter. Wide angle and tele auxiliary lens sets available. New price: $119.50. Current value: $45.

Variation: Anscoset III - 1964. Identical to the Uniomat III, but says "Anscoset III". Made for export to the USA. New price: $89.95. Current value: $30-45.

Minoltina-P - 1964. 35mm RF. Match

needle metering. Non-interchangeable Rokkor PF f2.8/38mm. Citizen shutter 1/30-250, B, ST, MX sync. New price: 13,700 Yen. Current value: $20-30.

Minoltina-S - 1964. 35mm rangefinder. Built-in meter. Rokkor QF f1.8/40mm lens. Shutter 1-500, B. New price: 20,000 Yen. Current value: $30-45.

GAF Ansco Autoset CdS - 1964. 35mm rangefinder. Built-in CdS meter. Made for the USA market. Ansco Rokkor f2.8/45mm, shutter 1/30-500 auto, B. New price: $79.95. Current value: $20-35.

Minolta 24 Rapid - 24x24mm on 35mm. Rangefinder; built-in CdS meter. Rokkor f2.8/32mm. Manual shutter speeds 1/30-250, B. Could also be used on automatic. New price: 15,800 Yen. Current value: $80.

Electro Shot - 1965. Auto 35mm RF. Non-interchangeable Rokkor QF f1.8/40mm. Auto shutter 1/16-1/500. This was the first electronically controlled 35mm lens/shutter camera. New price 22,140 Yen. Current value: $25-35.

Minolta SR-M - 1970. First 35mm SLR with integrated motor built in the body. Power supply was a grip on the side of the body. Minolta SR/SRT bayonet mount. Most common lens is the Minolta Rokkor MC RF f1.7/55mm. Horizontal cloth focal plane shutter, 1-1000, T,B. Sync at 1/60. There was no meter built into the body or provision for adding one. New price: 129,000 Yen with body and grip. Current value: $250-325.

Minolta XD-7, XD-11, XD - 1977. Made in black and chrome, this camera was marketed in Europe as the XD-7, in North America as the XD-11, and in Japan as the XD. This is the world's first multimode

exposure 35mm camera. Shutter or aperture priority and metered manual modes. X-sync at 1/100. Mechanical speeds "O", 1/100, B. Minolta bayonet mount for the shutter priority mode MD lens. Vertical traverse metal focal plane shutter with electomagnetic release. Electronic stepped or stepless speeds 1-1000, B. Black: $200-275. Chrome: $150-225.

MINOLTA 6X6cm TWIN LENS REFLEX CAMERAS
1937 Minoltaflex (I) (two models)
1939 Minolta Automat (two models)
1950-54 Minoltaflex II, IIB, III (three models)
1953-54 Minoltacord (three models)
1955 Minoltacord Automat (one model)
1955 Minolta Autocord L (one model, selenium metered)
1955 Minolta Autocord LMX (one model, selenium metered)
1955-65 Minolta Autocord (seven models, non-metered)
1957 Minolta Autocord RA (one model, non-metered)
1965 Minolta Autocord CdS (three models, CdS metered)

There are 24 different models of Minolta 6x6cm TLRs. Any internal or external change is considered to be a new model of that camera. All use either 120 or 220 rollfilm and have f3.5/75mm lenses. The shutters are Konan, Citizen, Seikosha and Optiper.

Minoltaflex (I) - 1937. The first Japanese TLR. 6x6cm on 120 rollfilm. Says "Minolta" on front, not "Minoltaflex". Promar Anastigmat f3.5/75mm taking lens, Minolta Anastigmat f3.2/75mm viewing lens. Crown II-Tiyoko 1-300,B. The main body is identical to Rolleicord, top of the hood is identical to Ikoflex. Had a unique side lock and shutter release to avoid double exposure. Also available with Zeiss lenses and Compur shutters. New price: 305 Yen. Current value: $125-175. *(illustrated top of next page)*

Minolta Automat - 1939. TLR for 6x6cm on 120 rollfilm. Promar f3.5/75mm taking and viewing lenses. Crown 1-300,B. Crank advance like early Rolleiflex. Hood like Ikoflex. New price: 493 Yen. Current value: $150-225.

Minoltaflex II, IIB, III - 1950-54. 6x6cm TLR. Rokkor f3.5/75mm lens in S-Konan Rapid 1-500 shutter, B. $50-80. *(illustrated top of next page)*

Minoltacord, Minoltacord Automat - c1955. TLR predecessors of the Minolta Autocord. Rokkor f3.5/75mm lens. Citizen 1-400 shutter. $60-90. *(illustrated top of next page)*

Minoltaflex (1937), Minoltaflex (1950's), Minoltacord, Minolta Miniflex, Minolta Autocord (non-metered), Minolta Autocord CdS

Minolta Autocord, Autocord RA - 1955-65. Non-metered models. Rokkor f3.5/75mm lens. Optiper MX 1-500 shutter. $60-90. *(illustrated above)*

Minolta Autocord L, LMX - Selenium meter. $90-110.

Minolta Autocord CdS I, II, III - CdS meter. $110-150. *(illustrated at top of page)*

Minolta Miniflex - 1959. TLR, for 4x4cm on 127 film. Minolta Rokkor f3.5/60mm lens. Optiper or Citizen MVL shutter 1-500, B. Less than 5000 made. New price: 12,700 Yen. Current value: $300+. *Note: There have been reports that the Miniflex has sold for thousands of dollars in Japan. However this has not been confirmed. Most reports around the USA/Canada and Europe have reported the sale of this limited production camera to be $300-450. (illustrated above)*

MINOLTA SUBMINIATURE CAMERAS:
Konan 16 - 1950 (Chiyoda Kogaku). 16mm subminiature, 10x14mm exposures. Chiyoko Rokkor f3.5/25mm lens. 25-200, T,B shutter. Push-pull advance and shutter cocking. New price: 7,750 Yen. Current value: $60-90.

Minolta 16 Model I - 1957-60. Subminiature taking 10x14mm exposures on 16mm film in special cassettes. Rokkor f3.5/25mm lens. Shutter has only three speeds, 25,50,200. No bulb. Push-pull advance. New price: 6,900 Yen. Blue: $100-150. Green: $75-100. Red: $60-90. Black: $35-50. Chrome finish is very common: $15-25.

Minolta 16 Model II - 1960-66. Identical in appearance to the Model I, but with f2.8 lens and shutter has five speeds 30-500, plus B. New price: 7,300 Yen. Very common: $15-25.

Minolta 16 Model P - 1960-65. Rokkor f3.5/25mm, shutter 1/100 only, sync. New price: 4,100 Yen. Very common: $15-20.

Sonocon 16mm MB-ZA - 1962. 16mm subminiature, 10x14mm exposures. Black body. Rokkor f2.8/22mm lens, shutter 30-500, B. This is actually a Minolta 16-II combined with a 7 transistor radio. New price: 6,900 Yen. Current value: $100-150.

Minolta 16 EE - 1962-64. Rokkor f2.8/25mm; shutter 30-500. Auto exposure using selenium cell. New price: 9,500 Yen. Current value: $20-30.

Minolta 16 EE II - 1963-65. Rokkor f2.8/25mm, shutter speeds H (High) and L (Low) (200 and 50). Auto exposure CdS metering. New price: 12,400 Yen. Current value: $20-30.

Minolta 16PS - 1964-74. Appearance is identical to the Model P, but shutter 30-100. Made only for export to the USA. New price: $26.90. Very common. Usually found like new, with case, box, and instructions for $15-25. Camera with case only: $10-18.

Minolta 16-MG - 1966-71. Rokkor f2.8/20mm, shutter 30-250. Match needle metering. Very common. Kit with case, chain, and MG flash: $25-35. Camera with case and chain only: $20-25.

Minolta 16 MG-S - 1969-74. Made in black or silver. Rokkor f2.8/23mm, shutter 30-500. Auto match needle metering. With case, flash, strap, instructions in presentation box: $35-50. Camera and case only: $25-35.

Minolta 16 QT - 1972-74. Rokkor f3.5/23mm, shutter 30-250. Auto metering. Black or chrome. Very common. Often found with case, electronic flash, etc. in presentation box. Like new: $35-50. Camera and case only: $20-30.

Maxxum - 1985. *Technical details/prices from your Minolta dealer. This is new merchandise. We're including it only because of its name.* This is a story of the mid-1980's world business atmosphere: International trade agreements, grey-market dealing, import and export restrictions, warranty contracts... all symbols of the times. Separate brand names for different countries led to the name Maxxum for the North American version of the camera called "7000 AF" in Europe and "Alpha 7000" in Japan. In spelling the name Maxxum, the decision was made to use an interlocking double X. That all sounds like a great idea, until giant Exxon sees the advertising. Exxon, of course, has used the interlocking double X in their trademark for some time. Now nobody at either Minolta or Exxon is worried that people will put cameras in their gas tank or tigers in their cameras, but from a legal viewpoint, if any infringements on a trademark are allowed, the protected design could soon become generic, unprotectable, and useless as an identifiable symbol for the original product.
So, now the innocent new baby, Maxxum, with cameras, lenses, and advertising materials already in distribution, faces a change. Minolta agreed to change the design of the Maxxum logo. Exxon agreed to allow a gradual phasing in of the changes

to avoid disrupting Minolta's production schedules. Now that's a reasonable way to conduct business. After all "we all make misteaks."

Will the double-crossed Maxxum be collectible? Of course, if you can afford to buy one and let it sit around. Will it be rare? Probably not. There were many produced and shipped.

MINOX - *Subminature cameras for 8x11mm exposures on 9.5mm film in special cassettes. The original model, designed by Walter Zapp, was made in 1937 in Riga, Latvia.*

Original model - (stainless steel body) - Made in Riga, Latvia by Valsts Electro-Techniska Fabrika. Guillotine shutter ½-1000. Minostigmat f3.5/15mm lens. Historically significant and esthetically pleasing, but not rare. Readily available in the $400-500 range, they sell well in the $300-400 range. The original zippered blue, brown, or black case with "Riga" markings will fetch an additional $25.

Minox "Made in USSR" - Stainless steel model made during the short time the Russians held Latvia before the German occupation. (Approximately Spring to Fall, 1940.) $700-850.

Minox II - 1949-51. Made in Wetzlar, Germany. Aluminum body. $60-85.

Minox III - 1951-56. Export model of the Minox A for the USA. $60-80.

Minox III, Gold-plated - With design pattern in metal, gold-plated, in crocodile case with gold chain. $1200-1800.

Minox III-S - c1954-63. Gold: $1000-1300. Black: $200-300. Chrome model, with case and chain: $50-70. *(illustrated top of next column)*

Minox III-S

Minox A - c1948. Wetzlar. Complan f3.5. Gold: 1200-1800. Chrome: $60-80.

Minox B - c1958-71. Built-in meter. Black: $90-125. Chrome: $50-70.

Minox BL - c1971-76. CdS meter. $70-95.

Minox C - c1969-79. Black: $80-120. Chrome (extremely common): $70-100.

M.I.O.M. (Manufacture d'Isolants et d'Objets Moules)

Lec Junior - Rigid, light brown bakelite body. 4x6.5cm exposures on rollfilm. $10-20.

Loisir - Plastic rollfilm camera for 8 or 16 exposures on 120 film. Radior lens, simple shutter, T & I. $10-20.

Miom - Rigid black bakelite body. 4x6.5cm on rollfilm. $15-25.

Photax - Streamlined black bakelite body. Helix lens mount. 6x9cm on rollfilm. $10-20.

MIRACLE - Japanese novelty subminiature of the Hit type. $10-15.

MIRANDA CAMERA CO. LTD. (Tokyo, Japan)
Miranda A - c1958. Second Miranda 35mm SLR. Same body design and features as the Miranda T, except: FP shutter 1-1000, Miranda Soligor f1.9/50mm lens, single-stroke winding lever, and rapid-rewind crank. $50-65.

Miranda C - 1958-60. 35mm SLR. Soligor f1.9/50mm interchangeable lens. FP shutter 1-500, B. Instant return mirror. $50-75.

Miranda D - 1960-62. 35mm SLR. Interchangeable Auto Soligor f1.9/50mm lens. FP shutter 1-500,B. Instant return mirror. $45-60.

Miranda F - c1963-66. Similar to the "C" and "D". Same lens and FP shutter. $45-65.

Miranda G - c1966-68. Similar, but FP shutter 1-1000, B,ST. $65-85.

Miranda T (Standard) - c1955. First Miranda-made 35mm SLR. Zunow f1.9/50mm interchangeable lens. FP shutter 1-500, B. Non-return mirror. $55-70.

MISUZU TRADING CO. (Japan)
Jilona Midget cameras - *A series of subminiature cameras. Similar in style to the cheap "Hit" cameras, but heavy cast metal construction. The earliest models were from the late 1930's, but the most commonly found ones in the U.S.A. are the post-war models listed here:*
Jilona Midget Model No. 2 - c1949. Identified on the top. $40-60.

Midget Model III - c1950. "Model III Midget" on top. Body release. $50-75.

MIYAKAWA SEISAKUSHO (Tokyo, Japan)
Picny - c1935. Compact camera for 3x4cm exposures on 127 film. Very similar in size and shape to the Gelto-D by Toakoki Seisakusho but rounded ends and better finish almost make it look like a stubby Leica. Even the collapsing lens mount is a direct copy of the Leica styling. Picny Anastigmat f4.5/40mm lens. Picny shutter 1/25-1/100, T,B. $75-100.

MIZUHO KOKI (Japan)
Mizuho-Six - c1952. Folding two-format camera for 120 film, 6x6cm and 4.5x6cm. Militar Speciial f3.5/80mm lens. NKS shutter 1-200,B. $30-45.

MOCKBA 5 (U.S.S.R) - c1938. Folding rollfilm rangefinder camera, copy of Super Ikonta C. 6x9cm or 6x6cm exposures. Netar Anastigmat f3.5/105mm lens. $80-100.

MOELLER (J. D. Moeller, Hamburg, Germany)
Cambinox - c1956. A combination of high quality 7x35 binoculars and a precision camera for 10x14mm exposures on 16mm film. Interchangeable f3.5/90mm

lenses. Rotary focal plane shutter 30-800. $500-750.

Moment (Momehm)

MOLLIER (Etablissements Mollier, Paris)
Le Cent Vues - c1925-30. An early camera for 100 exposures 18x24mm on 35mm film. Several variations. Early ones have a square cornered, vertically oriented metal body. The metal front has rounded corners. "Le Cent Vues" (100 views) written above the lens. Second c1926 has leather covered body with rounded ends. Hermagis Anastigmat f3.5/40mm in Compur shutter 1-300. $1100-1600.

MOLTENI (Paris, France)
Detective camera - c1885. Wooden body, 9x12cm plate camera of an unusual design. Front portion of body hinges up 180 degrees to rest on the top of the camera body, becoming the front of the viewfinder. Back of the body lifts up to form the back of the viewfinder. Brass fittings. Brass barrel Molteni Aplanat lens. Brass lens cap acts as the shutter. $1000-1400.

MOM (Magyar Optikai Muerek (Hungarian Optical Works), Budapest)
Fotobox - c1950. 6x6cm metal box camera. Large built in eye-level finder on top. Achromat f7.7/75mm lens, shutter 1/25-100. $45-55.

Mometta II - c1953. Rangefinder Leica copy. Ymmar f3.5/50mm lens. FP shutter 1/25-500. $75-100.

Momikon - c1950. Rangefinder 35. Ymmar f3.5/50mm lens. FP shutter 25-500. $75-100.

MOMENT (MOMEHM) - Russian copy of Polaroid 95. f6.8/135mm. "BTL" shutter, 10-200, B. Black bellows. Rare. $100-150.
(illustrated top of next column)

MONARCH MFG. CO. (Chicago) *Also spelled Monarck.*

Plastic novelty cameras - Half-frame 127. Minicam-style, horizontal or reflex-type bodies. Various names: Fleetwood, Flash Master, Flex-Master, Kando Reflex, Pickwik, Remington. $3-7.

Monarch 620 - Simple, cast aluminum camera for 4.5x6cm on 620 film. Also sold as the Photo-Master Twin 620. $8-12.

MONARCK MFG. CO. (Chicago) *Also spelled Monarch.*
Monarck - Plastic novelty cameras for full or half frames on 828 film. Minicam-style. $3-7.

MONO-WERK (Rudolph Chaste, Magdeburg, Germany)
Mono-Trumpf - c1914. 9x12cm folding bed plate camera. Mono Doppel Anastigmat f6.3/136mm lens. Ibsor shutter. $30-45.

MONROE CAMERA CO. (Rochester, NY) *(Incorporated in 1897, merged in 1899 with several companies to form Rochester Optical & Camera Co.)*
Folding plate cameras (bed types) - "cycle" style folding cameras. 4x5": $40-60. 5x7": $60-90.

Folding plate cameras (strut types) - c1898. They fold to a very compact size, only about 1½" thick including brass double plateholder. Sizes:
2x2½" (Vest Pocket Size) - $150-250.
3½x3½" (Pocket Size) - $100-150.

3¼x4¼" (Pocket A) - The last of the series by Monroe before the merger. $100-150.

Monroe Model 7 - A 5x7" "cycle" style plate camera. Double extension maroon bellows. RR lens, Gundlach shutter. This camera looks like the Rochester it is about to become. $75-125.

MONROE SALES CO.
Color-flex - c1947. Pseudo-TLR aluminum camera. Cream colored enamel and burgundy leatherette covering. $35-50.

MONTANUS (Solingen, Germany)
Montiflex - 6x6cm TLR. Steinheil Cassar f2.8/80mm. Prontor-SVS shutter. $75-100.

Rocca Super Reflex - c1955. 6x6cm TLR. Steinheil Cassar f2.8/80mm lens. Prontor 1-300 shutter, MX sync. $75-100.

MONTGOMERY WARD & CO.
Model B - 4x5" folding plate camera. Leather covered wood body. Rapid conv. lens. Wollensak shutter. $40-60. *Note: Most of the cameras sold through Montgomery Ward were not marked with the company name. Sears was one step ahead of Wards in that respect.*

Wardflex - c1941. 6x6cm TLR for 120 film. An Argoflex with the Wardflex name. f3.5/80 lens. TKK shutter 1-200, B. $20-30.

Wards 35 - c1956. An Adox Polo 1S with the Wards 35 name. Adoxar f3.5/45mm lens. Shutter 1-300. $15-20.

Wards xp400 - Simple 35mm camera with automatic diaphragm. Made in Japan. Meter cell surrounds the lens. $15-25.

MONTI (Charles Monti, France)
Monte Carlo, Monte Carlo Special - Folding rollfilm cameras for 6x9cm on 120 film. f3.5 or 4.5/90mm lens. $15-25.

MOORE & CO. (Liverpool, England)

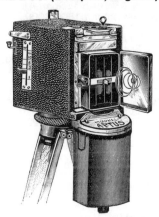

Aptus Ferrotype Camera - 1895-1930's. Black leather covered wood body, for 4.5x6.3cm plates. Meniscus lens. Suction bulb takes unexposed plate and swings it into position for exposures. $300-350.

MOORSE - (H. Moorse, London)
Single-lens Stereo - c1865. Unusual stereo camera for 9x18cm exposures on wet-plates. Camera sits in a track on the top of its case. Between the two exposures, the camera is moved along the track to give the proper separation for the stereo exposures. Meniscus lens. $3000-3500.

MORITA TRADING CO. (Japan)

Gem 16, Model II - c1956. Novelty subminiature for 14x14mm on paper-backed rollfilm. $65-85.

Kiku 16, Model II - c1956. Novelty subminiature, 14x14 exposures. Mensicus lens. B,I shutter. Same as Gem 16, Model II, above. $65-85.

MORLEY (W. Morley, Ltd., London, England)
Wet-plate camera - c1860. Quarter-plate bellows camera. Jamin-Darlot lens, waterhouse stops. $550-650.

Wet-plate stereo camera - c1860. Negretti & Zambra brass-barrel lenses. Waterhouse stops. $1800-2200.

MOSCOW (MOSKWA) - *Russian copies of the Zeiss Super Ikonta C.*
Moscow, Models (1)-5 - Industar f3.5/105mm or f4.5/110mm. Moment shutter 1-250. $75-125.

MOTOCA (Japan) - 35mm Leica copy. Lunar Anastigmat f3/45mm. Shutter 20-300. Fixed lens mount. $200-250.

MOUNTFORD (W.S. Mountford Mfg., NY)
Button tintype camera - Leather-covered cannon-style button tintype camera, taking 100 1" dia. tintypes. $800-1200.

MOURFIELD
Direct Positive Camera - Large brown-leathered camera. Prism mounted in front of lens. $120-140.

MULTIPLE TOYMAKERS (N.Y.C.)
Camera Kit, Wonderful Camera - c1973. Small plastic half-frame 127 camera in kit form. Simple assembly of five large pieces and a few small ones yields a camera named "Wonderful Camera" with f8 lens in 1/50 sec. shutter. The kit comes bubble packed on a card. Made in Hong Kong. $1-5.

MULTISCOPE & FILM CO. (Burlington, Wisc.)

Baby Al-Vista and Model 5D

Al-Vista Panoramic Cameras - patents 1891-1901. Takes panoramic pictures (model no. gives film height in inches) The standard five-format models take pictures in lengths of 4, 6, 8, 10, or 12 inches on rollfilm. The dual-format models take a standard proportion picture or double-width panoramic view.

Baby Al-Vista - $250-350.

Model 3B - Dual-format model. Picture 3½" high by either 4½ or 9" long. $250-300.

Model 4B - Standard five-format model. Pictures 4" high by 4,6,8,10, or 12" long. $200-250.

Model 4G - Dual format, 4" high by 5 or 10" long. $225-275.

Model 5B - Standard five-format model. Pictures 5" high by 4,6,8,10, or 12" long. $225-275.

Model 5C - Five panoramic formats on rollfilm or standard photos on glass plates with lens tube locked in center position and rear lens hood detached. A "semi-convertible" model. $250-350.

Model 5D - Like the 5B, but lengths of 6,8,10,12, and 16". $225-275.

Model 5F - The convertible model. This camera has two fronts which use the same back. One front is the swinging lens panoramic, and the other is a folding-bed front which looks like the typical folding plate cameras of the day. An unusual and rare set. $400-500.

Model 7D - Dual format, 7" high by 7½ or 15" long. Uncommon. $300-400.

Model 7E - Dual format, 7" high by 10½ or 21" long. Uncommon. $300-400.

Model 7F - Large size convertible model, similar to 5F above. The standard front has extra long bellows for use with convertible lenses, such as the 8½" rectilinear lens originally supplied. Complete: $600-700.

MUNDUS (France)
Mundus Color - c1958. Beige vertical camera for 8x14mm exposures on double 8 movie film. Resembles a movie camera. Interchangeable Berthiot f2.8/20mm lens. Shutter 1-300. $200-250.

MURER & DURONI (Milan, Italy)
Express - c1900. Magazine box camera for various sized plates: 4.5x6cm, 6x9cm, 7x8cm, 8.5x11cm (3¼x4¼") and 9x12cm. Murer Anastigmat f4.5 or 6.3, focal length depending on size of camera. Focal plane shutter. $75-125.

Folding plate cameras, focal plane models - Strut folding style. In all the sizes listed above. $100-125.

Muro - c1914. Vertical 4.5x6cm strut folding camera. Suter Anastigmat f5/70mm. FP shutter to 1000. $150-200.

Reflex - c1912. SLR for 6x9cm plates. Murer Anastigmat f4.5/120mm. Focal plane shutter 15-1000. $100-125.

Sprite - c1915. Vertical 4.5x6cm strut folding cameras. Made in 127 rollfilm and plate versions. Rapide Aplanat f8/70mm lens. Shutter 25-100. $100-125.

Stereo - c1920. Folding camera for 45x107mm. Focal plane shutter, 15-1000. Murer Anastigmat f8 or f4.5/60mm. $150-200.

Stereo Box - c1905. Magazine box camera for stereo exposures. 6x13cm or 8x17cm sizes. Rapide Rectilinear f10 lenses. $175-225.

Stereo Reflex - c1929. SLR for 45x107mm plates. F4.5 lenses. $400-450.

MUSE OPTICAL CO. (Tokyo, Japan)
Museflex - c1955. TLR for 3x3cm on paper-backed 35mm rollfilm. f5.6/55mm. Automatic shutter. (Note: We have seen several offered at prices from $250-350, but no confirmed sales. It appears to be a camera which would be worth $35-50 at best.) *(illustrated top of next page)*

MUTSCHLER, ROBERTSON, & CO.
Manufacturer of the "Ray" cameras, which were later sold & labeled under the "Ray Camera Co." name. See Ray.

Museflex

MW - Horizontally styled bakelite folding camera. Similar to Vokar A,B and Voigt Jr. Probably sold by Montgomery Ward, but we can find no catalog references. $15-20.

MYKRO FINE COLOR 16 - Japanese subminiature for 13mm wide exposures on 16mm film in special cassettes. Body style similar to the Whittaker Pixie. $35-65.

MYSTIC PLATE CAMERA CO. (NY) Mystic Button Camera - Button tintype camera. Spring loaded tube advances buttons for exposure. $250-350.

NAGEL (Dr. August Nagel Camerawerk, Stuttgart, Germany) *Formed by Dr. Nagel in 1928, when he left Zeiss Ikon. Sold to Kodak A.G. in 1932.*
Anca (10,14,25,28) - 1928-34. Folding plate cameras in 6.5x9cm and 9x12cm sizes. Most commonly found with Nagel Anastigmat f4.5, 6.3, 6.8 lenses in Pronto 25-100 shutter. $60-110.

Fornidar 30 - 1930-31. 9x12cm folding plate camera. Nagel Anastigmat f6.3/135, f4.5, or Laudar f4.5/135mm lens. Compur shutter 1-200. $75-100.

Librette (65,74,75,79) - 1933. 6x9cm folding rollfilm cameras. Most commonly found with Nagel Anastigmat f4.5, f6.3, or f6.8 lens in Pronto 25-100 shutter. $175-225.

Pupille - 1931-35. (Also called "Rollaroy" in England). 16 exposures, 3x4cm on 127 film. The version with Leitz Elmar f3.5/50mm lens used to bring nearly double the normal price, but at least four were sold at auction in 1984 in the $125-200. range. It is possible that a truly MINT example might bring a premium price from a Leica collector, but for practical purposes,

the price distinction no longer exists. Normally equipped with Schneider Xenon f2, Xenar 2.9, or 3.5/50mm in Compur 1-300 shutter. $115-200.

Ranca - 1930-31. 3x4cm on 127 film. Similar to Pupille, but cheaper. Has front-lens focusing. Nagel Anastigmat f4.5/50mm in Pronto or Ibsor 1-150 shutter. $200-250.

Recomar 18 - 1928-38. Folding-bed plate camera, 6x9cm. Compur shutter 1-250. With Leitz Elmar f4.5: $125-150. With normal lens; Nagel Anastigmat, Xenar, Tessar f3.8, 4.5, 6.3/105mm: $45-65.

Recomar 33 - 1928-39. Folding 9x12cm plate camera, double extension bellows. Compur 1-250, T, B. With Leitz Elmar f4.5/135mm: $125-150. With normal f4.5/135mm lens: $45-60.

Vollenda, 3x4cm - 1931-37. Folding bed rollfilm camera. Horizontal style. Pronto or Compur shutter. With Elmar f3.5/50mm: $125-150. With normal lens, such as Xenar or Radionar f3.5 or 4.5/50mm: $30-60.

Vollenda, 4x6.5cm or 6x9cm - c1930-

1937. Folding bed cameras for 127 or 120 rollfilm. With normal f4.5 lens: $30-45.

NATIONAL (Osaka, Japan)

Radio/Flash CR-1 - c1978. 110 cartridge camera with built-in flash and radio. $75-100.

NATIONAL CAMERA (England)
Folding field camera - c1900-05. Half-plate. Fine mahogany finish. Reversible back, tapered black bellows, Ross f6.3/7" homocentric lens. Thornton-Picard roller-blind shutter. $200-250.

NATIONAL CAMERA CO. (N.Y.C.)

Baldwin-Flex - TLR-style minicam for 3x4cm on 127 film. $5-10.

NATIONAL CAMERA CO. (St. Louis, Missouri)

Naco - Horizontal folding rollfilm, 8x14cm. Similar to the #3A Folding Hawk-Eye. Rapid Rectilinear f4 lens. Ilex 25-100 shutter, B.T. $30-45.

NATIONAL INSTRUMENT CORP. (Houston, Texas)

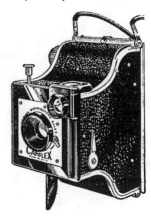

Camflex - 6x6cm aluminum box camera. $15-25.

Colonel - c1947. Aluminum 6x6cm box camera. $15-25.

NATIONAL PHOTOCOLOR CORP. (New York, NY)
One-Shot Color Camera - c1939. 9x12cm exposures on plates, sheet film or film packs. Goerz Dogmar f4.5/8¼" lens. Compound shutter 1-100, T,B. Single extension bellows. $350-500. *(illustrated top of next page)*

- 5x7" size - c1939. Similar to above, except for size. $350-500.

NATIONAL SILVER CO.
National Miniature - Black plastic minicam for half-frame 127. $3-7.

National Photocolor One-Shot Color Camera

NEGRETTI & ZAMBRA (London)
One-Lens Stereo Camera - c1865-70. Wet-plate sliding-box camera, 8x8cm. For stereo exposures, camera is mounted on top of its stoarge case and moved in its mount between exposures. Negretti & Zambra lens. Rare and desirable. Price negotiable. Estimate: $10,000+.

Stereo Camera - c1862. Mahogany sliding-box wet-plate camera. Brass-barrel Negretti & Zambra lenses. $3000-3500.

NEOCA CO.
Neoca I S - c1955. 35mm rangefinder. Neokor f3.5/45mm lens. Shutter 5-300, B. $30-40.

Neoca II S - c1957. 35mm rangefinder. Neokor f3.5/45mm lens. Rectus 1-300 shutter. $30-40.

Robin - Rangefinder 35. Neokar f2.8/45mm lens. Citizen MV shutter to 500. A number of different models, but all in the same price range. $20-30.

NETTEL KAMERAWERK (Sontheim-Heilbronn, Germany) *Formerly Sueddeutsches Camerawerk- Koerner & Mayer. Later became Contessa-Nettel in 1919 and Zeiss-Ikon in 1926.*

Argus - c1911. Monocular-styled camera, the precursor to the Contessa-Nettel Ergo. Right angle finder in monocular eyepiece. An unusual disguised camera, less common than the later Contessa and Zeiss models. British catalogs called it the "Intimo". $850-1250.

Deckrullo - c1908. A series of strut-folding

focal plane "klapp" cameras for glass plates. Focal plane shutter ½-2800.
- **9x12cm size** - Zeiss Tessar f6.3/135mm or Dogmar f4.5/150mm. $100-150.
- **13x18cm size** - Zeiss Anastigmat f8/210mm lens. $100-150.
- **18x24cm size** - Xenar f4.5/210mm. FP shutter. $150-200.

Folding plate camera, 9x12cm - Double extension bellows. Tessar f6.3/135mm lens. Dial Compur 1-250. $40-60.

Folding plate camera, 5x7" - Zeiss Anastigmat f8/210mm. $75-125.

Sonnet - c1913. 10x15cm folding plate camera. Single extension. Tessar f6.3/165mm, Compur 1-200. $60-90.

Sonnet (Tropical model) - 4.5x6cm. Tessar f4.5/75mm. Compound shutter 1-300. Teakwood with light brown bellows. $400-600.
- **6x9cm size** - Tessar f4.5/120mm in Compound shutter. $200-400.

NEUMANN (Felix Neumann, Vienna, Austria)
Magazine camera - c1895. Wood box for 12 plates 9x12cm. Leather changing bag, meniscus lens. $175-225.

NEUMANN & HEILEMANN (Japan)
Condor - Folding 120 rollfilm camera, half-frame. $35-50.

NEW HIT - 16mm subminiature made in Occupied Japan. $30-45.

NEW IDEAS MFG. CO. (New York)
Manufacturing branch of Herbert & Huesgen.

Magazine camera - c1898. Polished wood box detective camera. String-set shutter. $250-375.

Tourist Multiple - c1913. One of the earliest cameras to use 35mm motion picture film for still pictures, and the first to be commercially produced. Vertically styled body, leather covered. Tessar f3.5, Goerz Hypar f3.5, or Steinheil Triplar f2.5 lens, guillotine shutter. Film capacity of about 50 feet for 750 exposures 18x24mm. The outbreak of WWI slowed the tourist

f9/220mm lens. $225-325.

market for which this camera was intended, and probably only about 1000 were ever made. $1500-2200.

NEW TAIWAN PHOTOGRAPHIC CORP.
Yumeka 35-R5 - c1983. A poor quality transistor radio built into a poor quality 35mm camera. New in box: $15-25.

NEW YORK FERROTYPE CO.
Tintype camera - c1906. Professional model with three-section plateholder for postcards, 1½x2½" tintypes, and "button" tintypes. Two-speed Wollensak shutter. With tank and black sleeve. $150-200.

NEWMAN & GUARDIA (London)

Folding Reflex - c1921. A single lens reflex which takes 6.5x9cm plates. Ross Xpress f2.9 or f4.5 lens. Folds to compact size. $200-250.

New Ideal Sibyl - c1913. 6x9cm and 9x12cm plate sizes. f4.5/135mm Tessar. N&G shutter. $100-200.

New Special Sibyl - For 6x9cm exposures on 120 rollfilm. Ross Xpress f4.5/112mm. N&G Special shutter. $200-260.

Baby Sibyl - 4x6cm. c1913. Tessar or Ross Xpress f4.5/75mm. N&G shutter 2-200. $250-425.

Deluxe - c1896. Box-style camera with bellows extension. Zeiss Protar

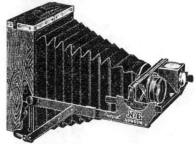

Nydia - c1900. Tapered bellows, folding

plate camera. Unusual design for folding. Bellows detach from lensboard, which then swings to the end of the body. 9x12cm and 10x13cm sizes. Wray Rapid Rectilinear or Ross f8 or 6.3 lens. Guillotine shutter 2-100. $400-500.

Newman & Guardia Trellis

Sibyl Excelsior

Sibyl - c1907-1920's. Folding-bed rollfilm or plate cameras, 6.5x9cm and 6.5x11cm sizes, including models Excelsior and Vitesse. Tessar f6.3/120mm or Ross f3.5 or 4.5 lens. N&G Special shutter. $175-225.

Sibyl Deluxe - 9x12cm. Double extension bellows. Zeiss Protar f6.3/122mm. N&G shutter. 2-100. $250-300.

Sibyl Stereo - 6x13cm filmpack camera. Trellis struts like other Sibyl cameras. Zeiss Tessar f4.5/120mm lens. Shutter 2-100. $1000-1400.

Trellis - c1930. Folding-bed plate camera in ¼ and ½-plate sizes, with typical N&G struts. Protar lens, N&G shutter. $250-350. *(ilustrated top of next column)*

Twin Lens Pattern - c1895. 9x12cm, box-TLR. Viewed through a chimney-like extension in the viewing hood. $300-400.

Universal Special Pattern B - Box magazine camera for 3¼x4¼" plates. Internal bellows allow front of box to slide out for copy work or close-ups. Zeiss f6.3 lens. N&G pneumatic shutter 2-100. $150-200.

NEWTON PHOTO PRODUCTS

Newton New Vue - c1947. All-metal bi-rail view. Gray enamel, nickel trim. Rotating back. Rapid front focus, micro focus at rear. With appropriate lens and shutter. $150-250.

NIAGARA CAMERA CO. (Buffalo, NY)

Niagara #2 - Box camera for 3½x3½" plates in double plateholders which load through hinged door on top. $25-35.

NICCA CAMERA WORKS (Japan)

Production began with two models of the Nippon camera in 1942, with and without rangefinder. The Nicca Original produced in 1948, is essentially identical to the Nippon except for top plate engraving and Nikkor rather than Kol Xebec lens. The Original was followed by the Type 3, IIIA, IIIB, IIIS, IIIL, 3S, 3F, 4, 5, and 33. Nicca also made cameras for Sears under the "Tower" name. Flash sync, lever wind, hinged backs and projected frame lines were added over the course of the production. The company was absorbed by Yashica in 1958 and the final two Nicca models were the Yashica YE (a Leica IIIc copy) and YF (a Leica M2 copy).
Nippon - $700-800.
Nicca Original - $400-500.
Other knob wind models - $100-150.
Lever wind models - $110-175.

NICHIRYO INT. (Japan)

Nicnon Binocular Camera - c1968-78.

Binocular camera for half-frame on 35mm. Nicnon f3.5/165mm. 3-speed shutter, 60-250. Viewing is done as with regular binoculars. A beam-splitting device in the right side enables the viewed object to be photographed. Motorized film transport. This camera was later distributed by Ricoh under the name "Teleca 35". $225-275.

NIELL & SIMONS (Cologne)
Lopa - Same as the Griffin Pocket Cyko. See Griffin (page 194).

NIHOH SEIKI (Japan)
Nescon 35 - c1950. 35mm viewfinder camera. Nescor f3.5/40mm. Shutter 25-200. $15-25.

NIHON SHOKAI (Tokyo)
Walz Automat - c1957. 4x4cm TLR. Zunow f2.8/60mm. Copal shutter 1-500, B. $100-150.

Walz Envoy 35 - Rangefinder 35. Kominar f1.9/48mm. Copal SLV shutter, 1-500, MFX sync. ST. Single stroke advance. $15-25.

Walz-wide - 35mm. Walzer f2.8/35mm lens. Copal shutter to 300. $30-40.

Walzflex - c1950's. 6x6cm TLR for 120 film. f3.5/75mm Kominar lens in Copal shutter. $20-30.

NIKO - Plastic body. 4x4cm on 127 film. $8-12.

NIKOH CO. LTD. (Japan)
Minimax-lite - c1981. Subminiature 8x11mm camera with built-in butane lighter. $50-60.

NIPPON KOGAKU K.K. (Tokyo) *Nippon Kogaku K.K. was formed in 1918 by the merger of some smaller optical firms. During the pre-war years, they made a large variety of optical goods for both the military and scientific communities. These included microscopes, telescopes, transits, surveying equipment, binoculars, periscopes, aerial lenses, sextants, microtesters and other related equipment. Because of the types of items produced, they were virtually unknown to the general public and to the world outside of Japan. With the advent of WWII, they were chosen to be the primary supplier of optical ordnance for the Japanese military establishment and grew to over twenty factories and 23,000 employees. Most of the optical equipment used by the Japanese Army, Air Force and Navy was produced by Nippon Kogaku. After the end of the war they were reorganized for civilian production only and were reduced to just one factory and 1400 employees. They immediately began to produce some of the fine optical* *equipment they made before the war for the scientific and industrial fields, but had yet to produce any cameras for general use. Before the war they had begun to make photographic lenses, including those for the famous Hansa Canon, and actually made all of Canon's lenses up to 1947. They also produced their lenses in a Leica-type screw mount as well as the early Canon bayonet.*

Sometime in 1945 or 1946, they decided that they should get into the camera field in an attempt to expand their product line. Since they were making lenses for 35mm cameras, it was a logical step to make a camera to use these same lenses. By September of 1946, they had completed the design of what was to become their first camera and decided on the name NIKON, from NIppon KOgaku. They studied the strong points of the two leading 35mm cameras of the day, the Contax and Leica, and combined many of the best features of both in the new Nikon design.

The majority of the information and photographs in the Nikon section are the work of Mr. Robert Rotoloni, a prominent collector and avid user of Nikon cameras. His interest in the field led him to write and publish a book entitled "The Nikon - An Illustrated History of the Nikon Rangefinder Series", C1981. Although his first book is out of print, Mr. Rotoloni has written a new edition entitled "Nikon Rangefinder Camera" published in 1983 by Hove Foto Books in England. In the U.S.A., autographed copies are available directly from the author at the address below. Since Mr. Rotoloni is also a respected dealer in collectible Nikon cameras, readers are invited to contact him with regard to buying or selling Nikons as well as exchanging information on the subject. As a courtesy, please include a stamped self-addressed envelope with queries. He may be reached at: P.O. Box 3213; Munster, IN 46321 USA. Tel. 312-895-5319.

Our second Nikon consultant is Dr. Burton Rubin, a well-known collector of Nikon and 35mm cameras. Dr. Rubin writes a monthly column, "The Collectible 35" for Photographic News. You may write to him at 4580 Broadway, New York, NY 10040.

Nikon I - 1948. Focal plane shutter to 500. Bayonet lens mount which continued to be used for later models. Unusual image size of 24x32mm. Despite printed information to the contrary, the exposure counter is NOT numbered past 40 in any case. Made for a little over one year, with a total production of about 750 cameras. Originally supplied with Nikkor 50mm f3.5 or f2.0 lens. Serial numbers 609-1 to 609-758, of which the first 20 or 21 were pre-production prototypes. Rare. Price negotiable. Estimate: $3000+.

Nikon M - August 1949 - December 1951. Total production of about 3,200 cameras. The 24x34mm format is a compromise between the 24x32 of the Nikon I and the standard 24x36. It is the only Nikon rangefinder camera to be identified on the camera. The letter "M" precedes the serial number on the top plate. Current value with normal f2.0 or f1.4 lens: 1949 type (no synch) $650-900. 1950 type (with synch) $400-600. *Note: Late M's with flash sync are considered by the factory to be S's, even though they have the M serial number.*

Nikon S - 1951-54. The first Nikon to be officially imported into the USA. Identical to the later Nikon M with flash sync (which the factory already called "S"). The only difference is that the serial number no longer has the "M" prefix (#6094000- on). 24x34mm format. Replaced in December 1954 by the S2. Quite common, and often seen advertised above and below this normal range. With f2 or f1.4 lens: $90-140.

Nikon S2 - Dec.1954-early 1958. New features include rapid wind lever, shutter to 1000, crank rewind, and a larger viewfinder window permitting 1:1 viewing. The top plate steps up over the new larger viewfinder, but the accessory shoe remains on the lower level, unlike the later S3. Over 56,000 produced, which is more than any other Nikon rangefinder camera. It was the first to have the 24x36mm format, be available in black, and the first to take a motor drive accessory. Current prices include f2.0 or f1.4 lens. Chrome: $140-190. Chrome with black dials: $175-230. Black: $500-750. *Note: Chrome model*

Black Nikon S2

Chrome Nikon S2

is very common and often seen advertised above and below the normal range.

Chrome Nikon SP

Black Nikon SP, with motor drive

Nikon SP - Sept.1957-at least 1964. The most famous and significant Nikon rangefinder camera, again showing innovation in camera design. It offered a removable back which could be replaced with a motor-drive back. Universal finder for six focal length lenses 28-135mm. Approximately 23,000 produced. The popular motor-drive back led the way for Nikon's dominance of motor-driven photography in the following two decades. Easily recognized by the wide viewfinder window which extends over the lens. The "Nikon" logo, no longer fitting above the lens, was moved off center below the shutter release. Prices include f2 or f1.4 lens. Chrome: $350-500. Black: $500-800. Add $400-500 for motor drive. *Note Chrome model is very common and often seen advertised above and below the normal range.*

Nikon S3 - Introduced in 1958, this popular version of the SP could also be motorized. At least 14,000 were made during its production run which continued at least until 1960. Styled similar to the SP, but with a rectangular viewfinder window, and the Nikon logo again centered over the lens. Two major features distinguish it from the earlier S2: The viewfinder window is larger on the S3. The top plate steps up in the center (accessory shoe is on the high side). Prices with f2 or f1.4 lens. Chrome: $275-400. Black: $500-800. Black "Olympic" with "Olympic" lens: $600-900.

Nikon S4 - Announced in 1959, this simplified version of the S3 was never imported into the USA, so they are seen less frequently in the United States than in Japan. At least 5,900 were made, all in chrome finish. With f2 or f1.4 lens: $500-700.

Nikon S3M - 1960. A modified S3 for half-frames, permitting 72 exposures per load. It was Nikon's first half-frame camera, and was made in black or chrome. Only 195 were reportedly made, although more may exist. Most were motorized. With f2 or f1.4 lens. Chrome: $3000-4000. Black: $3500-4500. Motor drive for S3M: $1500.

NIKON RANGEFINDER LENSES *All are Nikkor lenses in bayonet mount.*
- 21mm f4 black only, with finder: $500+.
- 25mm f4 chrome, with finder: $300+.
- 25mm f4 black, with finder: $350+.
- 28mm f3.5 chrome Type 1 or 2: $110-175.
- 28mm f3.5 black: $120-180.
- 35mm f3.5 MIOJ: $100-150.
- 35mm f3.5 chrome Type 1 or 2: $55-70.
- 35mm f3.5 black: $70-95.
- 35mm f3.5 Stereo Nikkor: Outfit with lens, prism attachment, UV filter, shade, and finder in leather case. Very rare. $2500-3500.
- 35mm f2.5 chrome: $50-75.
- 35mm f2.5 black Type 1: $75-100.
- 35mm f2.5 black Type 2 (An f2.5 lens, but in f1.8-type barrel. Not easily found): $125-175.
- 35mm f1.8 all black: $300-400.
- 35mm f1.8 black and chrome: $125-170.
- 50mm f3.5 Micro Nikkor: $300-400.
- 50mm f3.5 collapsible: Looks very much like the Leitz Elmar, but in Nikon mount. Sold only on Nikon I. $400-500.
- 50mm f2.0 collapsible: $150-250.
- 50mm f2.0 chrome: $35-55.
- 50mm f2.0 black: $45-65.
- 50mm f2.0 all black: $150-250.
- 50mm f1.5: $200-275.
- 50mm f1.4 chrome: $40-60.
- 50mm f1.4 aluminum: $200-275.
- 50mm f1.4 black and chrome: $50-65.
- 50mm f1.4 all black (early): $200-250.
- 50mm f1.4 Olympic: $200-250.
- 50mm f1.1 Internal bayonet: $300-375.
- 50mm f1.1 External bayonet: $325-375.
- 85mm f1.5: $250-375.
- 85mm f2 chrome: $60-80.
- 85mm f2 black: $90-130.
- 105mm f4: $125-175.
- 105mm f2.5: $70-110.
- 135mm f4 Short mount for bellows: $125-175.
- 135mm f4 Serial #611x: $250-275.
- 135mm f3.5 chrome: $55-70.
- 135mm f3.5 black: $60-80.
- 180mm f2.5: $250-350.
- 250mm f4 manual: $200-250.
- 250mm f4 preset: $150-200.
- 350mm f4.5: $250-375.
- 500mm f5: $350-450.
- 1000mm f6.3: $1000-2000.

NIKON RANGEFINDER ACCESSORIES

Finders
- Chrome optical; 35, 85, 105, 135mm: $20-35.
- 21mm optical: $75-100.
- 25mm optical: $50.
- 28mm optical: $35-50.
- 35mm mini for S2: $100.
- Chrome 24X32 Variframe: $500.
- Chrome MIOJ Variframe: $100-150.
- Chrome Variframe: $50-75.
- Black Variframe, with shoe: $150-175.
- Black Variframe, no shoe: $200.
- 28mm adapter for black Variframe: $250.
- Varifocal: $50.
- 28mm adapter for Varifocal: $100.
- Bright line; 35, 85, 105, 135mm: $60.
- Bright line 50mm: $200.
- Bright line, stereo: $300.
- Folding Sports finder: $150.

Reflex Housings
- Early type, copy of Leica PLOOT: $350.
- Second type, 45 degree: $250-300.
- Second type, 90 degree: $500.

Flash Equipment
- BCB: $40.
- BCB II: $30.
- BCB-3: $20.
- BC 4, BC 5, BC 6: $10.

Closeup Attachments
- For S with f2: $50.
- For S with f1.4: $65.
- For S2, either lens: $50.
- For SP, either lens: $50.

Copy Stands
- Model S: $250.
- Model SA: $225.
- Model P: $350.
- Model PA: $325.

Motor Drives:
- Black: $400.
- Chrome: $500.
- Chrome S 72 for S3M: $1500.

NISHIDA KOGAKU (Japan)
Wester Autorol - c1956. Folding bed camera for 6x6cm on 120 film. Wescon f3.5/75mm in NKK shutter 1-400, B. $25-35.

NITTO SEIKO (Japan)
Elega-35 - c1950's. Leica-styled 35mm camera. Eleger f3.5 screw-mount lens (not interchangeable with the Leica lenses). Rotary shutter. $250-350.

NOMAR No. 1 - Metal box for 127 film. Film spools behind plane of focus. Black or green enameled. $20-30. *(illustrated top of next page)*

NOMAR No. 1

NORISAN APPARATEBAU GmbH (Nuernberg, Germany)

Afex - Small bakelite camera for 25x25mm on standard 828 film. Similar to the Hacon and Nori, but with metal top and bottom plates. $35-45.

Hacon - c1935. Small bakelite camera for 25x25mm on rollfilm. $35-45.

Nori - c1935. Black bakelite camera for

25x25mm exposures on 35mm wide rollfilm. $35-50.

NORRIS - 120 folding camera. f2.9/75mm Cassar lens in Compur shutter. $25-35.

NORTH AMERICAN MFG. CO.

Namco Multi-Flex - Plastic twin-lens novelty camera for 16 exposures on 127. Similar to "Clix-O-Flex". $5-10.

NORTHERN PHOTO SUPPLY CO.
Liberty View - 8x10" view. $100-150.

NORTON LABORATORIES *In 1933, Universal Camera Corp. had Norton Labs design a camera. After a falling out between the two companies, Norton continued with the "abandoned" joint project, while Universal set about modifying and producing their own version, the Univex A. See Universal Camera Corp. for related models, including the Norton-Univex.*

Norton - c1934. Cheap black plastic camera for six exposures 1⅛x1½" on No. 00 rollfilm on special film spools. The end of the film spool extends outside the camera body and functions as a winding knob. Stamped metal viewfinder on back of body. $20-25.

Okam

NOVA - c1938. 3x4cm on 35mm wide rollfilm. Front extends via telescoping boxes. Special Anastigmat f4.5 lens. Shutter 25-100. $225-275.

NYMCO FOLDING CAMERA - c1938. Low-cost Japanese folding "Yen" camera for 3x5cm cut film in paper holders. Leatherette covered. Simple lens, single-speed shutter. $25-35.

OBERGASSNER (Munich)
Oga - 35mm viewfinder. Built-in meter. f2.8/45 lens. $10-15.

OEHLER (B.J. Oehler, Wetzlar, Germany)

Infra - c1951. Plastic 35mm with metal top and bottom. Extinction meter incorporated in top housing. Punktar f2.8/35mm lens in Prontor 25-200 shutter. 24x24mm. $25-45.

OKAKA KOGAKU (abbreviated OKAKO), Japan
Gemmy - c1950. Pistol-shaped subminiature camera for 10x14mm exposures on 16mm film in special cassettes. Trigger advances film. Fixed focus f4.5/35mm lens. Three-speed shutter, 25,50,100. Current estimate: $500-750.

Kolt - 13x13mm subminiature from Occupied Japan. Kolt Anastigmat f4.5. Iris diaphragm. Shutter, B, 25,50,100. $145-165.

OKAM - Czechoslovakia. c1935. Box camera for 4.5x6cm plates. Meyer f6/105mm lens in Patent 2 disc shutter 5-1000. Rare. Known sales range from $200-500. *(illustrated top of previous column)*

OLBIA
Clartex 6/6 - Bakelite camera for 6x6cm on 620 film. $15-25.

OLYMPIC CAMERA WORKS (Japan)

Olympic - Bakelite half-frame 127. f6.3/50mm helical focus lens. $65-95.

New Olympic - c1938. Bakelite rollfilm camera for 4x4cm on 127. Ukas f4.5/50mm lens. Shutter 25-150, T,B. $40-60.

Semi-Olympic - c1937. 4.5x6cm on 120. Bakelite body. f4.5/75mm lens. Shutter 25-150, T,B. $40-60.

Super-Olympic - c1935. Bakelite 35mm. f4.5/50mm lens, shutter 25-150,T,B. $65-95.

Vest Olympic - c1938. Half-frame on 127 rollfilm. f4.5 Anastigmat. $40-60.

O.P.L. Foca

OLYMPUS KOGAKU (Japan)

Olympus 35 IV

Olympus 35 - c1957-59. Rangefinder 35mm. Several variations. Commonly found with f2.8/48mm Zuiko, shutter 1-500. $30-40.

Pen, original model - c1960-66. For 18x24mm half-frame exposures on 35mm film. Zuiko f3.5/28mm lens. 5-speed shutter 25-200. $30-45.

Pen D - c1963-65. Zuiko f1.9/32. $40-60.

Pen F - c1963-66. Single lens reflex. Zuiko f1.8/38mm. Common. $75-125.

Pen FT - c1967-72. With f1.8/38mm

normal lens. Black model: $150-175. Chrome model is very common: $100-150.

OMI (Ottico Meccanica Italiana, Rome)

Sunshine - Small three-color camera/ projector. A few years ago, these sold for about $3000, since only a few were known to exist. Since that time, more have surfaced and we have seen them offered for as low as $500 in late 1984.

O.P.L.-FOCA (Optique et Precision de Levallois S.A., France)

Foca - c1955. 35mm Leica copies. Four models with 0, 1, 2, or 3 stars. Optar f3.5 or f2.8/50mm lens. FP shutter 1-1000. $80-110. *(illustrated top of previous column)*

Focaflex - c1960. Unusually styled 35mm SLR. By using a mirror instead of a prism, the top housing does not have the familiar SLR bulge. Styling is very much like the rangefinder cameras of the same era, but without any front windows on the top housing. Oplar Color f2.8/50mm lens. Leaf shutter B, 1-250. $60-95.

OPTIKOTECHNA (Prague, C.S.S.R.)

Spektaretta - c1939. Three-color camera, for 3 simultaneous filtered exposures on 35mm film. Body is styled like a movie camera. Spektar f2.9/70mm. Compur 1-250 shutter. $3000-3500.

Palmer & Longking Daguerreotype camera

ORION CAMERA, MODEL SIMPLICITE - Plastic novelty camera from Hong Kong. 3.5x4cm on 127. $4-8.

ORION WERK (Hannover)
Orion box camera - c1922. Meniscus f17 lens, simple shutter. For 6x9cm glass plates. $50-60.

Rio folding plate cameras - c1923. 6x9 and 9x12cm sizes. Leather covered wood body with metal bed. f4.5 or f6.3 Meyer Trioplan, Helioplan, or Orion Special Aplanat. Vario or Compur shutter. $25-40.

Orion Rio Tropical - c1920. Folding-bed 9x12cm plate camera. Teak and brass. Brown double extension bellows. Tessar or Xenar f4.5/150mm lens in Compur shutter 1-150. $400-600.

O.T.A.G. (Vienna, Austria)
Amourette - c1925. Early 35mm for 24x30mm exposures using special double cassettes. Trioplan f6.3 lens. Compur shutter 25, 50, 100. Down from earlier high prices to $350-400.

Lutin - Nearly identical to the better known Amourette. $350-400.

OTTEWILL (Thomas Ottewill, London)
Sliding-box camera - c1851. Mahogany wet-plate camera in 9x11" size. Camera is completely collapsible when front and back panels are removed. Ross or Petzval-type lens. $3000-3500.

OWLA KOKI (Japan)
Owla Stereo - c1958. For stereo pairs on 35mm film. Owla f3.5/35mm lenses. Shutter to 200. $125-175.

PALMER & LONGKING
Lewis-style Daguerreotype camera - c1855. half-plate. $5000-6000. *(illustrated top of previous column)*

PANAX - Plastic novelty camera of the "Diana" type. $1-5.

PANON CAMERA CO. LTD. (Japan)

Panon Wide Angle Camera - c1953. 140 degree panoramic camera. 2x4½" exposures on 120 rollfilm. Hexanon f2.8/50mm. Shutter 2, 50, 200. $650-825.

Widelux - Panoramic camera for 24x59mm images on standard 35mm film. Lux f2.8/26mm lens. Also sold under the Kalimar label. Various models. $400-500.

PAPIGNY (Paris)
Jumelle Stereo - c1890. For 8x8cm plates. Magazine back. Chevalier f6.5/100 lenses. Guillotine shutter. $175-225.

PARIS (Georges Paris)
GAP Box - Metal box camera. Black leatherette covering. 6x9cm. $12-18.

PARK (Henry Park, London)
Tailboard camera - c1890. Half-plate field camera. Rapid Rectilinear f8 lens. $200-225.

PARKER PEN CO. (Janesville, Wisc.)
Parker Camera - c1949. Plastic subminiature for 8 images, 13x16mm on a 147mm strip of unperforated 16mm film in a special sylindrical cassette. Parker Stellar f4.5/37mm lens in rotary shutter, 30-50. At least 100 cameras were used in a test marketing study by Parker and a Chicago advertising firm. At one time they were presumed to have been destroyed,

and only a few examples were known to exist. The collectible value reached a $750-1000 range. Within the last few years a significant number have surfaced and the price has again dropped to $400-500.

PDQ CAMERA CO. (Chicago)
PDQ Photo Button Camera - c1930. All-metal button tintype camera. Echo Anastigmat lens. $750-900.

Mandel Automatic PDQ, Model G - c1935. Large street camera for 6x9cm exposures rolls of direct positive paper. Built-in developing tank with tubes to change solutions. RR f6/135mm lens. $150-200.

PEACE - Very early "Hit" type subminiature. $150-225.

PEACE, PEACE BABY FLEX - Reflex style subminiatures for 14x14mm on rollfilm. $500-600.

PEARSALL (G. Frank E. Pearsall, Brooklyn, NY)
Compact - c1883. First camera to use the basic folding camera design, used by most American folding plate cameras into the 1920's. Full plate size. Only one known sale, in 1981, for $3200.

PECK (Samuel Peck & Co., New Haven, Conn.)
Ferrotype, 4-tube camera - c1865. Takes 1/9 plate tintypes. $800-1200.

Wet-plate camera - c1859. Full plate size. $900-1200.

PEERLESS MFG. CO.
Box camera - Early paperboard box camera for single 2½x2½" glass plates. $50-75.

PENROSE (A.W. Penrose & Co. Ltd.)
Studio camera - c1915. 19x19". $250-350.

PENTACON (VEB Pentacon, Dresden, Germany) *The Dresden factory of Zeiss Ikon was destroyed in 1945, and in 1948 the main offices were moved to the former Contessa factory in Stuttgart. Meanwhile, the Dresden operation became a public "Volks Eigener Betrieb", using the name "Zeiss Ikon VEB". This causes a certain confusion, especially with similar camera names and designs. After much dispute with the West German operation at Stuttgart, the Zeiss Ikon and Contax names were relinquished completely and the "VEB Pentacon" name became the banner for the combine which also included Balda and KW.*

Belmira - Unusual 35mm RF camera. Trioplan f2.8/50mm. Rapid wind lever at back. $50-65.

Consul - Rare name variation of the Pentacon (Contax-D). Identical except for the factory-engraved Consul name. $100-125.

Contax D - c1953. 35mm SLR. Standard PC sync on top. Zeiss Jena Biotar f2, or Hexar or Tessar f2.8. FP shutter to 1000. Four or five variations. Last version has auto diaphragm like Contax F, but is not marked F. Clean and working: $85-100.

Contax E - c1955. Like the Contax D, but with uncoupled selenium meter built onto prism. $150-250.

Contax F - c1957. Same as the Contax D, but with semi-automatic cocking diaphragm. Clean & working. $100-150.

Contax FB - Zeiss Biotar f2/58mm. Focal plane shutter 1-1000. $100-150

Contax FM - c1957. Zeiss Biotar f2/58mm. Automatic diaphragm. Interchangeable finder screen. $100-150

Contax "No name" - c1963. Rangefinder camera based on the Zeiss Contax II, redesigned to look more like the IIa or IIIa.

In reality, it is a Russian Kiev camera, made for the U.S.A. market without any name. With normal lens: $150-200.

Contax S - 1949-51. One of the first 35mm prism SLR's, along with the Rectaflex which appeared in 1948. Identifiable by sync connection in tripod socket. Biotar f2 lens. FP shutter 1-1000, B. Early models have no self-timer. Later models have a self-timer with lever below shutter release. Clean and working: $125-160.

Ercona, Ercona II - c1954. Folding bed rollfilm camera. 6x9cm or dual format 6x9cm and 6x6cm. Ludwig Meritar f4.5/105mm in Prontor-S 1-250, B. $25-35.

Hexacon - c1948. Same as the Contax D. Clean & working: $50-100.

Orix - c1958. Half-frame (18x24mm) on 35mm film. Precursor of the Penti. $25-50.

Pentacon - c1948-62. Same as the Contax D. 35mm SLR. Tessar f2.8/50mm lens. Focal plane shutter 1-1000. $55-95.

Pentacon "No-Name" - Like Pentacon, and has Pentacon tower emblem, but no name engraved. This should not be confused with the "No-Name Contax" which is a rangefinder camera. $200-300.

Pentacon F - c1957-60. Meyer Primotar f3.5/50mm or Tessar f2.8/50mm. $75-100. *(illustrated top of next column)*

Pentacon F

Pentacon FB - c1959. Built-in exposure meter. Tessar f2.8/50 or Steinheil f1.9/55 lens. $100-150.

Pentacon FBM - c1957. Built-in exposure meter. F2 or f2.8. $100-150.

Pentacon FM - c1957. Built-in exposure meter. Tessar f2.8/50mm lens. $75-100.

Penti - c1959. 18x24mm on 35mm film. Meyer Triplan f3.5/50mm lens. Gold colored body with enamel in various colrs: blue-green, red, cream, etc. $25-50.

Pentina - c1963. 35mm leaf-shutter SLR. Tessar f2.8 in breach-lock mount. Similar to Praktina. Rarely in working order. Repairmen hate them according to one source. Normally $60-75; more if clean & working.

Taxona

Pentona, Pentona II - Low-priced basic 35mm viewfinder camera. Meyer f3.5/45mm lens. Bright frame finder. $25-50.

Prakti - Motor drive 35mm camera, but motor drive rarely working. $50-65.

Ritacon F - Name variant of the Pentacon F. Very rare with this name. $150-200.

Taxona - c1950. For 24x24mm exposures on 35mm film. Novenar or Tessar f3.5 lens. Tempor 1-300 shutter. (This is the DDR successor to the pre-war Zeiss Tenax, made from captured Tenax I parts.) $75-100. *(illustrated top of next column)*

Werra - c1955. 35mm. Models I-IV. Jena Tessar f2.8/50mm. Compur Rapid 1-500 shutter. Olive green or black leather. $40-60.

What's in a name?
Trademark usage and export/import regulations led to various names being used on the East-German Contax SLR cameras. The Contax S was the earliest model (c1949-51) and does not exist with other name variations, because it was out of production before the trademark and name changes began. It is recognizable by sync. in tripod socket. There are three or four versions. Generally the earliest are finished best.
The following chart compares the original "Contax" model with name variants.

CONTAX Model (VEB Zeiss-Ikon)	FEATURES	NAME VARIATIONS of PENTACON MODELS
Contax S	Sync. in tripod socket	NONE
Contax D	Standard PC sync. on top	Pentacon, Consul, Hexacon*, Astraflex*, "No name"*
Contax E	Meter built onto top of prism	None known.
Contax F	Auto diaphragm	Pentacon F, Ritacon F
Contax FB	Auto diaphragm plus meter	Pentacon FB
Contax FM	Auto diaphragm plus interchangeable finder screen	Pentacon FM
Contax FBM	Auto diaphragm, meter, RF	Pentacon FBM

The model letters are based on the camera's features. F=Automatic Diaphragm, B=Built-in meter, M=Split-image finder screen

*Note: Hexacon and Astraflex are "House brands". The original Pentacon name has been obliterated and the store name riveted or glued on. The "No name" version has the Pentacon Tower emblem, but no camera name engraved.

PERFECT CAMERA - c1910. Simple cardboard box camera for 6x9cm single plates. $75-125.

PERKA PRAZISIONS KAMERAWERK (Munich, Germany)

Perka - c1922. Folding-bed plate camera. Double extension bellows. Tessar f4.5/150mm lens. Compur 1-200 shutter. Construction allows tilting of back and lensboard (standard) for architectural photos. $150-175.

PERKEN, SON, & RAYMENT (London)
Folding camera - c1890. Mahogany with brass trim. Optimus lens. ½-plate size. $150-225.

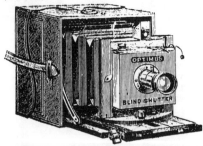

Optimus Camera DeLuxe - c1894. Black leather-covered folding camera. ¼-plate size. Opens like an early Folding Kodak. Extra Rapid Euryscope lens. Rack and pinion focus. Thornton-Pickard roller-blind shutter. Iris diaphragm. Estimate: $700-1000.

Optimus Detective - c1888. Mahogany bellows camera inside of a black leather covered box. ¼-plate size. External controls. Brass RR lens, waterhouse stops, rotary shutter. nearly identical to the Detective Camera of Watson & Sons. Estimate: $300-500. *(illustrated top of next column)*

Perken Optimus Detective

Studio camera - c1890's. Full-plate (6½x8½") size. $200-225.

Tailboard camera - c1886. ¼ and ½ plate sizes. Mahogany body with brass fittings. Ross lens, waterhouse stops. Maroon leather bellows. $250-300.

PETRI CAMERA CO. (Japan)

Penta - 1959-61. 35mm fixed pentaprism SLR. Orikkor f2/50mm lens. FP shutter ½-500, B. $30-50.

Petri 6x6 - c1948. Folding camera for 6x6cm exposures on 120 film. Ikonta copy. f3.5/75mm lens. Shutter 1-200, sync. Rangefinder. $25-35.

PFCA - Japanese novelty subminiature camera of the Hit type. Unusual streamlined top housing. Large flat advance knob. $10-15.

PHOBA A.G. (Basel, Switzerland)
Diva - 6x9cm folding-bed plate camera. Titar f4.5/105mm lens. Compur shutter. $25-35.

PHO-TAK CORP. (Chicago)
Foldex - c1950's. All metal folding camera for 620 film. Octvar or Steinheil lens. $5-10.

Macy 120, Marksman, Spectator Flash, Trailblazer 120, Traveler 120 - c1950's. Metal box camera for 6x9cm. $5-10.

Reflex I - c1953. TLR-styled box camera. $8-12.

PHOCIRA- Small box camera for 3x4cm on 127 film. Similar to Eho Baby Box. $50-75.

PHOTAVIT-WERK (Nuernberg, Germany) *Originally called Bolta-Werk.*
Photavit - A compact 35mm camera for 24x24mm exposures on standard 35mm film in special cartridges. $50-75. *(Complete description and photo are under the Bolta heading).*

Photina - c1953. 6x6cm TLR. Cassar f3.5/75mm lens in Prontor-SVS shutter. $35-50. *(illustrated top of next column)*

PHOTO DEVELOPMENTS LTD. (Birmingham, England)
Envoy Wide Angle - c1950. Wide angle camera for 6x9cm on 620 or 120 rollfilm, or cut film. f6.5/64mm Wide Angle lens. 82 degree angle of view. Agifold 1-150 shutter. $100-150.

PHOTO HALL (Paris)
Perfect Detective - c1910. Leather covered box camera for 9x12cm plates. Extra-Rapid Rectilinear lens. $150-200.

Photavit Photina

Perfect Jumelle - c1900. Single lens jumelle-style 6.5x9cm plate camera. Magazine back. Zeiss Protar f8/110mm. $150-200.

PHOTO-IT MFG. CO. (LaCrosse, WI)

The Photo-It - Round subminiature pinhole camera, 65mm dia. Stamped metal body. Cream enamel with brown lettering. Takes 8 exposures on a 12mm film strip wrapped on an octagonal drum. $1000-1500.

PHOTO-MAGASIN - c1895. French magazine camera for 6.5x9cm plates. Leather changing bag. String-set shutter. $400-475.

PHOTO MASTER - c1948. For 16 exposures 3x4cm on 127 film. Rollax 50mm lens, single speed rotary shutter. Brown or black bakelite or black thermoplastic body. $3-7.

PHOTO MASTER TWIN 620 - Simple cast-metal camera for 16 shots on 127 film. Identical to the Monarch 620, and probably made in the same factory in Chicago. $8-12.

PHOTO MATERIALS CO. (Rochester, NY)

Trokonet - c1893. Leather covered wooden magazine box camera. Holds 35 cutfilms or 12 glass plates, 4x5". Gundlach rectilinear lens, variable speed shutter. Inside the box, the lens is mounted on a lnesboard which is focused by rack and pinion. $400-600.

PHOTO-PORST (Hans Porst, Nuernberg) *Makers of Hapo cameras. Hapo = HAns POrst.*
Hapo 5, 10, 45 - c1930's. 6x9cm folding rollfilm cameras, made by Balda for Porst. Schneider Radionar f4.5/105mm or Trioplan f3.8/105mm lens. Compur or Compur Rapid shutter. $15-25.

Hapo 35 - c1955. Folding 35mm, made by Balda for Porst. Enna Haponar f2.9/50mm lens. Prontor-SVS 1-300 shutter. Coupled rangefinder. $15-25.

Hapo 36 - 35mm with non-coupled rangefinder. f2.8 Steinheil in Pronto shutter. $15-25.

Hapo 66, 66E - 6x6cm. Enna Haponar f3.3/75mm lens in Pronto sync. shutter, ½-200. $15-25.

PHOTO SEE CORP. (N.Y.C.)

Photo-See - An art-deco box camera and developing tank for photos in 5 minutes. An interesting, simple camera. According to a popular but untrue rumor, the viewfinders are on backwards and instructions were never printed. Actually the finders are as designed and instructions exist, though not often found with the cameras. These are usually found New in the box, with developing tank, and always with traces of rust from storage in a damp area. $15-25.

PHOTOLET - c1932. French subminature for rollfilm. Meniscus f8/31mm. Single speed rotary shutter. 2x2cm. Similar to the Ulca. $60-100.

PHOTOSCOPIC (Brussels, Belgium) - c1924. Unusually designed early 35mm camera for 50 exposures 24x24mm on 35mm film in special cassettes. O.I.P. Gand Labor f3.5/45mm lens. Pronto or Ibsor shutter. Metal body with black hammertone enamel. Tubular Galilean finder. Only 100 examples were made according to the inventor, Mr. A Van Remoortel, and several variations are known, including:
1. Pull-tab film advance like earlier Amourette camera. Full focusing.
2. Full focusing but with knob advance.
3. Fixed focus, knob advance. $400-500.

PIC - c1950. Unusual English disk-shaped plastic camera. 3x4cm exposures on rollfilm. Meniscus lens, rotary sector shutter. $100-200.

PICTURE MASTER - Stamped metal minicam for 16 exposures on 127 film. Body style identical to Scott-Atwater Photopal. $10-20.

PIGGOTT (John Piggot, London) Sliding-box wet-plate camera - c1960. Mahogany body. 8x8". Petzval-type lens. $1200-1800.

PIGNONS AG, (Ballaigues, Switzerland) *Pignons S.A. is a family business, founded in 1918 for making watches and clocks. Because of continual fluctuations in that business, the decision was made in 1933 to move into the photographic market by producing a camera which combined the advantages of reflex viewing and a rangefinder.*

The first of these prototypes appeared in 1939, and bore the name "Bolca", before the name "Alpa Reflex", which first was shown in 1944 at a public fair in Basel. The company remains in the camera business today, still producing exceptionally fine cameras which are virtually hand-made.

- Editor's note: The information in this section is primarily the work of Jim Stewart, whose particular interests revolve around Alpa, 35mm, and subminiature cameras. In addition to this section, he has made other important contributions to this guide.

Cameras are listed chronologically by year of introduction. Serial number ranges are approximate. Some prototypes fall into the 10000 and 25000 range. Display dummies are in the 29000 range. Discontinuance dates indicate the end of series production. Special orders of later bodies often occurred as long as parts were available. Almost any custom variation could be factory ordered.

There were many notable "firsts" by Alpa including the following:
1. First (and only) CRF in SLR (Model 7, 1952).
2. First with mirror tele lens (f6.3 Delft Fototel, 1950).
3. First mirror lock-up (1942, and with collapsible lens only 2" thick!).
4. First full auto diaphragm (1956).
5. First patented (1947) and produced (1963) TTL SLR.
6. First built-in multifocal finder (50, 90, 135mm; 1952).
7. First macro lenses as standard equipment (1959 to 11").
8. First Apochromat lenses (normal 1952, tele 1959).
9. Widest range of lenses (1.9mm to 5000mm) in the 1970's.

Bolca I - 1942-46 (#11000-13000). Waist-level SLR, eye-level VF and split-image CRF. Cloth FP shutter 1-1000. Berthiot f2.9/50mm in collapsible mount. Last run marked "Bolsey Model A". All are rare, especially the "Bolsey A". Bolca I: $350-500. Bolsey A: $400-600.

Bolca (Standard) - 1942-50. (#11000-13000). Similar to the Bolca I, but without reflex viewing. VF/CRF only. Sold in 1947 as "Alpa Standard". Very rare. $250-400.

Alpa (I) - 1947-52. (#13000-25000). Non-reflex type similar to the "Bolca" but with a modified lens bayonet. Angenieux f2.9/50mm in collapsible mount. $300-500. *A few have no slow speeds (25-1000 only): $600.*

Alpa Reflex (II) - 1947-52. (#13000-25000). Features of Alpa (I) above, but SLR & CRF. Full speed range. Also sold as "Bolsey Reflex". With f1.8/50mm rigid lens: $175-300. With Angenieux f2.9/50mm collapsible: $150-250.

Alpa Prisma Reflex (III) - 1949-52. (#13000-25000). WL reflex hood and finder replaced with 45 degree eye-level prism. (One of the earliest prism SLR's). Lenses as "Reflex" above, plus some late models have Xenon f2.0. $200-275.

Alpa 4 - 1952-60. (#30001-ca.39000). All new diecast magnesium alloy body. Integral magnifier hood for non-prismatic reflex viewing. Spektros f3.5/50mm collapsible lens. $250-300.

Alpa 5 - 1952-60. (#30001-ca.39000). As model 4, but integral 45 degree prism. Old Delft f2.8/50mm, rigid or collapsible mounts. $125-175.

Alpa 7 - 1952-59. (#30001-ca.39000). As model 5, but adds self-timer, superimposed image vertical base RF & multi-focal (35, 50, 135) built-in finder (first time done). Kern Switar f1.8. $150-175.

Alpa 6 - 1955-59. (#30001-ca.39000). As model 5, but adds split-wedge RF on ground glass, plus self-timer. $150-200.

Alpa 8 - 1958-59. (#37201-ca.39000). As model 7, plus prism RF of model 6. First auto lenses. Very short production run. $150-175.

Alpa 7s - 1958-59. (#37201-ca.39000). As model 7, but single frame (18x24mm) format. Rare. $350-400.

Alpa 4b - 1959-65. (#40701-48101). As model 4, but rapid return mirror and added advance lever. Normal auto lens mount redesigned and black finished. Old Delft f2.8/50mm, rigid mount only. $275-300.

Alpa 5b - 1959-65. (#39801-48101). As model 5, but rapid return mirror and added advance lever. Macro Kern Switar f1.8/50mm (focus to 8"). $125-175.

Alpa 6b - 1959-63. (#39601-48100). As model 6, but rapid return mirror and added advance lever. Macro Kern Switar f1.8/50mm (focus to 8"). $140-175.

Alpa 7b - 1959-65. (#40001-48101). As model 7, but rapid return mirror and added advance lever. Macro Kern Switar f1.8/50mm. $175-225.

Alpa 8b - 1959-65. (#40001-48101). As model 8, but rapid return mirror and added advance lever. Macro Kern Switar f1.8/50mm. $175-225.

Alpa 6c - 1960-69. (#42601-46500). Kern 45 degree prism replaced with standard pentaprism. Uncoupled selenium meter added. Macro Kern Switar f1.8/50mm. $145-175.

Alpa 9d - 1964-69. (#46501-52000). As model 6c, but top deck match-needle TTL CdS meter. Some gold or black finish with red or green covering. Macro Kern Switar f1.8/50mm. $235-275.

Alpa 9f - 1965-67. (#46201-46500). As model 9d, but without meter. Macro Kern Switar f1.8/50mm. Rare. $250-325.

Alpa 10d - 1968-72. (#58501-56400). New body with cross-coupled "zero center" match needle CdS meter. Normal lens reformulated. Kern Macro Switar f1.9/50mm. Gold or black with colored leather: $275-350. Chrome: $175-225.

Alpa 11e - 1970-72. (#57201-58300). As 10d, but lighted over-under exposure arrows, both off at correct exposure. Many all black, some gold or black with red or green covering. Kern Macro Switar f1.9/50mm. Black leather: $250-300. Colored leather: $300-375.

Alpa 10f - 1968-72. (#52501-56400). As 10d, but single frame 18x24mm format. Very low production. Rare. $300-350.

Alpa 10s - 1972. (#57101-?). As 10d, but no meter. Rare. $350-375.

Alpa 11el - 1972-74. (#58301-59500). As 11e, but both arrows lighted on correct exposure. Colored leather: $350-400. Black: $275-350.

Alpa 11si - 1976-80?(#60001-?). As 11el, but lighted arrows replaced by red, green, yellow diodes. Gold-plated: $2000. Majority of production black with black chrome top deck. $350-450.

Alpa 11fs - 1977-80?(#60001-?). As 11si, but single frame (18x24mm) format. Xenon f1.9/50mm. Rare. $375-475.

Alpa 11z - c1977-?(#61300-?). Special order single frame model. Similar to 11fs, but no meter, shutter 1/60 only, microprism screen only, no prism. Rangefinder. Very rare. $400-500.

PIONEER - Blue and black plastic camera of the "Diana" type. $1-5.

PIPON (Paris)

Magazine camera - c1900. Leather

covered wood box for 9x12cm plates. Aplanoscope f9 lens. $75-100.

Self-Worker - c1895. Jumelle camera for 9x12cm plates. Goerz Double Anastigmat 120mm lens. 6-speed guillotine shutter. $175-250.

PLANOVISTA SEEING CAMERA LTD. (London) *Imported a camera with their name on it, but it was actually a Bentzin camera. See Bentzin.*

PLASMAT GmbH

Roland - 1934-37. Telescoping front camera for 4.5x6cm exposures on 120 rollfilm. Coupled rangefinder. Designed by Dr. Winkler in association with Dr. Paul Rudolph, who designed the various Plasmat lenses. It was highly regarded for its 6-element Plasmat f2.7/70mm lens and sold new for $93-143. Rim-set Compur 1-250 shutter. After a rapid surge of speculative buying and high prices a few years ago, the Roland has rapidly fallen to its earlier range of $475-800.

PLASTICS DEVELOPMENT CORP. (Philadelphia, Penn.)
Snapshooter - c1970. Black plastic slip-on camera for 126 cartridges. $3-7.

PLAUBEL & CO. (Frankfurt, Germany)
Baby Makina - 1912-35. 4.5x6cm size. Anticomar f2.8/75mm. Compur shutter. $250-300.

Folding-bed plate cameras - 6x9 and 9x12cm sizes. Double extension bed and bellows. Anticomar or Heli-Orthar lens. Ibso or Compur shutter. $30-40.

Makina - 1920-33. Compact strut-folding 6.5x9cm sheet film camera. f2.9 Anticomar lens. Compur shutter. $160-250. *(illustrated top of next page)*

Plaubel Makina

Makina II - 1933-39. Anticomar f2.9/100mm lens converts to 73mm wide angle or 21cm telephoto by changing front elements. Compur shutter to 200. Coupled rangefinder. $115-150.

Makina IIS - 1936-49. Interchangeable Anticomar f2.9/50mm. All lens elements in front of the shutter, unlike the Makina II. Shutter 1-200. $150-190.

Makina IIa - 1946-1948. Fixed, non-changeable Anticomar f4.2/100mm or Xenar f4.5/105mm lens. Shutter to 1/400. Self-timer. $140-170.

Makina III - 1949-53. 6x9cm strut-folding camera. Anticomar f2.9/100mm lens. Rim-set Compur shutter 1-200. Coupled rangefinder. $150-200.

Makinette - c1931. Strut-folding camera for 3x4cm on 127 rollfilm. Anticomar f2.7/50mm in Compur 1-300. $800-800.

Roll-Op - c1935. Folding bed rollfilm camera, for 16 exposures 4.5x6cm on

120 film. Anticomar f2.8/75mm lens. Compur Rapid shutter 1-250. Coupled rangefinder. $110-175.

Stereo Makina, 6x13cm - 1926-41. Strut-folding stereo camera. Anticomar f2.9/90mm lenses in stereo Compur shutter 1-100. Black bellows. Black metal body, partly leather covered. $575-900.

Stereo Makina, 45x107mm - 1912-27. Similar, but f6/60mm Orthar or f3.9 Anticomar lens. $500-850.

Veriwide 100 - c1960. Wide angle camera for 6x9cm on 120 film. 100 degree angle of view. Super-Angulon f8/47mm in Synchro Compur 1-500 shutter, B, MXV sync. $450-625.

PLAVIC - c1920. Leather covered wood body. 6x9cm on rollfilm. Meniscus len, guillotine shutter. $20-30.

POCK (Hans Pock, Munich, Germany) Detective camera - c1888. Mahogany detective camera, concealed in a leather satchel. Gravity-operated guillotine shutter, 1-100. Magazine holds 15 plates 6x9cm. Voigtlander Euryskop fixed-focus lens. $2500-3000.

POCKET MAGDA - c1920. Compact French all-metal folding camera in 4.5x6cm and 6.5x9cm sizes. Meniscus lens, simple shutter. 4.5x6cm size: $400-500. 6.5x9cm size: $150-200.

POCKET PLATOS - French 6.5x9cm folding plate camera. Splendor f6.2/90mm lens in Vario shutter. $75-125.

POLAROID *Polaroid cameras, using the patented process of Dr. Land, were the first commercially successful instant picture cameras which were easy to use, and were not in need of bottles of chemicals, etc. The idea of in-camera development is not new; there are records of ideas for instant cameras from the first year of photography. In 1857, Bolles & Smith of Cooperstown, New York patented the first instant camera which actually went into production. Jules Bourdin of France invented a simple system which was successfully marketed as early as 1864. Many other attempts met with mediocre success, but Polaroid caught on and became a household word. Because of the success of the company, their cameras generally are quite common, and obviously none are very old. There is more supply than demand for most models in the present market. We are listing them in order by number, rather than chronologically. We have not listed cameras introduced after 1965, so this list is by no means a complete history of Polaroid.*

80 (Highlander) - 1954-1957. The first of the smaller size Polaroid cameras. Grey metal body. 100mm/f8.8 lens. Shutter 1/25-1/100 sec. Hot shoe. $5-10. *(illustrated top of next page)*

80A (Highlander) - 1957-1959. Like the 80, but with the shutter marked in the EV system. (Orig. price: $72.75) $5-10.

80B - 1959-1961. Further improvement of the 80A with new cutter bar and film release switch. $5-10.

Polaroid 80

95 - 1948-1953. The first of the Polaroid cameras, which took the market by storm. Heavy cast aluminum body, folding-bed style with brown leatherette covering. f11/135mm lens. Folding optical finder with sighting post on the shutter housing. Diehard collectors like to distinguish between the early models with the flexible spring sighting post and the later ones with a rigid post. $10-20.

95A - 1954-57. Replaced the Model 95. Essentially the same but sighting post was replaced with a wire frame finder, X-sync added, and shutter speeds increased to 1/12-1/100. 130mm/f8 lens. $10-20.

95B (Speedliner) - Like the 95A, but the shutter is marked in the EV (Exposure Value) system, rather than the traditional speeds. (Orig. price: $94.50) $10-20.

100 (rollfilm) - 1954-1957. (Not to be confused with the 1963 "Automatic 100" for pack film.) Industrial version of the 95A. Better roller bearings and heavy duty shutter. Black covering. $10-20.

100 ("Automatic 100") - 1963-1966. An innovative, fully automatic transistorized electronic shutter made the world stand up and take notice once again that the Polaroid Corporation was a leader in photographic technology. In addition to the marvelous new shutter, Polaroid introduced a new type of film in a flat, drop-in pack which simplified loading. Furthermore, the photographs developed outside the camera so that exposures could be made in more rapid succession. Three-element f8.8/114mm lens. Continuously variable speeds from 10 seconds to 1/1200. RF/viewfinder unit hinged for compactness. $10-15.

101, 102, 103, 104, 125, 135 - c1964-1967. Various low-priced pack cameras following after the Automatic 100. $5-10.

110 (Pathfinder) - 1952-1957. Wollensak Raptar f4.5/127mm lens and coupled rangefinder. Shutter 1-1/400 sec. $50-65.

110A (Pathfinder) - c1957-60. Improved version of the 110. Rodenstock Ysarex f4.7/127mm lens in Prontor SVS 1-1/300 shutter. Special lens cap with f/90 aperture added in 1959 for the new 3000 speed film. Charcoal covering. (Originally $169.50) $40-70.

110B - 1960-64. Like the 110A, but with single-window range/viewfinder. $40-65.

120 - 1961-1965. Made in Japan. Similar to the 110A, but with Yashica f4.7/127mm lens in Seikosha SLV shutter 1-1/500. Self-timer. Not as common in the U.S.A. as the other models, because it was made for foreign markets. $40-80.

150 - 1957-1960. Similar to the 95B with EV system, but also including CRF with focus knob below bed, parallax correction, and hot shoe. Charcoal grey covering. (Originally $110.) $7-15.

160 - 1962-65. Japanese-made version of the 150 for international markets. $7-15.

180 - 1965-1969. Professional model pack camera made in Japan. Tominon f4.5/114mm lens in Seiko shutter 1-1/500 with self-timer. Zeiss-Ikon range/viewfinder. Has retained its value as a usable professional camera. $175-220.

415 - Variation of the Swinger Model 20. $3-7.

700 - 1955-1957. Uncoupled rangefinder version of the 95A. $15-20.

800 - 1957-1962. All the features of the 150, but with carefully selected lens, electronically tested shutter, and permanently lubricated roller bearings. (Original price: $135 with flash, bounce bracket and 10 year guarantee.) $7-12.

850 - 1961-1963. Similar to the model 900, but with dual-eyepiece rangefinder & viewfinder. $8-12.

900 - 1960-1963. The first Polaroid with fully automatic electric-eye controlled shutter. Continuously variable shutter speeds (1/12-1/600) and apertures (f/8.8-f/82). $8-12.

Big Shot - 1971-73. Unusually designed pack-film camera for close-up portraits at a fixed distance of one meter. Since the lens is fixed focus, the rangefinder functions only to position the operator and subject at the correct distance. Built-in socket and diffuser for X-cubes. $5-10.

J-33 - 1961-1963. Newly styled electric-eye camera to replace the "80" series. Still using the 30 series double-roll films for 6x8cm pictures. $5-10.

J-66 - 1961-1963. Newly styled electric-eye camera, with simple f/19 lens. Tiny swing-out flash for AG-1 bulbs. $5-10.

Swinger Model 20 - 1965-1970 - White plastic camera for B&W photos on Type 20 roll film, the first roll film to develop outside the camera. If this is not the most common camera in the world, it certainly must be near the top of the list. Current value $5 per truckload, delivered.

Swinger Sentinel M15 - 1965-1970. Variation of the Swinger Model 20. Lacks built-in flash. $3-7.

SX-70 (Deluxe Model) - 1972-1977. The original SX-70 camera. Ingeniously designed folding SLR which ushered in a new era of instant photography. The miracle was watching the colored photo slowly appear in broad daylight after being automatically ejected from the camera. The technical and esthetic marvel was the compact machine which fit easily into a coat pocket. The basic folding design was not new. Perhaps one of Polaroid's engineers had seen the circa 1905 "Excentric" camera of R. Guenault, which is surprisingly similar. But Guenault would never have dreamed of an even more compact camera incorporating SLR focusing to 10½ inches, automatic exposure up to 14 seconds, and motorized print ejection, all powered by a disposable flat battery which came hidden in the film pack. This is a landmark camera, but quite common because it was so popular. $25-40.

POLYFOTO - c1933. Repeating-back camera, taking 48 ½x½" exposures on a 5x7" plate. Plate moves and exposure is made when a handle is cranked. $300-400.

PONTIAC (Paris)

Bakelite - Folding camera for 8 6x9cm exposures on 120 rollfilm. Bakelite body similar in style to the Gallus and Ebner cameras. Berthiot f4.5/105mm lens. Shutter 25-150. $20-40.

Lynx, Lynx II - Polished aluminum body. 16 exposures 3x4cm on 127 film. Berthiot Flor f2.8/50mm coated lens in Leica-style collapsible mount. Focal plane shutter. $40-60.

Super Lynx, I, II - c1950's. Made in Paris and Morocco. 35mm body has an aluminum finish, black enamel, or is leather covered. f2.8 or f3.5 Flor lens; Super Lynx has interchangeable lenses. Rarely seen with the fast f2.0 Salem Hexar lens. FP shutter. Some dealers really stetch the point by calling this a Leica copy. $150-200.

POPPY - Rare Japanese subminiature. Price negotiable. Estimate: $500-750.

POPULAR PHOTOGRAPH CO. (NY)
Nodark Tintype Camera - c1899. All wood box camera for 2½x3½" ferrotype plates. The camera has a capacity of 36 plate. With tank: $500-700. Less $100 if missing tank.

POTENZA - 110-cartridge camera shaped like a tire. New in box: $15-30.

POUVA (Karl Pouva, Freital, Germany)
Start - c1954. Telescoping camera for 6x6cm exposures on 120 rollfilm. $7-15.

PRECISION CAMERA INC.
(Minneapolis, MN)
Andante 100 - Large blue and gray plastic "school" camera. Twin lens reflex style. Uses bulk rolls of 35mm film. $50-70.

PREMIER INSTRUMENT CO. (NY)

Kardon - c1945. 35mm Leica IIIa copy. Made for the Signal Corps, and also for civilians. Ektar f2/47mm lens. Cloth focal plane shutter, 1 to 1000. CRF.

Back view of Kardon, Signal Corps model

Body: $175-225. With lens: $225-325.

PRESS VAN - c1953. Japanese strut folding rangefinder camera for 24x36mm on 35mm film, or 6x6cm on 120 film. Takumar f3.5/75mm in Seikosha Rapid shutter to 500, B,l. $250-350.

PRINCE - Japanese green and black bakelite subminiature. Scarce. $200-250.

PRINCESS MAY - c1900. Half-plate mahogany and brass field camera. Ross Anastigmat f8/7½" lens. $100-150.

PRINTEX PRODUCTS (Pasadena, CA)
Printex - c1946. Rigid-bodied, all-metal press camera. Telescoping lens mount rather than the bellows found on the popular Speed Graphics of its day. Made in 2¼x3¼" and 4x5" sizes. Uncommon. $75-125.

PRO CAMERA - Factory loaded disposable camera. 28x31mm on 35mm film. $12-18.

PROUD CHROME SIX III - c1952. Japanese Super Ikonta B copy. 6x6cm on 120. Coupled rangefinder. Congo f3.5/75mm in Proud Synchront 1-200 shutter, B. $75-100.

PUTNAM (E. Putnam, N.Y.)
Marvel - c1890. 5x8" horizontal folding view camera. Scovill Waterbury lens with rotating disc stops. $150-175.

PYNE (Manchester, England)
Stereoscopic Camera - c1860. Tailboard stereo, 8x17cm plates. Ross lenses. One sold at auction in 1979 for $4800.

Q.P. - (pronounced "Kewpie"). Japanese "Hit" type novelty camera for 16mm paper-backed rolls. $15-25.

Q.R.S.-DeVRY CORP. (Chicago)
Q.R.S. Kamra - c1928. Brick-shaped brown bakelite body. 40- 24x32mm exposures on 35mm film in special cassettes. Graf Anastigmat f7.7/40mm. Single speed shutter trips by counter-clockwise motion on winding crank. With crank intact: $75-100. As normally found with broken crank: $40-50.

RAACO - Box camera for 4.5x6cm. Cardboard construction. Meniscus lens. Segment shutter. $75-110.

RADIX - c1897. Box camera for 3¼x4¼" glass plates in standard double holders. Hinged door on side of camera to change and store plateholders. $25-40.

RAKSO - c1970's. Special purpose camera for close-up work. Body release. Single-speed flap shutter, exposing a self-erecting, single extension, telescoping front. Non-interchangeable front element. Built-in automatic flash. $10-12.

RALEIGH - 4x4cm novelty of the "Diana" type. $1-5.

RAY CAMERA CO. (Rochester, N.Y.)
Originally established in 1894 as Mutschler, Robertson & Co., the company began making "Ray" cameras in 1895. In 1898 the company moved to a new building and changed its name to "Ray Camera Co."In 1899, it became part of the new "Rochester Optical & Camera Co."
Box camera - For 3½x3½" glass plates. Rear section of top hinges up to insert holders. $30-40.

Ray No. 1, No. 4 - c1899. 4x5" wooden plate camera. Red bellows. Black leather covered. $40-60.

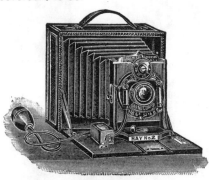

Ray No. 2 - 5x7" folding plate camera, similar construction to the No. 1. Dark mahogany interior, red bellows, double pneumatic shutter. $60-90.

Ray Jr. - c1897. for 2½x2½" plates. $40-60.

Telephoto Ray Model C - Folding bellows camera, 10x13cm. Wollensak Automatic shutter. $50-80.

RAYELLE - c1954. Side-loading metal box camera, 6x9cm on 120. Made in Italy. $5-10.

REAL CAMERA - Jpanese novelty subminiature of the Hit type. $10-15.

RECORD CAMERA - c1890. English mahogany twin-lens reflex style box camera. 3¼x4" plates. Fixed focus lens. T,I shutter. $800-1200.

RECTAFLEX (Italy)

Rectaflex Junior - c1952. 35mm SLR. f2.9/50mm Angenieux. 25-500 shutter. $100-150.

Rectaflex Rotor - c1952. 35mm SLR with 3-lens turret. With normal lens: $400-600. Wide angle, tele lenses, each $50-75. Add $50-75 for grip. Add $50-75 for gunstock.

Rectaflex Standard - 1948-56. One of the first prism SLR's, along with VEB Pentacon Contax S of early 1949. Schneider Xenon f2.0 or f2.8/50mm or Angenieux f1.8/50mm lens. Focal plane shutter 1-1000 (up to 1300 after 1952), sync. These standard (non-rotor) Rectaflex cameras are also designated Rectaflex 1000 and 1300 after their top shutter speed. Model 1000: $125-175. Model 1300: $100-150.

REDDING (H.J. Redding & Gyles, London, England)

Redding's Patent Luzo - c1889. Mahogany detective box camera. Brass fittings. 3x4" exposures on Eastman rollfilm. The first English rollfilm camera. f8 lens, sector shutter. Despite former high prices of 2500-3000, auction and sale prices from 1982-1985 have remained in the $650-1150 range.

REFLEX 66 - Post-WWII. Japanese copy of the Reflex Korelle. Anastigmat f3.5/75mm. FP shutter to 1000. $125-175.

REFLEX CAMERA CO. (Newark, NJ & Yonkers, NY) *(Originally located in Yonkers from about 1900-09, when they moved to Newark, NJ and took over the Borsum Camera Co.)*

Junior Reflex - c1930. Simple SLR box camera for 3¼x4¼" plates. Simple lens, 4-speed sector shutter coupled to mirror. $125-150.

Focal plane postcard camera - c1912. Vertically styled folding plate postcard camera. Focal plane shutter. Cooke Anastigmat or Ilex RR lens in plain mount. $140-160.

Reflex camera

Patent Reflex Hand camera - Early model leather covered 4x5" SLR box

camera. Internal bellows focus. Focal plane shutter. Red focusing hood. Fine finished wood interior. Without lens: $200-350.

Reflex camera - 4x5" slightly later model than the above listing. Leather covered wood box with tall viewing hood. Internal bellows focus. Euryplan Anastigmat 7" lens. $125-165. *(illustrated in previous column)*

5x7" Reflex - c1898. f16/210mm Anastigmat lens. $225-325.

REGAL FLASH MASTER - Black bakelite box camera wiht integral flash. Identical to Spartus Press Flash. $5-10.

REGAL MINIATURE - Plastic novelty camera for half-frame 828. $3-7.

REGENT - Japanese 14mm novelty camera. $10-15.

REICHENBACH, MOREY & WILL CO. (Rochester, N.Y.)
Alta D - 5x7" folding plate camera. $75-125.

REID & SIGRIST (Leicester, England)

Reid IA

Reid - c1953. Models I, IA, II, III. Leica copies. Collapsible Taylor Hobson f2/50mm lens. Focal plane shutter 1-1000, sync. $200-275.

RELIANCE - 4x4cm "Diana" type novelty camera. $1-5.

REPORTER MAX - c1960. Black plastic 6x6cm camera. Single-speed shutter. $10-15.

le REVE - c1908. French folding camera for 3¼x4¼" plates or special rollfilm back. Beckers f6.3 or Roussel f6.8/135mm Anastigmat lens. Unicum shutter. Red bellows. $150-200.

REVERE
Eyematic EE 127 - c1958. 127 film. Wollensak f2.8/58mm lens. $20-30.

Stereo 33 - Amaton, Enna Chromar S, or Wollensak f3.5/35mm. Shutter 2-200, MFX sync. Rangefinder. $95-125.

REX KAYSON - Japanese 35mm RF camera. f3.5/45mm lens. Compur 1-300 shutter. Looks like a small Leica M. $30-45.

REX MAGAZINE CAMERA CO. (Chicago)
Rex Magazine Camera - c1899. 4x5" format. Simple lens & shutter. Unusual plate changing mechanism. $150-200.

Rex Magazine Camera - 2x2" format. The baby brother of the above model. $200-250.

REYGONAUD (Paris)
Stand camera - c1870. Jamin Darlot lens. Brass trim. For 8x11cm plates. $400-550.

REYNOLDS & BRANSON
Field camera - c1890. Full or half plate size. Without lens: $75-125.

RICH-RAY TRADING CO.

Rich-Ray - Small bakelite camera for 24x24mm exposures on Bolta rollfilm.

Nearly identical to Start-35. Marked "Made in Occupied Japan" on the bottom; "Rich-Ray" on top. Simple fixed focus f5.6 lens with lever-operated f8 waterhouse stop. $15-25.

RICHARD (F.M. Richard)
Detective - c1895. Magazine box camera for 13x18cm plates. Rack and pinion focusing. $500-700.

RICHARD (Jules Richard, Paris)

Glyphoscope - c1905. 45x107mm stereo camera of simple construction. Black ebonite plastic or leather covered wood. Meniscus lens, guillotine shutter. Seen advertised at higher prices, but most confirmed sales are in the $25-50 range.

Homeos - c1914. The first stereo for 35mm film. 25 exposures on standard 35mm cine film. Zeiss Krauss Anastigmat f4.5/28mm. Guillotine shutter. Recent trends down from previous highs in the $2500-3500 range. $1300-2000. (Add $500-750 for viewer and printer.)

Homeoscope - c1900. Stereo cameras in 6x13 and 9x18cm sizes. $180-240.

Verascope, simple models - c1898. Fixed-focus lenses, single speed shutter.

All metal body. Basic camera: $65-85. Add $35-50 for magazine back. Add $100-150 for usable 127 or 120 film rollback.

Verascope, better models - With higher quality lenses/shutters. More common than the simple models. Basic camera: $75-100. Add $35-50 for magazine back. Add $100-150 for usable 120 or 127 film rollback.

Verascope F40 - c1950's. Stereo camera for 24x30mm pairs of singles. Berthiot f3.5/40mm lens. Guillotine shutter to 250. RF. Made by Richard in France but sold under the Busch name in the U.S.A. Generally considered to be one of the best stereo cameras, and not often found for sale. With printer and transposing viewer: $600. Camera and case: $300-400.

RICSOR - Rangefinder 35, similar to the Pax M2. Luna f2.8/45mm. $30-50.

RIDDELL (A. Riddell, Glasgow) Folding plate camera - c1880's. 9x12cm. Built-in roller-blind shutter. $150-200.

RIETZSCHEL (A. Heinrich Rietzschel GmbH Optische Fabrik, Munich, Germany) *Merged with Agfa in 1925, at which time the Rietzschel name was no longer used on cameras and the first Agfa cameras were produced.*

Clack - c1910. Folding bed camera for plates. 9x12cm or 10x15cm sizes. Red bellows, black leathered wood body, aluminum standard, nickel trim. f6.3 or f8 lens. $75-125.

Heli-Clack, horizontal type - c1910.

9x12cm or 10x15cm horizontal format folding plate cameras. Double extension bellows. Double Anastigmat f6.8 lens in Compound shutter. $50-80.

Kosmo-Clack Stereo - c1914. 45x107mm format. Double Anastigmat f6.3, Rietzschel f4.5/60mm lenses in Compur 1-250 shutter. Panoramic photos also possible. $125-150. A usable rollback would add $100-150 to this price.

Miniatur-Clack - c1920's. Small folding-bed camera for 4.5x6cm plates. Double extension bellows. Linear Anastigmat f4.5/165mm in Compound or Compur shutter. $100-150.

Reform-Clack - c1910-1920's. 6x9cm folding plate camera. Dialyt f6.8/105mm in Compound or Dial-set Compur 1-250. Double extension bellows. $30-40.

Universal Heli-Clack - Folding bed camera. Similar to the regular Heli-Clack, but with wide lensboard.
- Type I - Panoramic with single lens. 13x18cm size, with Linear Anastigmat f4.8/210mm lens: $100-125. 8x14cm size: $50-80. *(illustrated top of next page)*

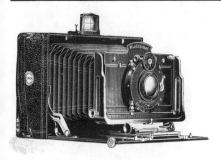

Universal Heli-Clack, Type I

Riken Golden Steky

- Type II - Stereo with two lenses in stereo shutter. 13x18cm size with Doppel Apotar f6.3/120mm stereo lenses: $350-450. 8x14cm size: $200-300.

Ricoh 16 - c1960. Subminiature for 10x14mm exposures on 16mm film. Rapid wind. Like the Golden Ricoh 16, but in chrome. Much less common. $100-125.

Ricoh 35 - c1955. Leica-style 35mm. f3.5, 2.8, 2 lens. $15-25.

Ricoh Six - Folding rollfilm camera. Orinar f3.5/80mm. Riken shutter. $35-50.

Ricoh Super 44 - c1959. 127 TLR. Riken f3.5/60mm. Shutter 1-400. $45-70.

- Type III - 3 lenses in Stereo-Panorama shutter. No sales data.

RIKEN OPTICAL (Japan)
Golden Ricoh 16 - c1955. Subminiature for 25 exposures 10x14mm on 16mm film. Interchangeable f3.5/25mm lens. Sync. shutter 50-200. Often found with case and presentation box for $100-125. Camera and normal lens only: $80-100.

Golden Steky - Subminiature for 10x14mm on 16mm film. Same as Golden Ricoh 16 except for name. Shutter 50-200. Fixed focus f3.5/25mm lens: $120-150. For $50 for f5.6/40mm telephoto. *(illustrated top of next column)*

Ricohflex

Ricoh Teleca 240 - c1970. Half-frame 35mm camera built into 7x50 binoculars. F3.5/165mm lens. Motorized film transport. Shutter 60-250. $225-275.

Ricohflex - c1953. Models (I), III, IV, V, VI, VII, VIIS. 6x6cm TLR. Ricoh Anastigmat f3.5 lens. $15-25. *(illustrated bottom of previous page)*

Ricohmatic 44 - c1959. Gray TLR, 4x4mm on 127. Built-in meter. Riken f3.5/80mm. Shutter 25-200, B. $40-60.

Ricolet - 1954. First Riken 35mm camera. No rangefinder. "RICOLET" on front of cast-metal finder housing. Viewfinder 35. Ricoh f3.5/45mm. Riken 25-50-100, B shutter. $20-30.

Super Ricohflex - TLR for 3 different film sizes: 6x6cm on 120, 4x4cm on 127, 24x36mm on 35mm. Ricoh Anastigmat f3.5/80mm. Riken shutter 10-300, B. $15-30.

Steky - c1949. Subminiature for 10x14mm on 16mm film. Stekinar

Robinson Luzo

f3.5/25mm Anastigmat lens. Shutter 25, 50, 100. $35-50.
Steky II, III, IIIa, IIIb - $30-45. *(Add $25 for tele lens.)*

RILEY RESEARCH (Santa Monica, CA)
Rilex Press - 2¼x3¼" press camera. Tessar f4.5 lens. Chrome and stainless. $100-150.

RILO - 6x9cm metal box camera, leatherette covering. $10-15.

RIVAL 35 - c1950. German folding 35mm.

Radionar or Ennagon f3.5/50mm in Prontor S shutter. $20-30.

RIVAL 120 - c1957. 6x9cm, black and chrome folding camera. $8-12.

ROBINSON (J. Robinson & Sons)
Luzo - c1889. Mahogany detective box camera. 6x6cm on plates or rollfilm. Aplanat f8/75mm. Rotary sector shutter. $650-1000. *(illustrated top of previous page)*

ROCAMCO PRODUCTS (Boonton, NJ)
Also known as Rochester Camera Co., New York City. Named for its president, Richmond Rochester.

Rocamco - c1936. Small metal box for 2.5x3cm on special 35mm film. $100-200.

Rocamco No. 3 Daylight Loading Rollfilm Camera - c1938. For 30x32mm on special rollfilm. Small bakelite camera. "A Rochester Product" molded on back. "No. 3 Daylight Loading Rollfilm Camera" designation is used on the original box. $25-40.

ROCHECHOVARD (Paris)
Le Multicolore - c1912. Magazine box camera for 9x12cm plates. Color filters could be moved into place, one at-a-time behind the lens for color separation plates. Rapid Rectilinear lens. Guillotine shutter. $800-1200.

ROCHESTER CAMERA MFG. CO.
ROCHESTER CAMERA & SUPPLY CO.
ROCHESTER OPTICAL COMPANY
ROCHESTER OPTICAL & CAMERA CO.
The Rochester OPTICAL Company was established in 1883 when W.F. Carlton took over the business of Wm. H. Walker & Co. The Rochester CAMERA Mfg. Co. was founded in 1891 by H.B. Carlton, brother of W.F. Thus there existed in Rochester, N.Y. two comtemporary companies, with similar names, and owned by brothers. Their major camera lines even had similar names. The Rochester CAMERA Mfg. Co. made POCO cameras, while the original Rochester OPTICAL Company began the PREMO camera line in 1893. To further complicate the name game, the Rochester Camera Mfg. Co. changed its name in 1895 to "Rochester Camera Co.", and in 1897 to "Rochester Camera & Supply Co.". In 1899, the two "Rochester" companies merged with the Monroe Camera Co, the Ray Camera Co. (formerly Mutschler & Robertson Co.), and the Western Camera Mfg. Co. of Chicago (mfr. of Cyclone cameras), to form the new "Rochester Optical and Camera Company". The new company retained the original products: Cyclone, Poco, Premo, and Ray. In 1903, George Eastman purchased the company and shortened the name again to "Rochester Optical Co.". In 1907 it became "Rochester Optical Division, E.K.C." and finally "Rochester Optical Department" in 1917. While the many name changes can seem confusing at first, they do help to date particular examples of cameras:
Rochester Camera Mfg. Co.: 1891-1895
Rochester Camera Co.: 1895-1897
Rochester Camera & Supply Co.: 1897-1899
Rochester Optical Co.: 1883-1899, (& 1903-1907, owned by Eastman)
Rochester Optical & Camera Co.: 1899-1903
Rochester Optical Div., EKC:1907-1917

ROCHESTER CAMERA MFG. CO.
Favorite - 8x10". c1890. Emile No. 5 lens with waterhouse stops. $125-175.

Folding Rochester - c1892. The first folding plate camera that they made. 4x5" and 5x7" sizes. Made only briefly. Seldom seen. $295-395.

Pocket Poco

Poco Cameras - Introduced in 1893. Listed here by size:
- **3¼x4¼", Pocket Poco** - Red bellows, single pneumatic shutter. $35-50.
(illustrated bottom of previous page)

- **4x5", Folding-bed plate cameras** - Models 1-7, A, B, C, including Cycle Pocos. Leather covered wood body and bed. Nicely finished wood interior. Often with B&L RR lens and Unicum shutter. $40-60.

- **5x7", Folding-bed plate cameras** - Models 1-5, including Cycle Pocos. Black leather covered wood body. Polished interior. Red bellows. RR lens. Unicum shutter. $55-85.

- **8x10" Poco** - Similar, but larger. Double extension bellows. B&L Symmetrical lens. $65-100.

Gem Poco - 4x5" box for plates. Focuses by sliding lever at left front. Shutter tensioned by brass knob on face. $35-50.

Gem Poco, folding - c1895. Very compact folding camera for 4x5" plates in standard holders. Red bellows. $75-100.

King Poco - c1899. 5x7" folding view, advertised as "Compact, elegant in design, and equipped with every known appliance. Especially adapted for those desiring the most perfect camera made." This was the top of the line. Not seen often. $125-180.

Telephoto Poco, Telephoto Cycle Poco:
- **4x5"** - c1891. Folding plate camera.

Triple extension red leather bellows. B&L lens in Auto shutter. Storage in back of camera for extra plateholders. $75-100.

- **5x7", 6½x8½"** - c1902. Folding plate cameras. Red leather bellows, double or triple extension. B&L RR lens, Auto shutter. $75-100.

Tuxedo - c1892. Leather covered 4x5" folding plate camera. Black wood interior, black wood front standard. This is an all-black version of the Folding Rochester camera. Brass trim. $225-295.

ROCHESTER OPTICAL CO.

Carlton - c1893-1903. All-wood, double extension view, similar to the Universal. Double swing back. Brass trim. With lens: $150-250.

Cyclone Cameras - (formerly Western, prior to 1899.)
Magazine Cyclone - No. 2, 4, or 5. c1898. For 3¼x4¼ or 4x5" plates. Black leathered wood box. Meniscus lens, sector shutter. $35-50.

Cyclone Junior - Plate box camera for 3½x3½" glass plates in standard holders. Top door hinges forward to load plateholders. A cheaper alternative to the more expensive magazine cameras. $25-35.

Cyclone Senior - Plate box camera, 4x5" for standard plateholders. $25-35.

Empire State View - c1895. Folding field camera. Polished wood. Brass fittings. 5x7" & 6½x8½": $60-100. 8x10": $75-125. 11x14": $60-90.

Handy - c1892. 4x5" detective box-plate camera. Internal bellows focus. A simple, less expensive version of the Premier. $100-160.

Ideal - c1885-95. Folding view cameras, 4x5" to 8x10" sizes. Cherry wood, brass trim. Ranging in price, depending on size, from $100-150.

Monitor - c1886. View camera in full plate and 8x10" sizes. Wood body folds in the "English" compact style. $100-150.

New Model View, New Model Improved View - Made in all the common sizes from 4x5" to 8x10". $125-200.

Peerless view - mid-to-late 1880's. Dark mahogany. $100-150.

Premier Cameras:

Premier folding camera

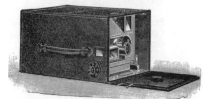

Detective box camera - c1891. Internal bellows focus with external control knob. Side panel opens to insert plate holders. 4x5 and 5x7" sizes. $90-140.

Premier folding camera - c1892. 4x5 or 5x7" size, for plates. Originally with shutter built into wooden lensboard: $300-400. Later with B&L pneumatic shutter: $175-225. *(illustrated in previous column)*

Premo Cameras - *See also Eastman for their continuation of the Premo line. Prices here are for cameras with normal shutter/lens combinations. (Often found with a B&L lens and Victor shutter.)*

Folding Premo Camera - 1893-84. This is the original folding plate model. Rapid Rectilinear lens, Star shutter. Sizes 4x5", 5x7", and 6½x8½". $100-125.

No. 2 Pony Premo

- 4x5" - c1900 folding plate cameras, including: Pony Premo, Premo Senior, Star Premo, Premo A-E, 3B, 4, and 7. Red bellows. $35-60.

- 5x7" - c1900. Folding plate cameras, including: Pony Premo, Pony Premo Sr., Premo No. 6, Premo B, and Premo Senior. Red bellows. $50-80.

Long Focus Premo - Triple extension red bellows. Sizes 4x5, 5x7, 6½x8½". $85-135.

Rochester Premograph

Premo Reflecting Camera - 1905-06. 4x5" single lens reflex camera with front bed and bellows (unlike the later Premograph, described below). Various B&L or Goerz lenses. FP shutter. Reversible back. Tall focusing hood supported by trellis strut. This is a rare model and should not be confused with the less rare Premograph. Price negotiable. Estimate: $600-900.

Reversible Back Premo - 5x7". Looks like a Long Focus Premo, but back shifts from horizontal to vertical. $85-135.

Rochester Universal

Rochester Stereo Camera - Wooden stereo field camera with folding tailboard. 5x7 or 6½x8½" size. B&L shutter. Red bellows. $250-350.

Premo Sr. Stereo - 1895-1900. 5x7" or full plate. Rapid Rectilinear lenses. B&L Stereo pneumatic shutter. Maroon bellows. Folding plate camera, a modification of the Premo Sr. $200-350.

Premograph - 1907-08. Simple box SLR. 3¼x4¼" filmpacks. $100-150. *(illustrated top of next column)*

Snappa - c1902. Unusual ¼-plate folding-bed view with integral magazine back.

319

Holds 12 plates or 24 cut films. Red bellows, nickel & brass fittings. RR lens. Quite rare. We have only one sale on record, in early 1982, at $585.

Universal - intro. 1888. Polished wood view, 5x7" or 6½x8½". Brass trim, brass barrel lens with Waterhouse stops. $125-165. *(illustrated on previous page)*

ROCKET CAMERA CO. LTD. (Japan)
General, Palmer, Rocket Camera - c1948. Simple metal box cameras, 4x5cm on 120 film. $3-6.

New Rocket - Early postwar Japanese novelty subminiature, 14x14mm. Some cameras are marked "Rocket Camera Co." below lens, others have "Tokyo Seiki Co. Ltd." Chrome: $140-160. Gold: $175-200.

RODEHUESER (Dr. Rodehueser, Bergkamen, Westf., Germany)
Panta - c1950. Cast metal body with telescoping front. 5x5.5cm on rollfilm. Steiner f3.5/75mm lens. Prontor 25-200 shutter. $30-40.

RODENSTOCK (Optische Werke G. Rodenstock, Munich)

Clarovid - c1932. Folding-bed rollfilm camera for 6x9cm exposures. Trinar Anastigmat f4.5 or f3.8/105mm lens. Rim-set Compur 1-250. Coupled rangefinder. $95-165.

Folding rollfilm camera - Models for 120 rollfilm, 4.5x6 and 6x6cm, or 116 rollfilm. Rodenstock Trinar f2.9 or Eurynar f4.5 lens. Rim-set Compur 1-250. $25-35.

Folding plate/sheetfilm camera - 9x12cm. f2.9, f3.8, or f4.5 Trinar. $25-35.

Perforette Super - c1950. 35mm viewfinder camera. Rodenstock Trinar Anastigmat f3.5/75mm. Prontor 1-175, B T. $20-30.

Robra - c1937. Folding camera, 4.5x6cm on 120. Robra Anastigmat f3.5/75mm. Compur shutter. $25-35.

Rodinett - Small rollfilm 3x4cm camera. Clamshell front doors. Body identical to the equally scarce Glunz & Bulter Ingo. $60-90.

Ysella - c1932. Strut folding camera with bed. Half-frame 127. Trinar f2.8 or 4.5/50mm in Compur shutter. $60-90.

ROGERS JUNIOR - Folding 6x9cm rollfilm camera. $15-20.

ROKUWA CO. (Japan)
Stereo Rocca - c1953. Plastic stereo camera for 23x24mm stereo pairs side-by-side on 120 rollfilm. Film travels vertically through camera. $100-135.

ROLCO - Japanese half-frame 127. Roko Anastigmat f3.5/60mm. $75-125.

ROLLS CAMERA MFG. CO. (Chicago)

Beauta Miniature Candid - Bakelite minicam for half-127 film. Originally sold as a punchboard premium. $3-7.

Rolls - Bakelite novelty camera for half-frame 127. $3-7.

Rolls Twin 620 - Cast aluminum box camera for 620 film. $8-12.

Super Rolls Seven Seven - Heavy cast metal camera for 4.5x6cm on 620 film.

T,B,I leaf shutter with body release. Named for its f7.7 Achromatic Rollax lens. Focuses by manually extending the front to proper footage mark. $10-15.

RONDO COLORMATIC - c1962. 35mm camera with meter cell surrounding lens. $10-15.

RONDO RONDOMATIC - c1962. Identical to the Colormatic. $10-15.

ROROX - 3x4cm on 127 film. Bottom loading. $30-45.

ROSKO - Novelty "Diana" type camera. Imitation meter grid on top housing. $1-5.

ROSKO BRILLANT 620, Model 2 - c1955. Black bakelite 6x6cm reflex style camera. Made by Goyo Co. It is an export model of the Palma Brillant Model 2 which used 120 film. $5-10.

ROSS (Thomas Ross & Co.)

Folding Twin Lens Camera - c1895. Boxy twin lens reflex style camera. Front double doors open straight out. Goerz Double Anastigmat f7.7/5" lens. $500-700.

Kinnear's Patent Wet-Plate Landscape Camera - 10x12" size. $500-550.

Stereo camera - ½-plate. Polished mahogany, tapered leather bellows. Ross lenses. Thornton-Pickard shutter. $500-700.

Sutton Panoramic Camera - c1861. This camera, made for Thomas Sutton by Ross, takes curved glass plates in special curved holders. And wet-plates at that! Only about 30 were made. The lens is water-filled and gives an angle of 120 degrees. Three of these cameras sold at auction in 1974 for approximately $24,000 to $27,000. In June 1983 there were two offered for sale at $14,000 and $17,000. Confirmed sales indicate a current value in the $12,000-14,000 range.

Wet-plate camera (sliding box style) - Recent sales have been in the $800-1200 range.

Wet-plate camera (tailboard style) - c1865. Mahogany camera with folding tailboard and bellows. Brass fittings. Euryscop lens with waterhouse stops. 12x12" plates. $750-950.

Wet-plate Stereo (sliding-box style) - Grubb lenses. $4000-5000.

Wet-plate Stereo (tailboard style) - c1865. Full plate size. Maroon square bellows. Ross Petzval 6" lenses, waterhouse stops. $2500-3500.

ROTH (L. Roth, Vienna)
Reflex, 4.5x6cm - c1926. SLR. Hugo Meyer Trioplan f6.3/75mm lens in FP shutter 10-1000. $300-350.

Reflex, 8x10.5cm - c1910. SLR. Hugo Meyer Trioplan f2.8/95mm lens in FP shutter 10-1000. $200-300.

ROUCH (W.W. Rouch & Co., London)
Eureka - c1888. Polished mahogany detective camera. Magazine for 12 exposures 8x8cm or ¼-plate size. Brass

barrel Rouch 150mm lens, rollerblind shutter. $350-500.

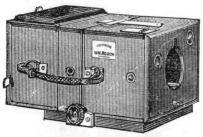

Excelsior - c1890. Mahogany detective camera, similar to the Eureka, but takes ordinary double slides as well as the Eureka magazine back. ¼-plate size. $350-500.

Patent camera - c1892. ½-plate mahogany field camera with brass fittings. Ross Rapid Symmetrical lens with Waterhouse stops. $125-175.

ROUSSEL (H. Roussel, Paris)

Stella Jumelle - c1900. 9x12cm plates. Roussel Anti-Spectroscopique f7.7/130mm in 7-speed guillotine shutter. Leather covered wood body. $175-225.

ROVER - Hong Kong "Diana" type novelty camera. $1-5.

ROYCE MFG. CO.
Royce Reflex - c1946. Twin lens reflex, cast aluminum body and back. Externally gear-coupled lenses. f4.5/75mm in Alphax shutter 25-150, T,B. $25-35.

ROYER (Fontenay-sous-Bois, France)
Altessa - c1952. Telescoping front camera for 6x9cm or 6x6cm on 120 film. Interchangeable Angenieux f3.5/105mm. $50-100.

Savoyflex - 35mm SLR. Som Berthiot f2.8/50mm. Prontor Reflex inter-lens shutter, 1-500. $50-75.

ROYET (Paul Royer, St. Etienne, France)

Reyna Cross III - Black painted cast aluminum bodied 35mm. f3.5 Berthiot or f2.9/45mm Cross. Two blade shutter 25-200, B. This camera was essentially a continuation of the Cornu Reyna line, but manufactured away from Paris which was under German occupation. See Cornu for similar models. $20-30.

RUBERG & RENNER
Ruberg - c1953. Metal body, 4x6cm on rollfilm. Front section screws out like the Photax. $25-35.

Ruberg Futuro - Metal body, 4.5x6cm on 127 rollfilm. Helical lens mount. $25-35.

RUTHINE - 35mm CRF camera. Friedrich Corygon f2.8/45mm lens. Shutter 25-100, B. $15-25.

RUVINAL - Models II, III. Japanese folding 120 or 620 camera. Pentagon f3.5/80mm lens. $15-25.

SAINT-ETIENNE (France)
Universelle - c1908. Vertical folding plate/rollfilm camera, along the lines of the Screen Focus Kodak, but with a removable back. Beckers Anastigmat f6.8/150mm in B&L Unicum shutter. $150-200.

SAKURA (Vest Pocket Camera) - c1937. Not related to the Sakura Seiki Co. which made the Petal camera. Actually this camera was made by the Konishiroku-Honten Co. Ltd. Small brown bakelite camera for ten exposures 4x5cm on 127 film. One of the very few cameras to use the 4x5cm format on 127 film. Rokuoh-Sha lens. $75-100.

SAKURA SEIKI CO. (Japan)
Petal - c1948. Subminiature camera about the size of a half-dollar. (Approximately 30mm dia.) Takes 6 exposures on circular film. Original price about $10. Two models:

- Octagonal model - This is the later version, but not as common. Made by Sakura and identified on the front as "Sakura Petal". $200-250.

- Round model - The more common early model, made by Petal Kogaku Co. Pre-dates the Sakura model. $100-135.

SALYUT-S - Russian Hasselblad 500C copy. Interchangeable Industar-24 f2.8/80mm. FP shutter 2-1500, T. $200-250.

SAN GIORGIO (Genova, Italy)
Janua - c1949. 35mm rangefinder Leica copy. Essegi f3.5/50mm. FP shutter 50-1000. Built-in meter. $500-750.

Parva - c1947. Subminiature for 16mm rollfilm. Less than 10 made. No known sales. rare. Estimate: $500+.

SANDERS & CROWHURST (Brighton, England)
Birdland - c1904. ¼-plate SLR. Extensible front. Waist-level focusing hood also allows for eye level focusing. Aldis Anastigmat f8 lens. FP shutter to 1000. $350-500.

SANDERSON CAMERA WORKS
(England) *Mr. Frederick H. Sanderson (1856-1929) was a cabinet maker, and a wood and stone carver. In the 1880's, he became interested in photography, particularly in architectural work, which required special camera movements not readily available on the cameras of the day. He designed his own camera, and in January of 1895 he had a patented new design. All Sanderson cameras incorporate his patented lens panel support system. The production models of the camera were built and marketed by Houghton's, with ads appearing as early as 1896.*

Sanderson Field camera - c1898. Half-plate mahogany folding camera. Double extension, tilt/swing back. Brass fittings. Sanderson's Patent Universal lens f8. $200-250.

Sanderson "Regular" and "Deluxe" Hand and Stand cameras - 3x4" to 4x5" sizes. Folding plate cameras with finely polished wood interior. Heavy leather exterior. $175-225.

Sanderson Tropical Hand and Stand cameras - ½-plate to 4x5" sizes. Polished teak with brass fittings. Goerz Dagor f6.8, Aldis f6.3, or Beck f7.7 lens. Compur shutter. Recent prices are down from prices in the $500-700 range a few years ago. $400-550.

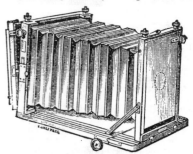

SANDS, HUNTER & CO., LTD. (London)
Field cameras - c1890. Tailboard or

folding bed styles. Full plate to 10x12" sizes. Rectilinear lens. $200-275.

SANEI SANGYO (Japan)

Samoca Super Rangefinder - c1956. 35mm camera for 36 exposures, 24x36mm on standard cartridges. Ezumar f3.5/50mm lens. Shutter 10-200. Coupled rangefinder. Versions with and without built-in selenium meter. $25-35.

Samoca 35, 35II, 35III - c1950's. Simpler models. $16-25.

SANEIKOKI (Japan)
Starrich 35 - Small bakelite camera for 24x36mm exposures on "Bolta" size 35mm paper-backed rollfilm. Similar to the ebony and Start cameras, but not as common. $30-45.

SANRIO CO. LTD. (Japan)

Hello Kitty Camera - c1981. 110 film plastic camera in bright colors. Rotating kitty acts as cover for lens and viewfinder. Built-in electric autowinder and electronic flash. A cute but expensive camera for the child who already has a silver spoon. Retail price near $100.

SANWA CO. LTD., SANWA SHOKAI (Japan)
Mycro (original model) - 1938. The pre-war model of the Mycro camera. There is no streamlined top housing as on the later (post-war) Sanwa Mycro cameras, but rather a square optical finder attached to the top.

Next to the finder is a small disc marked "T.A.Co.", but we have not yet discovered the name of the manufacturer. This early model is uncommon, and diehard subminiature collectors have been known to pay $75-100.

Mycro - 14x14mm novelty camera. Mycro Una f4.5/20mm. 3-speed shutter. There are a number of variations of the Mycro cameras, most of which sell for $20-35.

Mycro IIIA - Similar to the normal Mycro, but streamlined viewfinder. $45-60.

SATELLITE - "Hit" type subminiature. $10-15.

SAWYERS INC. (Portland, Ore.)
Mark IV (same as Primo Jr.) - c1956. TLR, 4x4cm on 127 film. Topcor f2.8 lens. Seikosha MX shutter to 500. Auto wind. $60-85.

Nomad 127, Nomad 620 - Brown bakelite box cameras. 4x6.5cm on 127 and 6x6cm on 620. $4-8.

View-Master Mark II Stereo - For stereo pairs on 35mm film. Trinar f2.8/20mm. $90-120.

View-Master Personal Stereo - c1960. For making your own view-master slides. Film was wound twice through the camera

Schatz Sola

with lenses raised/lowered for each pass. 69 stereo pairs, 12x13mm. Anastigmat f3.5/25mm lenses. 1/10-1/100 shutter. Quite common. Brown & beige model: $90-125. Black models with flash: $75-100. Mark film punch: $75-120.

Sawyers Europe: View-master Stereo Color - The European model. Made in Germany. For stereo exposures 12x13mm on 35mm film. Diagonal film path allows stereo pairs to be exposed on one pass of the film. Rodenstock f2.8/20mm lenses and single-speed shutter. $85-95.

S.C.A.T. (Societa Construzioni Articoli Technici, Rom)

Scat - c1950. Subminiature for 7x10mm exposures on 16mm film in special cassettes. f3.5 lens, single speed revolving shutter. Leather covered metal body. Uncommon. $100-150.

SCHAPP & CO. (Amsterdam)
Van Albada Stereo - c1900. 6x13cm box

stereo. FP shutter with variable tension and slit width. Four-element lenses in nickel-plated lens mounts with rotary stops. $600-850.

SCHATZ & SONS (Germany)
Sola - c1938. Unusually-shaped subminiature, 13x18mm on unperforated film in cassettes. Spring drive, 12 exposures per wind. Interchangeable Schneider Kinoplan f3/25 or Xenon f2/25 lens. Behind-the-lens shutter, 1-500, B. Waist-level or eye-level viewing. $1000-1500. *(illustrated top of previous column)*

SCHIANSKY
Universal Studio Camera - c1950. All metal, for 7x9¼" sheet film, with reducing back for 13x18cm (5x7"). Zeiss Apo-Tessar f9/450mm. Black bellows extend to 1 meter. Only 12 were made. One known sale in 1976 for $500.

SCHMITZ & THIENEMANN (Dresden)
Uniflex Reflex Meteor - c1931. SLR box for 6.5x9cm. Meyer Trioplan f4.5/105mm in self-cocking Pronto shutter 25-100. $150-175.

SCOTT-ATWATER MFG. CO. (Minneapolis, Minn.)
Photopal - Simple, stamped metal novelty camera, enameled black. 3x3.5cm or 4x6cm sizes. $25-35.

SCOVILL MANUFACTURING CO. (N.Y.)
Brief summary of name changes & dates: Scovill & Adams, 1889; Anthony & Scovill, 1902; Ansco, 1907. (See also Anthony and Ansco.) Scovill produced some excellent cameras, all of which are relatively uncommon today.

Antique Oak Detective - c1890. 4x5" box-plate camera finished in beautiful golden oak. String-set shutter, variable speeds. $400-500.

Book Camera - c1892. Camera disguised as a set of 3 books held with a leather strap. Rare. Estimate: $8000+. *(illustrated top of next page)*

Scovil Book Camera

Field/View cameras:
- **4x5"** - Square black box with folding beds on front and rear. Bellows extend both directions. Top and side doors permit loading the plateholders either way into the revolving back when only the front bellows are being used. Nickel plated Waterbury lens. $125-175.
- **8x10"** - ca. early 1880's. Light colored wood body. $125-175.

Irving - c1890. 11x14" compact folding view. RR lens, waterhouse stops. $250-350.

Knack Detective - c1891. The Antique Oak Detective camera with a new name. $400-500.

Mascot - c1890-1892. 4x5" format leather covered wood box camera. Similar to the Waterbury detective camera listed below, but with an Eastman Roll Holder. String-set shutter. $350-450.

Scovill Detective - c1886. Leather covered box detective camera for 4x5" plates in standard plateholders. Entire top of camera hinges open to one side to reveal the red leather bellows (and to change plates). The bottom of the camera is recessed, and the controls are located there, out of sight. A very uncommon detective camera. This camera was never shown close-up in original advertising in order to preserve its "concealed aspects". $550-650.

St. Louis - 8x10" reversible back camera No. 116. c1890. With lens: $125-175.

Stereo Solograph - c1899. A compact folding stereo camera for 4x6½. Stereo RR lenses in Automatic Stereo shutter. $275-375.

Triad Detective - c1892. Leather covered 4x5" box detective camera for plates, rollfilm, or sheet film. Variable speed string-set shutter. $200-350.

Waterbury Detective Camera, Original model - c1888. Black painted all wood box, or less common leather-covered model. Side door for loading plates. Focused by means of sliding bar extending through the base of the camera. Recessed bottom stores an extra plateholder. 4x5": $350-475. 5x7": $450-650.

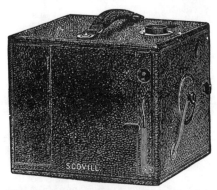

Waterbury Detective, Improved model
- c1892. Same as the original model, except focus knob is at top front. $250-375.

Waterbury Stereo - c1885. 5x8". All wood body. Scovill Waterbury lenses. $300-400.

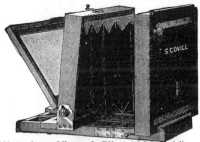

Waterbury View, 4x5" - c1888. Folding-bed collapsible bellows view camera. Eurygraph 4x5 RR lens, Prosch Duplex shutter. $135-175.

Waterbury View, 5x8" or 6½x8½" -

c1888. Horizontal format. Light wood finish. Brass barrel Waterbury lens. $125-175.

Wet-plate camera - c1860's. 4-tube wet-plate tintype camera for 4 exposures on a 5x7" plate. $1400-1800.

SDELANO: *Identifying mark on some Russian cameras beginning in the late 1950's. It means "Manufactured in the U.S.S.R." This is not a camera model or manufacturer's name.*

SDGD: *Brevete S.D.G.D. (Sans garantie du gouvernement) indicates French manufacture. According to French patent law, if an article is marked "brevete" (patented) it must also be marked "sans garantie du gouvernement" or S.G.D.G.*

SEARS (Seroco) *Seroco is an abbreviation for Sears, Roebuck & Co., whose cameras were made by other companies for sale under the Seroco name. The Conley company made many cameras for Sears after the turn of the century, and was purchased by Sears.*

Delmar - box camera for plates. Top rear door hinges up to insert plateholders. Storage space for extra plateholders. For 3¼x4¼ or 4x5" plates. $25-35.

Marvel S-16, S-20 - c1940. 116 or 120 rollfilm box cameras. Art-deco faceplate. $4-8.

Marvelflex - TLR. f4.5. $15-20.

Perfection - 4x5" plate camera. $30-40.

Seroco 4x5" folding plate camera - c1901. Black leathered wood body with polished interior. Red bellows. Seroco 4x5 Symmetrical lens and Wollensak shutter are common. $40-70.

Seroco 5x7" folding plate camera - similar to the above except for the size. $45-75.

Seroco 6½x8½" folding plate camera - Red double extension bellows. $75-105.

SEARS (cont.)

Seroco Magazine - c1902. 4x5" box camera. Leather covered, nickel trim. 12-plate magazine. $45-60.

Seroco Stereo - 5x7" plates. Leather covered mahogany body with polished interior. Red leather bellows. Wollensak Stereo shutter & lenses. $275-325.

Tower No. 5 - c1958. 4x4cm on 127 rollfilm. Styled like a 35mm. Blue-gray enameled with gray plastic partial covering. Made by Bilora for Sears and similar to the Bilora Bella. $8-12.

Tower 16 - c1959. A Mamiya-16 Super with the Tower name on it. $35-50.

Tower 35, Model 50

Tower, 35mm - c1955. Various models of 35mm cameras, styles vary from boxy to compact. Includes "Tower 35" Models 39, 41, 50, 55. Various features. $10-25.

Tower, Type 3 - Made by Nicca Camera Co. in Occupied Japan, and sold by Sears. Copy of a Leica III. Nikkor f2/50mm lens is the most common. With normal lens: $95-125. Body only: $60-75. *(illustrated top of next column)*

Sears Tower, Type 3

Tower 22, Tower 23, Tower 24 - c1955. 35mm SLR cameras. Sears version of the Asahiflex. Takumar f3.5/50mm. $50-110.

Tower 51 - c1955. Folding bed 6x9cm camera, identical to the United States Camera Corp. Rollex. $5-10.

Tower One-Twenty, One-Twenty Flash, Flash, Flash 120 - c1950's. 6x9cm box cameras. Leatherette or enamel finish. $1-5.

Tower 127EF - Horizontally styled cameras for 1⅝x1⅝" on 127 film. Electronic flash beside lens. Capacitor and electronics in detachable handle. Early example of a camera with built-in flash. $15-25.

Tower Automatic 127 - Horizontally styled white plastic body. Flash and meter built-in. 4x4cm on 127. Looks like the United States Camera Corp. Automatic 127. $5-10.

Tower Camflash 127, Camflash II 127 - Horizontal style 4x4cm, like the United States Camera Corp. Comet 127. Built-in flash. $5-10.

Sears Tower Junior

Tower Companion - Plastic 6x6cm box camera, identical to the Imperial Debonair. $1-5.

Tower Hide Away - Grey and green plastic box camera made by Imperial, same style as the Imperial Mark 27. Built-in flash with retractable cover. $1-5.

Tower Junior - c1953-56. Small bakelite box camera with eye-level finder. Made by Bilora for Sears and identical to the Bilora Boy. "Tower" on front, "Bilora" on back. $10-20. *(illustrated on previous page)*

Tower Pixie 127, Pixie II 127 - Gray plastic 4x4cm, 127 cameras. $1-5.

Tower Reflex - c1955. 6x6cm TLR. Isco Westar Anastigmat f3.5 lens. Pronto 25-200 shutter. Same as the Photina Reflex. $20-30.

Tower Reflex Type - c1955. Various styles of 6x6cm pseudo-TLR bakelite box cameras. $5-10.

Sears Tower Snappy

Tower Skipper - 4x4cm plastic box. Identical to the Mercury Satellite 127. $1-5.

Tower Snappy - Plastic 6x6cm 620 camera, identical to the Herbert-George Savoy. In colors. $1-5.

Tower Stereo - Made in Germany by Iloca for Sears. Same as Iloca Stereo II. Isco-Westar f3.5/35mm lenses. Prontor-S shutter 1-300. $85-100.

SECAM (Paris)

Stylophot cameras - c1950's "pen" style cameras, according to the name, but even if compared to the large deluxe European fountain pens, it ends up looking a bit hefty. The pocket clip is the closest resemblance to a pen. For 18 exposures 10x10mm on 16mm film in special cartridges. Shutter cocking and film advance via pull-push sliding mechanism which pushed film from cartridge to cartridge. Automatic exposure counter. Weight: 3 oz. (85 gr.) *Note: The same camera was also sold in Germany as the Foto-Fueller, listed in this guide under Knuik.*

Stylophot "Standard" or "Color" model - The cheaper of the two models, with fixed focus two-element f6.3 coated lens, single speed shutter (1/50). Also sold under the name "Private Eye". Original price: $15. Current value: $85-110.

Stylophot "Luxe" or "Deluxe" model - with f3.5/27mm Roussel Anastigmat lens. Iris diaphragm. Focus to 2½ ft. (0.8m). Single speed shutter (1/75) synched for flash. Original price: $33. This model is very uncommon. $125-150.

Stereophot - An unique stereo camera consisting of two Stylophot cameras mounted side-by-side on a special mounting plate. Awkward, maybe... but rare. $450-550. *(illustrated top of next page)*

Secam Stereophot

SEEMAN (H. Seeman)
Stereo camera - Black wooden strut folding camera, nickel-plated fittings. Goerz Dagor 120mm lenses. $300-450.

SEIKI KOGAKU CO. *(Seiki Kogaku means "Precision Optical" and this name was used on more than one occasion by unrelated companies. This company is not related to the Seiki Kogaku which made the early Canon cameras.)*

Seiki - Oval-shaped 16mm subminiature. Seek Anastigmat f3.5/25mm. B, 25, 50, 100 shutter. $500-700.

SEISCHAB (Otto Seischab, Nuernberg, Germany)
Esco - c1922. 400 exposure half-frame 35mm. Similar in style to the Leica Reporter. Steinheil Cassar f3.5/35mm. Dial-set Compur 1-300. $1500-2000.

S.E.M. (Societe des Etablissements Modernes; Aurec, France) *In 1942-45, during the German occupation of Paris, the Reyna Cross 35mm cameras were made in St. Etienne under license from Cornu. Once the war was over, the St. Etienne firm broke the ties with Cornu and re-established itself in the neighboring town of Aures under the S.E.M. name. The Reyna-Cross camera design, with some improvements, soon appeared as the Sem-Kim, and S.E.M. went on to design and build a number of small and medium-format cameras up through the early 1970's.*
Babysem - Grey-enameled 35mm. Some models are partially blue or red leather covered. Cross f2.9/45mm lens. Orec shutter 25-200 or 15-250. $20-30.

Colorado - Grey plastic dual-format camera. Takes 16 exposures 4x4cm or 20 exposures 24x35mm on 620 film. $20-30.

Kim - c1947. Simple cast aluminum 35mm camera. Successor of the Reyna-Cross. Cross Anastigmat f2.9/45mm. Shutter 25-200, later extended to 1-200. $20-30.

Semflex Joie de Vivre 45 - Light-gray plastic covered TLR. Metal faceplate. Berthiot f4.5/80mm lens. $35-50.

Semflex Standard - c1950. Twin-lens reflex camera for 6x6cm on 120 film. Several model variations. $20-40.

SEMI-PRINCE - c1937. Japanese copy of the Zeiss Ikonta A, 4.5x6cm. Schneider 4.5/75mm. Prontor 25-125 shutter. $25-35.

SEMMENDINGER (A. Semmendinger, Ft. Lee, NJ)
Excelsior - c1870. Wet-plate cameras in sizes 5x5" to 12x12". Large sizes have sliding backs. With lens: $500-800. Without lens: $250-350.

SENECA CAMERA CO. (Rochester, NY)
Box-plate camera - Fixed focus. All black. 4x5": $25-40. 5x7": $45-65.

Busy Bee - c1903. 4x5" box-plate camera. Fold-down front reveals a beautiful interior. $45-65.

Camera City View - c1907-25. 5x7" to 8x10" view cameras. Seneca Anastigmat lens. Ilex shutter. $85-135.

Chautauqua 4x5" - Folding plate camera. Wollensak lens. Seneca Uno shutter. A very plain all-black camera. $35-60.

Chautauqua 5x7" - All black "ebonized" model: $50-70. With polished wood interior: $100-150.

Chief 1A - c1918. 2½x4¼" on rollfilm. $12-18.

Competitor View - 5x7 or 8x10" folding field camera. Light colored wood or medium colored cherry wood. $90-135. *(illustrated top of next column)*

Seneca Competitor View

Duo - Not a camera name. This was the name for the medium-priced shutter in the Seneca line-up, with T,B,1,2,5,25,50,100.

Filmett - 1910-1916. Folding film-pack camera for 3¼x4¼" packs. Leather covered wood body. Black bellows. Wollensak Achromatic or Rapid Rectilinear lens. Uno or Duo shutter. $20-30.

Folding plate cameras:

SENECA (cont.)

- **3¼x4¼"** - Wollensak f16 lens. Uno shutter. $30-45.
- **3¼x5½"** - Black double-extension bellows and triple convertible lens. $30-45.
- **4x5"** - Black leathered body with nickel trim. Double extension bellows. Seneca Uno or Auto shutter. $40-60.
- **5x7"** - Similar, black or polished wood interior, black leathered wood body. 7" Rogers or Seneca Anastigmat lens in Auto shutter. $50-80.

No. 9 Folding Plate Camera - 4x5". Maroon bellows. Velostigmat lens. Compur shutter. $50-75.

Pocket Seneca Cameras:

No. 1 Seneca Junior - 2¼x3¼" exposure folding rollfilm camera. Strut-supported lensboard and hinged front-cover. Ilex shutter. $15-20.

Pocket Seneca No. 3A - Folding plate camera. Double extension bellows. Rapid

convertible lens, Auto shutter 1-100. $20-30.

Pocket Seneca No. 29 - c1905. Simple 4x5" folding plate camera. Seneca Uno shutter. f8 lens. $25-35.

Scout cameras:
No. 2A Folding Scout - c1916. Wollensak lens, Ultro shutter. $12-18.

No. 2C Folding Scout - c1916. $12-18.

No. 3 Folding Scout - c1916. Ultro shutter. $12-18.

No. 3A Folding Scout - c1916. Seneca Trio shutter. 122 film. $12-18.

Box Scout, No. 2, 2A, 3, 3A - $6-12.

Stereo View - c1910. 5x7" folding-bed collapsible bellows view camera with wide front lensboard. Style similar to the Competitor view. Wollensak lenses. $275-375.

Trio - Trio is a shutter name, not a camera name.

Uno - Not the name of a camera, but rather the low-priced shutter on Seneca cameras. Provides I,T,B speeds.

Seymore Brenda Starr

Seymore Dick Tracy

Vest Pocket - Compact folding camera for 127 film. f7.7 Seneca Anastigmat lens. Shutter 25-100. $25-45.

View Cameras:
- 5x7" - Seneca Rapid convertible or Goerz Syntor f6.8 lens. Ilex shutter 1-100. Black double extension bellows. Polished wood body. $85-125.

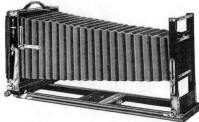

- 5x7" Improved - Wollensak Planatic Series III lens. Auto shutter. Black leather bellows. Fine wood body. $85-125.

- 6½x8½" Improved - Goerz Double Anastigmat f6.8/7" lens in Volute shutter. $80-120.

- 8x10", including the Improved model - With Wollensak Velostigmat Ser. 2, f4.5/ 12" lens or double anastigmat lens in Optimo or Wollensak Regular shutter. $90-145.

SEYMORE PRODUCTS CO. (Chicago, IL) *See alternate spelling "Seymour".*
Brenda Starr Cub Reporter - Bakelite minicam for 16 exposures on 127 film. Enameled 4-color illustrated faceplate. Probably the rarest and most desirable of the "Minicam" type cameras. $25-35. *(illustrated top of next column)*

Dick Tracy - Like the Seymour Sales Dick Tracy, but black faceplate. $12-20. *(illustrated next column)*

SEYMOUR SALES CO. (Chicago) *See also alternate spelling "Seymore".*
Dick Tracy - Black bakelite minicam for 3x4cm on 127 film. Picture of Dick Tracy and camera name are printed in red on the metal faceplate. $12-20. *See second variation above under "Seymore Products".*

Flash-Master - Inexpensive 3x4cm 127 rollfilm minicam with sync. $3-7.

S.F.O.M. (Societe Francaise d'Optique Mechanique)
Sfomax - c1949. Cast aluminum

subminiature with black or grey leatherette covering. Takes 20 exposures 14x23mm on unperforated 16mm film in special cartridges. S'fomar f3.5/30mm lens. Shutter 30-400 (early models 25-400). Split image rangefinder. $400-600.

SHACKMAN (D. Shackman and Sons, London, England)
Auto Camera, Mark 3 - c1953. 24x24mm on 35mm film in 250 exposures cassettes. Recording camera designed for scientific work. Motorized advance. Fixed focus Dallmeyer lens. Gray painted body. $50-100.

SHAJA - 9x12cm double extension plate camera. Tessar f4.5/135mm in Compur shutter. $25-35.

SHAKEY'S - Plastic novelty 4x4cm camera of the "Diana" type. Made in Hong Kong. $1-5.

SHALCO - 14x14mm Japanese novelty camera of the Hit type. $10-15.

SHANSHUI B - Chinese plastic 120 camera. $25-30.

SHAW (H.E. Shaw & Co.)

Oxford Minicam - Black plastic half-127, made by Utility Mfg. Co. for Shaw Co. $3-7.

SHAW-HARRISON
Sabre 620 - Plastic 6x6cm box camera. Various colors. $4-8.

Valiant 620 - Colored plastic 6x6cm box camera. Identical to the Sabre 620. $4-8.

SHAYO - Japanese novelty subminiature of the Hit type. $10-15.

SHEW (J. F. Shew & Co., London)
Day-Xit - c1910 variation of the Xit. Meniscus lens, synchro shutter. Black leathered wood body. $125-175.

Eclipse - c1890. 3¼x4¼" plates. Wray f8/5" lens in brass barrel. Thornton-Pickard

shutter. Mahogany with dark brown bellows. $150-250.

Guinea Xit - c1906. Mahogany gate-strut folding camera. Red bellows. 8x10.5cm on plates or cut film. Achromatic 5½" lens. Central rotary shutter. $125-175.

Xit, Aluminum Xit - c1900. Similar to the Eclipse with aluminum and mahogany construction. $125-175.

Xit Stereoscopic - Folding gate-strut stereo camera. $600-700.

SHIMURA KOKI (Japan)
Mascot - c1950. Vertical subminiature for 14x14mm on paper-backed "Midget" rollfilm. Mascot f4.5/25mm. Shutter 25-100, B. $250-350.

Shinano Pigeon

SHINANO CAMERA CO. LTD., SHINANO OPTICAL WORKS (Japan)

Pigeon - c1952. Viewfinder 35mm. Tomioka Tri-Lausar f3.5/45mm. Synchro shutter 10-200. Advance knob. $25-35. *(illustrated bottom of previous page)*

Pigeon III - c1952. Viewfinder 35mm. Tomioka Tri-Lausar f3.5/45mm. NYS shutter 1-100. Lever wind. $25-35.

SHINCHO SEIKI CO. LTD. (Japan)

Albert - A name variation of the Darling-16. "Albert Fifth Avenue New York" on metal faceplate. $180-200.

Darling-16 - c1950's. Vertically styled subminiature accepts 16mm cassettes for 10x12mm exposures. Bakelite body with metal front and back. $180-220.

SHINSEI OPTICAL WORKS (Japan)

Monte 35 - c1952. Inexpensive Japanese 35mm camera. Monte Anastigmat f3.5/50mm in Heilemann or SKK shutter. $15-20.

Showa Gemflex

SHOWA KOGAKU (Japan)

Gemflex - c1949. Subminiature TLR for 14x14mm on standard "Midget" paper-backed rollfilm. Gem f3.5/25mm, shutter 25-100. Early models: Back plate has serial number and "Made in Occupied Japan"; finder hood opens for eye level viewing. Later models: No serial number; not marked Occupied Japan; no eye-level viewing provision. $265-300. *(illustrated bottom of previous column)*

Leotax Cameras - *Prices include normal lens.*

Leotax Model I - 1940 Leica copy. Uncoupled rangefinder, no accessory shoe. $500-600.

Leotax Special, Special A - Wartime camera. External veiwfinder, no slow speeds, coupled RF. $300-500.

Leotax Special B - Wartime camera. External viewfinder, slow speeds. $275-400.

Leotax Special DII - 1947. Internal viewfinder, no slow speeds. $250-400.

Leotax DII MIOJ - $125-175.

Leotax Special DIII - 1947. Internal viewfinder, slow speeds. $250-400.

Leotax DIII MIOJ - $125-175.

Leotax DIV - 1950. Rangefinder magnification 1.5X, no sync. $125-175.

Leotax S - 1952. RF magnification 1.5X, sync. $100-175.

Leotax F - 1954. Fast speed dial now 25-1000. Slow speed dial. $90-150.

Leotax T - 1955. Top speed 1/500. Slow speed dial. $90-150.

Leotax K - 1955. No slow speeds. $110-160.

Leotax T2 - 1958. Slowest speed on fast speed dial now 1/30. Slow speed dial, no self-timer. $125-200.

Leotax K3 - 1958. Slow speeds limited to ⅛ & 1/15. No self timer. $125-200.

Leotax TV - 1957. Slow speeds, self timer. $125-200.

Leotax FV - 1958. Lever wind, self timer, slow speeds to 1000. $160-225.

Leotax TV2 (Merit) - 1958. Lever wind, self timer, slow speeds to 500. $160-225.

Leotax T2L (Elite) - 1959. Lever wind, no self timer. $160-225.

Leotax G - 1961. Small dial. $200-250.

Semi-Leotax - Folding camera for 4.5x6cm exposures on 120 film. f3.5 lens. $35-50.

SIGRISTE (J.G. Sigriste, Paris)
Sigriste - c1900. Jumelle-style camera 6.5x9cm or 9x12cm sizes. Zeiss Tessar f4.5. Special Focal Plane shutter 40-2500. (This shutter had speeds to 1/10,000 on some cameras.) Rare. $3000-4000.

Sigriste Stereo - Rare stereo version of the above. One was offered for sale in late 1984 at $5000, which seems like a realistic figure.

SIL-BEAR - "Hit" type camera. $10-15.

SIMCO BOX - 6x6cm reflex style box camera made in Germany. Stamped metal with black crinkle-enamel. $5-10.

SIMDA (Le Perreux, France)

Panorascope - c1955. Wide angle stereo camera for 16mm film. Fixed focus Roussel or Angenieux f3.5/25mm lenses. Stereo shutter 1-250, sync. Black or grey covered metal body. Less than 2500 were made. $400-500.

SIMMON BROTHERS, INC. (N.Y.)
Omega 120 - c1954. A professional rollfilm press camera for 9 exposures 2¼x2¾" on 120 film. Omicron f3.5/90mm lens. Sync shutter 1-400. Coupled rangefinder. $125-195. *(illustrated top of next column)*

Simmon Omega 120

Signal Corps Combat Camera - Cast magnesium camera with olive drab finish for 2¼x3¼" filmpacks only. Wollensak Velostigmat f4.5/101mm in Rapax shutter. $125-175.

SIMONS (Wolfgang Simons & Co., Bern, Switzerland)

Sico - c1923. Dark brown wooden body with brass trim. For 25 exposures 30x40mm on unperforated 35mm paper-backed rollfilm. Rudersdorf Anastigmat f3.5/60mm lens in focusing mount. Iris diaphragm to f22. Dial Compur shutter 1-300. $1500-1800.

SIMPRO CORP. of AMERICA
Simpro-X - Novelty camera front for 126 cartridges. Film cartridge forms the back of the camera. $1-5.

SIMPRO INTERNATIONAL LTD.
Slip-on - 126 film cartridge forms the back of the camera body. $1-3.

SINCLAIR (James A. Sinclair & Co. Ltd., London)

Traveller Una - c1930. Similar to the Una, but made of Duralumin, a special metal, almost as light as aluminum, but stronger. 6x9cm. Xenar f4.5/105mm. Compur shutter. $1200-1500.

Tropical Una - Similar to the Una, but polished mahogany with brass fittings. 6x9cm to ½-plate sizes. $800-1200.

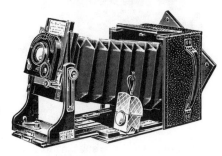

Una, Una Cameo - c1895. Folding plate camera, 6x9cm to 4x5" sizes. Heavy wood construction. Goerz Double Anastigmat f6.8 lens. Revolving back. $200-250.

Una Deluxe - c1908. Same as the Una, but hand-stiched brown leather exterior. $650-850.

SING 88 - 14x14mm novelty subminiature, a later rectangular version of the "Hit" types. $10-20.

SIRCHIE FINGER PRINT LABORATORIES INC. (Raleigh, NC)
Finger Print Camera - All-metal close-up camera with built-in lights. Various models for 2¼x3¼" filmholders, filmpacks, or for 3¼x4¼" Polaroid pack film. Raptar f6.3 lens. Alphax 25-150 shutter. 6x9cm or 8x10.5cm size. $45-85.

SIRIO (Florence, Italy)
Elettra I - c1950. Viewfinder 35mm. Fixed

Semitelar f8/50mm. Shutter 25-200. $100-150.

Elettra II - c1950. Viewfinder 35mm. Scupltor f5.6/40mm. Shutter 25-200. $125-175.

SITACON CO. LTD. (Taiwan)
Sitacon ST-3 - c1982. Inexpensive 35mm novelty camera. Identical to the Windsor WX-3. New: $8-12.

SKAIFE (Thomes Skaife, Londond)
Pistolgraph - c1858. Brass miniature camera for 28mm dia. exposures on wet-plates. Dallmeyer Petzval-type f2.2/40mm, waterhouse stops. Double-flap shutter. One known sale at auction in August 1977 for $15,000.

SKYVIEW CAMERA CO. (Cleveland, OH)
Skyview Aerial Camera Model K - Small hand-held aerial camera for 2¼x3¼" filmpacks. One-piece cast aluminum body with integral finder. Hinged aluminum back. Wollensak Aerialstigmat f4.5/5" lens. $35-50.

SMITH (Gosport, England)
Detective camera - Polished mahogany magazine box camera for 12 plates 3¼x4¼" distributed by Smith. Built-in leather changing bag. Brass trim. Two waist level viewfinders with brass covers. Guillotine shutter. $400-600.

SMITH (James H. Smith, Chicago, IL)
Known mainly for the manufacture of professional equipment.

Multiplying Camera - c1870's. 4¾x6½" plate can be moved hoizontally and vertically to take 2 to 32 exposures on it. Polished mahogany body; sliding back. Brass trim. Bellows focus. Portrait lens. pneumatic flap shutter. $500-750.

SNAP 16 - Black and gold cardboard half-127 box camera. $15-25.

SOENNECKEN & CO. (Munich)
Folding camera - 6x9cm. Double extension. Steinheil Unofocal f5.4/105mm lens. $20-30.

SOHO LTD. (London)

Soho Vest Pocket camera

Soho Altrex - c1932. 6x9cm folding bed rollfilm camera. Leather covered body. Kershaw Anastigmat lens, 7-speed shutter. $15-25.

Soho Cadet - c1930. 6x9cm folding bed rollfilm camera. Meniscus lens. 2-speed shutter. Brown bakelite body. $40-50.

Soho Myna Model SK12 - Metal folding-bed rollfilm camera with self-erecting front. 6x9cm on 120. $15-25.

Soho Vest Pocket - c1930. Strut-folding camera for 4x6.5cm on 127 film. Leather covered. Single Achromatic lens, 3-speed shutter. $15-25. *(illustrated top of next column)*

SOKOL AUTOMAT - c1970's. Russian 35mm with Industar 70 f2.8/50mm lens in 30-500 shutter. Rapid wind lever. $15-25.

SOUTHERN (E.J. Southern Ind., New York City)

Mykro-Fine - Japanese subminiature of the Hit type. This one actually has the U.S. distributor's name on the shutter faceplate. $15-20.

SPARTUS CORP. (Chicago, Ill.) *Began as Utility Mfg. Co. in New York about 1934, which sold out to the Spartus Corp. of Chicago in the 1940's. During the 1940's, several names were used including Falcon Camera Co., Spencer Co., and Spartus Corp., all of which were probably the same company. In 1951, the firm was purchased by its Sales Manager, Harold Rubin, who changed the name to Herold Mfg. Co. Meanwhile, the former President of Spartus, Jack Galter started a new company called "Galter Products" about 1950.*
See also "HEROLD" for later model Spartus cameras.

Cinex - Reflex-style novelty camera for 3x4cm on 127. Bakelite body. Identical to Spartus Reflex. $5-10. *(illustrated top of next page)*

Spartus Cinex

Spartus folding cameras - including Spartus 4, Spartus Vest Pocket. $8-12.

Spartus 35, 35F - $10-15.

Spartus box cameras - including Spartus 116, 116/616, 120, 620, Rocket. $1-5.

Spartus Full-Vue - Reflex-style 120 box camera. $5-10.

Spartus Junior Model - Bakelite folding vest-pocket camera for 4x6.5cm on 127 film. Like the earlier Utility Falcon Junior Model, but with different back latches. $5-10.

Spartus Press Flash - 1939-50. Bakelite box camera with built-in flash reflector. This camera was advertised in April 1939 under both the Spartus Press Flash (Utility Mfg. Co.) and Falcon Press Flash names. As far as we know, it is the first camera to have a built-in flash reflector. It also exists under other names, such as Galter Press Flash and Regal Flash Master. Historically significant and interesting from a design standpoint, yet common. $5-10. *(illustrated top of next page)*

Spartus Super R-I - TLR-style camera, non-focusing finder. $5-10.

Spartus Press Flash

Spartus Vanguard - 4x4cm plastic box camera. $1-3.

Spartacord - Brown plastic TLR. $10-15.

Spartaflex - Plastic TLR. $5-10.

SPECIAL CAMERA - Japanese novelty folding "Yen" camera for sheet film in paper holders. Ground glass back. $15-25.

SPEED-O-MATIC CORP. (Boston, Mass.)
Speed-O-Matic - An early instant-picture camera with meniscus lens, single speed shutter. $20-30. (Clear plastic salesman's "demo" model - $35-50.)

SPEEDEX - 14x14mm "Hit" type Japanese novelty subminiature. $5-10.

SPIEGEL
Elf - Metal box camera, 6x9cm on 120. $8-12.

SPIROTECHNIQUE (Levallois-Perret, France)
Calypso - c1960. The first commercially produced camera which was specifically designed for underwater use without any external housing. It takes standard 24x36mm frames on 35mm film, and the overall size is about the same as a normal 35mm camera. Features interchangeable lenses (Angenieux f2.8/45mm, Flor f3.5/35mm, or Berthiot Angulor f3.3/28mm.) Guillotine shutter 30-100. Body covering is a grey plastic imitation sealskin. Nikon bought the design and the Calypso evolved into the successful line of Nikonos cameras. Uncommon. $125-175. *(illus. on rear cover.)*

SPLENDIDFLEX - 4x4cm reflex-style plastic novelty camera. $1-5.

S.P.O. (Societe de Photographie et d'Optique, Carpentras, France)
Folding camera - 6x9cm folding rollfilm

camera, self-erecting. Anastigmat Sphinx Paris f6.3/105mm. $10-15.

SPUTNIK (CNYTHNK) (U.S.S.R.)
Sputnik Stereo - c1960. 6x13cm stereo pairs on 120 film. f4.5/75mm lenses, shutter 15-125. Ground glass focus. $225-275.

SPY CAMERA - Plastic 127 camera, made in Hong Kong. $1-5.

STANDARD CAMERAS LTD. (Birmingham)
Conway Camera - Box camera for 6x9cm on 120 rollfilm. Several variations. $5-15.

STAR LITE - Inexpensive reflex-style camera. $5-10.

STAR-LITE - Japanese "Hit" type novelty camera. $10-15.

STARLITE - Inexpensive 35mm, 24x36mm. $10-15.

STEGEMANN (A. Stegemann, Berlin)
Field camera - 13x18cm. Mahogany body. Single extension square cloth bellows. Normally with Meyer or Goerz lens. $150-175.

STEINECK KAMERAWERK (Tutzing)

Steineck ABC Wristwatch camera -

1949. For 8 exposures on circular film in special magazine. Steinheil f2.5/12.5mm fixed focus lens. Single speed shutter. $400-450.

STEINER OPTIK (Bayreuth, Germany)
Hunter 35 - c1950. 35mm viewfinder camera. Steiner f3.5/45mm lens, shutter 1/25-1/100. $10-20.

STEINHEIL (Optische Werke C. A. Steinheil Soehne, Munich)
Casca I - c1949. Viewfinder 35. Culminar f2.8/50mm lens in special mount. Focal plane shutter 25-1000. $100-150.

Casca II - c1948. Similar to Casca I, but with coupled rangefinder. $125-200.

Detective camera - c1895. Magazine camera for 12 plates, 9x12cm. Wood body with nickel trim. Steinheil or Periskop lens. Rotary or guillotine shutter. $550-750.

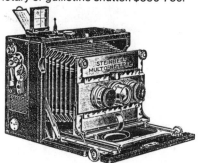

Multo Nettel - c1910-12. Folding-bed stereo camera for 3½x5½" (9x14cm) plates. Three convertible lenses on one lensboard allow for stereo or single exposures with a choice of several focal lengths. FP shutter. $375-450.

Tropical camera - 9x12cm plates. Double extension brown tapered bellows. Fine wood with nickel trim. $400-600.

STELLAR - Japanese novelty subminiature of the Hit type. $10-15.

STELLAR FLASH CAMERA - "Diana" type novelty camera with sync. $1-5.

Stereocrafters Videon II

STELLARFLEX - Twin lens reflex style novelty camera for 4x4cm on 127 film. Identical to the Bedfordflex and a few other names. $1-5.

STEREO CORPORATION (Milwaukee, Wisc.)

Contura - ca. mid-1950's. Stereo camera designed by Seton Rochewhite, who also designed the Stereo Realist for the David White Co. It was styled by reknowned product stylist Brooks Stevens, who was also responsible for the Excalibur automobile. It was engineered to be the finest stereo camera ever made. The f2.7/35mm Volar lenses focus to 24 inches with a coupled single-window rangefinder. Probably the first camera to incorporate "Auto Flash" which adjusted the diaphragm automatically based on the focus distance. The camera reached the production stage too late, just as stereo camera sales were plummeting, and a corporate decision was made to abandon the project. Ultimately, 130 cameras were assembled and sold to stockholders for $100 each. The rarity and quality of this camera keep it in demand among collectors. There are usually more offers to buy than to sell in the range of $500-600.

STEREOCRAFTERS (Milwaukee, WI)

Videon - c1950's. Stereo camera for standard 35mm cassettes. Black metal and plastic construction. Iles Stereon Anastigmat f3.5/35mm lenses. Sync. shutter. $55-75.

Videon II - Similar to the Videon, but top and faceplate are bright metal. $85-125. *(illustrated top of next column)*

STERLING - Hit type novelty camera. $10-15.

STIRN (C. P. Stirn, Stirn & Lyon, N.Y., Rudolph Stirn, Berlin)

Concealed Vest Camera, No. 1 - c1886. For 6 photos 1¾" diameter on 5" diameter glass plates. Original price, $10.00, and early ads proclaimed, "Over 15,000 sold in first 3 years." Needless to say, many are lost. $550-750. The original wooden box, which also allows the camera to be used on a tripod, doubles the value of the camera.

Concealed Vest Camera, No. 2 - Similar to the above, but for 4 exposures, 2½" (6.5cm) dia. $1000-1400.

Magazine camera - c1891. Mahogany box camera for 12 plates 6x8cm. Leather changing bag. Aplanetic lens. Rotating shutter. $500-800.

STOCK (John Stock & Co., New York, NY)

Stereo Wet-plate cameras, 5x8" - Very early models of heavier construction: $2000-3000. Later models, more common, lighter construction: $1000-1300.

STOECKIG - (Hugo Stoeckig, Dresden) **Union camera** - Early folding plate cameras with leather covered wood body and finely polished interior. 9x12 and 13x18cm sizes. With Meyer Anastigmat f7.2 or Union Aplanat f6.8 lens in Union shutter. Double extension bellows. $70-100.

SUGAYA KOKI, SUGAYA OPTICAL CO., LTD. (Japan)
Mycro Myracle, Model II - Hope Anastigmat f4.5. Shutter 25-100. Red, blue, or black leather. $35-50.

Rubix 16 - c1950's. Subminiature for 50 exposures 10x14mm on 16mm cassette film. Several variations. Hope f3.5/25mm lens. Shutter 25-100. $65-95.

SUMNER (J. Chase Sumner, Foxcroft, Maine)
Stereo rollfilm box camera - similar to the No. 2 Stereo Kodak box camera. $350-400.

SUNART PHOTO CO. (Rochester, N.Y.)
Sunart folding view - c1898. Various Vici and Vidi models. Black leather covered wood body with polished cherry interior. Double extension bellows. B&L RR lens. Unicum shutter. 5x7": $75-135. 4x5": $65-125.

Sunart Jr. - 3½x3½ and 4x5" plate box cameras, similar in style to the Cyclone Sr. $35-50.

SUNBEAM CAMERA CO.
Sunbeam Minicam - Black bakelite minicam for 16 exposures 3x4cm on 127 film. $4-8.

SUNBEAM SIX TWENTY - Gray plastic twin-lens 6x6cm box camera. Sunbeam label conceals the Spartus name beneath. $4-8.

SUNNY - Small Japanese bakelite camera for 24x24mm exposures on 35mm film. Cartridge-to-cartridge film advance with standard 35mm cartridges elimates the need to rewind. Combination eye-level direct or reflex finder with semi-silvered mirror. $30-40. *(illustrated top of next column)*

Sunny

SUPER CAMERA - Japanese paper covered wooden "Yen" cameras for sheet film in paper holders. Folding style: $15-20. Box Style: $10-15.

SUPERIOR FLASH CAMERA 120 - Synchronized metal box camera, 6x9cm. $1-5.

SUTER (E. Suter, Basel, Switzerland)

Detective magazine camera - c1890. Early model for 12 plates, 9x12cm.

Periskop lens, guillotine shutter. Polished wood with nickel trim. $500-600.

Detective magazine camera - c1893. Later model for 20 exposures on 9x12cm plates. Suter f8 lens with iris diaphragm, rotating shutter. Leather covered mahogany box with brass trim. $500-650.

Stereo Detective - c1895. Polished wood stereo box camera for 9x18cm plates. Not a magazine camera. $800-1100.

Stereo Detective, Magazine - c1893. Leather covered stereo magazine camera, for 6 plates 9x18cm. The built-in magazine changing-box sits below the camera body and is operated by pulling on a knob. f10/90mm Rectilinear lenses. Coupled rotary sector shutters. $800-1000.

Stereo Muro - c1890's. Press-type body, side struts, 9x18cm plates. f5/85mm Suter lenses. FP shutter 30-1000. $300-400.

SUZUKI OPTICAL CO. (Japan)

Camera-Lite - Cigarette-lighter spy camera which looks like a Zippo lighter. Very similar to the Echo 8. A supply of Camera-Lites was discovered at a flea market about 1966-67, but released slowly into the collector market. This helped to maintain the same market value for several years. $175-225.

Echo 8 - 1951-56. Cigarette-lighter camera. Designed to look like a Zippo lighter, it also takes 5x8mm photos with its Echor f3.5/15mm lens on film in special cassettes. There are at least two sizes, the larger measuring 17x47x58mm and the earlier but more common smaller size measuring 15x42x56mm. There were also different film cassettes, either "square" or "rapid" shaped. Also sold under the name

Europco-8. $175-225. With presentation box and film slitter add $100.

SWALLOW - Hit type novelty subminiature. $10-15.

TAHBES (Holland)
Populair - c1955. All metal camera with telescoping front. Nickel-plated body with chrome front. $50-60. *(illust. on front cover.)*

TAISEI KOKI (Japan)
Welmy Six - folding camera for 6x6cm on 120 film. Terionar f4.5/75mm or f3.5/75mm lens. Shutter 1-300. Eye-level and waist-level finders. $25-35.

Welmy 35 - Non-rangefinder folding 35mm camera. f3.5 or f2.8/50mm lens. $20-25.

Welmy M-3 - Rangefinder model with Terionar f3.5/45mm in 5-300 shutter. $20-25.

Welmy Wide - c1958. 35mm camera with Taikor f3.5/35mm lens. $20-25.

TAIYODO KOKI (T.K.K., Japan)

Beauty Canter - c1957. Rangefinder 35mm. f2.8 lens. $20-30.

Beauty Super II - c1959. 35mm RF. Canter f2.8/45mm in Copal SV shutter. Lever advance. $20-30.

Beauty Super L - c1959. Similar to Super II, but with built-in meter with booster. Canter-S f1.9/45mm. $25-35.

Beautycord - 6x6cm TLR for 120 film. Beauty f3.5/80mm in 10-200 shutter. $20-25.

Beautyflex - c1954. 6x6cm TLR. f3.5/80mm Doimer Anastigmat lens. Simple shutter. $20-25.

Epochs - c1948. Heavy cast metal subminiature for 14x14mm on "Midget" size rollfilm. Identical to the Vestkam and Meteor cameras. "Epochs" on top only, not on shutter face. This name is not common. $100-150.

Meteor - c1949. Same as Epochs, except for name. "Meteor" name on top and shutter face. This name is not common. $100-150.

Vestkam - c1949. Same as Epochs and Meteor, except for name. Marked "Made in Occupied Japan". This is the most common name. $80-125.

TAIYOKOKI CO., LTD. (Japan)
Viscawide-16 - c1961. Panoramic camera for 10 exposures 10x46mm on specially loaded 16mm film. Lausar f3.5/25mm lens. Shutter 60-300. 120 degree angle of view. $150-200. *(illus. on rear cover.)*

TALBOT (Romain Talbot, Berlin) *Makers of the Errtee cameras. In German, the letters R.T. (for R. Talbot) are pronounced "Err-Tee".*

Errtee button tintype camera - A cylindrical "cannon" for 100 button tintypes 25mm diameter. Processing tank hangs below camera and exposed plates drop through chute. Laack f4.5/60mm lens. Single speed shutter. $700-1000.

Errtee folding plate camera - 9x12cm. Double extension bellows. Laack Pololyt f4.5/135mm lens. Compur shutter 1-200. $25-35.

Errtee folding rollfilm camera - 6x9cm on rollfilm. Anastigmat Talbotar f4.5/105mm in Vario shutter 25-100. Brown bellows and brown leather covering. $30-45.

TALBOT (Walter Talbot, Berlin)

Invisible Camera - c1915-1930. Unusual camera shaped like a 7cm wide belt, 34cm long, with a film chamber at each end. The camera is made to be concealed under a vest with the lens protruding from a buttonhole. The versions advertised around 1930 are made for 35mm daylight-loading cartridges, but these ads usually mention that the camera had been in use for "over 15 years", (before there were standard

35mm cartridges.) We suspect that they were not commercially available in the early years. This suspicion is based on the lack of advertising until the late 1920's, and also because of their rarity in the current collector market. Rare. Price negotiable.

TALBOT & EAMER CO. (London)

Talmer - c1890. Magazine box camera with changing bag. 8x10.5cm plates. $300-350.

TANAKA OPTICAL CO., LTD. (Japan)

Tanack, Type IV-S - Copy of Leica IIIb. Tanar f2/50mm lens. Shutter 1-500. $75-125.

TARGET (Paris)
New Folding Stereo - Folding bed stereo camera for 9x18cm plates. Leathered wood body with polished wood interior and nickel trim. Stereo shutter built into wooden lensboard. Focusing knob on the front of the bed. $250-300. *(illus. on front cover.)*

TAUBER - c1920's. German 9x12cm folding plate camera. Rapid Aplanat f8/135mm lens. $25-35.

TAYLOR (A & G Taylor, England)
View camera - Tailboard style ½-plate mahogany view. Clement & Gilmer brass barrel lens, iris diaphragm. $175-225.

TECHNICOLOR CORP.
Techni-Pak 1 - c1960. Plastic 126 factory loaded cartridge camera. Camera must be returned for processing and reloading. $1-5.

TEDDY CAMERA CO. (Newark, NJ)
Teddy Model A - c1924. Stamped metal camera in bright red and gold finish. Takes direct positive prints 2x3½" which develop in tank below camera. Original price just $2.00 in 1924. Current value with tank: $300-400.

TEEMEE - Japanese novelty subminiature of the Hit type. $10-15.

TELLA CAMERA CO. LTD. (London)
No. 3 Magazine Camera - c1899. Leather covered box camera for 50 films in a filmpack. Taylor Hobson f6.5, pneumatic shutter. Detachable rise/cross front. $350-500.

TENNAR, TENNAR JUNIOR - c1954. Folding cameras for 6x9cm, 620 film. Made in Italy. $12-18.

TEX - c1949. German miniature for 3x4cm on unperforated 35mm film. Collapsing Vidar or Helur f4.5/50mm lens, Singlo or Compur shutter. Most common with Helur in Singlo. Body identical to the Nova camera. $75-100.

THOMAS (W. Thomas, London)
Wet-plate camera - c1870. Folding-bed bellows camera for ½-plates. Brass trim. f11 lens. $800-1200.

THOMPSON (W. J. Thompson Co., NY)
Direct positive street camera - Box-style street tintype camera. Plates, devloping tank, etc. all packed inside the camera's body. $125-150.

THORNTON-PICKARD MFG. CO. (Altrincham, England)
Duplex Ruby Reflex - c1920-30. SLR. Aldis Anastigmat f4.5. FP shutter. $75-100. *(illustrated on next page)*

Thornton-Pickard Photographic Rifle

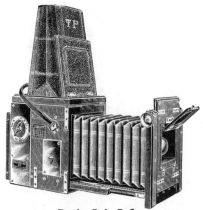

Duplex Ruby Reflex

Duplex Ruby Reflex, Tropical - SLR. 6x9cm and ¼-plate sizes. Teak and brass. Double extension orange bellows. Focal plane shutter to 1000. Cooke Anastigmat f6.3 lens. $1800-2200.

Folding plate camera, 5x7" - c1890. Zeiss Unar f5/210mm lens. Focal plane shutter 15-80. $150-180.

Imperial Pocket - c1916. Folding-bed plate cameras. Lower priced models have wood body, single extension metal bed. Better models have all metal body, rack focusing. $25-35.

Imperial Stereo - c1910. Folding bed camera, 9x18cm. Accomodates single or stereo lensboards. $250-350.

Junior Special Reflex - c1928. Press-type SLR, 6x9cm on plates or 120 rollfilm back. Black leather covering. Dallmeyer Anastigmat f4.5/130mm. FP shutter 10-1000, T. $75-90.

Limit - c1912. Small rigid body camera for 4.5x6cm plates or rollfilm. Cooke f6.3/55mm in telescoping mount. FP shutter 15-100, T. $800-1000.

Photographic Rifle - c1915. Rifle-type camera, 4.5x6cm on 120 rollfilm. Used in WWI to train British R.A.F. machine gunners. f8/300mm. Central shutter. $500-800. *(illustrated above)*

Puck Special - 4x5" plate box camera. Focus and shutter adjustable. $50-60.

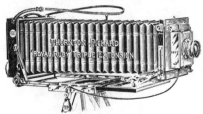

Royal Ruby - Folding plate camera, similar to the Ruby, but triple extension bellows. $175-250.

347

Ruby Reflex

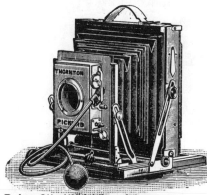

Ruby - 3¼x4¼" folding plate camera. Revolving back, fine wood interior, various correctional movements. Cooke Anastigmat f6.5 lens. $80-100.

Ruby Deluxe - c1912. Mahogany ¼-plate SLR with brass binding. Goerz Dogmar or

Ross Xpres f4.5 lens. Focal plane shutter 10-1000. $125-225.

Ruby Reflex - c1928. 4x5" SLR. Ross Homocentric f6.3/6". FP shutter. $150-250.

Rubyette No. 1, No. 2 - c1934. SLR. 6x9cm for plates or rollfilm. Dallmeyer Anastigmat f8, f4.5 or f2.9 lens. FP shutter 10-1000. $150-250.

Special Ruby Reflex - 2¼x3¼". Cooke Anastigmat f4.5/5" lens. Focal plane shutter. $125-175.

Stereo Puck - c1920's cheap rollfilm box for 6x8.5cm on 120 film. Meniscus lenses, simple shutter. Black covered wood body. $75-100.

Victory Reflex - c1925. 2¼x3¼" SLR Dallmeyer or Cooke lens. $75-100.

THORNWARD DANDY - Detective-type box-plate camera for 4x5" plates. $40-60.

THORPE (J. Thorpe, NY)
Four-tube camera - c1862-64. Wet-plate camera with 4 lenses for up to 4 exposures on a 5x7" plate. One on record in 1980 with wet-plate holder and dipping tank for $1250.

THOWE CAMERAWERK (Freital & Berlin)
9x12cm folding plate camera - c1910. Leather covered wood body. Doxanar f6/ 135mm. Shutter 25-100. $25-35.

Field camera, 9x12cm - Horizontal format. Rear bellows extension. Blue square bellows with black corners. Meyer Primotar f3.5/115mm. $100-150.

TIME-FIELD CO. (Newark, Delaware USA)
Pin-Zip 126 - c1984. Cardboard camera with drilled brass pinhole. Uses 126 cartridge film. An interesting modern pinhole camera, named for the sound made by the light as it enters the pinhole. $5-10.

TIRANTY (Paris)
Stereo Pocket - Jumelle type stereo camera for 45x107mm plates. Transpar f4.5/54mm lenses in Jack shutter 25-100, B,T. With magazine back: $125-175.

TISDELL & WHITTELSEY (pre-1893)
TISDELL CAMERA & MFG. CO. (post-1893) (New York)

T & W Detective Camera - c1888. Detective box camera for 3¼x4¼" plates. All wood box. Truncated pyramid rather than bellows for focusing. Achromatic meniscus lens. Rare. One sold a few years ago for $1200, and another for $2800.

Tisdell Hand Camera - c1893. In 1893, the name of the T & W Detective Camera was changed to "Tisdell Hand Camera". Leather covered. Internal bellows focus. $400-650.

TIVOLI - c1895. English ½-plate camera. Mahogany body. Rectilinear lens. $175-225.

TIZER CO. LTD.
Can Camera 110 TX Coca-Cola - c1970's. Camera the size and color of a Japanese 250ml Coke can. 110 cartridge film. Synched and non-synched versions. Fixed focus. Single speed shutter. $70-80. *See Eiko Co. Ltd. for later can cameras from Hong Kong.*

TOAKOKI SEISAKUSHO (Japan)
Gelto D III - c1930's. ½-frame 127 film camera. Grimmel f3.5/50mm collapsible

lens. Gold and chrome finish. $50-75.

TOGODO OPTICAL CO. (Japan)
Established in 1930 by Masanori Nagatsuka and named for Admiral Tougo of the Japanese Navy. ("Togodo" and "Tougodo" are roman spelling variations of the same name.)

TOHOKOKEN CAMERA CO.
Camel Model II - c1953. Inexpensive 35mm camera with styling similar to Canon, but with front shutter and no rangefinder. Even the type style for the name "Camel" is similar to the style used by Canon. Camel f3.5/45mm. Nippol 1-200 shutter. $30-45.

TOKIWA SEIKI CO. (Japan)
Firstflex - c1951-55. A series of 6x6cm TLR cameras. f3.5/80mm. Some models have shutters to 1/200, others have MSK 1-400 shutter, B. Cheaply made. $15-25.

Firstflex 35 - 1954. 35mm SLR with waist-level finders. Removeable bayonet-mount lens. Leaf shutter. $75-100.

Soligor I, II, Semi-Auto - 6x6cm TLR for 120 film. Soligor f3.5/80mm, Rektor rim-set shutter. $25-35.

Soligor 35 - c1955. 35mm SLR. Waist-level finder. Interchangeable Soligor f3.5/50 lens. Leaf shutter 1-200, B. Built-in meter. Same camera as the earlier Firstflex 35, but sold originally with a different lens. $60-90.

Soligor 45 - c1955. Viewfinder 35mm. Soligor f4.5/40mm. Shutter 25-100. $20-35.

Soligor 66 - c1957. 6x6cm SLR. Interchangeable Soligor f3.5/80mm. FP shutter 25-500, T,B. $60-100.

TOKYO KOGAKU (Japan)
Laurelflex - c1954. 6x6cm TLR. Toko f3.5/75mm. Seikosha Rapid 1-500, B. $30-40.

Minion - c1938. Folding bed camera for 4x5cm on 127 film. Toko f3.5/60mm. Seikosha Licht 25-100, B,T. $50-75.

Minion 35 - c1948. Viewfinder 35mm. Toko f3.5/40mm. Seikosha Rapid 1-500, B. $50-75.

Primo Jr. - c1958. 4x4cm TLR for 127 film. Sold in the U.S.A. by Sawyers. $80-110.

Teleca - c1950. 10x14mm subminiature. 16mm telephoto camera built into binoculars. Non-prismatic field glasses have camera mounted on top center. $300-375.

Topcon RE Super - Introduced 1963. The first fully 35mm SLR with fully coupled through the lens metering system. (Note that the Mec-16 SB subminiature already had a coupled behind the lens metering system in 1960.) Removable prism. FP shutter 1-1000. With f1.4/58mm lens: $100-150.

TOKYO KOKI CO. (Japan)

Rubina Sixteen Model II - Subminiature for unperforated 16mm film in special cassettes. Made in Occupied Japan. Ruby f3.5 lens. $100-125.

TOKYO SEIKI CO. LTD. - see Rocket Camera Co.

TOMIOKA (Japan)
Pigeon 35 - c1950. Viewfinder 35. Triplet Tomioka Tri-Lausar f3.5/45mm. N.K.S. 1-200, B shutter. $20-30.

TOP CAMERA - Bakelite Japanese subminiature camera with metal front and back. The entire camera is finished in grey hammertone enamel so it looks like an all-metal camera. Rectangular shape is similar to the Minolta-16, but construction quality is more like the Hit-types. Takes 14x14mm exposures on standard "Midget" size rollfilm. Meniscus lens, single speed shutter. $50-75.

TOPPER - Cheap plastic box camera for 127 film. Long shutter release plunger on left side. $3-7.

TOUGODO OPTICAL (Japan)
Hobiflex, Model III - c1950. 6x6cm TLR. Externally gear-coupled lenses. Hobi Anastigmat f3.5/80. Shutter to 200. $20-25.

Hobix, Hobix Junior - Compact camera for 24x36mm on 828 film. All-metal. Meniscus f11/40mm. Shutter, T,I, X sync. $20-30.

Leader - c1950's. Japanese 35mm stereo. Looks like the Windsor Stereo. Black bakelite with aluminum trim. Leader Anastigmat f4.5/45mm lenses, 3 speed shutter 1/25-1/100. Takes single or stereo exposures. $75-125.

Meikai - c1937. Twin lens reflex for 35mm film. In addition to the normal viewfinder for eye-level framing, this uniquely Japanese design incorporates a waist-level reflex finder with true twin-lens focusing. The lenses are located side-by-side, which allowed the overall size to be only barely larger than a standard 35mm rangefinder camera. The first two models used "No Need Darkroom" sheet film in paper holders for daylight developing. (See "Yen-Kame" for description of this process.) The first rollfilm versions c1939 used 16-exposure spools of paper-backed 35mm wide rollfilm for 3x4cm exposures. Meikai f3.5 or f4.5/50mm Anastigmat. Later models used standard 35mm film, and had f3.8/50mm Meikai Anastigmat. Early sheetfilm or rollfilm versions: $400-450. Standard 35mm models: $300-350.

Meikai EL - Cheap 35mm novelty camera. $8-12.

Meisupi, Meisupi II - c1930's. Side-by-side twin lens camera for 4x5cm on special film cassettes. Uncommon. $300-500. *(illustrated top of next column)*

Tougodo Meisupi

Meisupii Half - Simple inexpensive 35mm half-frame camera. $8-12.

Stereo Hit - c1955. Plastic stereo camera for 127 film. f4.5 lens. Synch shutter. $75-125.

Tougo Camera - 1930. The Tougo Camera was the first of the popular "Yen" cameras from Japan, produced by Tougo-do in the Kanda district of Tokyo. The camera itself is of simple construction, with a wood body with a paper covering, ground glass back, and simple shutter. The most historically significant feature was the novel film system, which incorporated a 3x4cm sheet of film in a paper holder. The disposable film holder also carried the film through the developing process without the need of a darkroom. The process used a red-colored developer, which effectively filtered daylight into red light. Its simplicity made it very popular, and soon there were many other simple "Yen" cameras on the market. An early example (clearly identified "Tougo Camera" on the shutter face) would easily fetch $50+ from a knowledgeable collector, while the later versions usually sell for $10-15.

Toyoca 16 - c1955. 14x14mm subminiature, styled like a miniature 35mm. "Toyoca 16" on top. Two models;

essentially identical except that the "improved" model has exposure counting numbers on the winding knob. $80-95. *Not to be confused with at least two other styles of "Toyoca" which are cheaper novelty cameras of the "Hit" type. $100-125.*

Toyoca 35 - c1955. 35mm camera styled like Nikon S-2. Lausar f2.8 or Owla f3.5/ 45mm lens. $30-35.

Toyocaflex - c1953. 6x6cm Rolleicord copy. Tri-Lausar f3.5/80mm. Synchro NKS 1-200 shutter. $25-35.

Toyocaflex 35 - c1955. Side-by-side 35mm TLR. Direct and reflex finders. Owla Anastigmat f3.5/45mm viewing and taking lenses. NSK shutter 1-300, B. $350-500.

TOWN - An unusual marriage of two

Japanese specialties of the postwar period. This camera is styled just like the Hit types, but is considerably larger, taking 24x24mm exposures on "Bolta-size" rollfilm. "Made in Occupied Japan" on front. Unusual and uncommon. Only one known sale, in 1984 for $100.

TOY'S CLAN

Donald Duck Camera - Plastic camera shaped like Donald Duck's head. The lens is in one eye and the viewfinder in the other. The tongue serves as a shutter release lever. Takes 3x4cm photos on 127 film. Made in Hong Kong. We saw one at a German auction in the 1970's, but never again until 1984 when a small number, new in boxes, came into circulation and rapidly began selling to avid duck fans for $60-90.

TOYO KOGAKU (TOKO), Japan

Mighty - c1947. Made in Occupied Japan. Subminiature for 13x13mm exposures on "Midget" size rollfilm. Meniscus lens, single speed shutter. With auxiliary telephoto attachment in case: $75-125. Camera only: $50-75.

Tone - c1948. Subminiature for 14x14mm on "Midget" size rollfilm. Made in Occupied Japan. Eye-level and waist-level finders. f3.5/25mm lens in 3 speed shutter. $75-100.

TOYOCA - Lightweight Japanese novelty camera of the Hit type. $10-15. *Not to be confused with the heavy "Toyoca 16" made by Tougodo.*

TRAID CORPORATION (Encino, CA)

Fotron & Fotron III - Grey and black plastic cameras of the 1960's, originally sold by door-to-door salesmen for prices ranging from $150 to $300 and up. The cameras were made to take 10 exposures 1x1" on special cartridges containing 828 film. They featured many high-class advancements such as built-in electronic flash with rechargeable batteries, electric film advance, etc. At the time these cameras were made, these were expensive features. Still, the Fotron camera campaign is considered by some to be the greatest photographic "rip-off" of the century. $25-35.

TRAMBOUZE (Paris)

Plate camera - 13x18cm. Brass barreled f8 lens. $175-225.

TRAVELER - 14x14mm "Hit" type Japanese novelty subminiature. $10-15.

TRAVELLER - Simple plastic Hong Kong 6x6cm TLR-style novelty camera. Shutter 25, 50. $10-15. *(illustrated top of next column)*

TRU-VIEW - 4x4cm "Diana" type novelty camera. $1-5.

Traveller

TRUMPFREFLEX - German-made 6x6cm TLR sold in the U.S. by Sears. Probably made by Balda. Looks very similar to the Balda Reflecta. Parallax correction accomplished by the taking lens tilting up at close focusing distances. Normally found with Trioplan f3.5/75mm lens. Shutter 1-300. $20-25.

TRUSITE CAMERA CO.

Girl Scout Official Camera - Like the Trusite Minicam, but with Girl Scout faceplate. $25-35.

Trusite Minicam - c1947. Cast metal minicam for 3x4cm on 127 film. $5-10.

T.S.C. TACKER - 14x14mm subminiature from Occupied Japan. f4.5 lens, rotary disc stops. Shutter 25, 50, 100, B. $150-175.

TSUBASA SEMI, SEMI SUPER CHROME - Folding bed camera, 4.5x6cm on 120. Bessel f3.5 or Lucomar f4.5 lens. Shutter 25-150. $25-35.

TSUBASAFLEX JUNIOR - Inexpensive 6x6cm TLR. Lenses externally gear-coupled. $20-25.

TURILLON (Louis Turillon, Paris)

Photo-Ticket No. 2 - c1905. Aluminum jumelle-style rollfilm camera; No. 2 for 4x5cm, No. 3 for 4.5x6cm. Petzval-type f4.5/95mm. FP shutter. $800-1200.

TURRET CAMERA CO. (Brooklyn, N.Y.)

Panoramic camera - c1905. For 4x10" panoramic views. $700-900.

TYLAR (William T. Tylar, Birmingham, England)
Tit-bit - c1895. Makes 2 exposures on a 6x9cm plate. Lens is mounted on circular plate which is rotated to position it over one half of the plate to make the first exposure, then rotated again over the other side to make the second exposure. $250-350. *(illustrated top of next column)*

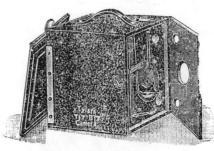

Tylar Tit-bit

TYNAR CORP. (Los Angeles, CA)

Tynar - c1950. For 14 exposures, 10x14mm on specially loaded 16mm cassettes. f6.3/45mm lens. Single speed guillotine shutter. Shaped like a small movie camera (similar to Universal Minute 16). $20-30.

UCA (Uca Werkstatten fuer Feinmechanik & Optik, Flensburg, Germany) *Associated with the Elop Kamerawerk of Flensburg.*

Ucaflex - c1950. 35mm SLR. Elolux f1.9/50mm lens. Focal plane shutter, 1-1000.

Also sold under the name Elcaflex. $175-275.

United Optical Merlin

UCET - Box camera for 6.5x11cm. $5-10.

ULCA CAMERA CORP. (Pittsburgh, PA)
Ulca - c1935. 20x20mm on rollfilm. Meniscus lens, simple shutter. Cast steel body. $25-45. *Note: Ulca cameras were also made in England and Germany. The shutter settings are the best indication of country of origin. TMS & STM are German. STI- English. TSL- American.*

UNDERWOOD (E. T. Underwood, Birmingham, England)

Field camera - 8x11cm. Rear extension, square leather bellows. Underwood f11 brass-barrel lens with iris diaphragm. Thornton-Pickard shutter. Swing-out ground glass. $150-200.

UNGER & HOFFMAN (Dresden)
Verax - Precision folding plate cameras, in 4.5x6 and 6.5x9cm sizes. Single extension bellows. f3.5 or 4.5 lens. Compound shutter 1-300. Ground glass back. $50-75.

UNION-BOX - c1950's. Box camera for 6x6cm. M & Z shutter. Union-Box nameplate below lens. $25-35.

UNITED OPTICAL INSTRUMENTS (England)
Merlin - c1936. Cast-metal 20x20mm subminiature. Black, blue, or green crackle-finish enamel. No identification on the camera except small name decal on some examples. $50-100. *(illustrated at left)*

UNITED STATES CAM-O CORP.
CAM-O - TLR "School camera". 250 exposures 4x6.5cm on 70mm film. Wollensak Raptar f4.5/117mm. Alphax shutter. $35-50.

UNITED STATES CAMERA CORP. (Chicago)

Box and TLR cameras - cheap cameras such as Reflex, Reflex II, Vagabond, etc. $1-5.

Auto Fifty - TLR for 6x6cm on 120. Biokor f3.5/80mm. Synchro MX 1-300, B. Made in Japan. $25-40.

Rollex 20 - Folding 6x9cm rollfilm camera with self-erecting front. Cheap construction. $4-8.

USC 35 - Viewfinder 35mm. Made in Germany. Built-in extinction meter. Steinheil Cassar f2.8/45mm. Vario 25-200 shutter. $15-25.

UNIVERSAL CAMERA CORP. (NYC) *The Universal Camera Corporation was founded on January 26, 1933 in New York by Otto Wolff Githens and Jacob J. Shapiro. Githens, a former New York loan company executive and Shapiro, ex-vice president of an Indianapolis insurance firm formed the company on the assumption that what America needed most was a photographic line that would be affordable to everyone. The company boasted of manufacturing "more cameras per year than any other company in the world". That claim may very well have been true. Their first* venture, Univex Model A, at a cost of $.39, sold over 3 million in 3 years. Universal's early success was not solely attributed to the sale of inexpensive cameras; but more so to the sale of the low-cost six exposure rollfilm that was necessary to utilize these cameras. The #00 rollfilm, which was packaged in Belgium on a special patented V-spool, sold for only $.10 in the United States. Twenty-two million rolls were sold by 1938. The special Univex films proved to be one of the major factors responsible for the company's collapse twenty years later.

Universal became involved with home movies in 1936, when it introduced the model A-8 camera for just under $10 and its companion P-8 projector for less than $15. They used a special Univex Single-8 film, manufactured by Ansco. In the next two years, 250,000 cameras and 175,000 projectors were sold.

During Universal's brief existence, it manufactured almost forty different still and movie cameras and a complete line of photographic accessories. The 1939 New York World's Fair provided Universal with an opportunity to exhibit the newly introduced non-standard 35mm Mercury and the new B-8 and C-8 movie cameras.

Universal verged on bankruptcy in 1940, when all film shipments from Belgium were temporarily suspended because of the war in Europe. Two years later there was still a film shortage, even though Universal was now packaging its film in the United States. The U.S. entry in the war brought Universal a government contract to manufacture binoculars, gunsights, and other optics, and by 1943 Universal had acquired $6,000,000 in sales from the United States government.

After the war, Universal returned to its pre-war line of cameras, some of which were given different names. Having gained experience in optics during the war years, Universal was now able to manufacture most of their own lenses. Universal again met with financial difficulties during the 1948-49 recession. At that time, Universal's prized post-war Mercury II was, for the most part, rejected by the public, mainly because the price had been set at more than triple that of the pre-war Mercury! Two other reasons for the eventual failure of Universal presumably were the $2,000,000 investment into the poorly designed Minute-16 and another investment into a complicated automatic phonograph. Neither of these items proved profitable. Consequently, Universal declared bankruptcy on April 15, 1952.

Universal never gained much respect from the photographic industry, because its business practices were generally believed to be somewhat unethical. Nevertheless, the one thing that Universal will always be remembered for is the originality and ingenuity it displayed in designing some of the most unusual cameras in America.

Our thanks to Cynthia Repinski for her help with the Universal Camera Company in this section and in the movie camera section at the end of the book. Cindy is an active collector of all products of the Universal Camera Co. (See her ad at the back of the book.) If you have questions on rare Universal items, you may contact Cindy at N80 W13004 Fond du Lac Ave. Apt. 24, Menomonee Falls, WI 53051.

Buccaneer - 1945-52. Bakelite 35mm camera. CRF. f3.5/50mm Tricor lens. Chronomatic shutter 10-300. Built-in extinction meter, flash sync. $20-25.

Corsair I & II - c1941. For 24x36mm exposures on perforated 35mm film in special cartridges. Univex f4.5/50mm lens in rimset shutter 25-200. $20-25.

Duovex - c1938. Two Univex A's mounted in a special attachment for stereo work. Manufactured by Pacific Coast Merchandise Co. of Los Angeles and sold as a package with a simple metal viewer and 12 mounting cards. Scarce. With viewer and original box $250-300. Camera only $130-140.

Iris - c1940. Heavy cast-metal camera for 6 exposures 1⅛x1½" on No. 00 Universal

film. Vitar f7.9/50mm lens. Ilex shutter. Common. $10-15.

Iris Deluxe - c1940. Similar to the standard Iris, but with leatherette covering and chromium finish. Late Deluxe models had an adjustable focus lens, focusing to 4'. Some models have been fitted with a flash unit which required drilling and mounting. There is currently no price difference with or without the flash. Not common. $20-28.

Mercury (Model CC) - 1938-42. The first Mercury model. Takes 18x24mm vertical exposures on Universal No. 200 film, a special 35mm wide film. Wollensak Tricor

Mercury II (Model CX)

f3.5/35mm lens. Rotating focal plane shutter, 1/20-1/1000. Common. $20-35.

Mercury (Model CC-1500) - 1939-40. Similar to the standard model CC but with 1/1500 shutter speed. Wollensak Hexar f2.0 or f2.7 lens. Scarce. $120-140. *Note: This price is for the combination of the rare body and the rare Hexar lens. One without the other would only bring half as much.*

Mercury II (Model CX) - c1945. Similar to Mercury CC, but for 65 exposures on standard 35mm film. Universal Tricor f2.7 or f3.5/35mm. Rotary shutter 20-1000. Common. $20-35. *(illustrated bottom of previous column)*

Meteor - For 6x6cm on 620 rollfilm. Telescoping front. Extinction meter. $8-12.

Minute 16 - c1950's. 16mm subminiature which resembles a miniature movie camera. Meniscus f6.3 lens. Guillotine shutter. Very common. With flash and original box: $35-40. Camera only: $10-15.

Norton-Univex - c1935. Cheap black plastic camera taking 6 exposures on Univex #00 film. Because of the overwhelming success in 1933 of the Univex Model A, the Norton camera made by Norton Labs never gained public interest when introduced in 1934. The Norton-Univex appeared in 1935, after Norton Labs sold the remains of their line to Universal. Not common. $15-25.

flash & box: $8-12. Camera only: $1-5.

Roamer I - Folding camera for 8 exposures 2¼x3¼" on 620 film. Coated f11 lens, single speed shutter, flash sync. $8-12.

Roamer II - similar. f4.5 lens. $8-12.

Roamer 63 - Folding camera for 120 or 620 film. Universal Anastigmat Synchromatic f6.3/100mm lens. $8-12.

Stere-All - c1954. For pairs of 24x24mm exposures on 35mm film. Tricor f3.5/35mm lenses, single speed shutter. $40-55.

Uniflex, Models I & II - c1948. TLR for 120 or 620 rollfilm. Universal lens, f5.6 or 4.5/75mm. Shutter to 200. $10-20.

Twinflex - c1941. Plastic TLR for 1⅛x1½" (29x38mm) on No. 00 rollfilm. Meniscus lens, simple shutter. $20-25.

Uniflash - cheap plastic camera for #00 rollfilm. f16/60mm Vitar lens. With original

Univex, Model A - c1933. The original small black plastic gem for No. 00 rollfilm. Similar to the Norton, which was originally designed for Universal Camera Corp. Wire frame sportsfinder attached to front of camera, and molded plastic rear sight. Cost $0.39 when new. $8-15.

Univex, Model A, Century of Progress - c1933. Special commemorative model of the simple Model A camera made for the Chicago World's Fair. $50-75.

Univex AF, AF-2, AF-3, AF-4, AF-5 - ca. late 1930's. A series of compact collapsing cameras for No. 00 rollfilm. Cast metal body. Various color combinations. $10-18.

Univex AF, Special models - c1938. Special faceplates and colors transformed the normal Univex AF into a promotional or premium camera. These include such models as the Official Girl Scout model, G.E. Toppers Club Convention, or the Hollywood. $25-45.

Vitar - c1952. Viewfinder 35mm. Extinction meter. Telescoping Anastigmat f3.5/50mm lens. This camera was a promotional item and supposedly never advertised to the public. Not common. $20-25.

Zenith - c1940. Lightweight aluminum body, leatherette covering, chrome finish. Six exposures on Univex #00 film. Univex f4.5/50mm, shutter 25-200. Lens focuses to 3½'. Rare. $75-150.

UNIVERSAL RADIO MFG. CO.
Cameradio - ca. late 1940's. 3x4cm TLR box camera built into a portable tube radio. Like the Tom Thumb listed under Automatic Radio Mfg. Co. $100-125.

UTILITY MFG. CO. (New York & Chicago)

Misc. cheap cameras, 3x4cm - including Carlton, Falcon Midget, Falcon Minette, Falcon Miniature, Falcon Minicam Junior, Falcon Model V16, Falcon Special, Rex Miniature, Spartus Miniature, etc. $3-7.

Falcon - 4x6.5cm folding 127 camera. Cast metal body with black or colored enamel. $10-15.

Falcon De-Luxe - Half-frame 127. Wollensak f3.5/50mm. Alphax 25-200 shutter. Telescoping lens mount. $15-20.

Falcon Junior - Bakelite folding vest-pocket camera for 4x6.5cm on 127 film. At least two different faceplate styles with different art-deco patterns. Colored models: $10-20. Black: $5-10.

Falcon Minicam Senior - Half-frame (3x4cm) camera for 16 exposures on 127 film. Cast aluminum body with leatherette covering. Minivar 50mm lens. Optical finder is in an elongated top housing, as though styled to look like a rangefinder. Has a body release, which is unusual for this type of camera. The same camera was also sold under the Falcon Camera Co. name in Chicago. $10-15.

Falcon Model Four - 6x9cm self-erecting folding camera. Pre-1940 model has black art-deco shutter face. $10-15.

Falcon Model V-16 - Bakelite folding vest-pocket camera identical to the Falcon Junior, but for 16 exposures 3x4cm (½-frame) on 127 film. Colored models: $10-20. Black: $5-10.

Falcon Press Flash - Bakelite 6x9cm box camera, with built-in flash for Edison-base bulbs. Forerunner of Spartus Press Flash. The first camera with built-in flash, introduced in April 1939 under the Falcon Press Flash and Spartus Press Flash name. $5-10.

Falcon-Flex, 3x4cm - TLR-style novelty camera for 127 film. Cast aluminum body. Similar in style to the Clix-O-Flex. $10-15.

Falcon-Flex, 6x6cm - Pseudo-TLR box camera. Cast aluminum body. $8-12.

Girl Scout Falcon - Half-frame 127. Green front plate with Girl Scout logo. $10-15.

VAN DYKE BITTERS CAMERA - Box camera for 9x9cm dry plates in double holders. An early example of a camera used as a premium. $60-80.

VANGUARD - Cast metal camera styled like a 35mm, but for 4x4cm on 127. Telescoping front. $8-12.

VANITY FAIR
Character 126 cartridge cameras - "Recent" collectibles. Prices are for NEW condition.
Barbie Cameramatic, Holly Hobbie, Sunny-Bunch, Super Star - $4-8.

Incredible Hulk, Spider-Man - $9-15.

VARIMEX (Poland)

Alfa 2 - c1963. Vertical format 35mm. Aqua body, cream colored trim. Emitar f4.5/45mm. Shutter 30-125. Unusual style. $75-125.

VARSITY CAMERA CORP.

Varsity Model V - Streamlined oval bakelite camera for 1⅜x1⅜" exposures on rollfilm. Also called the "Streamline Model V". $5-15.

VAUXHALL - Folding camera for 12 or 16 exposures on 120 film. Styled like Zeiss Super Ikonta. f2.9 lens. Coupled rangefinder. $30-40.

VEGA (Geneva, Switzerland)

subject-to-lens distance. $50-75.

VICTORY MFG. CO.
Lone Ranger - Photo-ette novelty camera for 28x40mm on 828 with drawing of Lone Ranger on his horse. $15-20.

VIDMAR CAMERA CO. (New York, NY)

Vega - c1900. Folding book-style camera for plates. The camera opens like a book, the lens being in the "binding" position, and the bellows fanning out like pages. Plate changing mechanism operated by opening and closing the camera. $500-700.

Vidax - c1948. Rollfilm press-type camera for 3 formats on 620 film: 6x9cm, 6x6cm, 4.5x6cm. Also accepts cut film or filmpacks. Ektar f4.5. Built-in RF. $250-350.

VENA (Amsterdam, Netherlands)
Venaret - Telescoping camera for 6x6cm exposures on 120 film. f7.7/75mm doublet lens. Simple shutter 25, 50. Leather covered metal body. Nickel trim. $15-20.

VICAM PHOTO APPLIANCE CORP. (Philadelphia, PA)
Vicamphoto - A compact "school camera" for bulk rolls of 35mm unperforated film. Fixed focus lens. Small compartment on front conceals the string used to measure

VIFLEX - c1905. Unusual SLR box camera for 4x5" plates, or sheetfilm.

When folded, viewing hood becomes carry case. $200-250.

VINTEN (W. Vinten, Ltd., London)
Aerial reconnaissance camera - For 500 exposures 55mm square on 70mm film. Black laquered body. Anastigmat f2/4" lens. $100-150.

VIVE CAMERA CO. (Chicago)
Folding B.B. - Folding "cycle" style camera for 4x5" plates. $40-60.

M.P.C. (Mechanical Plate Changing) - c1900. Magazine plate box cameras. Side crank advances plates. Two sizes: for 4¼x4¼" or 4x5" plates. Focusing model was called "Vive Focusing Portrait and View Camera". $45-60.

Souvenir Camera - c1895. Small cardboard box camera for single plates, 6x6.5cm. "Vive Souvenir Camera" in gold letters on front. $75-125.

Vive No. 1 - c1897. The first commercially successful U.S. camera to use the dark-sleeve to change plates in a camera. Actually, the Blair Tourograph had a sleeve (mitt) in 1879, but there was very limited production. For 12 plates 4¼x4¼". Simple lens and shutter. $60-90.

Vive No. 2 - c1897. An improved model of the Vive No. 1, with a self-capping shutter, and viewfinder at the center front. $55-85.

Vive No. 4 - c1899. Focusing model. $55-85.

Vive Stereo - For stereo pairs on 3½x6" plates. Similar to the No. 1, but stereo. $400-500.

Vive Tourist - c1897. Like the Vive No. 1, but for 4x5" plates. $55-85.

VOIGT JUNIOR MODEL 1 - Horizontally styled bakelite folding camera for 6x6cm on 120 film. Identical to the Vokar, Model B. Not made by Voigtlander, but "Voigt" is written on the camera in script deceptively similar to Voigtlander. Similar cameras also sold under the Wirgin Deluxe and Vokar names. $15-25.

VOIGTLÄNDER & SON (Braunschweig)
Please note that the Voigtländer name has never had the letter "h" in it until collectors started spelling it incorrectly.

Alpin - 1907-28. Folding plate camera for horizontal format 9x12cm plates. Light metal body, painted black. Black tapered triple extension bellows. Voigtländer Collinear f6.8/120mm or Heliar f4.5/135mm lens. Koilos, Compound, or Compur shutter. $125-150.

Alpin Stereo-Panoram - c1914-26. Stereo version of the Alpin camera in the

10x15cm size. Stereo Compound or Compur shutter. $350-450.

Avus - folding plate cameras:
- 6.5x9cm - Skopar f4.5/105mm. Compur 1-250. $40-50.

- 9x12cm - Skopar f4.5/135mm. Compur. $40-50.

Bergheil folding plate cameras - c1914-1920's. *Note: Models in colors other than black are listed below under Bergheil Deluxe. Actually, the 4.5x6cm and 6x9cm sizes are less common in the standard black color that in the deluxe versions, but lack the appeal of the colored leather models.*
- 4.5x6cm - Folding plate camera with double extension bellows. Heliar f4.5/80mm lens, Compur 1-300 shutter. Rare in this size. $150-200.

- 6x9cm - c1930. Heliar f4.5/105 lens. Compur 1-250. Bayonet system for interchanging of lens/shutter units. $75-95.

- 9x12cm - c1925. Double extension. Heliar f4.5/135mm lens. Compound or Compur shutter. $75-95.

- 10x15cm - c1924. Radionar f6.8, Skopar f4.5/165 or Kollinear f6.3/165mm lens. Compur shutter. $75-100.

Bergheil Deluxe - *There are two distinct styles of the Bergheil Deluxe. The most deluxe and desirable is the small 4.5x6cm model with BROWN leather and bellows and GOLD metal parts. The larger versions with green Russian leather covering and green bellows are a step up from the normal black models, but are not truly "Luxus" models.*

- 4.5x6cm, Deluxe - Brown leather, brown bellows, gold colored metal parts. Heliar f4.5/75mm lens; Compur 1-300 shutter. $400-600.

- 6x9cm, Deluxe - Green leathered body and green bellows. f3.5 or 4.5/105 Heliar lens. Compur 1-200 shutter. Nickel trim. $125-175.

- 9x12cm Deluxe - Green leather and bellows. $100-140.

Bessa cameras:

Folding rollfilm models - c1931-49. Various shutter/lens combinations, including Voigtar, Vaskar, and Skopar lenses f3.5 to f7.7. Single, Prontor, or Compur shutters. Better models with f3.5 or f4.5 lens tend to fall in the range of $20-35. Models with f6.3 or f7.7 lens usually sell for $10-25.

Bessa 6x6

Bessamatic - 35mm SLR. Skopar f2.8/50mm lens. Common. $50-75.

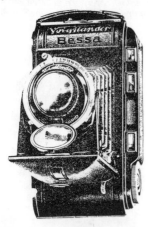

Bessa RF - c1936. f3.5/105mm Heliar, Helomar, or Skopar lens. Compur shutter. $75-110.

Bessamatic Deluxe - c1963. Similar, but diaphragm and shutter speed visible in finder. Externally recognizable by the small T-shaped window above the meter cell. With Septon f2 lens: $75-125. With Skopar f2.8: $50-75.

Bessa I - f3.5/105 Skopar or Helomar, or f4.5 Vaskar lens. $40-50.

Bessa II - c1950. Coupled rangefinder. With Apo-Lanthar f4.5 (rare): $500-750. With Heliar f3.5 or Skopar f3.5/105mm: $175-300.

Bessa 6x6 "Baby Bessa" - c1930. f3.5/75mm Voigtar or Skopar, or f4.5 Vaskar lens. Common. $25-45. *(illustrated top of next column)*

Bijou - c1908. The first miniature SLR, 4.5x6cm plates. All-metal box body, tapers toward the front. Helical focusing lens, Ross WA Xpress f4/4". $500-550.

Heliar Reflex

Brillant - c1933. Cheap TLR camera. 75mm f6.3 or 7.7 Voigtar, f4.5 Skopar, or f3.5 Heliar lens. Quite common. $15-25.

Daguerreotype "cannon" - Reproduction of the original 1841 Voigtländer brass Daguerreotype camera. 31cm long, 35cm high. Makes 80mm diameter image. $1000-1500.

Dynamatic, Dynamatic II - c1961. 35mm with automatic electronic meter. Lanthar or Color-Skopar f2.8/50mm in Prontormat-SV or Prontor-Matic-V shutter. $30-50.

Folding plate cameras (misc. models) - $25-35.

Folding rollfilm cameras (misc. models) - $15-45.

Heliar Reflex - c1902. Boxy SLR for 9x12cm plates. Heliar f4.5/180mm. FP shutter 20-1000. $150-250. *(illustrated top of next column)*

Inos, Inos II - c1930's. Folding bed camera with self-erecting front. For 6x9cm exposures on 120 film. Compur to 250, or Embezet shutter to 100. With Skopar f4.5/ 105mm: $45-65. With Heliar: $50-80.

Inos II, Two-format model - For 6x9cm or 4.5x6cm with reducing masks. Skopar f4.5/105mm lens. Compur 1-250 shutter. $50-75.

Jubilar - Folding camera for 6x9cm on 120 rollfilm. Voigtar f9 lens. $13-18.

Perkeo I - c1960. Folding camera for 6x6cm exposures on 120 film. Prontor shutter. f4.5 Vaskar lens. $25-45.

Perkeo II - similar, but with f3.5 Color Skopar in Synchro-Compur shutter. $45-65.

Perkeo E - Like the Perkeo II, but with rangefinder. Color-Skopar lens in Prontor SVS shutter. $125-150.

Perkeo, 3x4cm - c1938. Folding camera with self-erecting front. For 16 exposures 3x4cm on 127 film. Camera can be focused before opening, via external knob. Heliar or Skopar f3.5 or 4.5/55mm lens. $125-225.

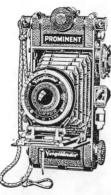

Prominent - c1932. Folding camera for 6x9cm on 120 film, or 4.5x6cm with reducing masks. Self-erecting front. Coupled split-image rangefinder. Extinction meter. Heliar f4.5/105mm lens in Compur 1-250 shutter. $300-450. *(Like several other desirable cameras, this one hit a peak a few years ago and has settled back to a more stable price.)*

Prominent - ca. mid-1950's. With f2 Ultron or f1.5 Nokton: $75-125.
Prominent II - $125-150.

Stereflektoskop - c1913-1930's. Stereo cameras with plate changing magazine. 45x107mm and 6x13cm sizes. Three Heliar f4.5 lenses in Stereo Compur shutter. This is a three-lens reflex, the center lens for 1:1 reflex viewing. This style was later used in the Heidoscop and Rolleidoscop cameras:

45x107mm size - $200-300.
6x13cm size - $270-400.

Stereophotoskop - Rigid-body stereo camera for 45x107mm plates. Magazine back for 12 plates. $175-225.

Superb - c1933. TLR for 120 film. A prism reflects the settings for easy visibility. With Heliar: $175-225. With f3.5/75mm Skopar: $125-175.

Vag - c1920's. Folding plate cameras,

6x9cm and 9x12cm sizes. f6.3 Voigtar or f4.5 Skopar lens in Ibsor or Embezet shutter. $25-35.

Virtus - c1935. Similar to the Prominent, but smaller, and more common. For 16 exposures on 120 film. Automatically focuses to infinity upon opening. Heliar f3.5/75mm. Compur shutter 1-250. $125-175.

Vitessa Cameras: *A series of smartly-styled folding 35mm cameras introduced in 1950. "Barn-doors" on front. Several variations: Originally had smooth top without shoe. Manual parallax correction. Pressure plate hinged to body, not back. Ultron f2 lens only. Second variation, still 1950, had the pressure plate on the back door. Third model, 1951, has sync contact on door, accessory shoe top, and automatic parallax correction. f2.0 or f2.8 lens.*

Vitessa - c1950. 35mm camera. f2.8 Color Skopar or f2 Ultron lens. Synchro Compur 1-500 shutter. Coupled rangefinder. Common. $60-85.

Vitessa L - c1954. Like Vitessa (1951 type) but with selenium meter. Ultron f2/50mm lens. Coupled rangefinder. $85-110. *(illustrated top of next column)*

Vitessa N - c1951. Same as 1951 Vitessa, but f3.5 Color Skopar only. $50-75.

Vitessa L

Vitessa T - f2.8/50mm Color Skopar lens. Compur 1-500 shutter, sync. Coupled rangefinder. Common. $60-80.

Vito II

Vito - c1950. Folding style 35mm. Skopar f3.5/50mm lens in Compur 1-300. $25-35.

Vito II - c1950. 35mm. Color Skopar f3.5 or Ultron f2 lens in Prontor or Compur. $30-40. *(illustrated bottom of previous page)*

Vito IIa - Less common than the Vito and Vito II. $30-45.

Vito III - c1950. Folding style with coupled rangefinder. f2 Ultron. Synchro Compur 1-500 shutter. $75-125.

Vito B

Vito BL

Vito B - Normally with f3.5 Color Skopar in Pronto or Prontor SVS shutter. Less common with f2.8 Color Skopar in Prontor SVS. $25-30. Add $10-20 for Ultron f2 lens. *(illustrated bottom of previous column)*

Vito BL - c1957-59. Color-Skopar f2.8/50mm. Built-in exposure meter. $15-20. *(illustrated bottom of previous column)*

Vito C - f2.8/50 Lanthar. Prontor shutter. $20-35.

Vito Automatic - f2.8/50mm Lanthar. Prontor Lux shutter. $20-30.

Vitomatic (I), II, IIa, Ia, Ib, IIb, IIIb - f2.8 Skopar lens in Prontor shutter. $25-45. Add $10-20 for Ultron f2 lens.

Vitrona - c1964. 35mm with built-in

electronic flash. f2.8/50mm Lanthar lens. Prontor shutter 1-250. Batteries and electronics are housed in detachable handle. Never made in any large quantity, because they were novel and expensive. $34-45.

VOKAR CORPORATION (Dexter, Michigan) *Formerly "Electronic Products Mfg. Corp." of Ann Arbor, Michigan.*

Vokar, Models A, B - c1940. Bakelite folding camera for 6x6cm on 120. Also sold under the Voigt Junior and Wirgin Deluxe names. $15-25.

Vokar I, II - c1946. 35mm RF cameras. f2.8/50mm Vokar Anastigmat lens in helical mount. Leaf shutter 1-300. $55-85.

VORMBRUCK CAMERABAU (W. & P. Fertsch, Germany)
Feca - Folding plate camera, made in 6x9cm and 9x12cm sizes. Tessar or Xenar f4.5 lenses. Double extension bellows, GG back. $30-40.

VOSS (W. Voss, Ulm, Germany)
Diax (I), Ia, Ib, II, IIa, IIb - c1948-1950's. 35mm rangefinder cameras. Xenon f2/45mm lens in Synchro-Compur 1-500 shutter. Coupled rangefinder on models II, IIa, IIb. Models Ia, IIa, and IIb have interchangeable lenses. $25-40.
(illustrated top of next column)

Diax II

Diaxette - c1953. Low-priced viewfinder 35mm based on the early Diax I body. Non-interchangeable Steinheil Cassar f2.8/45mm. Prontor 25-200. $15-30.

VREDEBORCH (Germany)
Alka Box - c1953. Metal box camera, 6x9cm on 120. $8-12.

Felica - c1954. Metal box camera for 6x6cm on 120 film. Meniscus lens, zone focus, simple shutter 25, 50, B. Light gray colored. $5-10.

Junior - c1954. Same as the Felica, but with the "Junior" name. $5-10.

Nordetta 3-D - c1951. Strut-folding stereo, taking two 42x55mm exposures on 127 rollfilm. f4.5/75mm lenses. Guillotine shutter. Cheap construction, but not too common. $85-150.

Texar Box - Metal box caemra for 6x9cm on 120 film. $5-10.

Vrede Box - c1953. Metal box camera with paper covering. PC flash sync. $5-10.

WABASH PHOTO SUPPLY (Terre Haute, IN)
Direct positive camera - c1935. Wood body. Ilex Universal f3.5/3" portrait lens. Dimensions 5x8x20". With enlarger and dryer: $150-180.

WALDORF CAMERA CO.

Waldorf Minicam - Black bakelite half-127 camera. Made by Utility Mfg. Co. for Waldorf. $3-7.

WALES-BABY - Plastic half-127 novelty camera. $1-5.

WALKER MANUFACTURING CO. (Palmyra, N.Y.)
TaklV - c1892. Cardboard and leatherette construction. Multiple exposures for four pictures, each 2½x2½" on dry plates. Rotating shutter and lens assembly. Septums for four exp. at rear. $800-1200.

WALKLENZ - Japanese novelty subminiature of the Hit type. $10-15.

WALLACE HEATON LTD. (London)
Zodel - Folding 6.5x9cm plate camera. Zodellax f4.5/120mm lens in Compur shutter. $25-35. *(illustrated top of next column)*

Wallace Heaton Zodel

WALTAX - c1950's. Japanese folding "Ikonta-style" camera for 16 exp. on 120 rollfilm. Kolex f3.5/75mm lens in Dabir shutter. $25-40.

WALTAX JR. - Copy of Ikonta A. For 16 exposures 4.5x6cm on 120 film. f4.5/75mm lens. Shutter 25-150. $25-40.

WANAUS (Josef Wanaus & Co., Vienna)
Full-plate view camera - c1900. Field-type camera for 13x18cm plates. Light colored polished wood, nickel trim. Gustav-Rapp Universal Aplanat lens, waterhouse stops. Geared focus, front and rear. $175-200.

WATSON (W. Watson & Sons, London)

Acme - c1890. 8x10" folding bellows field camera. $150-200.

Alpha - c1892. Tropical hand camera with extreme rising front. 9x12cm or 4x5"

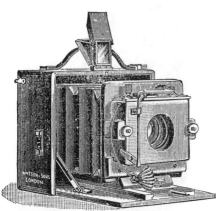

sizes. Mahogany body with brass reinforcements, maroon bellows. B&L lens, Unicum shutter. $400-475.

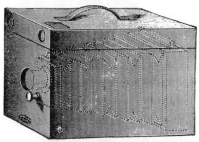

Detective Camera - intro. 1886. Black leather covered box contains a ¼-plate bellows camera. Box also holds three double plateholders behind the camera, or Eastman's roll-holder also could be used. External controls in bottom of box. Two waistlevel viewfinders in the lid. Rapid Rectilinear lens, adjustable guillotine shutter. Focus by means of a lever in the bottom of the box, from 15' to infinity. $500-800.

Field camera - c1885-1887. Tailboard style in sizes from ½-plate to 8x10". Fine wood body, brass trim. Thornton-Pickard

roller-blind shutter. Watson f8 brass barrel lens. $275-350.

Stereoscopic Binocular Camera - c1900. English imported version of the Bloch Stereo Physiographe. Krauss Tessar lenses. 45x107mm. $1000-1500.

Twin Lens Camera - c1899. An early twin lens style camera for quarter plates. Black leather covered mahogany body. Rapid Rectilinear lens, iris diaphragm. Thornton-Pickard T,I shutter. Reflex viewing. $300-400.

Vanneck - intro. 1890. Plate-changing compartment holds 12 3¼x4¼" plates. Rapid Rectilinear lens. First SLR with instant return spring mirror. Leather covered body. $350-450.

WAUCKOSIN (Frankfurt, Germany) Waranette - Folding rollfilm camera for 5x8cm. f6.3/85mm Polluxar lens in Vero shutter 25-100. $25-35.

WEBSTER INDUSTRIES INC. (Webster, NY) *Founded c1947. In 1953 the company name was changed to "Monroe Research", then within a few months to "Zenith Film Corp." Cameras and printed materials are also found using the name "Winpro Camera Co." and sometimes the city is listed as Rochester, of which Webster is a suburb.*

Winpro 35 - 1947-55. Grey or black "Tenite" plastic 35mm. Rotary shutter, 50, B. Early models not synchronized. Non-interchangeable Crystar f8/40mm. $15-20.

WEIMET PHOTO PRODUCTS CO.

Rocket - Inexpensive plastic 3x4cm camera. $3-7.

WELTA KAMERAWERKE (Waurich & Weber, Freital, Germany)
Dubla, 9x12cm - c1932. Two-shuttered triple extension plate camera. Xenar f4.5/150 lens; Compur and FP 1/10-1000 shutters. $120-140.

Dubla, 10x14cm, - Two-shuttered folding plate camera. Goerz Dogmar f4.5/165mm in Compur front shutter to 200. Rear focal plane shutter to 1000. $120-140.

Gucki - c1932. Strut-folding 127 rollfilm camera. 3x4cm and 4x6.5cm sizes. Some models have a folding bed in addition to the struts. Schneider Xenar f2.9 or Radionar f3.5. Compur shutter. $45-70.

Peerflekta (I), II, V - c1956. 6x6cm TLR for 120 film. Pololyt f3.5/75mm lens in Prontor shutter 1-300. $25-30.

Perfekta - c1934. Folding TLR of unusual design for 6x6cm exposures on 120 film. Meyer f3.5 or Tessar f3.8/75mm lens. Compur shutter 1-300. $125-200.

Perle - Folding 120 rollfilm cameras for 12 exposures, 6x6cm or 16 exposures,

4.5x6cm. f2.8 Xenar or f2.9 Cassar lens. Compur shutter. $40-55.

Reflekta - 6x6cm TLR for 120 film. f3.5 or 4.5 Pololyt lens. Blitz shutter. $20-30.

Superfekta

Solida - c1933. Folding 6x9cm rollfilm camera. Coupled rangefinder. Schneider Radionar or Xenar f4.5/105mm. Compur 1-250, T,B. $60-90.

Superfekta - c1932. Folding 6x9cm TLR for 120 film. An unusual design, similar to the Perfekta, above. Pivoting back for taking horizontal pictures. f3.8/105mm Tessar or Trioplan lens. Compur shutter. $175-300. *(illustrated bottom of previous page)*

Trio - 6x9cm on 120 film. f4.5/105mm lens in rimset Compur shutter. $15-20.

Welta 35 - c1936. Folding 35mm optical viewfinder. Similar to the Retina cameras of the same time period. Trioplan f2.9/50mm. Ring Compur or Vebur shutter. $20-35.

Welta, 6x6cm - 120 rollfilm camera. f4.5 Weltar, or f2.8/75mm Tessar lens. Compur shutter. $15-25.

Weltax

Welta folding plate cameras:
- 6x9cm - Orion Rionar, Meyer Trioplan, Tessar, or Xenar f4.5/105mm lens. Ibsor shutter 1-125. $30-50.

- 9x12cm - f3.5 Rodenstock Eurynar or f4.5 Doppel Anastigmat 135mm lens. Compur shutter. $25-35.

Weltaflex - c1950. TLR for 6x6cm on 120 film. Ludwig Meritar f3.5/75mm lens in Prontor 1-300 shutter. $25-30.

Weltax, Weltax Jr. - c1939. 4.5x6 and 6x9cm models for 120 film. Xenar or Tessar f2.8, or Trioplan f3.5/75mm lens in Compur or Prontor shutter. $25-35. *(illustrated bottom of previous page)*

Welti (I), Ic, II - c1935. Folding 35mm. Tessar f2.8 or Xenar f3.5/50mm lens in Vebur, Cludor, or Compur shutter. $25-35.

Weltini - c1937. Folding 35mm with coupled rangefinder. f2 Xenon or f2.8 Tessar lens in Compur shutter. $30-40.

Weltix - Folding 35mm. f2.9/50mm Steinheil Cassar lens in Compur shutter. $25-35.

Weltur - c1930's. For 16 exposures 4.5x6cm on 120 film. Similar to the Super Ikonta. Coupled rangefinder. With one of the many available 75mm lenses: f2.8 Xenar, f2.9 Trioplan, f2.8, 3.5, or 3.8 Tessar. $75-125.

WENK (Gebr. Wenk, Nuernberg, Germany)

Wenka - Post-war 35mm camera with interchangeable Leica-thread Xenar f2.8/ 50mm lens. Behind the lens shutter. $90-150.

WESTERN CAMERA MFG. CO. (Chicago) *The Cyclone cameras listed here were made in 1898, before Western became a part of Rochester Optical & Camera Co. in 1899. See Rochester for later models.*
Cyclone Jr. - 3½x3½" plate box camera. $25-35.

Cyclone Sr. - 4x5" plate box camera. Not a magazine camera. Top rear door to insert plateholders. $25-30.

Magazine Cyclone No. 2 - $30-45.
Magazine Cyclone No. 3 - 4x5". $30-45.
Magazine Cyclone No. 4 - 3¼x4¼". $30-45.
Magazine Cyclone No. 5 - 4x5". $30-45.

Pocket Zar - c1897. Cardboard box camera for 2x2" glass plates. $60-90.

WESTFÄLISCHER KAMERA & APPARATEBAU *This small company existed only a few years.*
Navax - c1953. Viewfinder 35mm. Röschlein Pointar interchangeable f2.8/ 45mm. FP shutter 5-1000, sync. Very low production. One sold on auction in March 1983 for $190.

WHITE (David White Co. Milwaukee, WI)

Realist 35 - Non-stereo 35mm made for David White by Iloca; identical to Iloca Rapid A. f3.5 or 2.8 Cassar lens. $25-35.

Realist 45 - 1953-57. Stereo 35 made for White by Iloca. f3.5 Cassar lenses. $80-110.

Stereo Realist - c1950's. 35mm stereo

camera. Movable film plane controlled by focus knob. With f2.8 lenses, case, flash: $225-265. With f3.5 lenses, case, flash: Like all common cameras, these tend to have a wide range of prices, often advertised for more than "book" price. But they are nearly always available in excellent condition for $75-110.

Stereo Realist Custom 1050 - With matched color corrected, coated "rare earth" f2.8 lenses. Shutter 1-200,T,B. Black coarse-grained kangaroo leather covering. $300-400.

Stereo Realist Macro - c1971. Probably less than 1000 were produced. Matched f3.5 lenses, focused at 4-5". Sync shutter to 125. $800-1000.

Stereo Realist Viewer - The better viewers would add about $65-75 to the price of a camera.

WHITEHOUSE PRODUCTS (Brooklyn, N.Y.)
Beacon, Beacon II - Plastic rollfilm camera for 127 film. Plastic lens, simple spring shutter. Colored models: $8-12. Black: $4-8.

Beacon 225 - Similar to the other Beacons, but 6x6cm on 620. Colored: $8-12. Black: $4-8.

Charlie Tuna - 126 cartridge camera, shaped and colored like Starkist's Charlie

Tuna. Truly a novelty camera in "good taste". Sorry, Charlie. $60-85. *There is a companion radio, somewhat smaller, but also shaped like Charlie Tuna. Beware if your collecting takes such a turn, because you'll also need a Coke can radio to match your Coke can camera... then a Rolls Royce automobile to go with your "Rolls" camera...*

WHITTAKER (Wm. R. Whittaker Co., Ltd., Los Angeles, Calif.)

Micro 16 - c1950's. Subminiature for 16mm film in special cassettes. Cartridge to cartridge feed. Meniscus lens, single speed shutter. Black, blue, or green: $25-40. Chrome: $20-30.

Pixie - Black plastic 16mm subminiature wriststrap camera. $20-40. With flash, wrist strap, etc.: $35-60.

Pixie Custom - Marbelized brown plastic body. Gold-plated metal parts. $150-175.

WILCA KAMERABAU (West Germany)

Wilca Automatic - Subminiature for 24 exposures 10x19mm on 16mm film in special cassettes. Wilcalux Filtra f2/16mm lens. Sync. Prontor shutter. Coupled selenium meter. Rare, reportedly less than 100 made. $350-500.

WILLIAMSON MANUFACTURING CO. LTD. (London, England)
Pistol Aircraft camera - c1930. 6x9cm plate or filmpack camera, with a pistol grip. Dallmeyer Ross Xpress f4.5/5" lens. Behind the lens louvre shutter 50-200. $300-500. *(illustrated top of next column)*

Williamson Pistol Aircraft Camera

WINDSOR - 4x4cm "Diana" type novelty camera. $1-5.

WINDSOR WX-3 - Inexpensive plastic 35mm from Taiwan. Like new: $8-12.

WINDSOR CAMERA CO. (Japan)
Cameras were probably made by Tougodo or Toyo Kogaku for marketing under the Windsor name.
Windsor 35 - c1953. 35mm RF, made in Japan. f3.5/50mm lens. Shutter 1-200, B. $15-20.

Windsor Stereo - c1954-60. Black bakelite 35mm stereo camera. Windsor f4.5/35 lenses. Windsor 1/25-1/50. $75-100.

WINDSORFLEX - Plastic 4x4cm novelty TLR. $1-5.

WING (Simon Wing, Charlestown, MA)

Multiplying View Camera - c1862. Multiple images on single 5x7" collodion plate. Mahogany body, vertical and lateral back movements, shadow box front. $700-900.

New Gem - c1901. For 15 exposures on 5x7" plates. Sliding front lens panel. $700-1000.

WIRECRAFT CO.
Jewel Sixteen - Small 3x4cm plastic novelty camera, similar to the Cardinal. $3-7.

SHUTTER RELEASE—

Wirgin Baky

WIRGIN (Gebr. Wirgin, Wiesbaden, Germany)

Baky - c1936. Bakelite folding bed camera for 16 exposures 4.5x6cm on 120 film. Black or brown bakelite body. Schneider Radionar or Cassar f2.9 lens in Compur, Compur-Rapid, or Prontor II shutter. Body release, folding optical finder. Also sold in England as the Westminster Victoria and Norfolk Miniature. There is no identification on the camera itself. $40-60. *(illustrated bottom of previous page)*

Edina - c1954. Viewfinder 35mm. Edinar f2.8 or f3.5/45mm. Vario 25-200 or Velio 10-200 shutter. $15-25.

Edinex - c1930's-1950's. Compact 35mm camera, almost identical to the Adox Adrette. Also sold in the USA under the name "Midget Marvel" although not marked as such. Telescoping front. Film loads from bottom. Late models such as IIIS with coupled rangefinder: $30-45. Early models, without rangefinder, with f4.5, 3.5, 2.8, or f2 lens. $20-35.

Edinex 120 - c1953. Folding rollfilm camera for 2 formats: 6x9, 4.5x6cm. $15-25.

Edixa - Viewfinder 35mm. Commonly found with Isconar f2.8/43mm in Prontor SVS shutter. $20-25.

Edixa 16, 16M, 16MB, 16S - c1960's. Subminiature cameras for 12x16mm exposures on 16mm film. Schneider Xenar f2.8/25mm lens. $25-40.

Edixa Electronica - c1962. 35mm SLR. Fully automatic with selenium meter.

Culminar or Xenar f2.8/50mm lens. Compur sync shutter 1-500. $45-60.

Edixa Reflex, Edixaflex - c1960. 35mm SLR. Exakta mount f2.8 Isconar or Westanar lens. Focal plane shutter 1 to 1000. $30-50.

Edixa Stereo - 35mm stereo. Steinheil Cassar f3.5/35mm lenses. Vario shutter. $70-90.

Edixa Stereo II, IIa - Rangefinder 35mm stereo camera. No meter. Steinheil f3.5. Pronto or Prontor SVS shutter to 200, ST. $70-100.

Edixa Stereo III, IIIa - Rangefinder 35mm stereo camera. Built-in light meter. Prontor SVS shutter. $100-145.

Gewirette - c1937. Same as the "Klein-Edinex". 3x4cm exposures on 127 film.

Telescoping front. Film loads from the top. $60-80.

Klein-Edinex - c1938. 127 film. Marketed in the U.S.A. under the name "Gewirette". We can find no original advertising with the "Klein Edinex" name, but it has appeared in some collector publications. Similar in appearance to the 35mm Edinex, but for 3x4cm exposures on 127 film. Gewironar f4.5, Steinheil Cassar, or Schneider Xenar f2.9/50mm lens. $60-80.

Midget Marvel - see Edinex.

Wirgin Deluxe - Bakelite bodied folding camera for 6x6cm on 120 film. Similar to Vokar Model B and Voigt Jr. Art-deco metal plates on top, bottom, and front door. $15-25.

Wirgin folding rollfilm camera - 6x9cm on 120 film. Schneider Radionar f4.5, or Gewironar f8.8 or 6.3 lens. $13-23.

Wirgin 6x6cm TLR - c1950. Rodenstock Trinar f2.9/75mm. Built-in extinction meter. $25-40.

WITT (Wilhelm Witt, Hamburg, Germany)
Iloca I, Ia, II, IIa - c1950's. Basic 35mm cameras. f2.9 or f3.5/45mm Ilitar lens in Prontor shutter. Models II and IIa with coupled rangefinder. $20-30.

Iloca Quick A - c1954. Viewfinder 35. Ilitar f3.5/45mm. Vario 25-200 shutter, B. $13-17.

Iloca Rapid, Rapid B, Rapid IIL - c1950. Coupled rangefinder, 35mm. Rapid wind. Cassar f2.8/50mm. $15-25.

Iloca Stereo, Original Model - Individually focusing lenses. Apertures and shutters coupled through tube at bottom. Unusual. $100-125.

Iloca Stereo, Models I & II - c1950's. 35mm stereo camera for 24x24mm pairs. Ilitar f3.5 lenses, 35mm or 45mm. Prontor-S shutter to 300. $70-90.

Iloca Stereo Rapid - c1955. 35mm stereo, 23x24mm pairs. CRF. Rapid wind. Cassarit f2.8 or Cassar f3.5 lenses. Prontor SVS 1-300 or Vero 25-200. Rangefinder version of the Realist 45. $250-350.

Photrix Quick B - 35mm. Cassar f2.8/50mm, Prontor-SVS to 300. $12-18.

WITTIE MFG. & SALES CO.

Wit-eez - Black bakelite minicam, styled like the Rolls. $3-7.

WITTMAN (R. Wittman, Dresden, Germany)
Tailboard camera - c1880. Tailboard camera for 13x18cm plates. Square bellows. Wittman Universal Aplanat lens, waterhouse stops. $250-350.

WITTNAUER

35mm cameras - c1959. Misc. models

including Adventurer, Automaton, Challenge, Continental, Legionaire, Scout. RF. Chronex f2.8/45mm lens. $15-20.

WOLLENSAK OPTICAL CO.

Wollensak Stereo, Model 10 - 35mm stereo camera. f2.7 lenses; shutter to 300. Similar to the Revere Stereo 33, but faster lenses and shutter, and in black leather, not brown. $175-225.

WONDER CAMERA - Magazine box camera for 2½x3½" glass plates. $60-90.

WONDERFLEX - c1965. Hong Kong plastic novelty TLR-style camera, 4x4cm. Same camera sold as Bedfordflex, Splendidflex, etc. $1-5.

WRATTEN & WAINWRIGHT (London)

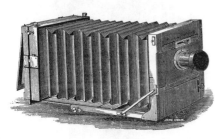

Tailboard camera - c1890. Mahogany 5x8" view. Maroon square bellows. A&N Auxiliary 6½x8½" lens. $200-250.

WRAY OPTICAL WORKS (London)
Peckham Wray - 1955. 4x5" SLR. Looks like an overgrowm 35mm SLR. Wray Lustvar interchangeable f4.8/135mm. FP shutter 5-800 and Compur shutter 1-500. $140-190.

Stereo Graphic - Made under license to

Graflex. Same as the Graflex version, but with Wray lenses. $75-125.

Wrayflex - c1950. The only commercially successful English-made 35mm SLR. Originally for 24x32mm, later for standard 24x36mm. Wray f2/50mm interchangeable lens. FP shutter ½-1000. $100-125.

WUENSCHE (Emil Wuensche, Reick b/Dresden)
Field cameras - c1900. Wood body. For 5x7" or 10x15" plates. Wuensche Rectilinear Extra Rapid f8 brass barrel lens. $125-150.

Lola - c1905. Strut-folding stereo, for 9x18cm plates. Leather-covered wood body, nickel trim. Anastigmat f7.7/90mm lenses. $250-350.

Mars 99 - c1895. Leather covered box camera for 9x12cm plates. Aplanat f12/150mm lens. Rotating shutter. $250-300.
Mars Detective - c1893. Polished mahogany 12-plate magazine camera. ¼- or ½-plate sizes. Aplanat f8/130mm. Rotary shutter. $350-400.

Postage stamp camera - c1907. Twelve lens camera makes twelve 24x30mm exposures on a ½-plate. Wood body with wooden door (flap shutter) covering the lenses. $1500-2000.

Reicka - c1912. Folding 9x12cm plate camera. Leather covered wood body. Double extension bellows. Rodenstock Heligonal f5.4/120mm lens in Koilos 1-300 shutter. $40-60.

YALE CAMERA CO.
Yale Camera - c1910. Small paper box camera for 5x5cm glass plates. Single plates must be darkroom loaded. Similar to the Zar, but with exposed brass shutter pivot. $60-90.

YAMASHITA (T. Yamashita, Japan)
Boltax I, II, III - c1938. Small viewfinder

35mm, 24x24mm. Picner f4.5/40mm, Picny-D 25-100,B shutter. $75-100.

YAMATO KOKI KOGYO CO. LTD.
YAMATO CAMERA INDUSTRY CO. LTD.
(Tokyo)
Bonny Six - Zeiss Ikonta B copy. Bonny Anast. f4.5/75mm. $25-35.

Konair Ruby - c1955. Rangefinder 35. Konair f3.5/45mm lens in Sunchro 10-300 shutter. $20-30.

Pax - c1950. Models M2, M3, M4, Ruby. Small rangefinder 35mm styled after the Leica. Luminor f2.8 or f3.5/45mm or Color Luna f2.8/45mm lens. Synchro shutter 10-300. $25-45.

Pax Golden View - Deluxe version of the Pax. All metal parts are gold-colored. Green leather covering. $75-100.

YASHICA (Japan)

Yashica 44 - c1956. TLR for 4x4cm on 127 film. f3.5 lens. $30-50.

Yashica 44A - c1960. 4x4cm TLR for 127. Various colors, including blue, grey,

or black enamel with grey leatherette. $30-45.

Yashica 44LM - c1959. Built-in meter. $40-60.

Yashica A - c1960. TLR for 6x6cm on 120. Yashikor f3.5/80mm. Copal 25-300 shutter. $25-35.

Yashica Atoron - c1965. Subminiature for 8x11mm on 9.5mm film (Minox cassettes). Yashinon f2.8/18mm fixed focus lens. With case, flash, filters in presentation box: $30-40. Camera only: $20-30.

Yashica Atoron Electro - c1970. 8x11mm subminiature. Black finish. CdS meter. Yashinon DX f2.8/18mm focusing lens. Outfit with case, flash, filters, presentation box: $50-65. Camera only: $30-50.

Yashica C - c1958. TLR, 6x6cm on 120. Yashikor f3.5/80mm. Copal MX 1-300 shutter. $25-35.

Yashica D - c1959-74. 6x6cm TLR. Yashikor f3.5/80mm in Copal MXV 500 shutter. $30-50.

Yashica EE - c1962. Viewfinder 35mm. Yashinon f1.9/45mm. Copal SVA 1-500, MX sync. Meter cell around lens. $25-35.

Yashica Rapide - c1962. Half-frame 35mm. Unusual style: stands vertically like a pocket-sized transistor radio. Interchangeable Yashinon f2.8/28mm lens in Copal 1-500 shutter. Built-in meter. $40-60.

Yashica Sequelle - c1960. 18x24mm half-frame 35mm. Styled like a movie camera. f2.8/28mm Yashinon lens in Seikosha-L shutter. Built-in meter. $60-80.

Yashica Y16 - c1958. Subminiature for 10x14mm on 16mm cassette film. f2.8 or 3.5/25mm Yashinon lens. $15-20.

Yashica YE - c1959. Rangefinder 35mm, made by the newly acquired Nicca factory. Has similarities to the Leica IIIg and M3 cameras. Interchangeable Yashikor f2.8/50mm. FP shutter 1-500, B,T. Rapid wind lever. $125-175.

Yashica YF - c1959. Leica M3 copy. (Actually a continuation of the Nicca camera line. Yashica had purchased Nicca in 1958.) Interchangeable Yashinor f1.8/50mm lens. FP shutter 1-1000. $125-175.

Yashica YK - c1960. Rangefinder 35mm. Yashinon f2.8 lens. Between-the-lens 25-300 shutter. Single-stroke advance lever. $20-35.

YASHINA SEIKI CO. LTD. (Japan)
Pigeonflex - c1953. 6x6cm TLR. Tri-Lausar f3.5/80mm. NKS shutter 1-200, B. $35-45.

YEN-KAME (Yen cameras): *A unique and inexpensive camera type which flourished during the 1930's in Japan, and continued to be popular after WWII. They are occasionally found with "Made in Occupied Japan" markings. The cameras are simple ground-glass backed box or folding cameras which take single sheets of film in paper holders. The negative could be processed in daylight by dipping the entire paper holder into a red-colored developer and then a green-colored fixer. The red coloring in the developer eliminated the need for a darkroom, and the slogan "No Need DarkRoom" is often printed on the camera faces. This slogan is also used to identify the film type. There are many names on the low-priced cameras, and several are listed alphabetically in this guide. We do not have space to give each "brand" a separate listing, but some of the names you might encounter are: Amco, Asahi, Asahigo, Baby, Baby Reflex, Baby Special, Baby Sports, Camera, Camerette, Collegiate, Highking, Hitgo, Kamerette, Kamerette Junior Nos. 1-4, Kamerette Senior No. 1, Katei, King, King Super, Koseido, Light, Lion, Maruso, Milbro, Million, Nichibei, Nymco Folding Camera, Pocket, Special Camera, Special King, Super Camera, Tokyo, Tougo Camera, Victory Camera, and Yuuhigo. There are even generic versions with no name at all. To the street vendors and the public, the name was not as important as the low-cost magic of the camera. Generally, the box camera versions sell for $10-15. Folding models $15-20.*

ZEH (Paul Zeh Kamerawerk, Dresden)
Bettax - c1936. Folding 6x6cm rollfilm camera. Radionar f4.5/100mm in Compur. $25-40.

Goldi - c1930. Folding-bed camera for 16 exposures 3x4cm on 127 film. f2.9 or 4.5 Zecanar lens. Vario, Prontor, or Compur shutter. $45-60.

Zeca, 9x12cm

Zeca, 6x9cm - Folding sheet-film camera. Steinheil f6.8 or Periskop f11 lens. Vario shutter, 25-100. $20-35.

Zeca, 9x12cm - Folding sheet-film camera. 135mm lenses: f6.3 Schneider Radionar, f6.8 Jena, f2.9 Zecanar or Xenar. Leather covered wood body. $20-30. *(illustrated bottom of previous column)*

Zeca-Flex - c1930's. Folding 6x6cm TLR for 120 film. f3.5/75mm Schneider Xenar lens. f2.9 viewing lens. The folding style 6x6cm reflex never became popular, so this model, along with the Perfekta and Superfekta from the neighboring suburb of Freital, was not made in large quantities. $550-650.

ZEISS, ZEISS IKON A.G. *(Before 1926, the Carl Zeiss Optical Co. was located in Jena. In late 1926, the largest camera manufacturers in Germany, Contessa-Nettel, Ernemann, Goerz, Ica, and Carl Zeiss merged to form Zeiss-Ikon, and the headquarters became Dresden. In 1946, after WWII, Zeiss-Ikon A.G. located in Stuttgart, West Germany. Some camera models were still being made in the Jena and Dresden factories, but they were not really "Zeiss Ikon" cameras, even though some bore the Zeiss Ikon trademark. (We have listed these models under the manufacturer Pentacon.) Camera production ceased in 1971 with assembly continuing into 1972.*

In a single year Zeiss Ikon offered in their catalog 104 different model names with an average of 3 separate formats and more than 3 lens and shutter combinations per format- 936 choices or "stock" models in that one catalog. The most variations that year were offered in the Deckrullo (later called "Nettel") press camera. One could order it in 4.5x6, 6.5x9, 9x12, 10x15, and 13x18cm formats plus all except the smallest in tropical style with varnished teak and brown leather bellows.

With an actual count of 30 different lenses for the 9 types, one had 39 possible choices for this single model! This was in the 1927 catalog before any of the really famous Zeiss Ikon cameras like the Contax, Contarex, Contaflex, Kolibri, and Super Ikontas had been introduced.

From the above you can get some idea of the complexity of identiying and pricing all Zeiss Ikon cameras so please regard this list as covering only the more usual types and/or those of exceptional value. Where the Zeiss Ikon model number is available this number is included in the description to help in identification. Often, these numbers appear on the camera body. Sometimes, especially on U.S.A. models, they are not on the camera itself, but only in the catalog. The number is usually expressed as a fraction; for example, a 9x12 Ideal is 250/7 and a 6.5x9cm Ideal is 250/3. Basically, the first half of the number designates the camera model. The second half of the number indicates negative size and is standard from one model to another. The chart below (listed in "Zeiss Historica" Journal Vol. 3 No. 1) gives the size numbers used on Zeiss Ikon still cameras from 1927 to 1960, after which decimal numbers for models were used. (The focal length of the most usual lens for the format is also shown.) A new or improved model usually changes only the last digit of the first number, generally increasing it by one. Hopefully this information will help the user of this guide to locate his Zeiss camera by name, number, illustration, or a combination of the three.

Number	Metric size	F.L.
- - -	4.5x6cm	75mm
- - -	22x31mm	45, 50mm
1	45x107mm	twin 65mm
2	6x9cm	105mm
3	6.5x9cm	105mm
4	6x13cm	twin 75mm
5	8.5x11.5cm	135mm
6	8x14cm	150mm
7	9x12cm	135mm
8	9x14cm *(Ica)*	- - -
9	10x15cm	165mm
10	9x18cm (Ica)	- - -
11	13x18cm	210mm
12	4x6.5cm	75mm
13	13x18cm (Ica)	- - -
14	5x7.5cm	90mm
15	6.5x11cm	120mm
16	6x6cm	80mm
17	8x10.5cm	120mm
18	3x4cm	50mm
20	18x24cm	- - -
21	24x30cm	- - -
24	24x36mm	50mm
27	24x24mm	40mm

Baby Box Tengor 54/18 (1931)

Baby Box Tengor 54/18 (1934)

Zeiss Ikon cameras have attracted a following whose buying habits resemble those of Leica collectors in some respects. This has led to a wider range of prices based on condition. Since most items are not rare, their condition is a very important consideration in establishing prices. The prices here are from our database, showing cameras in condition range 4 to 5. Items in condition range 2-3 would bring a bit more. Range 6 to 9 would not only bring less money, but also be harder to sell. It should also be noted that cameras bearing the Zeiss-Ikon logo are generally worth from 10% to 50% more than their counterparts from the earlier companies, which accounts for the somewhat higher prices here than in the Contessa, Ernemann, Goerz, and Ica sections of this guide.

Editor's note: We are deeply indebted to Mr. Mead Kibbey for the excellent job of researching and assembling this section of the book. Mr. Kibbey is widely respected as one of the world's foremost authorities on Zeiss-Ikon. In addition to his Zeiss collecting, Mead also serves as an officer of the Zeiss Historica Society.

Adoro - see Tropen Adoro

Baby Box Tengor - Baseball sized box camera with name on front or back. 3x4cm on 127 film. Note: Shutter won't work unless wire front sight is lifted.

54/18 - 1931. Frontar f11 lens. Plain leather front. $40-60. *(illustrated top of previous page)*

54/18 - 1934-38. Metal front plate with "Baby Box" under lens. $25-60. *(illustrated top of previous page)*

54/18(E) - 1931-34. Focusing Novar f6.3 lens. Black metal front plate. $40-75.

Baby Deckrullo (12, 870) - 1926-29. 4.5x6cm plate camera. Strut-folding, with bed. Focal plane shutter to 1200. Zeiss Tessar f4.5 or f2.7/80mm lens. Camera focus knob on top. $250-375.

Baby Ikonta (520/18) - 3x4cm rollfilm. Novar f3.5/50mm (1936): $45-85. Tessar f3.5/50mm (1936): $80-110. Novar f6.3 or Tessar f4.5 (1932): $40-80.

Baldur Box (51) - 1934-36. Inexpensive black box camera for 16 exposures 4.5x6cm on 120. Frontar f11/90mm. Shutter 1/30, T. Rare, but usually selling for around $20-35. *(illustrated top of next column)*

Baldur Box 51/2 - 1934-36. For 8 exposures 6x9cm on 120 film. Goerz Frontar f11/115mm lens. Shutter 1/30, T. Very rare. Estimate: $25-50.

Baldur Box, 51

Bebe (342) - 4.5x6cm strut camera with unpleated bellows. Front cell focus. Tessar f4.5 or Triotar f3.5/75mm in dial set Compur (1928): $200-300. Tessar f3.5 in rimset Compur (1930): $250-375.

Bebe (342/3) - 6.5x9cm folding camera. Tessar f4.5/105mm or rimset Compur with Tessar f3.5. $200-300.

Bob (510, 510/2) - 1934-41. Inexpensive black folding cameras, 4.5x6 and 6x9cm sizes. Nettar lens. Gauthier shutter 25-75, B, T. $25-35.

Bob IV, V - 1927. (Cameras left over from Ernemann.) Sizes: 4x6.5, 6x6, 6x9, 6.5x11, 7.25x12.5cm. 33 different lens/shutter combinations. 7.25x12.5cm size: $50-90. Other sizes: $25-50.

Bobette I (549) - 1929. Strut folding camera for 22x31mm on rollfilm. With Ernoplast f4.5/50 or Erid f8/40: $150-175. With Frontar f9/50mm: $55-75.

Bobette II (548) - 1929. Folding camera for 22x31mm on rollfilm. Leather covered body. Black bellows. Ernostar f2/42mmor Ernon f3.5/50mm lens. Shutter ½-100. The first miniature rollfilm camera with f2 lens. $250-500.

Box Tengor 54 - 1934-39. 4.5x6cm (½-frame) on 120 film. Goerz Frontar f11 lens, rotating waterhouse stops, 1 close up lens controlled from the front of the camera. Single speed shutter. Flash synch. Diamond shaped winding knob. 2 ruby windows. $15-25.

Box Tengor 54/14 - 5x7.5cm on 127 film. Frontar f11. Plain leather front. Winding knob on bottom right side, as viewed by operator. First model (1926-28) has two finder lenses vertical at upper front corner. Quite rare. $60-100. Second model (1928-34) has two finder lenses horizontal across the top of the front. $50-90.

Box Tengor 54/2 - 6x9cm on 120 film. Frontar f11 lens.
- 1926-28. Plain leatherette front. Viewfinder objectives vertical in upper front corner. Winding knob at bottom. $10-25.
- 1928-34. Plain leatherette front. Viewfinder objectives horizontal across front. Winding knob at top. Stops and closeups. $10-25.

- 1934-38. Extended hexagon front plate around lens with stops and closeup settings around it. Black enamel trim around front edge of camera. Diamond shaped winding knob at top of operator's right side. $10-25.
- 1938. Same as the previous listing, but release button moved to the top of camera on operator's right. $15-25.

Box Tengor 55/2 - 1939. Same as the 54/2 of 1938, but serrated round winding knob with leatherette center, black front trim, and double exposure interlock on winding knob. $15-25.

Box Tengor 56/2 - 1948-56. Chrome trim.

Lever shutter release on lower right side, flash contact on lower left (from operator's viewpoint). Frontar f9 lens, internal sync. $20-45.

Box Tengor 54/15 - 6.5x11cm (2½x4¼") on 116 rollfilm. Fairly rare, since this size was not offered after 1938/39. Goerz Frontar lens.

- 1926-28. Ground glass viewfinder windows. Viewfinder objective lenses vertical in upper corner. Winding knob at bottom. $20-40.

- 1928-33. Viewfinder objectives horizontal across top of front. Winding knob at top. Shutter has mirror on front. Close up lenses and diaphragm control on metal strips pulled up on top of camera. $20-40.

- 1933-38. Similar to the 1928-33 model, but metal plate like elongated hexagon on front around lens. Brilliant viewfinders with square lenses. Close up and diaphragm settings on front metal plate around lens. $25-50.

Citoskop (671/1) - A top quality stereo camera for 45x107mm cut film or plates. Sucher Triplett f4.5/65mm viewing/focusing lens located between the Tessar f4.5/65mm taking lenses. All metal pop-up viewing hood with newton finder lens at front. "Citoskop" on front of camera. Fairly rare. Estimate: $300-500 with Zeiss-Ikon markings. (Contessa-Nettel Citoskop sells for $235-275.)

Cocarette - 1928-29. Rollfilm is loaded by removing the winder and film track from the side of the camera, somewhat like a Leica (the back does not open). (Also made in a plate back model.) Single extension. Derval, Klio, and Compur dial set shutters.

ZEISS (cont.)

Frontar, Periskop, Novar, Dominar, and Tessar lenses. 64 different lens/shutter combinations. Made in black models. #514 in 5 sizes. #517, #518: lever focus, vertical lens adjustment, each in 2 sizes. #519: lever focus, no vertical lens adjustment, in 3 sizes. $30-50. *(In 1930, #517, #518, #519 were made with rimset Compur. Add $5-10 for these rimset models.)*

Cocarette Luxus (521/2, 521/15, 522/17) - 1928. 6x9 and 8x10.5cm sizes. Brown leather covering, polished metal parts. Double extension. Dial set Compur. Dominar f4.5/105mm: $85-130. Tessar f4.5/105: $150-300.

Colora (10.0641) - 1963-65. An inexpensive 35mm camera. "Colora" on top. Novica f2.8/50mm (a fairly unusual lens). Prontor 125 shutter, X sync. $20-30.

Colora F (10.0641) - 1964-65. Similar to the Colora, but AG-1 flash bulb socket under the accessory shoe. Shoe tips back to become the flash reflector and to uncover the socket. Rewind knob has flash calculator in top. $15-25.

Contaflex (860/24) - TLR 35mm camera. 80mm viewing lens. 8 interchangeable taking lenses, 35mm to 135mm. First camera with built-in exposure meter. $600-950 if excellent to mint. (Worth much less if meter is broken, shutter jammed, or Albada finder discolored.) In average condition, these regularly sell at auction in the $400-700 range.

Contaflex TLR lenses:
- 35mm Orthometer or Biotar: $450-600.
- 50mm Sonnar f2 or f1.5: $100-200.
- 50mm Tessar f2.8: $100-200.
- 85mm Sonnar f2: $300-450.
- 85mm Triotar f4: $325-450.
- 135mm Sonnar f4: $350-500.
- 35mm viewfinder: $200.

Contaflex I (861/24) - 1953-58. 35mm SLR. Tessar f2.8/45mm. Synchro-Compur. No exposure meter. Readily available. $45-65.

Contaflex II (862/24) - 1954-58. Like the I, but with built-in exposure meter. Readily available. $50-70.

Contaflex III (863/24) - 1957-59. 35mm SLR. Tessar f2.8/50mm, interchangeable front element. Knob for film advance and shutter tensioning. No meter. Not as common as Contaflex II. $50-70.

Contaflex IV (864/24) - 1957-59. Like the III, but with built-in exposure meter. Door covers the meter. LVS settings. Readily available. $50-70.

Contaflex Alpha (10.1241) - 1958-59. Same as the Contaflex III, but with the less expensive Pantar f2.8/45mm lens. Interchangeable front element for Pantar series lenses. $40-60.

Contaflex Beta (10.1251) - Like the Alpha, but with exposure meter. $45-65.

The Contaflex Rapid, Prima, Supers, and S Automatic all have rapid film advance, accessory shoe on prism housing, and interchangeable magazine backs.

Contaflex Rapid (10.1261) - 1959-61. Tessar f2.8/50mm, interchangeable front element. Rarely offered for sale. $60-85.

Contaflex Prima (10.1291) - 1959-65. Like the Rapid, but with Pantar f2.8/45mm. Uncovered match needle exposure meter on operator's right side. Quite rare. $60-90.

Contaflex Super (10.1262) - 1959-62. Same as the Rapid, but with coupled exposure meter. Uncovered meter window in front of prism housing. Meter adjustment wheel on front of camera, operator's left. No other Contaflex has this external wheel. Common. $60-90.

Contaflex Super (New Style- 10.1271) - 1962-67. "Zeiss-Ikon" printed on front of larger exposure meter window. No external setting wheel as above. Tessar f2.8/ 50mm. Shutter says "Synchro-Compur X" under lens. Exposure meter window on top has two red arrows and no numbers. Inside viewfinder tiny "2x" visible at top of exposure meter slot. No automatic exposure control. Common. $60-90.

Contaflex Super B (10.1272) - 1963-68. Looks like the new style Super, except has numbers in exposure meter indicator on top and in viewfinder. Shutter says "Synchro-Compur" under lens. Automatic exposure control. $75-100.

Contaflex Super BC (10.1273) - 1967-1970. Similar to above except no external exposure meter window. Has internal through-the-lens CdS meter. Black rectangle over the lens, with "Zeiss-Ikon". Battery compartment with square door at 9 o'clock from lens. Chrome: $100-150. Add $50-75 for black model.

Contaflex S Automatic (10.1273-BL) - 1970-72. "Contaflex S" on front of prism housing. "Automatic" above lens on shutter. $160-250.

Contaflex 126 (10.1102) - 1970-73. For 28x28mm on 126 cartridge film. Fully automatic exposure control. "Contaflex 126" on front. Interchangeable f2.8/45mm Tessar or Color Pantar. Not unusual to find an outfit with camera and four lenses; f2.8/45, f2.8/32, f28./85, and f4/135 for $150-250. With f2.8/45mm lens only, very common: $60-100.

Contaflex SLR lenses, for full frame models
- Teleskop 1.7x (fits models I and II only) (11.1203) With bracket: $50-80.
- Steritar A (Stereo prism for above) (20.2004, and 812). $125-175.
- 35mm f4 Pro-Tessar (11.1201, and 1003). 49mm external filters. $35-45.
- 35mm f3.2 Pro-Tessar (11.1201). 60mm external filters. $50-90.
- 85mm f4 Pro-Tessar (11.1202, and 1004). 60mm external filters. $50-80.
- 85mm f3.2 Pro-Tessar (11.1202). 60mm external filters. $60-95.
- 115mm f4 Pro-Tessar (11.1205). 67mm external filters. $85-120.
- Pro-Tessar M-1:1 (11.1204). High resolution close copy lens. $90-125.

- Monocular 8x30B - see Contarex lenses below.

For Alpha, Beta, Prima, and Contina III
- 30mm f4 Pantar (11.0601). $25-40.
- 75mm f4 Pantar (11.0601 or 1002). $60-80.
- Steritar D (20.2006 or 814). $75-125.
- Steritar B (20.2005 or 813) (for Contaflex III through S). $150-200.

Contaflex 126 lenses
- Distagon f4/25mm (11.1113). Very rare. No sales records. Estimate: $150.
- 32mm f2.8 Distagon (11.1101). Mint: $18-30.
- 45mm f2.8 Color Pantar (11.1102). $12.
- 45mm f2.8 Tessar (11.1103). $18.
- 85mm f2.8 Sonnar (11.1104). $45-75.
- 135mm f4 Tele Tessar (11.1105). $25-40.
- 200mm f4 Tele Tessar (11.1112). $100-200.

Contarex Cameras - *All models of this superbly made 35mm camera except the microscope version have the word "Contarex" on front. KEH Camera Brokers, Atlanta assisted in pricing this series.*

Contarex "Bullseye" (10.2401) - 1960-67. Large round coupled exposure meter window over lens. Interchangeable Planar f2/50mm. Early models had no data strip slot at rear. $125-200.

Contarex Special (10.2500 body) - 1960-66. No meter. Interchangeable reflex or prism view hood. "Contarex" in script-like letters. $275-400.

Contarex Professional (10.2700 body)
- 1967-68. No meter. Only prism viewer.

"Professional" on front. Very rare. Less than 1000 made, and almost no mint examples remaining. $250-350.

Contarex Super (10.2600 body) - 1968-1972. "Super" on front. First model has through-the-lens meter switch on front at 2 o'clock from the lens (opposite from focus wheel). Second model has switch on top under the winding lever. Front switch: $300-500. Top switch: $400-600. *A very nice example of the second model, in black, with f2 Planar recently brought $660 at auction.*

Contarex Electronic (Super Electronic) (10.2800 body) - 1970-72. "Electronic" on front. Chrome or (rarer) black body. Mint: $650-850. Excellent: $500-650.

Contarex Hologon (10.0659 outfit) - 1970-72. "Hologon" on front. Fixed focus lens f8/15mm, linear type (not a fisheye). With camera, grip, cable release, special neutral density graduated filter, and case for all: $850-1200. Camera only: $700-900.

Contarex Microscope Camera - "Zeiss Ikon" in block letters on top. No lens, viewfinder, or exposure meter. Interchangeable backs. Quite rare. $300-400.

Contarex Lenses - These lenses, made between 1959 and 1973 by Carl Zeiss, Oberkochen are seldom equalled and never surpassed even with today's technology. Up to 1965, 135mm and shorter lenses have chrome finish, and 180mm and longer have black finish. After 1965, all were black finished.
- 16mm f2.8 fisheye Distagon (11.2442) 1973. Rare. $400-700.
- 18mm Distagon f4 (11.2418) 1967-73. With adapter ring for B96 filters. $300-425.
- 21mm Biogon f4.5 (11.2402) 1960-63. (For Bullseye only.) $140-195. *Add $100 for finder.*
- 25mm Distagon f2.8 (11.2408) 1963-73. Black: $350-425. Chrome: $225-325.
- 35mm Distagon f4 Chrome (11.2403) 1960-73. $75-115.
- 35mm Blitz Distagon f4 Black (11.2413) 1966-73. Built-in flash automation. $80-130.
- 35mm f4 PA Curtagon (11.2430) 1973. Made by Schneider, but mounted and sold by Zeiss Ikon, Stuttgart. Automatic stop down. Perspective control by lateral movement of up to 7mm in any of four directions. Rare. $350-500 with B56 filter ring.

- 35mm f2 Distagon (11.2414) 1965-73. $225-325.

- 50mm f4 S-Planar (11.2415) 1963-68. For critical close ups to 3". $300-500.
- 50mm f2.8 Tessar (11.2501). Black: $125-175. Chrome: $85-110.
- 50mm f2 Planar Chrome (11.2401) 1960-73. $45-75.
- 50mm f2 Blitz Planar Black (11.2412) 1966-73. $75-110.
- 55mm f1.4 Planar (11.2407) 1965-73. Black: $200-245. Chrome: $130-165.
- 85mm f2 Sonnar (11.2404) 1960-73. Black: $190-235. Chrome: $160-195.
- 85mm f1.4 Planar 1974. Very rare. Estimate: $600-750.
- 115mm f3.5 Tessar (11.2417) 1960-73. For use with bellows. Estimate: $350-400. Bellows: $100. Bellows with cable socket: $125.
- 135mm f4 Sonnar (11.2405) 1960-73. Black: $90-130. Chrome: $80-120.
- 135mm f2.8 Olympia-Sonnar (11.2409) 1965-73. $250-300.
- 180mm f2.8 Olympia-Sonnar (11.2425) 1967-73. Fairly rare. $400-700.
- 250mm f4 Sonnar (11.2406) 1960-63. Manual preset ring focus. $125-180.
- 250mm f4 Olympia-Sonnar (11.2421) 1963-73. Knob focus auto stop-down. $300-380.
- 400mm f5.6 Tele Tessar (11.2434) 1970-73. Very rare. Estimate: $700-1200.
- 500mm f4.5 Mirotar (11.2420) Catadioptric. 1963-73. Very rare. $1500-2000.
- 1000mm f5.6 Mirotar (11.2422) Catadioptric. 1964-70. Super rare. $2500-3500.
- 40/120mm f2.8 Vario-Sonnar (11.2423) 1970-73. Rare. $1000-1400.
- 85/250 f4 Vario-Sonnar (11.2424) 1970-73. Very rare. $1500-2500.

- Monocular 8x30B with 27mm threaded at eyepiece to fit Contaflex SLR or on Contarex by use of an adapter. First model (1960) (20.1629) with eyepiece focus and line for 140 feet. $80-120. Second model (1963) with front end focussing and a distance scale. (This second model is the most common type seen.) $120-160. Third model (1969) (11.1206) has porro prism with front end focus. This model is straight and looks like a small refracting telescope. $175-225.
- Adapter to use monocular with 50mm f2 Planar: $40-50.
- Adapter to use monocular with 50mm f1.4 Planar: $70-90.

Contax Series - Introduced in 1932 as a top quality rangefinder 35mm system camera, it was manufactured until 1961 with the exception of the 1944-52 period. Dr. Stanley Bishop assisted in the preparation of this section.

Contax I (540/24) - 1932-36. Identifying features: black enamel finish, square appearance, "Contax" in white on upper front and winding knob on front to operator's right of lens.

Contax I(a) - Serial numbers starting with "AU" or "AV". No low (below 1/25) shutter speeds, no "foot" on tripod socket and often had one or more raised "dimples" over ends of shafts on front of camera. Viewfinder window closer to center of camera than rangefinder window. With contemporary lens: $550-650.

Contax I(b) - Same as the I(a) in appearance except front bezel extends across front to viewing and rangefinder window. $450-600.

Contax I(c) - "Foot" on tripod socket, slow speeds added, guard attached to lens bezel surrounds slow speed setting ring. Like the above models, it has no button to unlock infinity stop when external bayonet lenses are in use. $400-575.

Contax I(d) - Same as the I(c), but button to release infinity lock present at 1 o'clock from lens, and distance scale around base of lens mount now finished in chrome with black numbers rather than in black with white numbers as on earlier models. $400-575.

Contax I(e) - Same as I(d), except viewfinder window moved to outside of rangefinder window, and a shallow vertical groove in front bezel between lens mount containing word "Contax" and focus wheel. $350-550.

Contax I(f) - Same as I(e), but has four screws in accessory shoe, and the marker for setting shutter speeds changed from an apparent slotted screw head to a small pointer. $300-500.

Contax II (543/24) - 1936-42. Identified by satin chrome finish on top and trim. Winding and speed setting on top right (viewed from behind), shutter speeds to 1250, and rangefinder and viewfinder windows combined. A superb rugged camera with no external variations during its production life. It can be differentiated from the postwar Contax II(a) by its larger size, a narrow frame around the small rangefinder window, and the absence of sync connection on upper back. With Sonnar f2/50mm: $80-150.

Contax III (544/24) - 1936-42. Same as the Contax II, except had built in, uncoupled exposure meter on top and rewind knob was much higher. $80-150.

"No Name" Contax, Contax D, and Contax F - Using captured parts and personnel, other variations of the Contax II and Pentaprism versions were produced after WWII in East Germany. They tended to be of inferior quality and sell in the range of $50-150. These cameras are covered in more detail under the manufacturer "Pentacon" on pages 295-297.

Contax II(a) (563/24) - 1950-61. An excellent quality camera produced at Stuttgart and identified by satin chrome top, "Contax" on front, wide frame around right rangefinder window, sync fitting on back near top, and film speed and type indicator on rewind knob.

- First model: all numbers on speed setting dial are black. Sync attachment looks like flat plunger in socket. Requires special attachment to convert mechanical motion to electric contact. (#1361 for bulbs, #1366 for electronic flash.) $100-150.

- Second model: Same, but numbers on speed dial in color (1-1/25 black, 1/50 yellow, 100-1250 red) and regular p.c. flash connector at rear. Many of these are still in use. $150-200.

Contax IIIa - Same as the IIa, except uncoupled exposure meter on top. First model (black dial): $120-150. Second model (colored dial): $125-200. (Mint condition brings 25-35% more.)

Prewar Contax Lenses - Earliest were black enamel and heavy chrome trim. These are worth from a little to a lot more than the later satin chrome versions. All these lenses plus innumerable Contax accessories are described in a book published by David Gorski. Even the view finders in the Contax series are collected and vary from $20 up to several hundred dollars in value. Serial numbers range from about 1,350,000 to 2,700,000.
- 28mm f8 non-coupled wide angle Tessar: $75-110.
- 35mm f4.5 Orthometer. Rare: $300-500.
- 35mm f2.8 Biogon (fits only pre-war Contaxes): $50-85.
- 40mm and 42.5mm f2 Biotar. Black: $800-900. Chrome: $740-800.
- 50mm f3.5 Tessar: $60-90. *Add $10-20 if black fonrt ring (for Contax I).*
- 50mm f2.8 Tessar: $50-80. *Add $10-20 if black front ring (for Contax I).*
- 50mm f2 Sonnar: Rigid mount: $35-60. Collapsible mount: $20-25.
- 50mm f1.5 Sonnar: $25-55. *Add $10 for black.*
- 85mm f4 Triotar: Black: $90-125. Chrome: $70-85.
- 85mm f2 Sonnar: Prewar black: $140-160. Prewar chrome: $90-110.
- 135mm f4 Sonnar: Black: $125. Chrome: $70.
- 180mm f6.3 Tele Tessar K (direct mount): Black: $700-800. Chrome: $550-675.
- 180mm f2.8 Sonnar (direct mount): $1450-1600.
- 180mm f2.8 Sonnar in flektoskop (inverted image), with case: $950-1200.
- 300mm f8 Teletessar K (direct or Flektoskop mount): $1300-1800.
- 500mm f8 Fern (distance) lens in direct or Flektoskop mount. Rare. $3200-4200 with Flektoskop and case.

Postwar Contax lenses - Chrome finish throughout range. Fern 500mm, Sonnar f2.8/180mm, and Tessar f3.5/115mm offered in black also.
- 21mm f4 Biogon (563/013): $100-150. (Add $90 for finder.)

- 25mm f4 Topogon. Very rare, no recent ones for sale. Estimate: $400-600.
- 35mm f3.5 Planar (563/014): $100-160.
- 35mm f2.8 Biometar: $110-175.
- 35mm f2.8 Biogon (563/09): $110-160.
- 50mm f3.5 Tessar (543/00): $95-145.
- 50mm f2 Sonnar (543/59): $20-40.
- 50mm f1.5 Sonnar (543/60): $25-50.
- 75mm f1.5 Biotar. Super rare. One known sale at $1100.
- 85mm f4 Triotar (543/02): $70-100.
- 85mm f2 Sonnar (563/05): $85-130.
- 115mm f3.5 Panflex Tessar (5522/01), for bellows. Rare. $500-700.
- 135mm f4 Sonnar (543/64): $60-110.
- 180mm f2.8 Sonnar, direct or Flektoskop mount. Rare. One recent sale at $1200.
- 300mm f4 Sonnar, direct or Flektoskop. Rare. One recent sale at $2300.
- 500mm f8 Tele-Lens. Flektoskop or Panflex mount and case. (In October 1952, this lens cost $835.) Infrequently offered for sale. One recently purchased at auction for about $2000.

- Stereotar C outfit (810/01, 20.2000). Twin lens assembly, separating prism, special viewfinder, close up lenses, and leather case: $1000-1600.

Contessa Series - Post-war 35mm full frame cameras.

Contessa-35 (533/24), 1950-55 - A fine quality folding 35 with center door somewhat like a Retina. Built-in dual-range, uncoupled exposure meter. "Contessa" in gold on leather door covering, and round rangefinder window directly above lens. Shutter will not fire unless camera has film and it is advanced. Tessar f2.8/45mm. First version (1950-53), Compur Rapid, X sync: $50-90. Second version (1953-55), Synchro Compur, MX sync: $60-110.

Contessa-35 (533/24), 1960-61 - Very different from the first 2 versions. Rigid lens mount. Built-in exposure meter. "Contessa" on top. Tessar f2.8/50mm. Pronto 30-250. $20-35.

Contessa LK (10.0637) - 1963-65. "Contessa LK" on top. Coupled match needle exposure meter. No rangefinder. Tessar f2.8/50mm, Prontor 500 LK shutter. $25-40.

Contessa LKE (10.0638) - 1963-65. "Contessa LKE" on top. Like the LK, but with coupled rangefinder. $30-50.

Contessa LBE (10.0639) - 1965-67. "Contessa LBE" on top. Like the LKE, but automatic flash control by linkage between distance and aperature setting. $30-50.

Contessa S-310 (10.0351) - 1971. Small very well made rigid mount automatic 35, with manual overide. "S-310" on front. Tessar f2.8/40mm. Pronto S500 Electronic shutter, exposures to 8 seconds. $35-50.

Contessa S-312 (10.0354) - "S-312" on front. Like the S-310, but with coupled rangefinder. $75-125.

Contessamatic E - (10.0645) - 1960-63. "Contessa" on top-front of lens mount. No name on top. Tessar f2.8/50mm. Prontor SLK "Special" shutter, 1-500, MX sync. Coupled rangefinder. Exposure meter. $25-40.

Contessamatic - 1960-61. Same as the "E", but no rangefinder, and Prontor SLK shutter. $25-40.

Contessamat - 1964-65. "Contessamat" on top. Fully automatic. Color Pantar f2.8/45mm. Prontormatic 30-125 shutter. Coupled exposure meter. No rangefinder. $25-40.

Contessamat SE (10.0654) - 1963-65. "Contessamat SE" on top. Like the Contessamat, but with coupled rangefinder, Prontormatic 500 shutter, 30-500. $30-45.

Contessamat STE - 1965. "Contessamat STE" on top. Like the SE, but Tessar f2.8/50mm in Prontormatic 500 SL shutter, 1-500. $30-60.

Contessamat SBE (10.0652) - 1963-67. "Contessamat SBE" on top in black. "Flashmatic" in red letters. Like the STE, but covered flash contacts on top. Automatic flash control by linking distance and diaphragm settings. $30-65.

Contina I (522/24) - 1952-55. 35mm folding camera with center door. "Contina" in gold letters on door. Model number on leather of back by back latch. Novar f3.5/

45mm in Prontor SV or Tessar f2.8/45mm in Synchro Compur. X sync. $15-35.

Contina Ia (526/24) - 1956-58. Rigid mount lens. "Contina" under the lens and on bezel at 1 o'clock from lens. Model number in leather on back next to catch. Novicar f2.8/45mm (1956-57) or Pantar f2.8/45mm (1958). $15-35.

Contina II (524/24) - 1952-53. 35mm folding camera with center door. "Contina" on door. Model number in leather of back near catch. Uncoupled built-in rangefinder. Opton-Tessar f2.8/45mm in Synchro Compur 1-500, MX or Novar f3.5/45mm in Prontor SV. $30-40.

Contina IIa (527/24) - 1956-58. Rigid mount lens. "Contina" on front under lens. Model number on back. Rapid wind lever. Built in uncoupled exposure meter, match needle on top. Novar f3.5/45mm or Novicar f2.8/45mm. Prontor SVS 1-300, MX sync. $30-45.

Contina III (529/24) - 1955-58. A system camera, with the same specifications as Contina IIa, except Pantar f2.8/45mm convertible lens. "Contina" on front bezel. Model number on back. Uses all lenses of the Contaflex Alpha series. $40-70.

Contina III Lenses
- 30mm f4 Pantar (1001): $25-45.
- 75mm f4 Pantar (1002): $60-80.
- Steritar D for 3-D pictures (814): $75-125.
- 30mm wide angle finder (422): $25-35.
- Telephoto finder (423): $25-35.
- Telephoto rangefinder (correct field of view for 75mm Pantar) (425): $50-100.
- Universal finder for all items above (426): $50-70.

Contina III Microscope Camera - Body of the Contina III, but modified for use with standard Zeiss Microscope Connecting funnel. No lens. Ibsor B self-cocking shutter, 1-125, X sync. No exposure meter, rangefinder, viewfinder or name, except

"Zeiss-Ikon" in middle of back. Usual shutter release button does not release shutter, but must be depressed to advance shutter. Rare. $40-70.

Contina (10.0626) - 1962-65. Rigid mount 35mm. "Contina" on top. Color Pantar f2.8/45mm. Pronto shutter to 250, X sync, self-timer. $20-40.

Contina L (10.0605) - 1964-65. "Contina L" on top. Like the Contina, but with built-in uncoupled exposure meter. Prontor 250 shutter, 30-250. $20-40.

Contina LK (10.0637) - 1963-65. "Contina LK" on top. Like the "L", but coupled exposure meter. $25-45.

Continette (10.0625) - 1960-61. "Continette" on front beside viewfinder. Rigid mount 35mm, without rangefinder or exposure meter. Pronto shutter 30-250, ST. Lucinar f2.8/45mm. (This lens was not used on any other Zeiss Ikon camera.) $20-40.

Deckrullo, Deckrullo Nettel - 1926-28. (Made by Contessa-Nettel Camerawerk before 1926, now by Contessa-Nettel Div. of Zeiss-Ikon.) This camera continued after 1929 as the Nettel camera (870 series). Strut-folding cameras. Focal plane shutters to 2800. (See also Baby Deckrullo.) **6.5x9cm (36), 9x12cm (90)** - Zeiss Tessar f4.5 or f2.7, or Triotar f3.5. $60-150. **10x15cm (120), 13x18 (165)** - Zeiss Tessar f4.5 or Triotar f3.5. $60-150.

Deckrullo Tropical, Deckrullo Nettel Tropical - Same shutter and lens combinations as the Deckrullo. $400-550.

Donata (227/3, 227/7) - 1927-31. Inexpensive folding plate camera, 6.5x9 and 9x12cm sizes. Name usually on or under handle. Dominar or Tessar f4.5 lens in Compur shutter. $25-55.

Era-box

Elegante (816) - 1927-34. Field camera with rigid front. Square bellows. Wood with brass. $300-400.

Era-Box - 1934-38. Inexpensive version of the Box Tengor. "Era-Box" around lens. 4.5x6cm or 6x9cm on 120. $15-30. *(illustrated bottom of previous column)*

Ergo (301) - 1927-31. Detective camera made to look like a monocular. Shoots at right angles to direction of viewing. "Ergo" in eyepiece area. 4.5x6cm plates. Tessar f4.5/55mm. Self-cocking shutter. Very rare. $800-1000.

Ermanox (858) - 1927-31. 4.5x6cm plate camera. Ernostar f1.8/85mm or rare f2 lens. FP shutter 20-1200. Rigid helical focusing. $800-1200.

Ermanox (858/3, 858/7, 858/11) - 1927. Strut-folding, bellows camera. Ernostar f1.8 lens, FP shutter to 1000. 6.5x9cm (858/3) is fairly rare: $500-1000. 9x12cm (858/7) is super rare: $3000-5000. 10x15 and 13x18cm sizes are listed in original catalogs, but are so rare that they are impossible to price.

Ermanox Reflex - 1927-29. Reflex 4.5x6cm plate camera. Ernostar f1.8/105mm lens in rigid helical focus mount. FP shutter 20-1200. $1500-2500.

Erni (27, 27/3) - 1927-30. Box plate camera. Celluloid "ground glass". Very rare. Estimate: $150-250.

Favorit (265, 265/7, 265/9, 265/11) - 1927-35. Black bodied plate camera of excellent quality. Name or number usually on handle, number on outside of door near hinge. Interchangeable lenses on all but the 4.5x6cm size. Tessar or Dominar f4.5 lens. 13x18cm size: Very rare. Estimate: $150-300. Other sizes: $100-180.

Favorit Tropical (266, 266/7, 266/9) - 1927-31. Teakwood plate camera of excellent quality. Brown leather handle with name and model number. Tessar or Dominar f4.5 in Compur shutter. Price varies, depending on size and condition. $400-600.

Hochtourist - c1927-31. Double extension wood view camera. Brass trim. Square bellows. Vertical and horizontal front movements. Sizes 5x7", 8x10", and 10x12". Usually without model name on camera, but with "Zeiss-Ikon" round metal plate. Very rare. No active trading exists. Infrequent sales records indicate prices in $100-300 range. *See D.B. Tubbs "Zeiss Ikon Cameras 1926-39" for pictures.*

Hologon - see Zeiss Contarex Hologon.

Icarette - 1927-36. In formats 4x6.5, 6x6, 6x9, 6.5x11, and 8x10.5cm, plus one model which used 6x9cm rollfilm or 6.5x9cm plates. Most say "Icarette" on handle or in leather on body. There were over 60 different lens/shutter combinations offered and 4 qualities of bodies, #509, #500, #512, and the fanciest #551/2. There are simply more kinds of Icarettes than most people want to hear about. Interest is still light in this series and the price range is $20-60.

Icarex - 1967-73. *An intermediate priced 35mm system camera. All had cloth focal plane shutter, ½-1000, B, X sync.*

Icarex 35 (10.2200) - Bayonet mount. Interchangeable viewing screens, viewfinders, and lenses. With Color Pantar f2.8/50: $85-110. With Tessar f2.8/50mm: $90-120. Add $20-40 for black body.

Icarex 35 "TM" - Threaded 42mm lens mount, marked "TM" at 1 o'clock from the lens. With Tessar f2.8/50mm: $125-175. With Ultron f1.8/50mm: $135-185.

Icarex 35 CS - Either of the Icarex 35 models becomes an Icarex 35 CS by the addition of a pentaprism viewfinder containing a through-the-lens CdS meter.

The finder says "Icarex 35 CS" on its front, and looks like a part of the camera. $65-125.

Icarex 35S - intro. 1970. Available in TM (10.3600) and BM (10.3300) models. This camera differs from the Icarex 35 in that the viewfinders and view screens are not interchangeable. The CdS meter is built in and coupled with stop-down metering. Five Zeiss lenses were available for the TM model, nine for the BM model. Chrome or black versions. Some of the early black models are marked "Pro". With Pantar: $75-110. Tessar f2.8: $80-125. Ultron f1.8: $110-180. For black models, add $20-40.

Icarex SL-706 (10.3700) - 1972-73. An improved type of Icarex, with "SL-706" on body at 11 o'clock direction from the lens. Zeiss lenses. Open aperture metering. These cameras were remaindered out by Cambridge Camera at $257, with case, and most are seen in mint condition. With Ultron f1.8: $165-200.

Icarex Lenses - All take 50mm bayonet or 56mm screw-over filters and shades.
Bayonet mount:
- 35mm f3.4 Skoparex (11.2003): $60-90.
- 50mm f2.8 Color Pantar (11.2001): $20-40.
- 50mm f2.8 Tessar (11.2002): $30-50.
- 50mm f1.8 Ultron (11.2014): $75-110.
- 90mm f3.4 Dynarex (11.2004): $70-120.
- 135mm f4 Super Dynarex (11.2005): $65-100.
- 200mm f4 Super Dynarex (11.2008): $140-215.
- 400mm f5 Telomar (11.2010). Rare: $275-475.
- 36-82mm f2.8 Zoomar (11.2012): $180-300.
Thread mount:
- 25mm f2.8 Distagon (11.3503). Rare: $110-170.
- 35mm f3.4 Skoparex (11.3510): $65-95.
- 50mm f2.8 Tessar (11.35??): $40-60.
- 50mm f1.8 Ultron (11.3502): $80-100.
- 135mm f4 Super Dynarex (11.3511): $70-110.

Ideal 9x12cm, #250/7

Ideal - 1927-38. A fine quality double extension folding plate camera usually having the name and model number stamped on the leather body covering under the handle. The 9x12cm size was the most common, followed by the 6.5x9cm. They were offered with Compur shutters, and Dominar, Tessar, or Double Protar lenses, the Tessars being by far the most common. Interchangeable lens/shutter on all but the 6.5x9cm. All had special "pop-off" backs. 13x18 (250/11), very rare: $75-125. 10x15 (250/9), rare: $50-100. 9x12 (250/7): $30-50. 6.5x9 (250/3): $30-60.

Ikoflex cameras - 1934-60. *Twin lens reflex for 6x6cm format. Name on front.*

Ikoflex, original (850/16) - c1934. "Coffee can" model. All black enamel finish on body. Novar f4.5 or 6.3/80mm lens. Derval, Klio, or Compur-Rapid shutter. Identified by: 2 film counters (for 120 and 620 films); lever focus under lens; "Ikoflex" on shutter above lens. Earliest version

has ribbed finder hood. Second type has leathered hood like later models. Formerly sold for $75-125, but several recent sales have been in the range of $100-175.

Ikoflex I (851/16) - 1936-50. Chrome trim. Tessar or Novar f3.5/75mm. Compur shutter to 300 until 1939, then Klio to 250. Identified by chrome plate at top front with "Ikoflex". First year had lever focus, later a knob. $30-50.

Ikoflex Ia (854/16) - 1952-56. "Ikoflex" in chrome against a black background on front of viewfinder. Novar or Tessar f3.5/75mm. Identified by Prontor SV shutter to 300. Does not have a folding shutter release. $50-75.

Ikoflex Ib (856/16) - 1956-58. Similar to the Ia. Tessar or Novar f3.5/75mm in 1956-57; Novar only in 1957-58. Focusing hood opens and closes with single action, magnifies over diaphragm and shutter speed dials. Prontor SVS shutter. Folding shutter release. No exposure meter. $45-70.

Ikoflex Ic (886/16) - 1956-58. Similar to the Ib, but with built-in exposure meter. Needle visible on ground glass inside hood. $60-85.

Ikoflex II (851/16) - 1937-39. Chrome plate with "Ikoflex" on front. Tessar f3.5/75mm. Compur Rapid to 300. Auto film counter and double exposure prevention. Identify by: Viewing lens appears to stick out further than other models and is in chrome tube. Compur Rapid shutter. Focus lever in 1937, knob in 1938-39. $60-85.

Ikoflex IIa - 1950-52. Similar to the Ikoflex II, but has flash sync, magnifiers on peep windows over shutter speed, and aperature settings dials which are set by levers under shutter housing. $60-85.

Ikoflex IIa (855/16) - 1953-56. Similar to the earlier IIa, but viewing lens black with peep windows directly over it, and shutter and aperature set by wheels. Unlike the Favorite, does not have LVS settings. $60-100.

Ikoflex III (853/16) - 1939-40. Only Ikoflex with huge Albada finder on front of viewing hood (like Contaflex TLR). Crank to advance film and wind shutter. Tessar f2.8/80mm. Compur Rapid 1-400 or 500. $120-250.

Ikoflex Favorit (887/16) - 1956-60. Last of the Ikoflex line. Tessar f3.5/75mm. Synchro Compur shutter. Built in exposure meter. Shutter and aperature settings by wheels. LVS. Cross coupled. $125-185.

Ikomatic A (10.0552) - 1964-65. Inexpensive square-looking, for 126 cartridge film. Color Citar f6.3/45mm lens.

Shutter 1/90 for daylight, 1/30 for flash. Built in electric eye exposure control. Hot shoe. "Ikomatic A" on lower front of camera. $10-25.

Ikomatic F (10.0551) - 1964-65. Same general appearance as the "A", but has Frontar fixed focus lens. No exposure control. Built-in pop-up reflector for AG-1 bulbs on top of camera. "Ikomatic-F" on lower front. $10-25.

Ikonette (504/2) - 1929-31. Small rollfilm camera for 127 film. Frontar f9/80mm. Self-cocking shutter. The whole back comes off to load the film. There were at least 2 variations in the body catch mechanism. $30-50.

Ikonette 35 (500/24) - A unique 35mm camera (for Zeiss) made entirely of grey high impact plastic. Body is curved into a kidney shape and a single lever on the front winds the film, advances the counter, and cocks the shutter on a long stroke. The same lever then releases shutter on a short stroke. No flash sync. Red flag appears in the viewfinder when the shutter is cocked. Two-tone grey and blue plastic case with name on front available (1256/24). $15-35.

Ikonta cameras - 1929-56. Early models also known as Ikomats in the U.S.A. All had front cell focus lenses. *see also Baby Ikonta.*

Ikonta (520/14) - 1931. 5x7.5cm. With Tessar f4.5/80mm in Compur shutter: $30-45. With Novar f6.3/80mm in Derval shutter: $25-35.

Ikonta A (520) - 1933-40. 4.5x6cm on 120 film. Compur shutter. With Tessar f3.5/80mm: $35-50. With Novar f4.5/80mm: $30-40.

Ikonta A (521) - Postwar version of the 4.5x6cm size. With Tessar f3.5/75mm in Synchro Compur shutter: $50-80. With Novar f3.5 or 4.5/75 in Prontor: $40-60.

Ikonta B (520/16) - 1937-39. For 12 exposures 6x6cm on 120. With Tessar f3.5/75mm in Compur Rapid: $30-55. With Novar f3.5 or f4.5/75mm in Compur or Klio shutter: $25-35.

Ikonta B (521/16) - 1948-53. Similar to the 520/16, but with chrome lens mount and more chrome trim. $30-55.

Ikonta B (523/16) - 1954-56. Also similar, but with chrome top plate. Prontor SV or Synchro Compur shutter. $45-65.

Ikonta B (524/16) - 1954-56. Built in uncoupled rangefinder. With Tessar f3.5/

ZEISS (cont.)

105 in Synchro Compur: $60-100. With Novar f3.5 or f4.5/105mm in Prontor SV shutter: $50-70.

Ikonta C (520/2) - 1930-40. 6x9cm on 120. With 105mm lenses: Tessar f4.5: $30-50. Tessar f3.8 (1936-37 only): $35-45. Novar f6.3: $25-40.

Ikonta C (521/2) - Postwar. With Tessar f3.5/105: $40-60.

Ikonta C (523/2) - 1950-56. 6x9cm. Heavy chrome trim at top. Tessar f3.5, Novar f3.5, or Novar f4.5/105mm lens. $35-75.

Ikonta C (524/2) - 1954-56. Like the 523/2 but with built in uncoupled rangefinder. $60-100.

Ikonta D (520/15) - 1931-39. Ikomats seem to be more common in this size than Ikontas. Early versions for 116 film, later for 616 film. With Tessar f4.5/120mm in Compur: $35-50. With Novar f6.3/120mm in Derval shutter: $30-40.

Ikonta 35 (522/24) - 1949-53. Folding 35mm with central door and very rigid front standard. Novar f3.5/45mm, Tessar f2.8/45mm, or Xenar f2.8/45mm (1949-51 only). "Ikonta" in leather on back. Later models had accessory shoe. $25-45.

Juwel (275/7) - 1927-38. 9x12cm plate camera. Superb quality, all metal, leather covered with rotating back. "Juwel" or "Universal Juwel" on or under the handle. Rising/falling, shifting/tilting front. Pop-off backs. Triple extension by means of two rack-and-pinion knobs on folding bed; one moves back and front, one moves lens standard. Interchangeable bayonet lenses. Price depends on condition and lens. $300-400.

Juwel (275/11) - 1927-39. 13x18cm. As

above except lens interchanges with aluminum "board". This camera used extensively by Ansel Adams. With a Triple convertable Protar, this was Zeiss's most expensive camera throughout the prewar years. Quite rare, still usable. With Tessar f4.5/210mm: $300-500. With Protar: $450-700.

Kolibri (523/18) - 1930-35. A compact rollfilm camera giving 16 exposures 4x6.5cm on 127 film. "Kolibri" below lens in leather. Lens extends for picture taking on brightly polished chromed tube. Came with unique shaped case in brown or black. Looking at hinge on right side of open case is a screw in "foot" which is inserted in lens mount for vertical still pictures. With Telma shutter: Novar f4.5/50mm: $75-120; Novar f3.5/50mm, rare: $100-175. With Rimset Compur shutter: Tessar f3.5/50, most common: $150-225; Tessar f2.8/50, rare: $200-325; Biotar f2/45mm, super rare (also called "Night Kolibri"): $450-550. Microscope version with no lens or shutter, very rare: $200-300.

Kosmopolit - 1927-34. Wood double extension field camera with brass trim. Reversing back, vertical and horizontal front movements (no swing). Tapered bellows. 5x7" (818, 818/11) or 7x9½" (819, 818/20) size. Very seldom offered. $200-300.

Lilliput - 1927-28. Tiny strut folding plate camera. Celluloid "ground glass". Struts are inside the bellows. f12.5 lens. 4.5x6cm (361) or 6.5x9cm (370). $100-150.

Lloyd (510/17) - 1928-31. Black leather covered folding rollfilm camera, can also take cut film. Ground glass focusing by sliding out a back cover plate. "Lloyd" in leather on front. Tessar f4.5/120 in Compur. $30-45.

Magnar-Kamera - c1906. (Carl Zeiss, Jena.) Elongated focal plane box camera with telescoping tube in front. Designed for Magnar f10/800mm telephoto lens. Newton finder or monocular finder. A very rare camera. Only one known sale, at auction in Germany for DM 3000 (about $1500 at the time).

Maximar A (207/3) - 1927-39. 6.5x9cm folding plate camera. Slide in holders. "Maximar" on or below handle in leather. Tessar f4.5/105mm in Compur. $40-65.

Maximar B (207/7) - 1927-39. Similar to the "A", but for 9x12cm. Tessar f4.5/135mm in Compur. $45-75.

Maximar (207/9) - 1927-37. Similar, but 10x15cm. Tessar f4.5/165mm in Compur. Rare. $60-90.

Minimum Palmos Stereo - c1908 (Carl Zeiss, Jena). Strut-camera for stereo or panoramic exposures on 9x18cm plates. Focal plane shutter 10-1000. With single f6.3/112mm lens for panoramic use: $200-250.

Miroflex A (859/3) - 1927-36. Folding 6.5x9cm SLR plate camera. Focal plane shutter 3-2000. Can be used as a press camera by leaving the mirror up, focusing hood folded, and using the wire finder. "Miroflex" in leather on front. With Tessar f4.5/120mm: $200-300. With Tessar f3.5/135mm or Bio Tessar f2.8/135mm: $240-350.

Miroflex B (859/7) - Similar to the "A", but 9x12cm. More common. With Tessar f4.5/165mm: $120-200. With Tessar f3.5 or Bio Tessar f2.8/165mm: $150-250.

Nettar - Bob (510) was known as the Nettar (510) in England. From 1937-41 these were inexpensive folding rollfilm cameras. "Nettar" on leather. 4.5x6cm (515), 6x6cm (515/16), and 6x9cm (515/2). From 1949-57 they were a fancier style with body release and chrome top: 6x6cm (518/16) and 6x9cm (517/2). With Novar or Nettar lens: $20-40. With Tessar: $30-50.

Nettax (538/24) - 1936-38. 35mm. Looks somewhat like a Contax II, but has rotating rangefinder window attached to interchangeable lens. Focal plane shutter to 1000. With Tessar f2.8/50mm, quite rare: $400-500. With Tessar f3.5/50mm, rarest: $450-650. For additional Triotar f5.6/105mm lens, add $375-500.

Nettax (513/16) - 1955-57. Folding 6x6cm rollfilm camera. Chrome top. Built in uncoupled exposure meter. Novar f4.5/75mm, Pronto shutter. $50-80.

Nettel - 1929-37 (some sizes discontinued before 1937). "Nettel" below the focal plane shutter winding/setting knob. Black leather covered press camera. 4.5x6cm (870), 6.5x9cm (870/3), 9x12cm (870/7), 10x15cm (870/9), 5x7" (870/11) sizes, with the 9x12cm being the most common. $60-150.

Nettel, Tropen (Tropical) - Focal plane press camera made of polished teak with brown leather bellows. 6.5x9cm (871/3), 9x12cm (871/7), 10x15cm (871/9), 5x7" (871/11) sizes. $200-600.

Nixe - 1927-34. High quality double extension folding cameras. "Nixe" on handle or in body leather. Dominar, Tessar, or Double Protar lens. 551/17 for 8x10.5cm rollfilm or 9x12cm cut film: $45-70. 551/6 for 8x14cm rollfilm or 9x14cm cut film: $50-80. *(illustrated top of next column)*

Nixe

Onito - 1927-29. Inexpensive single extension folding plate cameras. Novar f6.3 lens, lever focus. 6.5x9cm (126/3) or 9x12cm (126/7). $25-35.

Orix (308) - 1928-34. Quality double extension folding press camera, 10x15cm plates. (Special spring back model also made.) Rack-and-pinion focus. Usually seen with Tessar f4.5/150mm lens. $50-100.

Palmos-O - 1927-28. 4.5x6cm plate camera with struts and folding door. Sold in Europe in 1927 only as the "Minimum Palmos". High-speed Tessar f2.7/80mm lens. Focal plane shutter 50-1000. Rare. $350-500.

Perfekt - c1927-31. Double extension, polished mahogany view camera. Tapered bellows. Vertical and horizontal front movements. Sizes 5x7" (834, 834/11, 835, 835/11) and 18x24cm (836, 837, 834/20, 835/20). Usually without model name on camera, but with "Zeiss-Ikon" round metal plate. Very rare. No active trading exists. Infrequent sales records indicate prices in $100-300 range.

Piccolette (545/12) - 1927-30 in Germany, 1927-32 in the U.S.A. Inexpensive all metal strut camera for

4x6.5cm on 127 film. Metal front pulls out for use. "Zeiss-Ikon" above lens, "Piccolette" below. Achromat f11, Novar f6.3, or Tessar f4.5/75mm lens. $60-75.

Piccolette-Luxus (546/12) - 1927-30. Deluxe model with folding bed and lazy tong struts. Brown leather covering and bellows. Dominar or Tessar f4.5/75mm lens, dial-set Compur shutter. $150-200.

Plaskop - 1927-30. Stereo box cameras.
602/1 - 45x107mm. "Plaskop" under left lens (viewed from front). f12 lenses. No brilliant finder. $75-125.
603/1 - 45x107mm. "Plaskop" in oval on left (viewed from front). Better model than the 602/1, with Novar f6.8/60mm lenses. No brilliant finder. $130-200.
603/4 - 6x13cm. Like the 603/1, but a larger size. Brilliant finder in top center. $150-250.

Polyskop - 1927-30. Precision stereo box cameras. Black leather covering. Septum magazine for 12 plates. Brilliant finder in top center. Tessar f4.5 lenses in Compur dial set stereo shutter. 45x107mm (609/1), or 6x13cm (609/4). $150-300.

Simplex (112/7) - 1928-30. Inexpensive folding camera for 9x12cm plates. "Simplex" in leather under handle. "Zeiss Ikon" under lens on front of front standard. Frontar f9/140 or Novar f6.3/135mm. $20-50.

Simplex (511/2) - 6x9cm brown plastic rollfilm camera. "Simplex" on body. Several variations of struts and hardware exist. Nettar f6.3/150mm in Telma or Derval shutter. $25-50.

Simplex-Ernoflex - SLR. "Ernemann" on side in 1927-29 version, "Simplex Ernoflex" over lens from 1930-on. Ernoplast f4.5 or f3.5, Ernon f3.5, or Tessar f4.5 lens. Helical focusing. Focal plane shutter 20-1000. 4.5x6cm (853), 6.5x9cm (853/3), or 9x12cm (853/7). Rare. Hard to set price. 4.5x6cm size: $400-550. 6.5x9cm or 9x12cm size: $175-225.

Sirene - Inexpensive folding plate camera. "Sirene" under handle. In 1927 only: 6.5x9cm (135/3), 9x12cm (135/7; this number was later used on Volta). $25-35. 1930-31: 3¼x4¼" (8x10.5cm, 135/5) made for the American market. Dominar f4.5/135mm lens. Compur shutter. Rare. $45-55.

Sonnet - 1927-30. Teakwood folding plate camera. Brown leather covering on door and brown bellows. "Sonnet" inside door at front. Radial lever focusing. Dominar or Tessar f4.5, or Novar f6.3 lens. Originally came with 3 German silver film holders. 4.5x6cm (303), 6.5x9cm (303/3): $300-600.

Stereo-Ernoflex (621/1) - 1927-29. Top quality folding stereo. Door on hood extends across entire top of camera. Ernotar f4.5, Ernon or Tessar f3.5/75mm lenses. Focal plane shutter 20-1000. $1000-1500. *(illustrated on p.161 under Ernemann)*

Stereo-Simplex-Ernoflex (615/1) - 1927-30. Medium quality non-folding stereo box camera. "Ernemann" on front between lenses. Viewing hood cover is on half of the camera's top, the other half has a pop-up frame finder. Ernon f3.5 or Tessar f4.5/75mm or 80mm lenses. FP shutter. $400-600. *(illustrated on p.162 under Ernemann)*

Stereo Ideal (651) - 6x13cm folding plate stereo camera, black leather covering. Identified on the handle. 1927 version with Dial-set Compur shutters, 1928 version with Compound shutters. Tessar f4.5/90mm. $200-300.

Stereo Ideal (650) - Similar to the 651, but a larger 9x18cm size for films. Compur shutter. Tessar f4.5/120mm lenses. $250-400.

Stereo Nettel - 1927-30. Scissors strut stereo cameras. Black leather covering. Knob focus. Tessar f4.5 lenses. Focal plane shutter. Wire finder. Removable roller blind inside separates the two images, or allows for full frame use. 6x13cm (613/4): $250-350. 10x15cm (613/9): $200-300.

Stereo Nettel, Tropical - Same as the Stereo Nettel, but in teakwood with brown bellows. 6x13cm (614/4) or 10x15cm (614/9). $350-600.

Stereo Palmos - c1905-11 (Carl Zeiss Optical Co.) Folding-bed stereo camera for 9x12cm plates. FP shutter 25-1000. Zeiss Tessar f6.3/84mm lenses. Rack focusing. $300-500. *(illustrated top of next page)*

Stereo Palmos

Stereolette-Cupido (611) - 1927-28. 45x107mm folding plate stereo camera. Black leather covering. "Stereolette-Cupido" on handle, "Stereolette" on outside of door. $150-250.

Steroco (612/1) - 1927-30. 45x107mm plate stereo box camera, tapered shape, leather covered. "Steroco" on upper front, "Zeiss-Ikon" below. Tessar f6.3/55mm lenses in Derval or Dial-set Compur. Rare. $150-250.

Suevia - c1926-27. 6.5x9cm folding-bed plate camera. Nostar f6.8 or Contessa-Nettel Periskop f11 lens in Derval 25-100 shutter. Uncommon. $50-65.

Super Ikonta Series - *Top quality black leather covered folding rollfilm cameras, with coupled rangefinder of the rotating wedge type gear coupled to front cell focussing lens. The early cheaper lens models were sometimes called "Super Ikomat" in the U.S.A. before WWII. Introduced in 1934, they were continued in gradually improving forms until 1959 or 1960. The most recent models with MX sync have increased in value because they have been rediscovered as usable cameras... a lower cost nostalgic alternative to such modern cameras as the new folding Plaubel Makinas.*

Super Ikonta A (530) - 1934-37. 16

exposures 4.5x6cm on 120 film. Usually seen with Tessar f3.5/70mm uncoated lens. No sync. Body release 1935-37. Direct finder (not Albada). $100-180.

Super Ikonta A (530) - 1937-50. Same as the above, but with body release, Albada finder, and double exposure prevention. Usually with Tessar f3.5/75mm lens. Novar f3.5 lens is rare. Schneider Xenar in 1948. No sync. $110-200.

Super Ikonta A (531) - 1950-56. Chrome top. Normal lens is Tessar f3.5/75mm. Compur Rapid, X sync, until 1952; later MX sync; and finally Synchro Compur. $250-400. *The latest model with Synchro Compur is increasing in demand as a usable camera, and in Excellent to Mint condition will bring at least $100 more the the prices indicated.*

Super Ikonta B (530/16) - 1935-37. Eleven exposures 6x6cm on 120. Separate rangefinder/viewfinder windows. f2.8/80mm or (rarely) f3.5/80mm Tessar. Compur Rapid to 400. No sync. Lens/shutter housing black enameled.

Some of the earliest say "Super Ikomat" on the door. $85-125. *In 1936 a model was produced in meters with European tripod socket and "Super Six 530/16" on the back of the camera and front of the ER case. These are rare, but only a modest premium seems obtainable.*

Super Ikonta B (532/16) - 1937-56. Single window range/viewfinder. Lens/shutter housing in black enamel through 1948, chrome after 1948. "Super Ikonta 532/16" in back leather. Tessar f2.8/80mm. Compur Rapid shutter, no sync to 1951. Synchro Compur shutter, MX sync 1951-on. (Some Compur Rapid models c1951 have X sync.) Compur Rapid: $90-180. Synchro Compur: $250-300.

Super Ikonta BX (532/16) - 1937-52. 12 exposures 6x6cm on 120. Double exposure and blank exposure prevention. Uncoupled exposure meter. "Super Ikonta-533/16" in leather on back. Tessar f2.8/80mm in Compur Rapid to 400. Exposure meter in DIN or Scheiner before 1948, ASA after 1948. $90-165.

Super Ikonta BX (533/16) - 1952-57. Uncoupled exposure meter in chrome and lower profile than the 1937-52 type. "Super Ikonta 533/16" on back. Synchro

Compur MX shutter to 500. Coated Tessar or Opton Tessar lens. $165-250.

Super Ikonta III (531/16) - 1954-58. A redesigned "B" with no exposure meter. Smaller than the "B". No "front window" at lens for rangefinder. Synchro Compur MX shutter to 500. Novar or Tessar (until 1956) f3.5/75mm. $100-140.

Super Ikonta IV (534/16) - 1956-60. Like the III, but with built in exposure meter using the LVS system (where you lock in a guide number on shutter, after which shutter and diaphragm settings move together). "534/16" in leather on back by latch. Tessar f3.5/75mm only. (During 1983, KEH Camera sold off NEW Super Ikonta IV's for $395.) $150-300.

Super Ikonta C (530/2) - 1934-36. "Super Ikonta" or "Super Ikomat" in leather on front. "530/2" in back leather by hinge. Black enamel finish, nickel plated fittings. No body release. Triotar f4.5/120 in Klio shutter, or Tessar f4.5 or f3.8/105mm in Compur to 250 or Compur-Rapid to 400. $100-175.

Super Ikonta C 531/2, 1936-38

Super Ikonta C 531/2, 1950-55

Super Ikonta C (531/2) - 1936-50. Front of rangefinder is chrome. "531/2" in leather by back hinge. Body release, double exposure prevention. Albada finder. Tessar f3.8/105 until 1938, Tessar f4.5 or f3.5/105 after 1938. Compur to 250, or Compur-Rapid to 400. $130-200.

Super Ikonta C (531/2) - 1950-55. "531/2" in leather by back latch. Double exposure and blank exposure prevention. Tessar f3.5. Compur Rapid, X sync, or Synchro Compur, MX sync. This model is both a user and collector type and many are sold in Japan. VG to EXC: $350-450. *Add $100 if mint. (illustrated top right)*

Super Ikonta D (530/15) - 1936-39. "530/15" by back latch. Bright chrome on front of viewfinder. Albada viewfinder with ½-frame marks. Body release. No double exposure prevention. Compur to 250 or Compur Rapid to 400. No sync. $150-175.

Super Nettel (536/24) - 1934-37. 35mm folding bellows camera. Black enamel and leather. "Super Nettel" in leather on door. Focal plane shutter 5-1000. 1934-36, Tessar f3.5 or f2.8/50mm lens; 1935-37, Triotar f3.5/50mm. $150-250. *This normal range is well substantiated, but one example in extraordinary condition brought well over $600 at an October 1984 auction!*

Super Ikonta D (530/15) - 1934-36. "Super Ikomat" or "Super Ikonta" in front leather. "530/15" in leather by back hinge. Black enamel on rangefinder. 6.5x11cm on 616 film, mask for ½-frame (5.5x6.5cm). Flip-up mask in viewfinder for ½-frame. No body release. Tessar f4.5/120mm in Compur to 250, or Triotar (rare) f4.5/120mm in Klio shutter 5-100. $135-220.

Super Nettel II (537/24) - 1936-38.

Similar to the first model, but with polished chrome door and matte chrome top. Tessar f2.8/50mm. Has increased considerably in the last two years. $400-800.

Symbolica (10.6035) - 1959-62. 35mm viewfinder camera. Coupled match needle exposure meter. "Symbolica" on top. Tessar f2.8/50mm, front cell focus. $25-45.

Taxo - Inexpensive folding plate camera, single extension. "Taxo" on body under handle. Periskop f11/105, Novar f6.3/105 or f6.3/135, Frontar, or Dominar lens. Derval shutter. Two variations:
1927-31 - Focus by sliding front standard on track, 6.5x9cm (122/3) or 9x12cm (122/7). $20-35.
1927-30 - Focus by radial lever, 6.5x9cm (126/3) or 9x12cm (126/7). $25-35.

Taxona - see PENTACON VEB.

Tenax - 1927. Popular strut-folding plate cameras. "Tenax" or "Taschen Tenax" on front or top. These appear to be clean up items which were never actually manufactured by or marked "Zeiss Ikon". 4.5x6, 6.5x9, and 45x107mm (stereo) sizes. Various lenses. $80-150.

Tenax I (570/27)

Tenax I (1948)

Tenax I (570/27) - 1930-41. 35mm camera for 50 exposures 24x24mm on a 36 exposure roll. "Tenax" under lens. No rangefinder. Novar f3.5/35mm lens. Compur shutter, cocked and film advanced by left-hand lever. $35-75. *(illustrated bottom of previous column)*

Tenax I - 1948. Like the 570/27, but with coated Tessar f3.5/37.5mm lens. Flash sync contact on top of shutter. Possibly East German. "Zeiss Ikon" above lens, "Tenax" below. Earlier data indicated higher prices, but recent sales are in the same range as the pre-war models $35-75. *(illustrated bottom of previous column)*

Tenax II (580/27) - 1937-41. More expensive and earlier version with coupled rangefinder, interchangeable lenses, and shoe for viewfinders and contameter (1339). Most often found with Tessar f2.8/40mm: $180-260. With Sonnar f2/40mm: $200-325. For the Orthometar f4.5/27 (wide angle) or Sonnar f4/75 (telephoto) with viewfinder, add $300-500.

Tenax Automatic (10.0651) - 1960-63. Full frame 35mm. "Tenax" at 11 o'clock from lens on exposure meter window. Automatic exposure control by selenium cell. No rangefinder. Tessar f2.8/50mm in Prontormat shutter. Front cell focus. $25-45.

Tengoflex (85/16) - 1941-42. Box camera for 6x6cm exposures on 120 film. "Tengoflex" on front. Large brilliant finder on top, giving the appearance of a twin

ZEISS (cont.)

lens reflex. Extremely rare. No recent sales data. Several sales 1974-81 in the range of $275-325.

Tessco (761) - 1927. Double extension 9x12cm folding plate camera. "Tessco" in leather of handle. Seen with one of five different lenses, from Periskop f11 to Tessar f4.5. Rare. $50-100.

Trona (210 series) - 1927-30. Quality folding plate camera, double extension, screw controlled rise and shift. "Trona" and model number under handle. Dominar or Tessar f4.5 lens. 9x12cm (210/7): $40-60. 6.5x9cm (210/3) or 8.5x11cm (210/5): $50-100. *The 8.5x11cm (210/5) was apparently made for the English and American market for use with 3¼x4¼" film. This size is rare.*

Tropen Adoro

Trona (212/7) - c1928-36. 9x12cm folding plate camera similar to the 210 series. Tessar lens, Compur shutter. $50-70.

Trona (214 series) - 1929-38. A fancier version, with aluminum ground glass back (frequently exchanged for a regular back). Tessar f3.5 lens in Compur shutter (rimset after 1930). "Trona" and model number on body under handle. 6.5x9cm (214/3): $70-125. 9x12cm (214/7): $60-100. (Slightly less for f4.5 models.)

Tropen Adoro - 1927-36. Polished teak, folding plate camera. Brown leather covering on door and back. Brown double extension bellows. "Tropen Adoro" and model number on leather of door. Tessar f4.5 lens, Compur shutter. Sizes: 6.5x9cm (230/3), 105 or 120mm lens. 9x12cm (230/7), 135 or 150mm lens. 10x15cm (230/9), 165 or 180mm lens. $300-500. *(illustrated top of next column)*

Tropica - 1927-31 (to 1935 in foreign catalogs). A heavy polished teak folding plate camera, the second most expensive camera in 1930 Zeiss line. Strongly reinforced with German silver corners and battens. No leather anywhere on the outside, even the door on the ground glass back is teak. Black bellows. Back rotates a quarter turn. "Zeiss-Ikon" between pull knobs on front stand. 14 different lenses available, all in Compur shutter. Sizes 9x12cm (285/7) and 10x15cm (285/9) are both rare. The 5x7" (285/11) is VERY rare. Sales records are hard to find. Estimate: $450-1000.

Unette (550) - 1927-30. Wood box camera, with leatherette covering. For paper-backed rollfilm, 22x31mm. "Unette" on front in leatherette over lens, "Zeiss-Ikon" over lens, "Ernemann" on side. Metal frame finder at top rear. f12.5/40mm lens. Very rare. Only one known sale in 1980 at $225.

Victrix (101) - 1927-31. Small folding plate camera for 4.5x6cm. "Victrix 101" in leather on camera top. "Zeiss Ikon" on lens, between pulls, and on door. Novar f6.3/75, Dominar f4.5/75, or Tessar. Compur shutter. $85-150.

404

Volta - 1927-31. Inexpensive single extension folding plate cameras. "Volta" on body under handle, "Zeiss Ikon" on door. Dominar or Tessar lens, Klio or Compur shutter. Radial arm focusing in 6.5x9cm (146/3) or 9x12cm (146/7). Focusing by slide front standard in 6.5x9cm (135/3) or 9x12cm (135/7). (10x15cm and 13x18cm sizes were sold in 1926/27 as clean up of old stock on hand at the time of the union.) Although Voltas are not common, there is little interest in them. $25-45.

ZENIT (Russia)
Photo Sniper - Zenit E camera with a special Tair-3 f4.5/300mm lens attached to a pistol-type grip. $150-200.

Zenit, Zenit 3, Zenit 3M, Zenit B - 35mm SLR cameras. Fixed pentaprism. FP shutter 30-500, B. $20-40.

ZENITH CAMERA CORP.
Comet - c1947. Plastic camera for 4x6cm on 127 film. Vertical style. Telescoping front. $8-12.

Comet Flash - c1948. Plastic camera with aluminum top and bottom. 4x6cm on 127. $8-12.

Sharpshooter - c1948. Black & silver metal box camera. Identical to the J.E. Mergott Co. JEM Jr. $4-8.

ZENITH EDELWEISS - Folding rollfilm camera for 6x6cm on 620 film. $12-18.

ZENITH FILM CORP.
Winpro 35, Synchro Flash - c1948. Gray plastic 35mm. f7/40mm. $15-25.

ZION (Ed. Zion, Paris)

Pocket Z - Folding strut-type camera for 6.5x9cm plates. Rex Luxia or Boyer Sapphir lens. Dial Compur shutter. Leather bellows. Metal body. $75-125.

ZODIAC - Novelty 4x4cm "Diana" style camera. $1-5.

ZORKI (USSR) *Manufacturers of 35mm cameras, copies of various Leicas.*
Zorki - c1952. Leica II copy. f3.5/50mm Industar or f2/50mm Jupiter lens. $60-90.

Zorki 2 - Leica copy. $60-90.
Zorki C - Leica thread lenses. $40-50.
Zorki 2C - $60-100.
Zorki 3 - c1955. f2.8 lens. Coupled rangefinder. $40-60.

Zorki 4 - c1955. Jupitar f2/50mm. FP shutter 1-1000. CRF. This is the most common model. $35-60.

Zorki 5 - Industar f3.5/50mm. FP shutter 25-500. CRF. Rapid advance lever. $40-60.

ZUIKO OPTICAL CO. (Japan)
Honor - c1959. 35mm Leica copy. CRF. Konishiroku Hexar f3.5/50mm lens. FP shutter 1-500. $125-175.

ZULAUF (G. Zulauf, Zurich)
Bebe - Compact camera for 4.5x6cm plates. Before 1911 it was distributed by Carl Zeiss and Krauss. It became a part of the Ica line in 1911. The logo G.Z.C. is in an oval on the camera. $150-175.

MOVIE CAMERAS

COLLECTING MOTION PICTURE CAMERAS

Many photographic and persistence of vision developments, over a long period of time, led to the advent of motion pictures. True motion picture cameras, as we know them, did not come into being until the 1890's, and few such cameras were made during that very early period. Some were one-of-a-kind. The very few surviving pre-1900 cameras are in museums and private collections with perhaps a very few in attics, basements or warehouses throughout the world.

From about 1900 on, a variety of motion picture cameras appeared. Some were manufactured for sale to the growing number of motion picture studios; others were made by the studios themselves. A small number were made for amateurs.

The collecting of motion picture cameras from this period on can be a fascinating hobby. The limited number of early cameras available makes collecting challenging. In addition, some of the early cameras do not carry identification because some manufacturers borrowed freely from the designs of others and there were many patent infringment problems. This lack of identification calls for research by the collector to identify some of the cameras.

In the early motion picture days there were many film widths. The 35mm width pioneered by Edison (U.S.A.) and Lumiere (France) became the standard for professional motion pictures. Most of the cameras available to collectors are of the 35mm variety and they are found in a wide array of sizes, shapes, and configurations.

It is interesting to note, however, that even before 1900 there were 17½mm cameras and projectors for use by amateurs. Several amateur cameras using different 17½ film perforation configurations were made over the years. Cameras using 10, 11, 15, 20, 32, 40, 60, and 70mm film widths were also made. Motion picture cameras were made that used glass plates and circular discs of film for sequential exposures.

In 1912, Pathe of France introduced a 28mm projector and a large library of 28mm feature films for home use. A limited number of 28mm cameras followed. Also in 1912, Edison introduced a 22mm projector (3 rows of pictures per width) and a library of their films, but no 22mm cameras were offered to the public.

Movie cameras did not become available in appreciable numbers until after the introduction of the amateur film formats of 16mm in the U.S.A. and 9½mm in Europe in 1923. Amateur motion pictures then became very popular because the new 16 and 9½mm cameras were easy to use and the new reversal films were economical and had a safety film base.

With the subsequent introduction of 8mm cameras and film in 1932 and Super 8 in 1965 the motion picture camera collector can specialize in many ways, for example: particular format, country of origin, chronological period, manufacturer, or first models, etc. To those just entering the fascinating hobby of motion picture camera collecting: Happy Collecting.

Much of the information in the movie section is due to the efforts of several collectors who specialize in movie equipment. Wes Lambert is a long time collector who specializes in the very early motion picture cameras. He lectures and displays his cameras in museums, cinema schools and camera clubs. He provided most of the information and photographs for the early 35mm cameras and a few of the smaller ones, as well as price estimates for these rare early cameras. He will correspond with other movie camera collectors. Contact him at: 1568 Dapple Ave., Camarillo, CA 93010. Tel 805-482-5331.

Cynthia Repinski provided the information on the cameras of the Universal Camera Corp. of New York City. Cindy specializes in both movie and still cameras from Universal. She is an active collector and trader. See her full-page ad in the advertising section at the back of this book.

Most of the 8 and 16mm camera information, and price data on all sizes is the work of Joan McKeown.

AGFA (Berlin)

Agfa Movex 16-12B

Movex 8 - c1937. 8mm movie camera taking a 10m length of single-8 film in Agfa-Kassettes. Black lacquered metal body; rectangular shape. Optical eye-level finder. Spring motor drive, 16 fps.

The six most basic motion picture camera movements are illustrated here in chronological order. Almost all motion picture movements are derived from these six. These models were made by Eric Berndt and are now in the Smithsonian Institution.

Top, left to right:
Demeny Beater movement, patented 1893;
Lumiere-Pathe movement, patented 1895;
Geneva Star movement, patented 1896;
Prestwich movement, patented 1899.

Bottom left to right:
Williamson movement, patented 1908;
Chronik movement, patented 1913.

Interchangeable Agfa Kine Anastigmat f2.8/12mm focusing lens. $25-30.

Movex 8L - c1954. 8mm movie camera taking a 10m single-8 Agfa-Kassette. Black lacquered metal body; rectangular shape. Optical eye-level finder. Spring motor drive, 16 fps. Agfa Kine Anastigmat f2.8/12mm fixed focus lens. Coupled meter. $10-15.

Movex 16-12B - c1928. 16mm movie camera taking a 12m Agfa-Kassette. Black leather covered metal body; rectangular shape. Waist-level brilliant finder and eye-level Newton finder. Spring motor drive, 16 fps. Agfa Kine Anastigmat f3.5/20mm

focusing lens. $55-80. *(illustrated on previous page)*

Movex 30B, 30L - c1932. 16mm movie camera taking 100' spools. Blue leather covered metal body, oval in shape. Optical eye-level finder. Spring drive. Model 30L has 8-12-16 fps; Model 30B also has 32 fps. Interchangeable Kine Anastigmat f2.8/20mm focusing lens. $85-100.

Movex 88 - c1957. 8mm movie camera, using double 8 film on 25' spools. Grey leather covered metal body. Optical eye-level finder. Spring motor, 16 fps. Agfa Kine Anastigmat f2.5/11mm lens. Made in focusing and fixed focus versions. $10-15.

Movex 88L - c1958. Similar to the Movex 88, but with built-in coupled meter. Agfa Movexar f1.9/13mm focusing lens. $20-30.

Movex Automatic I - c1958. Double-8 movie camera using 25' spools. Gray leather covered metal body. Optical eye-level finder. Spring motor, 16 fps. Agfa Movestar f1.9/12.5mm focusing lens. Automatic light meter. $10-15.

AKELEY CAMERA, INC. (New York)
Carl Akeley, a famous naturalist, scientist, and inventor, found fault with the best available motion picture cameras for use in photographing wild animals in Africa. He then designed this camera system.

Akeley 35mm Motion Picture Camera - 1914. The Akeley camera features interchangeable taking and viewing lens pairs, and can use very long telephoto lenses. The viewfinder eyepiece optics are articulated. A unique dual gyroscope mechanism built into the tripod head provides a very smooth one hand pan and tilt. The 200 foot film magazines are the displacement type and include the supply/takeup sprocket for fast reload. The Akeley was affectionately known as the "pancake" and was a favorite of newsreel and sports cameramen for decades. Range: $500-1500. *Camera shown is Serial No. 2.*

ANSCO
Cine Ansco - c1930. The first 16mm amateur movie camera from Ansco. Includes Models A & B. Black or brown leather covered metal body; rectangular in shape. Optical eye-level finder. Spring motor, 8-64 fps. Interchangeable fixed focus Agfa Anastigmat f3.5 lens. $25-40.

Ansco Risdon Model A - c1931. 16mm movie camera taking 50' spools. Black crinkle-finish lacquered metal body. Optical eye-level finder. Spring motor, 16 fps. B&L Ilex f3.5/1" fixed focus lens. $20-25.

ARGUS
Automatic 8 - 8mm movie camera. Two-tone green lacquered metal body. Battery-operated motor. Cinepar f1.8/13mm lens. Coupled meter. $10-15.

BARKER BROS. (LOS ANGELES, CA)

King Barker 35mm Motion Picture Camera - 1917. This camera, known as "The Educator" was manufactured by the Angeles Camera Co. for Barker Bros., a pioneer California furniture Co. It is almost identical to an early English Williamson type camera but "The Educator" can also be used as a projector and a printer. The camera was often used to photograph local events in small towns for projection in the local theater. This camera was also sold under the Omnio Mfg. Co. name. Range: $350-1000.

BELL AND HOWELL (Chicago, IL, USA)

Eyemo, 35mm

Bell & Howell Cine Camera #2709 - This excellent studio camera was considered a revolutionary design when introduced in 1912. It features all metal construction with an external dual magazine. A four lens turret is incorporated and preview viewing and focusing can be accomplished through the taking lens. The most sophisticated feature is the fixed registration pins that engage two film perforations during exposure. This feature and the overall precision of this camera led to its use in studios throughout the world. Although initially a hand crank camera, electric motor drive was soon used. Bell and Howell 2709 cameras are plentiful but are quite expensive for the collector as ther are still in use as animation and special effects cameras. Range: $1000-3500.

Eyemo 35mm Motion Picture Camera - 1926. The Eyemo camera is the 35mm version of the very successful Filmo 16mm camera introduced 3 years earlier. The Eyemo is a rugged camera that found great use in newsreel photography. Many Eyemo cameras were used by the U.S. Military during World War II. Range: $40-80. *(illustrated on previous page)*

Filmo 70 - 1923. 16mm motion picture camera. The Filmo camera was introduced shortly after the Cine Kodak and Victor 16mm cameras. The Filmo is an excellent design that had previously appeared briefly as a 17½mm camera. A compact die cast metal body encloses 100' film spools and a heavy spring drive motor. It has a rugged version of the very successful Lumiere/Pathe film transport movement. Range: $30-60.

Filmo 70A - c1924. 16mm movie camera taking 100' spools. Black crackle-finish metal body. Eye-level finder. Spring motor wound by large key on the side. 8-16 fps. Interchangeable Taylor Hobson f3.5/1" fixed focus lens. $25-40.

Filmo 75 - c1928. 16mm movie camera taking 100' spools. Black, brown, or grey leather covered metal body. Leather is

tooled with intricate patterns. Oval shape. Eye-level finder. Spring motor, 16 fps. Interchangeable Taylor Hobson f3.5/20mm fixed focus lens. $50-65.

Filmo-121 - c1934. 16mm magazine movie camra. Brown leatherette and brown lacquered aluminum body. Optical eye-level and waist-level finders. Spring motor 16-24 fps. Interchangeable Cooke Anastigmat f2.7/1" fixed focus lens. $18-24.

Filmo 127-A - Single 8mm movie camera. Spring motor 8-32 fps. Interchangeable Mytal Anastigmat f2.5/12.5mm lens. $5-10.

Filmo 141-A, 141-B - intro. 1938. 16mm magazine movie cameras. Black painted metal body. Optical eye-level finder. Spring motor. Model A has 8-32 fps; Model B has 16-64 fps. Interchangeable Taylor Hobson f3.5/1" lens. $25-35.

Filmo Aristocrat Turret 8 - c1940. Same as the Filmo Sportster, but with 3-lens turret. $5-10.

Filmo Auto Load - c1940. 16mm magazine movie camera. Brown plastic covered aluminum body. Eye-level finder. Spring motor, 8-32 fps. Interchangeable Lumax f1.9/1" lens. $13-17.

Filmo Companion (Double Run Eight)- c1941. Double-8 spool load movie camera. Brown leatherette and painted metal body. Eye-level finder. Spring motor, 8-32 fps. Interchangeable Anastigmat f3.5/12.5mm fixed focus lens. $5-10. *(illustrated top of next page)*

Filmo Sportster (Double Run Eight) - c1940. Double-8 movie camera. Early models only say "Filmo Double Run Eight". Later models also say "Sportster". Grey body. Similar to the Filmo Companion, but 16-64 fps. $5-10.

Filmo Companion

Magazine Camera-172 - c1947. 8mm magazine movie camera. Brown leatherette covered metal body. Eye-level finder. Spring motor, 16-64 fps. Interchangeable focusing Comat f1.9, f2.5, f3.5/½" lenses. Available in single lens or 2-lens turret models. $15-25.

Magazine Camera-200 - c1952. 16mm magazine movie camera. Chromed metal body with tan leather. Optical eye-level finder. Spring motor, 16-64 fps. Interchangeable Taylor Hobson Cooke f1.9/1" lens. Available in single lens, 2-lens turret, and 3-lens turret models. $15-25.

200EE - c1956. 16mm magazine movie camera. Chromed aluminum body with black leather. Optical eye-level finder. Battery-operated motor, 16-64 fps. Super Comat f1.9/20mm fixed focus lens. Automatic electric eye. $20-35.

252 - intro. 1954. 8mm movie camera, referred to in ads as the Monterey. Two-tone brown die-cast aluminum body. Optical eye-level finder, marked for telephoto attachment. Spring motor, 16 fps. Super Comat f2.3/10mm fixed focus lens. "Sun Dial" diaphragm setting allows

the user to set the dial for the lighting conditions and the diaphragm is set accordingly. Available in single lens or 3-lens turret models. $5-10.

319 - Double-8mm movie camera. Two-tone brown body. Spring motor, 10-40 fps. Super Comat f1.9/10mm lens. $4-7.

BELL MANUFACTURING CO. (Des Plaines, IL)
Bell Motion Picture Camera, Model 10 - c1936. 16mm movie camera taking 50' spools. Black crinkle painted metal body. Oval shape. Small sportsfinder. Spring motor. Fixed focus lens. $40-60.

BOLEX (Paillard-Bolex, Switzerland)

Bolex C8

B8, C8, L8 - c1940-55. A series of double 8mm cameras, with only minor differences in body design or features. C8 and L8 have a single interchangeable lens; B8 has a 2-lens turret. L8 is 16 fps; B8 and C8 are 8-64 fps. Spring motor. Black leather covered metal body. f1.9 to f2.8 lenses available. $15-25.

Bolex D8L

B8L, C8SL, D8L - c1958. Like the B8, and C8 models above, but with built-in light meter. B8L and D8L are 2-lens and 3-lens turret models, 12-64 fps. C8SL has a single lens and 18 fps. D8L: $65-90. B8L: $50-65. C8SL: $20-30.

H8 - intro. 1936. Same body style as the H16, but for 8mm movies. Heavier construction than the later L8, B8, and C8 models. Black leather covered metal body. Optical eye-level finder. Spring motor, 8-64 fps. Interchangeable focusing lenses on a 3-lens turret. Meyer Kino Plasmat f1.5/12.5mm, Meyer Trioplan f2.8/36mm and f2.8/20mm. With 3 lenses: $95-120.

H-16 - intro. 1935. 16mm movie camera for 100' spools. Automatic film threading. Black leather covered metal body. Optical eye-level finder. Spring motor, 8-64 fps. Interchangeable lenses mounted on a 3-lens turret. Meyer Trioplan f2.8/75mm, Meyer Plasmat f1.5/6mm and f1.5/25mm. $150-200.

H-16 Leader - c1950. Similar to the Standard F-16 (above), but with thru-the-lens waist level reflex viewing. Achromatic eyepiece. $100-135.

H-16 Reflex - c1950. Similar to the Standard H-16 (above), but with an eye-level reflex thru-the-lens viewfinder. $200-250.

BOLSEY - *See the still camera section for a description of the Bolsey 8 (page 60).*

BRUMBERGER
8mm-E3L, T3L - 8mm movie camera with 3-lens turret. Grey and black body. Brumberger f1.8/13mm normal lens. With normal, tele, and wide angle lenses: $10-20.

Empire 35mm Motion Picture Camera - c1912. This wood body, hand crank amateur camera is simple and basic in design. It has 100' internal magazines and a fixed focus f6.3/50mm lens. The price was modest and the operation elementary. The English Ensign and Jury cameras are almost identical. Range: $350-1000.

CAMERA PROJECTOR LTD. (London, England)

Midas 9½mm Motion Picture Camera/ Projector - 1933. The Midas 9½mm camera is unusual in that it is both a camera and a projector. An internal battery pack provided power to drive the camera. As a projector it was hand cranked and illuminiation power was provided by the battery pack. Range: $30-60.

CAMERAS LTD. (Slough, England)
Dekko - c1934. 9.5mm movie camera taking 10m Pathe-size cartridge. Black bakelite art deco body. Optical eye-level

body. Spring motor, 16-64 fps. Interchangeable Taylor Hobson f2.5/23mm fixed focus lens. $20-30.

CAMPRO LTD. (Home Cine Cameras, Ltd., London)
Campro - c1927. 35mm movie camera that could also be used as a projector by attaching two special lamp housings. Black metal and wood body is partly leather covered and partly painted. Folding Newton finder. Hand crank, one rotation per 8 frames. Uses 100' spool. Dallmeyer focusing f3.5 lens. $250-280.

Campro Cine Camera-Projector - c1935. 9.5mm movie camera, taking 10m Pathe cartridges (later model also used Campro-cassettes). Black crinkle finish metal body. Sportsfinder on top. Spring motor, 16 fps. f3.5 fixed focus lens. Camera could also be used as a projector with an accessory attachment. $35-40.

CHRONIK BROS. MFG. (New York) *The Chronik Brothers were tool and die makers.*

Chronik Bros. 35mm Motion Picture

Camera - 1908. This camera is a typical example of the Chronik Brothers' excellent workmanship and design. The unique film transport is a Chronik patent. The camera features through the lens viewing and convenient control on the lens diaphragm and focusing. Range: $700-1500.

CORONET (Birmingham, England)
Coronet, Models A, B - c1932. 9.5mm movie cameras taking 10m Pathe cassettes. Black leather covered metal body. Optical eye-level finder. Spring motor, 16 fps. Coronar Anastigmat f3.9 lens with four stops. $20-30.

DEBRIE (Etablissements Andre Debrie, Paris)

Parvo Interview 35mm Motion Picture Camera - 1908. This wood body, hand crank studio camera has co-axial 400' internal film magazines. It features critical focusing on the film, variable shutter, frame rate indicator, lever control for focus and lens aperture setting, and a precise footage counter. The design and workmanship on this camera are of excellent quality. A metal body model was also made that could use an electric motor drive. Range: $350-1000.

Sept 35mm Motion Picture Camera System - 1922. This precision, compact, 35mm movie camera is extremely versatile. It is spring motor driven and takes 250 exposures on a short length of film. It is a pin registered camera system for a: motion picture camera, sequential camera, still camera, and with the addition of a lamphouse, motion picture projector, film strip projector, still enlarger and negative film to positve film cine printer. From these seven functions comes the name "Sept". The Sept design is based on an earlier Italian camera. A 1925 model Sept

DITMAR (Vienna, Austria)

has a larger spring motor. Range: $100-150.

DEVRY CORPORATION (Chicago, IL)
DeVry, 16mm - c1930. Various models were made with only slight variations. Black cast metal body; large rectangular shape. Models for 100' and 400' spools. Folding Newton finder. Spring motor; some models also have a hand crank. Interchangeable Graf f3.5/20mm fixed focus lens. $25-35.

DeVry Standard Automatic - 1926. 35mm motion picture camera. The DeVry is a spring motor, metal body newsreel-type cine camera, using 100' film spools. The design is rugged. It was nicknamed "The Lunch Box" because of its rectangular shape. Some DeVry cameras were actually launched in captured German V2 rockets at the White Sands Missile Range after World War II. The DeVry also found use as a rapid sequential still camera in sports work. Range: $60-150.

Ditmar, 9.5mm - c1938. 9.5mm movie camera taking 10m Ditmar cassettes. Black leatherette covered metal body. Eye-level finder. Spring wind motor, 16-32 fps. Steinheil Cassar f2.9/20mm fixed focus lens. Built-in light meter. $30-40.

DRALOWID-WERK (Berlin)
Dralowid Reporter 8 - c1953. 8mm spool load movie camera. Green leather covered metal body. Eye-level finder. Spring motor is wound by pulling a cord. Minox Wetzlar Dralonar f2.5/12.5mm fixed focus lens. $45-65.

EASTMAN KODAK CO. (Rochester, NY)

Brownie Movie Cameras - c1951-63. Double-8 spool load movie cameras. Various models with single lens or 3-lens turret. Brown leatherette or brown lacquered bodies. Folding frame or Newton finders. Spring wind motor, 16 fps. Interchangeable fixed focus f1.9 or f2.7 lenses. Turret models also have wide angle and tele lenses. Turret models: $10-15. Single lens models: $5-10.

Cine-Kodak - 1923. (Called Model A beginning in 1925 when the Model B was

introduced.) This is the first Kodak movie camera. It introduced the new Eastman 16mm safety film for the amatuer. A substantial cost savings was brought about by the small 16mm format and the fact that the original film was processed by Eastman to a positive rather than a negative, thereby eliminating the extra step to make a positive print. Hand crank, one rotation per 8 frames. All metal black painted body, large boxy square shape. Eye-level finder. Kodak Anastigmat f3.5/ 25mm focusing lens. This camera underwent minor changes over the next few years, including the addition of a waist-level finder. Range: $175-230.

Cine-Kodak Model B - 1925-31. 16mm spool load movie camera. Rectangular and not as boxy looking as the Model A. Black, brown, or grey leather covered metal body. Newton finder and waist level brilliant finder. Spring motor, 16 fps. Kodak Anastigmat f3.5/25mm fixed focus lens. $15-20.

Cine Kodak Model E

Cine Kodak Model BB, Model BB Junior - c1929. 16mm spool load movie cameras. Metal body covered with black, blue, brown, or grey leather. Newton finder. Fixed focus f3.5 or focusing f1.9/ 25mm Kodak Anastigmat lens. Spring motor, 16 fps. $15-25.

Cine Kodak Model E - c1937-46. 16mm movie camera taking 100' spools. Black crinkle finish metal body. Optical eye-level finder. Spring motor, 16-64 fps. Interchangeable Kodak Anastigmat lens: fixed focus f3.5/20mm or focusing f1.9/ 25mm. $25-40. *(illustrated bottom of previous column)*

Cine Kodak Model K - 1930-46. 16mm movie camera taking 100' spools. Black, blue, brown, or grey leather covered metal body. Folding Newton finder and waist level brilliant finder. Spring motor, 8-16 fps. Interchangeable Kodak Anastigmat f1.9/ 25mm focusing lens. $25-40.

Cine Kodak Model M - 1930-34. Less expensive version of the Model K (above). Fixed focus f3.5/20mm lens. No waist level finder. 16 fps only. $25-40.

Cine Kodak 8, Models 20, 25, 60 - c1932-47. 8mm spool load movie cameras.

Leather covered metal body in black, brown, or grey. Newton finder in the handle. Spring motor, 16 fps. Kodak Anastigmat 13mm lens: Model 20 has f3.5 fixed focus; Model 25 has f2.7 fixed focus; Model 60 has interchangeable f1.9 focusing lens. $5-10.

**Cine-Kodak Special (1933-47);
Cine-Kodak Special II (1948-61) -** 16mm magazine movie cameras. Left side of body is the magazine containing the film spools. The magazine can be removed at any time and replaced by another. 100' and 200' magazines were available. 2-lens turret with interchangeable focusing Kodak Anastigmat f1.9/25mm and f2.7/15mm lenses. Spring motor 8-64 fps. $170-300.

**Magazine Cine-Kodak Eight Model 90 (1940-46);
Cine-Kodak Magazine 8 (1946-55) -** Similar to the Model 60 (above), but magazine load. Optical eye-level finder. 16-64 fps. $5-10.

**Magazine Cine Kodak (1937-45);
Cine Kodak Magazine 16 (1945-50) -** Body style and features similar to their 8mm counterparts, but for 16mm movies using 50' magazines. $20-30.

Kodak Cine Scopemeter - c1959.

Double-8 spool load movie camera. Built-in meter. Optical eye-level finder in housing with meter. Spring motor, 16 fps. 3-lens turret with Ektanar f1.9 normal, tele, and wide angle lenses. $5-10.

ERCSAM (Paris)
Auto Camex - c1960. 8mm spool load movie camera. Reflex viewing. Spring motor, 8-64 fps. Focusing Pan-Cinor zoom lens. $30-50.

Camex Reflex 8 - c1956. First 8mm movie camera with continuous reflex viewing. Double-8 film on 25' spools. Spring motor, 8-32 fps. Interchangeable Som Berthiot f1.9/12.5mm focusing lens. $50-75.

ERNEMANN AG (Dresden, Germany)
Kino I - 1902. Ernemann entered the amateur motion picture field with this very early, center perforation, 17½mm motion picture camera. It has a leather covered wood body. The Kino I is a well built movie camera using a Williamson type film transport with a quality Ernemann lens and a variable shutter. Range: $1000-2000.

Kino II - 1904. This versatile 17½mm, center perforation, amateur camera/printer/projector has features unusual even for professional motion picture cameras of its time. A fast lens was used. The intermittent film transport utilized an eight arm Geneva cross movement. A reciprocating glass platen at the aperture applies pressure during exposure. The Kino II shown has a large co-axial film magazine and a studio type viewfinder that has straight and reflex viewing. Range: $1000-2000.

Kino Model E - 1917. 35mm motion picture camera. This wood body, hand crank studio camera has co-axial 400' internal film magazines. Its appearance and operation are very similar to the 1908 Debrie Parvo camera. Range: $700-1500.

Normal Kino Model A - 1908-18. The Normal Kino Model A 35mm motion picture camera is a wood-bodied hand cranked field camera. The film magazines are internal, one above the other. Some Kino cameras have Lumiere/Pathe type film transports and some have Williamson type transports. The Model A has a 200' film capacity; the B, 400'; and the C, 100'. Range: $350-1500.

ERTEL WERKE (Munich, Germany)

Ertel - 1920. The Ertel 35mm motion picture camera is a well made, wood body, hand cranked field camera. Several models with minor differences were made. Lens focus and aperture control is accomplished by conveniently placed levers. Range: $350-1000.

EUMIG (Vienna, Austria)
Eumig C-3 - c1955. Double-8 movie camera taking 25' spools. Grey or black patterned metal body. Optical eye-level finder. Spring motor, 8-32 fps. f1.9/12.5mm lens. $5-10.

Eumig C16 - c1956. 16mm movie camera for 100' spools. Lacquered metal body with green leather. Spring motor, 16-64 fps. Semi-automatic coupled meter. Eumigar f1.9/25mm focusing lens. $150-180.

Eumig Electric - c1955. Double-8 movie camera for 25' spools. Green crinkle finish metal body. Eye-level finder. Battery driven motor, 16 fps. Eugon f2.7/12.5mm. $5-10.

GERMAN-AMERICAN CINEMATOGRAPH AND FILM CO.
(New York and Berlin) *Everhard Schneider, the founder of the German-American Cinematograph and Film Co. designed and made a series of cine cameras as well as motion picture projectors, printers and film perforators. Edison filed suit against Schneider in 1898 for patent violation. This German-American Co. did not survive World War I.*

Everhard Schneider 35mm movie cameras. Top photo c1898, bottom photo c1910

Everhard Schneider 35mm Motion Picture Camera - c1898. This very early motion picture camera was the first of a series of fine equipment. It has an external film supply magazine and an internal take-up magazine. Although some mechanical parts of the camera are castings, several are hand made. Range: $2000-3500. *(illustrated on previous page)*

Everhard Schneider 35mm Motion Picture Camera - c1910. This camera is an example of Schneider's less elaborate, wood body, hand crank, field type motion picture camera. 200' co-axial internal magazines are used. Range: $500-1000. *(illustrated bottom of previous page)*

GUSTAV AMIGO (Berlin, Germany)

Amigo 35mm Motion Picture Camera - 1920. Though basic in design, the Amigo is a well constructed field camera and is capable of fine work. A Williamson type film transport is used. Range: $350-700.

HOUGHTON

Ensign Auto-Kinecam 16 Type B - c1935. 16mm movie camera taking 100' or 200' spools. Crinkle-finish black metal body. Eye-level finder near the top, Newton finder mounted on the side. Spring motor, 8-32 fps and hand wind. Interchangeable Dallmeyer Anastigmat f2.9/1" lens. $20-40.

ICA A.G. (Dresden, Germany)

Kinamo 35mm Motion Picture Camera - 1924. This compact, hand cranked, amateur camera uses 50' magazines. It has a leather covered metal body. An accessory spring motor drive was also available. It is of quality design and construction. In 1926, the ICA company joined with Contessa-Nettel-Werke, Zeiss, Goerz, and Ernemann to form the Zeiss Ikon Co. Production of the Kinamo continued and more versatile models were produced. Range: $80-150.

INDUSTRIAL SYNDICATE OF CINOSCOPE (Italy and Paris, France)

Cinoscope - 1924. This leather covered

metal hand crank 35mm camera was made in Italy and sold in France. The camera has a Kador f3.5/50mm lens. It uses 100' magazines and has Geneva Cross film transport. With the addition of a lamphouse and reel arms, the camera can be used as a projector. Range: $500-1000.

INTERNATIONAL PROJECTOR CORP. (New York)
Simplex Pockette - c1932. 16mm magazine movie camera. Aluminum body with black or grey covering. Sportsfinder on side; optional optical eye-level viewfinder attaches to top. Spring motor, 12-16 fps. Interchangeable Kodak Anastigmat f3.5/1" focusing lens. $10-17.

IRWIN CORP. (New York)
Irwin Magazine Model 16 - c1930. 16mm movie camera taking 50' magazines. Rectangluar metal body. Optical eye-level finder. Spring motor, 16 fps. f4.5/1" lens. $5-10.

KEYSTONE MFG. CO. (Boston)
Capri Models - c1950's. Models K-25, K-27, K-30. 8mm spool load movie cameras. Grey or brown leather covered body. Single lens and 3-lens turret models. Elgeet f1.9 lens. $4-10.

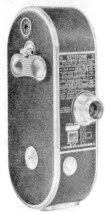

Keystone K-8, K-22 - 1930's-1940's. Like the "A" models, but for 8mm film. $4-9.

KLIX MANUFACTURING CO. (Chicago)

Keystone A Models - c1930's-1940's. A series of 16mm spool load cameras (models A, A-3, A-7, A-9, A-12). Oval metal bodies are either leather covered or lacquered. In black, brown, or grey. Eye-level finder. Spring motor, 12-64 fps on most models. Some models have an interchangeable lens. $20-30.

Keystone Movie Camera, Model C - c1931. 16mm spool load movie camera. Black crinkle finish metal body. Eye level finder. Hand crank. Oval body like the later "A" models. Ilex f3.5/1" lens. $35-45.

Klix 35mm Motion Picture Camera - 1918. This compact amateur hand crank cine camera has an unusual reciprocating shutter. A Geneva Cross film transport movement is used. A heavy flywheel helps for smooth cranking. This camera has 25' film magazines. A larger Model 2 camera has 100' magazines. Both cameras can be used as projectors with the addition of an adapter kit that includes a lamphouse, reel arms, special shutter, etc. Range: $250-500.

L.A. MOTION PICTURE CO.
(Los Angeles, CA) *Also known as Angeles Camera Co. Produced original Cine camera designs and also made close copies of the designs of others. During WWI they were able to meet requirements of domestic studios for European type cameras that were not available. They also made cameras that were sold under the brand names of others.*

35mm Motion Picture Camera - c1914-23. There is no model name on this well made, metal bodied, hand crank camera. It has several features, including 400' internal co-axial magazines. Range: $500-1000.

LUBIN (Sigmund Lubin, Philadelphia, PA) *Sigmund "Pop" Lubin, a European imigrant, was quite knowledgeable in optics, chemistry, and mechanics. He was a very early motion picture entrepreneur. He manufactured motion picture equipment for his own studio use. At one time, however, he did offer a camera, a projector, and a phonograph for use by those starting in the motion picture business, for a modest $150. The buyers later found that the camera and projector used only film supplied and printed by Lubin. Much of his equipment was very similar to that of other manufacturers but his versions were always an improvement. He did hold motion picture equipment patents and was involved with Edison in the Motion Picture Patent Company, a trust formed to control the motion picture industry.*

Lubin 35mm - 1908. This motion picture

camera was the workhorse of the Lubin studios. It is very similar to the Pathe studio camera but has heavier gearing, a metal body, and a speed governor. Range: $1500-3500.

MILLER CINE CO. (England)
Miller Cine Model CA - c1953. 8mm spool load movie camera. Brown leather covered metal body. Eye-level finder. Spring motor, 8-64 fps. Interchangeable Anastigmat f2.5/12.5 fixed focus lens. $5-10.

MITCHELL CAMERA CORPORATION (Glendale, CA)
Mitchell - 1920. The Mitchell studio camera was a major milestone in motion picture camera design when introduced in 1920. It is somewhat similar in appearance to the earlier Bell and Howell 2709 studio camera, but has a simpler through-the-taking-lens previewing system. The Mitchell registration pins are reciprocal and hold the film perforations precisely during exposure. A wide range of accessories are available. The low operational noise level of the Mitchell compared to the Bell and Howell, soon had it replacing the Bell and Howell after the advent of sound movies. The Mitchell soon became the most popular studio camera. It is still in use to this day and its current high price is based on its status as a usable camera. Range: $2000-5000.

MOVETTE CAMERA CORP. (Rochester, NY.) *Reorganized as Movette, Inc. after 1918.*

Movette, 17½mm - 1917. This amateur hand cranked motion picture camera uses 17½mm film that has two round perforations on each side of the picture frame. The shutter has a fixed opening and the lens has a fixed aperture and focus. The camera used a simple type film magazine. The processed positive print on safety film was returned from Eastman on a similar magazine for use in the companion projector. A library of feature films was offered. This home motion picture system featured simplicity. Range: $350-700.

MOY (Ernest F.) LTD. (London)

Moy and Bastie's 35mm Motion Picture Camera - 1909. This wood body camera used internal 400' magazines, one above the other. The Moy uses a variable shutter and a unique film transport movement called a drunken screw. Critical focusing is accomplished by viewing the image through the film. A variant of this model has the lens mounted on what would normally be the side and has dual shutters so it can be used as a projector head. Range: $350-1000.

NEWMAN & SINCLAIR (London)
Auto Kine Camera, Model E - c1946. 35mm spring driven movie camera, 10-32 fps. Holds spools up to 200'. Polished, patterned Duralumin body. Eye-level finder. Ross Xpres f3.5 lens. $150-190.

NIPPON KOGAKU (Japan)
Nikkorex 8, 8F - c9162. Slim 8mm spool load movie cameras. Battery operated motor, 16 fps. Chrome with brown covering. Nikkor f1.8/10mm fixed focus lens. Electric eye CdS exposure meter. The model 8 has a folding optical eye-level finder. Model 8F has a thru-the-lens reflex finder. $15-25. *(illustrated top of next column)*

NIZO (Niezoldi & Kramer GmbH, Nizo-Braun AG, Munich)
Cine Nizo 8E Models A, B, C - c1930's. 8mm spool load movie cameras. Black leather covered rectangular metal body.

Nikkorex 8

Spring motor, 6-64 fps. Interchangeable Voigtlander Skopar f2.7/12.5mm focusing lens. In addition to the optical eye-level finder found on the Model A, Models B and C have a waist level finder. $40-50.

Cine Nizo 9.5 Model A - c1925. Boxy 9.5mm movie camera using Pathe cassettes. Black leather covered metal body. Eye-level finder. Spring motor, 16 fps, and hand crank. Meyer Trioplan f3.5/77mm fixed focus lens. "N.K.M" manufacturers plate on front. $30-50.

Cine Nizo 9.5, Model F - c1925. Boxy 9.5mm movie camera using Pathe cassettes. Black leather covered metal body. Folding Newton finder. Spring motor, 16-32 fps. Steinheil Cassar f2.8/20mm fixed focus lens. $30-50.

Cine Nizo 16B - c1927. Similar to the Cine Nizo 9.5 Model A, but for 16mm film. $30-50.

Cine Nizo 16L - c1930's. 16mm movie cameras taking 50' spools. Black crackle finish metal body. Optical eye-level finder. Spring motor, early version 8-24 fps, later one for 8-64 fps. Interchangeable Meyer f1.5/20mm focusing lens. $30-50.

Exposomat 8R - c1955. 8mm movie camera taking a 25' Rapid cassette. Grey crinkle finish metal body. Eye-level finder. Built-in meter. Spring motor, 16-24 fps. Ronar f1.9/12.5mm fixed focus lens. $15-25.

Heliomatic 8 S2R - c1951. 8mm spool load movie camra. Grey crinkle finish metal body. Spring motor, 8-64 fps. Coupled meter. Focusing Rodenstock Heligon f1.5/12.5mm and Euron f2.8/37.5mm lenses. $30-45.

PATHE FRERES, PATHE S.A., (Paris) *A major European motion picture company, they introduced the 28mm movie format, and reduced a large 35mm feature movie library to 28mm safety film to increase their home movie business. The 28mm format provided a modest savings in film size, cost, and more importantly, the use of fire resistant film in the home. 28mm projectors were made by Pathe of France and subsequently by Hall Projector and Victor Animatograph of the USA. A few 28mm cameras were made so that the amateur could make his own 28mm movies for the home use.*

Motocamera - c1928. 9.5mm movie camera taking 10m Pathe cassettes. Spring motor, 16 fps. Leather covered metal body. Eye-level finder built into the camera body instead of the folding frame finder found on the earlier Pathe Baby. Krauss Trinar f3.5/20mm fixed focus lens. $15-25.

Motocamera Luxe - c1932. Similar, but with 3 speeds and Zeiss or Krauss f2.9 or f2.7 lens. $15-25.

Motocamera 16 - c1933. 16mm movie camera using cassettes. Black leather covered metal body. Spring motor, 16 fps. Krauss Trinar f3/25mm lens. This 16mm model is not nearly as common as the 9.5mm model listed above. $80-120.

Pathe, 35mm - 1905. Motion picture studio camera. This leather covered wood body hand crank camera uses external 400' magazines mounted on top. The film transport mechanism is based on the movement used in the pioneer Lumiere Cinematograph camera and is still used in the modern Bell & Howell Filmo and Eyemo cameras. In the years just before WWI the Pathe was used on more movies throughout the world than any other camera. It is difficult to find a pristine Pathe as they were heavily used and generally modified to update them. Lubin,

Angeles and Wilart made similar cameras in the USA. Range: $500-2000.

Pathe, 28mm - 1912. This is a scaled down version of their successful 35mm field camera. An economical 28mm version of the English Williamson/Butcher type camera was also offered later by Pathescope of America. Range: $500-1000.

Pathe Baby - 1923-25. 9.5mm hand cranked movie camera, taking 9m Pathe cassettes. One rotation per 8 frames. Extremely compact leather covered metal body. Folding sportsfinder. Roussel Kynor f3.5/20mm fixed focus lens. The 9½mm width amatuer film format was introduced in Europe at about the same time 16mm film was introduced in the USA. The 9½mm film perforations are in the center of the film, between frames. The picture format extends to almost the width of the film thereby providing efficient film use. The film has a safety, reversal type base that could be processed by the user. 9½mm movie cameras were popular in Europe and the British empire. Range: $15-25.

Pathe Baby, with motor - c1926-27. Similar to the original model, but body is about twice the width to accomodate the spring motor. 16 fps. Hermagis f3.5/20mm fixed focus lens. $20-25.

Pathe Baby, with Camo motor - Larger motor than the listing above. Marked "Camo" and "Swiss movement Suisse". Kynor f3.5/20mm lens. $30-40.

Pathe Mondial B - c1932. Similar to the Motocamera (above), but slightly smaller body, and black painted instead of leather covered. Trioplan f2.8/20mm lens. $25-35.

Pathe National I - c1930. 9.5mm movie camera taking 9m Type H Pathe cassette. Black painted metal body. Eye-level finder. Spring motor, 16 fps. Krauss Trinar f3.5/20mm fixed focus lens. $20-30.

Pathe National II - c1940's. Improved version of the National I. Grey crinkle finish body. 8-32 fps. Interchangeable Som Berthiot focusing f1.9/20mm lens. $20-30.

PRESWITCH MANUFACTURING CO. (London, England)

Preswitch 35mm Motion Picture Camera - 1908. This wood body camera uses internal 400' magazines, one above the other. The patented Preswitch film transport movement is used. The lens is focused by rack and pinion. The lensboard swings out for access to the variable shutter. Critical focusing is accomplished by viewing the image through the film. 200' models were also made. The Pitman and DeFranne cameras, made in the U.S.A. are almost identical to the Preswitch. Range: $350-1000.

REVERE CAMERA CO. (Chicago)
Revere, 8mm - 1940's-1950's. Turret models, including 44, 60, 63, 67, 84, 99:

$5-10. Various single lens magazine models, including 40, 61, 70, 77, 88, and Ranger and spool load model 55: $5-10.

Revere Magazine 16 - c1948. 16mm magazine movie camera. Brushed chrome and grey or brown leather covered metal body. Optical eye-level finder. Spring wind, 12-48 fps. Interchangeable Wollensak Raptar focusing lens. Single-lens models have f1.9/1" lens. Turret models also have f2.7/17mm and f4/3" lenses. $10-20.

SIEMENS & HALSKE AG (Berlin)
Siemens B - c1933. 16mm movie camera taking special 50' Siemens magazines. Black leather covered body. Optical eye-level and waist level finders. Spring motor, 8, 16, 64 fps. Busch Glaukar f2.8/20mm focusing lens. $35-55.

Siemens C - c1934. Similar in style and features to the Siemens B, but with 8, 16, 24, 64 fps and a better lens. Meyer Siemar f1.5/20mm focusing lens. $40-55.

Siemens C II - c1938. Similar to the Siemens C, but lens is coupled to the meter. Meyer Optimat f1.5/20 focusing lens. $50-60.

Siemens F - c1936. Similar to the Siemens C, but interchangeable Dallmeyer f1.5/1" lens. $60-100.

SINEMAT MOTION PICTURE CO. (USA)
Sinemat Duplex 17½mm Motion Picture Camera - c1915. This amateur, hand-cranked, metal body motion picture camera used standard 35mm film that was split lengthwise, providing perforations only on one side. A fixed focus, fixed opening lens is used. The camera can be opened in such a manner that it can be used as a projector. The single opening shutter is disengaged and a dual opening shutter is engaged when used as a projector. Range:$250-700. *(illustrated top of next page)*

Sinemat Duplex, 17½mm

SOCIETY OF CINEMA PLATES (Paris)

Olikos - 1912. The Olikos uses 18 glass plates, 9.5x9cm, to produce a 90 second movie. The camera, with the addition of a lamphouse is used as a projector. A conventional lens, shutter, and hand crank is used. A unique mechanism takes each plate through a sequence of positions at the focal plane of the camera. Each plate, in turn, is automatically positioned so a series of seven pictures is taken from right to left on the top of the plate. The plate is then immediately moved up and another sequence of seven photographs is taken from left to right and so on for a series of 12 rows of seven or 84 photographs on each plate. Each following plate is automatically positioned and sequenced for a total of a 1512 frame movie. The plate positioning mechanism is precise enough so that the time interval between photographs is acceptably consistent. Few Olikos camera were made. Range: $1500-2500.

SPORT-2 - c1960. Double-8 movie camera. Battery operated motor. T-40 f2.8/10mm lens. $15-20.

STEWART-WARNER (Chicago)
Companion 8 (Model 532B) - intro. 1933. 8mm spool load movie camera. Smaller version of the Hollywood camera listed below. Black lacquered metal body, oval shaped. Spring motor, 12, 16, 48 fps. Interchangeable Wollensak Velostigmat f3.5/12.5mm lens. $5-10.

Hollywood (Model 531-B) - c1931. 16mm spool load movie camera. Black lacquered metal body, oval shape. Eye-level finder. Spring motor, 8-64 fps. Stewart Warner f3.5/25mm lens. $5-15.

URIU SEIKI (Tokyo)
Cinemax 85E - c1960's. Double-8 movie camera. Spring motor, 12-48 fps. Cinemax Auto Zoom 8.5-42.5mm f1.6 lens. Automatic meter. $3-7.

U.S.CINEMATOGRAPH CO. (Chicago)

35mm Motion Picture Camera - c1916. This wood body, leather covered field camera has 200' co-axial internal magazines. Its film transport movement is somewhat unique. It has a variable shutter and through the film critical focusing. This camera was also sold under the name "Davsco". Range: $350-700.

UNIVERSAL CAMERA CO. (Chicago)
Not to be confused with the later "Universal Camera Corporation" of New York City.
Universal 35mm Motion Picture Camera - 1914. This camera, in the classic early English design, has internal 200' film magazines, one above the other. (400' cameras were made for the US Army during World War I.) The film transport mechanism is similar to the early French Lumiere/Pathe movement. The wood body is painted black or khaki and the front and side doors are aluminum with a distinctive

Victor (description on next page)

engine turned finish. While primarily a field camera, the Universal with added features became a studio camera. Range: $350-700.

UNIVERSAL CAMERA CORPORATION (New York City) *Not to be confused with the earlier "Universal Camera Co." of Chicago.*
CINE 8 CAMERAS:
A-8 - c1936. Die-cast metal, black finish. Interchangeable f5.6 Ilex Univar lens. Collapsible viewfinder. Used Univex 30' patented spools of Single-8 film. Common. $10-15.

B-8 - c1939. "True View" model. Die-cast metal, antique bronze finish. Built-on telescopic viewfinder above the body. Interchangeable f5.6 Ilex Univar lens. Used Univex Single-8 film. $20-25.

C-8 - c1939. "Exposition" model. Die-cast metal, antique bronze finish. Built-in viewfinder. Interchangeable f4.5 Ilex Univar lens. Used Univex Single-8 film. $20-25.

C-8 Turret model - c1939. Same features as the standard C-8, but with 3-lens turret. Sold with f4.5 or f3.5 Ilex Univar lens. Optional Univar lenses were: f2.7/½", f1.9/½", f3.5/1" Telephoto, f3.5/1½" Telephoto. Scarce with f3.5, f1.9 and a Telephoto lens: $150-175. Also uncommon with f4.5 or f3.5 only: $45-65.

D-8 - c1941. Dual 8mm "Cinemaster" model, taking Univex Single-8 or standard Double-8 film. Die-cast metal. Built-in viewfinder. Interchangeable f4.5 Ilex Univar. Single speed. Scarce. $65-85.

E-8 - c1941. Dual 8mm "Cinemaster" model, taking Univex Single-8 or standard Double-8 film. Die-cast metal, antique

bronze finish. Interchangeable Ilex Univar f3.5/½". Built-in combination extinction meter and viewfinder. Three speeds. Scarce. $60-80.

F-8 - c1941. Dual 8mm "Cinemaster" model. Similar to E-8, but with grey satin finish and front and rear chrome plates. $20-25.

G-8 - c1948. Dual 8mm "Cinemaster II" model. Similar to F-8, except for minor improvements in the film transport system. Sold with f3.5 or f2.5 Ilex Univar lens. Common. $15-25.

H-8 - c. late 1940's. "Cinemaster II" model. Identical to G-8, except only standard Double-8 film could be used. This was the last cine camera made by Universal. Scarce. $60-80.

VICAM PHOTO APPLIANCE CORP. (Philadelphia, PA)

Baby Standard - 1923. 35mm motion

picture camera. This wood body, hand cranked camera featured simple design and construction, rather than small film size, to provide economical use for the amateur. A fixed focus lens is used with a two opening waterhouse stop bar. Internal 25' film magazines are used. A removable port in the rear allows the use as a projector. A die cast aluminum body model was also offered. Range: $80-150.

VICTOR ANIMATOGRAPH CO. (Davenport, IA)
Victor - 1923. This basic hand crank 16mm camera was produced shortly after the introduction of the Cine Kodak 16mm system. It uses a double push claw for a film transport. The fixed focus lens is fitted with wheel stops. Range: $80-150. *(illustrated top of previous page)*

Victor, Models 3, 4, 5 - late 1920's- early 1940's. 16mm movie cameras taking 100' spools. Black or brown crinkle lacquered finish on metal body. Newton finder and reflex critical focus eyepiece. Spring motor, 8-64 fps. Interchangeable lenses. Model 3 for single lens: Wollensak Cine Velostigmat f3.5/1" fixed focus. Models 4 and 5 have a 3-lens turret with focusing lenses: Wollensak f2.7/17mm, Cooke f3.5/2", and f1.9/1". With 3 lenses: $75-110. With single lens: $35-45.

VITAGRAPH COMPANY OF AMERICA (New York)

Vitagraph - 1915. This wood body, hand crank camera was a ruggedly built in-house design of the Vitagraph Studios. The design is complex and it is a fine looking camera with lots of external brass. It is somewhat unique for this type of camera in that it is loaded from its right camera side rather than the left. Range: $700-2000.

VITASCOPE CORP. (Providence, RI)
Movie Maker - c1931. 16mm movie camera, taking 50' spools. Hand crank, one rotation per 8 frames. Black crinkle finish metal body. Small waist level finder. Simple lens. $10-17.

WILLIAMSON LTD. (London, England)

Williamson 35mm Motion Picture Camera - 1909. This wood body camera uses internal 400' magazines, one above the other. The patented Williamson film transport movement and a variable shutter are used. Critical focusing is accomplished by viewing the image through the film. 200' models were also made. A 100' basic design camera, similar to Empire was made. Some Williamson cameras are called tropical models and have numerous brass inlays to reduce expansion and shrinkage in the wood body. Range: $350-1000.

WITTNAUER CAMERA CO. (NYC)
Wittnauer Cine-Twin - c1960. Battery powered 8mm spool load movie camera. Die cast body. Electric eye exposure meter. 3-lens turret with f1.6 zoom lens and matching optical zoom viewfinder. When mounted on the base containing the electric motor and blower, it becomes a projector. $50-75.

WOLLENSAK OPTICAL CO. (Chicago)
Model 8 - Grey and black 8mm movie camera. Eye-level finder. Elgeet f1.9/½" focusing lens. $3-7.

Model 46 - c1958. 8mm spool load movie. Electric eye. 3-lens turret with Raptar f1.8 normal, tele, and wide angle lenses. $5-10.

YASHICA (Japan)

Yashica 8, T-8 - c1959. 8mm spool load movie cameras. Grey and black die-cast aluminum bodies. Spring motor, 16 fps on model 8, 8-64 fps on model T-8. Zoom-type viewfinder for 6.5-38mm lenses. Model 8 has a single interchangeable Yashikor f1.9/13mm lens. T-8 has a 2-lens turret for Yashinon f1.4/13mm normal, 38mm tele, or 6.5mm wide angle lenses. $5-10.

ZEISS

Kinamo S10 - c1928. 16mm movie camera taking a 10m special Zeiss magazine. Black leather covered metal body. Optical eye-level finder. Spring motor, 16 fps. Very small body compared to other 16mm movie cameras. Zeiss Tessar f2.7/15mm fixed focus lens. $40-55.

Movikon 8 - c1952. 8mm movie camera taking 25' spools. Interesting horizontal body design. Brown or grey crinkle finish metal body. Eye-level finder. Spring motor. Early version only 16 fps; later for 16-48 fps. Focusing Zeiss Movitar f1.9/10mm lens. $35-50.

Movikon 16 - c1936. 16mm spool load movie camera. Black leather covered metal body. Eye-level and waist-level finders, and separate critical focus sight. Spring motor, 12-64 fps. Interchangeable Sonnar f1.4/25mm lens. $200-245.

ZIX COMPANY (Detroit, MI)

Zix - 1920. The Zix is a wood body, leather covered, hand crank 35mm motion picture camera for amateur use. It is unusual in that the shutter is mounted forward of the lens, the lens is mounted midpoint in the camera box and the film plane is at the rear of the camera. The lens is focused by a knob on the side. The film transport is Geneva Cross. The camera can be used as a projector. Range: $250-500.

NON-CAMERAS

This section of the book lists items which look like cameras but actually serve a different purpose. Funcional cameras are in the main section of this guide. Many of these are recent items. Their "collectible" value is generally not based on rarity or demand, but more realistically is the retail price at which they currently are or recently were available. On these items, we have listed their approximate retail price. Items which have not been available new for some time have prices which reflect the current market value rather than the original price.

They are grouped by function, and the functional types are in alphabetical order, i.e. Albums, Banks, Candy, etc. This list is only a sampling of the many camera-like novelites which have been produced. Readers contributions are welcomed to expand this section.

Piccolette Camera Bank

ALBUMS

ALBUM - Photo album shaped like 35mm SLR. Holds 24 prints 3¼x5". $4.

BANKS

INSTAMATIC CAMERA BANK - Black plastic body. Printed front behind clear plastic. Styled like a simple Kodak Instamatic camera, including Kodak logo on front. Molded into the back is "Instant Savings for Instamatic Cameras". $1-2.

KODAK BANK - Early cast metal type. Shaped like a Brownie box camera. The door reads "Kodak Bank". This bank was not made by Kodak. Manufacturer unknown. Marked "Patent Pending 1905". It was offered for sale as late as 1914 by Butler Brothers, a toy distributor. We have seen these offered in recent years for high prices, but have no confirmed sales data.

PICCOLETTE CAMERA BANK - Ceramic coin bank shaped like Piccolette camera. $15. *(illustrated top of next column)*

POCKET COIN BANK - Black plastic coin bank shaped like 110 pocket camera. "Pocket Coin Bank" on aluminum-colored top. $1-3.

ROLLEICORD - Ceramic bank styled like Rolleicord TLR. White iridescent glaze with gold trim. Clear plastic lenses. $20-30.

TUPPERWARE - Black plastic bank with

grey plastic knobs and lens. Lettered rings around lens set combination "tumblers" to open lens. "Tupper Toys" on front of top housing. $3-6.

BELT BUCKLES

LEWIS BUCKLES (Chicago)

Camera Buckles - c1980's. Cast metal belt buckles shaped like cameras or with bas-relief cameras as the major design. Available in various styles for different brands of cameras. About $5.

CANDY & GUM

AKUTAGAWA CONFECTIONERY CO. LTD. (Tokyo)
Chocolate Camera - c1981. A well-detailed scaled-down chocolate model of the Canon AE-1 camera. A perfect gift for the man who wants to have his camera and eat it too. Retail price: $3.75

DONRUSS CO. (Memphis, TN)

Hot Flash Chewing Gum - c1984. Red or yellow plastic container shaped like SLR. "Hot Flash" on front of prism. Lens removes to open. Contains small pellets of chewing gum. Retail: $.50.

CIGARETTE LIGHTERS

AKW (Tokyo)
Perfect-Lighter - Lighter shaped like 35mm camera. Metal covering with stamped cherry tree design. Tree trunk and branches on back. Some traces of Leica styling include slow speed knob and focus lever. "Perfect" engraved on top. Actuator button is marked "pushing". "AKW Tokyo" on bottom. With tripod: $30-40. *(illustrated top of next column)*

AKW Perfect-Lighter

CONTINENTAL CAMERA-LIGHTER - Bakelite-bodied lighter, styled like 35mm camera. Made in Occupied Japan. With tripod and cable release: $10-15.

K.K.W.
Camera-Lighter - Lighter styled like 35mm camera. Bakelite body with no name on back. Compass built into front. "Made in occupied Japan" on bottom. "K.K.W. CAMERA LIGHTER" on lens rim. With tripod: $15-25.

LUCKY-LITE CAMERA-LIGHTER - Cigarette lighter/telescope shaped like 35mm camera. Bakelite body. "Lucky-Lite" molded in back. Telescope through center of camera in lens position. Front lens focus. Made in Occupied Japan. $20-30.

LUMIX CAMERA-LIGHTER - Small cigarette lighter styled like Leica IIIc camera. "Winding knob" with numbered skirt functions as shutter release lock. Top housing profile is definitely Leica-styled (unlike other lighters). "Slow speed dial" on front. Viewfinder window and two round rangefinder windows on front. Side by side eyepieces on back. Focus lever on "Excellent Cherry" lens. Metal covering in either cherry blossom or leopard spot pattern. Made in Occupied Japan. $20-30.

MUGETTE CAMERA-LIGHTER - Small bakelite lighter styled like Piccolette camera. Made in Germany. $20-25.

NST
Phenix camera-lighter (bakelite body) - Lighter styled like 35mm camera. Black bakelite body. "Phenix" molded in back. Compass built into front. Made in Occupied Japan. "NST" on focus ring. With tripod: $10-15.

Phenix camera-lighter (metal covering) - Lighter styled like 35mm camera. Thin metal covering with stamped flower pattern on front. Back engraved with dragon design. Made in Occupied Japan. "NST" on focus scale. $15-20.

PEACE-GAS CAMERA-LIGHTER - Gas lighter styled like 35mm camera. "Peace-Gas" molded in back of bakelite body. No compass on front. With tripod and cable release: $15-25.

PERFEOT LIGHTER - Cigarette lighter styled as 35mm camera. "PERFEOT (sic) LIGHTER" on lens rim. No other identification. Thin metal covering stamped with cherry blossom pattern. "Made in Occupied Japan" on back. $20-25.

PHOTO-FLASH CAMERA-LIGHTER - Lighter styled like 35mm camera. "Photo-Flash" molded in back of bakelite body. Compass inset in front. "K.K.W. P.P 13449 Japan" on bottom. With tripod: $10-15.

S.M.R. (Japan)
PENTAX ME Cigarette Lighter - Cast metal table model cigarette lighter, styled

after the Pentax ME camera. The lighter insert is the refillable gas type. Retail price in 1983 about $35.00.

View Camera Cigarette Lighter - Cast metal table model cigarette lighter, styled after a folding-bed view camera. Refillable gas lighter insert. Current value $10-20.

SUN ARROW (Japan)

KadocK-II Personal Gaslighter - Lighter disguised as a 120 film roll. Styling imitates Kodak packaging. One version even imitates Kodak trade dress in yellow, red and black colors. Another version is in silver and black. $10-20.

CLOCKS

COPAL CO. LTD. (Japan)
Asanuma Clock - Brown plastic scale model of a studio camera on a stand. A mechanical digital clock is in the stand below the camera. The lens of the camera is marked "Asanuma & Co. Established in 1871". $30-40.

COASTERS

FRIENDLY HOME PARTIES INC. (Albany, NY)
Camera Coaster Set - Set of six wooden coasters with cork inserts. Storage rack designed like view camera on tripod. Chamfered edges of coasters resemble bellows. About $5. *(illustrated top of next page)*

Friendly Home Parties Coaster Set

COMPACTS

In addition to the camera-shaped compacts below, there are some real cameras which are built into makeup boxes, compacts, etc. These are listed in the main part of the book, under such names as Ansco Photo Vanity, Vanity Kodak cameras, and Kunik Petie Vanity.

GIREY

Kamra-Pak Vanity - Small metal compact shaped like a folding camera. Front door conceals mirror and makeup. Winding knob is a lipstick. Various colored coverings, including colored leatherettes and imitation mother-of-pearl. Metal parts in brass or chrome. Often found with U.S. Navy emblem. Some collectors have expressed the opinion that the resemblance to a camera is coincidental. The name "Kamra-Pak" used by Girey confirms their intentional design as camera look-alikes. That name is found on the original box, however, and not on the compact itself which has only the Girey name. $10-20.

Unidentified compact - Slightly larger than the common Girey Kamra-Pak. This compact has a door on each side. A mirror and makeup powder are on one side; a manicure set on the other. The winding key conceals the lipstick tube. Available in several finishes, including suede leather and brightly colored leather patterns. Complete: $30-40.

VENUS-RAY COMPACT - Brass-lacquered chrome compact with horizontal ribs. Shaped like a miniature Ikonta 6x6. Battery-powered lighted mirror in the door of the makeup compartment. The winding knobs conceal the batteries at the rounded ends of the body. $30-40.

CONTAINERS

GIBSON (C.R.) CO. (Norwalk, CT)
Camera Note Box - Cardboard box with note cards and envelopes. Exterior is extremely realistic lithograph of No. 2 Brownie. Design Copyright 1983 by Philip Sykes. Retail price $8.50. *(illustrated top of next page)*

IAN LOGAN LTD. (England)
Foto-File - Cardboard box for storing photographs. Styled to look like an Agfa box camera. $5-10.

Gibson Camera Note Box

CONVERTORS

For those who don't understand this modern science-fiction terminology, "convertors" are robot-like people who convert to mechanical objects. Ask your kids.

Mark MA-1 as camera and robot. The film can in upper photo gives a size reference.

CAMERA A-1 - Toy camera with converts to ray-gun and flashlight. Battery operated light and sound effects. $10-15.

CHIEN HSIN PLASTIC FAC. CO. LTD. (Taiwan)
Camera Pistol 116 - Toy disguised as a camera. Opens to become a cap gun. "Camera Pistol 116" on back. $4-8.

DAH YANG TOYS (Taiwan)
Camera-Cap Gun - Toy disguised as a camera. Opens to become a cap gun. $4-8.

MARK
MA-1 camera-robot - Small SLR-type camera converts to robot. Copyright 1984 by Select, New York and Mark, Japan. Retail about $2.50. *(illustrated in previous column)*

Snap-Shot Secret Gun CH-337 - Toy disguised as a camera. Opens to become a cap gun. "Snap Shot" on front. "Secret Gun" on back. $4-8.

DART & PELLET SHOOTERS

DART CAMERA - Manufacturer unknown. Metal camera, spring-loaded to shoot darts. Usually found without darts. $10-15.

JA-RU
Pellet Shooting Camera - Small camera-shaped pellet shooter. Comes with box of pellets which resembles film box. Retail in 1980: $1.25

DECANTERS & FLASKS

CAMERA-FLASK, Folding camera style (American) - Several different styles, shaped like a folding rollfilm camera in the closed position. Glass flask bottle inside leatherette covered wood body or leather covered aluminum body. $40-60.

MOVIE CAMERA (no name) - Ceramic decanter shaped like movie camera. Black glaze with gold trim. Two shot glasses for lenses. $10-20.

CAMERA-FLASK, Folding camera style (German) - Very well made, all metal with genuine leather covering. Winding knob conceals two metal shot glasses. Corner of camera body twists off to pour contents. Beautifully crafted. $100-150.

REFLEX SHOT - Ceramic decanter shaped like TLR. Black glaze with gold trim. Cork stopper in top. Two shot glasses for lenses. $10-20.

SCHNAPPS-O-FLEX - Ceramic decanter shaped like a TLR with a flash attachment on the left side. Black glazed with silver trim. The flash reflector removes to reveal the pouring spout for your favorite beverage. $10-15. *(illus. on front cover.)*

CANDID SHOT - Ceramic decanter styled like 35mm. Winding knob is cork stopper. Two shot glasses in pouch on strap. $10-20.

SWANK CAMERA FLASK - Plastic flask shaped like 35mm SLR. Winding knobs conceal spout and air vent. Clear slot on back and clear lens are useful to gauge level of contents. Comes with a small plastic funnel. $8-12.

UNIVEX MERCURY DECANTER -
Ceramic decanter shaped like Univex
Mercury camera. Glazed in all black, or
black body with white shutter housing,
lens, speed knobs, and VF window. $10.

DISHES

**KODAK MUG "You press the button
We do the rest" -** Ivory colored coffee
mug with brown printing. Drawing of
woman photographing young girl with
original Kodak Camera. Made in Korea.
About $5.

**McDONALDS
Great Muppet Caper drinking glass -**
c1981. Two different glasses with pictures
featuring Gonzo with his camera. One
depicts Gonzo in a hot air balloon, the
other in a bus. New in 1981. $.60 each.

**WILTON (Columbia, PA)
Kodak 1880-1980 Centennial Plate -**
Cast metal plate, 10" diameter. "A 100-year
start on tomorrow" on rim. Center area
has bas-relief scene of woman with the
original Kodak Camera, photographing a
young girl as a boy watches. Dealers ask
up to $65.

JEWELRY

CAMERA-CHARM JAS 300 - Small plastic
charm for charm bracelet. Styled like 35mm
RF camera. "JAS 300" on back. $.25

KODAK FILM NECKLACE - Tiny
reproduction of 35mm cartridge of
Kodacolor II, Agfa, or Fuji film. Only one
inch tall. Comes with neck chain and
matching box. $2.00

**KRUGENER DELTA-CAR LAPEL PIN
DVPCA 10th Anniv. -** Tiny replica of the
Krugener trademark (Delta camera on
wheels with rear cab). Fashioned in sterling
silver for the Delaware Valley Photographic
Collectors Assn. in 1984. About $20.

LIGHTS

FOTOX - Reddish-brown bakelite
flashlight styled like Piccolette. Unusual
bulb with solid glass front in lens position.

Made in Saxony. $20-35.

**SASPARILLA DECO DESIGNS LTD.
(New York, NY) Camera-lamp -** White
ceramic night-light designed like 35mm
camera. Made in Japan. Copyright 1980.
$22-27.

MASKS

**SPEARHEAD INDUSTRIES, INC.
(Minneapolis MN)**

Camera Mask - c1983. Rubber face
mask shaped like SLR camera and hands
holding it. Retail price about $6.

MOUSE, WORM, & SURPRISE CAMERAS

FRIEND BOY'S CAMERA - Eye-level style
Mouse camera. $2.

COMMONWEALTH PLASTICS CORP.
Jack-in-the Camera Sr. - Small black plastic "camera". When release lever is pressed, a small smiling face springs through the front of the lens. $1-5.

HIT-SIZE - Miniature worm camera about the size of a Hit-type novelty camera. $2.

KING FLEX - Miniature TLR-style worm camera. $1-5.

PANOMATIC 126 - Mouse camera shaped like 126 cartridge camera. Same old mouse in a new package. $3-6.

PRINCE FLEX - Miniature TLR-style worm camera. $2.

WONDER SPECIAL CAMERA - Eye-level style mouse camera. $3.

WONDERFLEX COMET SPECIAL CAMERA - TLR styled mouse camera. Also sold under the name "Wonderflex

Wonder Special Camera". Made in Japan. $4.

MUSIC BOX

GIRL HOLDING CAMERA - Ceramic figurine with music box in base. Girl holding camera. Cat seated on nearby chair. Music box plays "Everything Is Beautiful". Retail in 1983: $12.

ILLCO TOY CO. (Illfelder Toy Co. Inc., New York City.)
Cabbage Patch Kids Musical Toy Camera - Copr.1984. A music box shaped like a camera. Available in two styles: Lavender body with white trim (plays "Farmer in the Dell") and cream body with lavender trim (plays "Old MacDonald".) About $6.

Mickey Mouse Musical Toy Camera - Music box shaped like a camera. Turning lens winds the mechanism. Pressing the release plays "Rock-a-bye-Baby", and a small Mickey Mouse or Donald Duck head turns around on top. Red camera has Mickey head on top, Donald face on lens. Yellow camera has Donald head on top, Mickey face on lens. Retail about $6.

Smurf Musical Toy Camera - Blue plastic camera-shaped music box toy. Plays "Rock-a-bye-Baby". Smurf head turns around on top. Copyright 1982. Retail: about $5.

ORNAMENTAL

These are decorative, non-functional items.

CAMERA WITH BIRDIE - Miniature cast metal camera on tripod. Birdie on stick above lensboard. About $5.

DURHAM INDUSTRIES INC.
(New York, NY)
Holly Hobbie Doll House Camera -
Small cast metal view camera with tripod.
About $3-4.

HASSELBLAD PLUSH TOY - Oversized
stuffed Hassie. Black velour and gray
terry-cloth. $5-10.

LIMOGES MINIATURE CAMERA - Tiny
ceramic view camera with cobalt-blue or
white glazing. Gold trim and gold tripod.
Blue: $17. White: $15.

SHACKMAN (B.) & CO.
Glass Camera on Tripod - Small novelty
glass camera on metal tripod. Copyright
1981. $6.

PENCIL SHARPENERS

**PENCIL-SHARPENER CAMERA (Hong
Kong) -** Cast metal pencil sharpener
shaped like a view camera. Bellows made
of plastic. "Made in Hong Kong" on side of
bellows. Retail about $2.

**PENCIL-SHARPENER CAMERA
(Spain) -** Cast metal pencil sharpener
shaped like view camera. Bellows are also
cast metal (unlike Hong Kong copies).
Play/Me trademark and "Made in Spain"
on bottom. Retail about $3-4.

**PENCIL SHARPENER EGFECOLOR
400 -** Plastic pencil sharpener shaped
like a film can. Red, blue, and yellow label
mimics Agfacolor. Retail $1.50.

PENCIL SHARPENER ENJICOLOR F-II
- Plastic pencil sharpener shaped like a
film can. Red, green, and white label
mimics Fujicolor. Retail $1.50. *(illustrated
above)*

PENCIL SHARPENER KEEPCOLOR II -
Plastic pencil sharpener shaped like a film
can. Yellow black label mimics Kodacolor.
Retail $1.50. *(illustrated above)*

**PENCIL SHARPENER LANTERN
PROJECTOR -** Heavy metal construction,
shaped like an old-fashioned lantern slide
projector. $4.

PHONOGRAPHS

PETER PAN GRAMOPHONE - Portable
hand-cranked 78 rpm phonograph which
resembles a box camera when closed.
Black leather covered. $125-150.

THORENS EXCELDA - A portable hand-
cranked 78 rpm phonograph which packs
neatly into a metal case shaped like a
folding rollfilm camera. Available in black
or colored enamel finish. $100-150.

PLANTERS

NAPCO PLANTER - Ceramic plater
shaped like Mamiya RB-67 camera. Black
with silver trim. $8.

PRINTING FRAMES

ELVIN (Japan)
Magic Sun Picture 35mm Camera - A
small cardboard box with a hinged glass
back. Printed design resembles 35mm
camera. Box contains "printing-out" paper
for making prints from negatives by two-
minute exposure to sunlight. $2-3.
(illustrated top of next page)

Elvin Magic Sun Picture 35mm Camera

PUZZLES & GAMES

EASTMAN KODAK CO.
Kolorcube - Everybody has heard of Rubik's cube. This is a special version with the Kodak logo on each square of each side. $3-5.

KODAK DICE CUP - Red plastic dice cup with Kodak logo. Five yellow dice with Kodak logo included. $10-15.

RADIOS

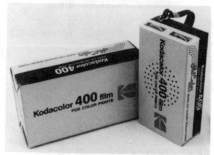

Kodacolor 400 Film Radio

AMICO - Transistor radio shaped like Olympus OM-1 camera. Speaker is in lens mount. $15-25.

KODACOLOR 400 FILM RADIO - Transistor radio shaped and colored like Kodak film box. Radio box also mimics Kodak film packaging. Made in Hong Kong. $15-25. *(illustrated bottom of previous column)*

SHIRASUNA DENKI MFG. CO. LTD.

Silver Pocket Radio - Early transistor radio in leather case designed to look like a camera case. Uses one "B" battery and one "A" battery. Small "filter case" on strap contains earphone and antenna wire. $40-50.

STEWART RADIO-LIGHT-MIRROR - Transistor radio shaped like a 110 pocket camera. Built-in flashlight. Battery compartment door has mirror inside. Made in Hong Kong. $5-10.

RUBBER STAMPS

Kodaclone Slide

BUTTERFLY ORIGINALS LTD. (Cherry Hill, NJ)
Cabbage Patch Kids Figurine Stamper - c1984. Small figurine of Cabbage Patch Doll holding a camera. The base has a rubber stamp (Smile!) and ink pad. Retail $2.50.

KODACLONE SLIDE - A cute rubber-stamp which mimics Kodak's logo on a 35mm slide mount. "Processed by clones" adds an interesting touch. $8-10. *(illustrated bottom of previous page)*

SASPARILLA DECO DESIGNS LTD.
Camera Salt & Pepper - Set of two miniature 35mm-styled ceramic shakers. One is black, the other is white. Retail $6.

WF

Camera-screwdriver-keychain - Small red plastic "camera" with screwdriver bit in lens position. Interchangeable bits store in body. Keychain attached to strap lug. "WF" molded in back. $5-10.

Wolff Prod. Camera Soap-on-a-rope

WOLFF PRODUCTS (Long Island City, NY) Camera Soap-on-a-rope - A six ounce bar of soap shaped like a camera. $7-10. *(illustrated bottom of previous column)*

BATTLESTAR GALACTICA - Small plastic squirt camera with Battlestar Galactica emblem on front. $3.

DICK TRACY SQUIRT GUN CAMERA - Square plastic squirt camera in Dick Tracy motif. $4.

FOTOMAT

Squirt Camera - Well-made squirt camera shaped and sized like a 126 cartridge camera. Made in Hungary. No relation to the Fotomat film stores in the U.S.A. $5-10.

JA-RU Trick Squirt Camera No. 803 - Retail $1.

SHIBA

Aqua Camera Flash Shiba - c1984. Small "camera" which squirts water from the "winding knob". Knob rotates to allow squirting in a different direction. The instructions suggest that after squirting somebody by taking their picture, you give them the chance to do the same to you (but only after you reverse the direction of the knob!) This double-trouble toy comes in red or black. Retail about $3.

Squirt Camera "Diana Style" - This "camera" looks exactly like the cheap "Diana-type" cameras for 120 rollfilm, but squirts water. $2.

T.H.
Water Camera No. 402 - Black plastic water camera. Chrome trim on front. "T.H." trademark and "No. 402" on back. Mushroom top on shutter release. Cloth strap. Retail: under $1.

T.K.
Water Camera No. 677 - Black plastic squirt camera. Chrome trim on front. "Made in Hong Kong" on back. Thin shutter button. Plastic strap. Retail: under $1.

VOHO

Squirt Camera - Small rubber squirt camera styled like a Hit camera. Cream colored body with aluminum paint on top, front, and "latch". "Made in Occupied Japan" molded into bottom. Also available in a black model. $3-5.

WATER CAMERA - Black plastic squirt camera. White top and bottom. Chrome lens rim. Made in Hong Kong. $1-3.

WATER CAMERA NO. 014 - Simple plastic squeeze-type squirt camera. Made in Hong Kong. Retail $.30.

STATUETTES & FIGURINES

ALDON PHOTOGRAPHER - Wooden figurine 30cm (12") tall. Man holds one camera to his face. Two other cameras hang at his sides. Made in China. Retail: $15.00

GIRL WITH CAMERA - Painted ceramic figurine. Girl with view camera. Camera rests on the face of a cat on a chair. Made in Taiwan. $10. *(illustrated below)*

LEFTON CHINA
Man with camera - Hand painted ceramic figurine. Man with camera on tripod. Powder flash unit in left hand. Box of plates at his feet. Made in Taiwan. Retail: about $30.

Left: Royal Crown Boy holding camera
Right: Girl with camera

ROYAL CROWN (Taiwan)
Boy Holding Camera - Figurine of boy seated on stump holding camera. Retail in 1983: $12.

SCHLEICH
Super Smurf Photographer - Small rubbery Smurf toy. Box camera camera on tripod. Copyright 1981. $12.

SHUTTER BUG - Comical furry figure holding camera. Large eyes, nose, and sandaled feet protrude from furry body. "Nikon" SLR camera in left hand. "SHUTTER BUG" placard between feet. $10.

SQUIRREL HOLDING CAMERA - Multicolored ceramic figurine, 4" tall. Made in Taiwan. $15. (illustrated above)

TOYS & GAMES
NOT OTHERWISE SPECIFIED

BEAR WITH FLASH CAMERA - Mechanical bear with camera. Wind-up mechanism raises camera to bear's eye and battery operated flash fires. Made in China. About $20.

EFS (Burlingame, CA)
Camp Out - Set of small toy camping items. Includes wrist compass, camera, canteen, flashlight, walkie-talkie, lantern, and radio. $1.50.

KNICKERBOCKER TOY CO. (Middlesex, NJ)
Snoopy The Astronaut - Snoopy doll with space suit, helmet, and camera. Also

includes moon shoes, life support system, vehicle, flag, and Woodstock. $20.

LEGO

Fabuland Patrick Parrot - Toy parrot with flash camera. Also has motorcycle and pipe wrench. Made to interlock with Lego building blocks. Copyright 1982. Retail: $3.

MATTEL
Fashion Photo Barbie - Imitation camera for fashion photography, connected to doll by a tube. Turning camera lens causes doll to change positions. Copyright 1977. $7.

WINROSS (Rochester, NY)

Kodak Truck 1880-1980 - Toy truck issued for the Kodak Centennial in 1980. Detachable semi-trailer with operable rear doors. Metal construction, white enameled with yellow trim. Dealers are asking $40-50 for these, but probably not selling many.

TOY CAMERAS

These are kid's toys that are made to look like and imitate the functions of real cameras.

ARCO INDUSTRIES LTD. (New York, NY)
Take-A-Picture - Toy camera styled after Kodak Colorburst 250 camera. Includes 12 pre-printed photos which eject when shutter is depressed. Made in Hong Kong. Copyright 1982. Retail: $3.

KENNER
Picture-Quick - Toy camera styled like Kodak EK-4 Instant Camera. Knob ejects pre-printed pictures through bottom slot. Dated 1977 on back. $7.

TOMY

Ring-a-dingy Camera - Child's toy shaped like a camera. Lens turns with clicking sound. Film advance lever clicks and returns. Shutter button rings bell. Copyright 1982. (Other Ring-a-dingy toys are Telephone, Typewriter, and Cash Register.) $5.

TOYPOWER MFG. CO. LTD.

Just Like Daddy's Camera - Toy camera with "simulated working flash". Detachable Kaleidoscope and zoom lenses. Copyright 1983. $5.

VIEWING DEVICES

CAMERA-VIEWER - Small viewer shaped like a camera with 18 views of the Canadian Rockies or some other scenic spot. $2.

CAMERA-VIEWER KEY CHAIN - Small SLR-shaped, with views of New York City, Toronto, or other major cities. Made in Hong Kong. $2. *(illustrated above)*

CHILD GUIDANCE PLAYTHINGS INC.
(Subsid. of Gabriel Industries, Inc. Bronx, NY)

Sesame Street Big Bird's 3-D Camera -

Three-dimensional viewer shaped like a camera. 24 different pictures with alphabet letters. Copyright 1978. Retail: $5.

FISHER-PRICE TOYS (East Aurora, NY)

Pocket Camera - Viewer shaped like 110 pocket camera with flashcube. Shutter advances 27 photos of zoo animals. $3-6.

HASBRO INDUSTRIES, INC.
(Pawtucket, RI)

Romper Room Snoopy Counting Camera - Children's viewer shaped like a camera. Snoopy on front, Woodstock on top. Teaches children to count. Number of characters in scene matches film counter digit. Retail in 1981: $6.

JA-RU (Jacksonville, Florida)

Home Movie Super-8 Auto-matic - c1984. Toy film viewer shaped like a movie camera. Includes interchangeable cylinders with translucent illustrations. New in package: $1-3.

STEVEN MFG CO. (Herman, MO)

Talking Vue Camera - Viewer shaped like a camera. 16 animal cartoon pictures. Six voice messages play when string is pulled. $8.

VEPLA-VENEZIA

Camera-Viewer Capri - Detailed SLR-shaped viewer. 14 views of the island of Capri. Made in Italy. $3-5. *(illustrated in previous column)*

INDEX

Beacon 225 (Whitehouse): 375
Bear Camera: 47
Bear with Flash Camera (Non-Camera): 439
Beau Brownie (EKC): 106
Beaurline Imp: 47
BEAURLINE INDUSTRIES INC.: 47
Beaurline Pro: 47
Beauta Miniature Candid (Rolls): 320
Beauty: 47
Beauty Super II (Taiyodo Koki): 344
Beauty Super L (Taiyodo Koki): 345
Beautycord (Taiyodo Koki): 345
Beautyflex (Taiyodo Koki): 345
Bebe (Ica): 208
Bebe (Zeiss): 384
Bebe (Zulauf): 405
BECK: 47
Beck Frena: 47
Beck Frena Deluxe: 47
Bedfordflex: 47
Bee Bee (Burleigh Brooks): 65
Beginners Camera (Aivas): 24
Beica: 47
BEIER: 48-49
Beier Beier-Flex: 48
Beier Beira: 48
Beier Beirax: 48
Beier Beirette: 48
Beier-Flex (Beier): 48
Beier Folding sheet film cameras: 48
Beier Precisa: 48
Beier Rifax: 48-49
BEIL & FREUND: 49
Beil & Freund Plate Camera: 49
Beira (Beier): 48
Beirax (Beier): 48
Beirette (Beier): 48
Bel-Park Photo: ADV
Belca Belfoca: 49
Belca Belplasca: 49
Belca Beltica: 49
BELCA-WERKE: 49
Belco: 49
Belco (Idam): 213
Belfoca (Belca): 49
Bell 14: 49
BELL & HOWELL: 49-50
BELL & HOWELL (Movie): 408-410
Bell & Howell 200EE: 410
Bell & Howell 252: 410
Bell & Howell 319: 410
Bell & Howell Cine Camera #2709: 408-409
Bell & Howell Colorist: 49
Bell & Howell Dial 35: 49
Bell & Howell Double Run Eight (Companion, Sporster): 409
Bell & Howell Electric Eye 127: 49
Bell & Howell Eyemo 35mm: 408,409
Bell & Howell Filmo 127-A: 409
Bell & Howell Filmo 141-A: 409
Bell & Howell Filmo 141-B: 409
Bell & Howell Filmo 70: 409
Bell & Howell Filmo 70A: 409
Bell & Howell Filmo 75: 409
Bell & Howell Filmo Aristocrat Turret 8: 409

Bell & Howell Filmo Auto Load: 409
Bell & Howell Filmo Companion: 409,410
Bell & Howell Filmo Sportster: 409
Bell & Howell Filmo-121: 409
Bell & Howell Foton: 50
Bell & Howell Infallible (Electric Eye 127): 49
Bell & Howell Magazine Camera-172: 410
Bell & Howell Magazine Camera-200: 410
Bell & Howell TDC Stereo Vivid: 50
Bell & Howell Vivid: 50
BELL CAMERA CO.: 49
Bell Kamra: 49
BELL MFG. CO. (Movie): 410
Bell Model 10: 410
Bell's Straight-Working Panorama Camera: 49
Bella 44, 66 (Bilora): 53
Bellcraft Can-Tex: 50
BELLCRAFT CREATIONS: 50
BELLIENI: 50
Bellieni Jumelle: 50
Bellieni Stereo Jumelle: 50
Bellina 127 (Bilora): 53
Bellows: ADV
Belmira (Pentacon): 295
Belplasca (Belca): 49
BELT BUCKLES (Non-Camera): 428
Beltica (Belca): 49
Ben Akiba (Lehmann): 237
BENCINI: 50
Bencini Animatic 600: 50
Bencini Comet: 50
Bencini Cometa: 50
Bencini Eno: 50
Bencini Koroll: 50
Bencini Koroll 24: 50
BENETFINK: 50-51
Benetfink Lightning Detective: 50
Benetfink Lightning Hand: 50
Benetfink Speedy Detective: 50-51
BENSON DRY PLATE & CAMERA CO.: 51
Benson Street Camera: 51
Benson Victor: 51
BENTZIN: 51-52
Bentzin Astraflex II (Primarflex II): 51
Bentzin Plan Primar: 51
Bentzin Planovista: 51
Bentzin Primar: 51
Bentzin Primar Folding Reflex: 51
Bentzin Primar Reflex: 51
Bentzin Primarette: 51
Bentzin Primarflex: 51
Bentzin Stereo Reflex: 51
Bera (Mashpriborintorg Vega): 259
Bera 2 (Mashpriborintorg Vega): 259
Bergheil (Voigtlander): 363
Bergheil Deluxe (Voigtlander): 363
BERMPOHL & CO. K.G.: 52
Bermpohl Miethe's Three-color camera: 52
Bermpohl's Naturfarbenkamera: 52
Bernard Faultless Miniature: 52
BERNARD PRODUCTS CO.: 52
BERNING: 52-53
Berning Robot I: 52
Berning Robot II: 52
Berning Robot IIa: 52

Bolsey C22: 59
BOLSEY CORP. OF AMERICA: 58-60
Bolsey Explorer: 59
Bolsey Explorer "Treasure Chest" Outfit: 59
Bolsey Jubilee: 59
Bolsey La Belle Pal: 59
Bolsey PH324A: 59
Bolsey Reflex: 60
Bolsey Uniset 8: 60
Bolseyflex (Bolsey): 59
BOLTA-WERK: 60
Bolta Photavit: 60
Boltavit (Bolta): 60
Boltax III (Yamashita): 379-380
Bonita 66 (Bilora): 53
Bonny Six (Yamato): 380
Book Camera (Scovill): 325-326
BOREUX: 60-61
Boreux Nanna: 60-61
BORSUM CAMERA CO.: 61
Borsum 5x7 New Model Reflex: 61
Borsum 5x7 Reflex: 61
Boston Bull's-Eye: 61
BOSTON CAMERA CO.: 61
BOSTON CAMERA MFG. CO.: 61
Boston Hawk-Eye Detective: 61
Boucher (Macris-Boucher): 256
BOUMSELL: 61-62
Boumsell Azur: 61
Boumsell Box Metal: 61
Boumsell Longchamp: 62
Boumsell Photo-Magic: 62
BOWER: 62
Bower 35: 62
Bower-X: 62
Box cameras: see Manufacturers' names
Box Metal (Boumsell): 61
Box Scout cameras (Seneca): 332
Box Tengor (Goerz): 179
Box Tengor (54) (Zeiss): 384
Box Tengor (54/2) (Zeiss): 385
Box Tengor (54/14) (Zeiss): 384-385
Box Tengor (54/15) (Zeiss): 385
Box Tengor (55/2) (Zeiss): 385
Box Tengor (56/2) (Zeiss): 385
Boy (Bilora): 54
Boy Holding Camera (Non-Camera): 438
Boy Scout Brownie (EKC): 104
Boy Scout Camera (Herbert George): 200
Boy Scout Kodak (EKC): 104
Boy Scout Memo (Ansco): 31
BRACK & CO.: 62
Brack Field camera: 62
Brass Bound Instantograph (Lancaster): 234
BRAUN: 62
Braun Gloriette: 62
Braun Norca: 62
Braun Pax: 62
Braun Paxette: 62
Braun Paxina: 63
Braun Super Colorette: 63
Braun Super Paxette: 63
Brenda Starr (Seymore): 333
Brillant (Voigtlander): 365
Brin's Patent Camera: 63

British (Chapman): 80
BRITISH FERROTYPE CO.: 63
British Ferrotype Co. Telephot Button Camera: 63
BROIS: 63
Brois Thompson's Revolver Camera: 63
Brooklyn Camera: 63
BROOKLYN CAMERA CO.: 63
Brooks Veriwide (Burleigh Brooks): 65
BROWNELL: 63
Brownell Stereo Camera: 63
Brownie (Original) (EKC): 104-105
Brownie 127 (EKC): 105
Brownie Auto 27 (EKC): 105
Brownie box cameras (EKC): 104-105
Brownie Bull's-Eye (EKC): 106
Brownie Bullet (EKC): 106
Brownie Bullet II (EKC): 106
Brownie Chiquita (EKC): 107
Brownie Fiesta (EKC): 107
Brownie Flash (EKC): 107
Brownie Flash IV (EKC): 107
Brownie Flash 20 (EKC): 107
Brownie Flash B (EKC): 107
Brownie Flash Six-20 (EKC): 107
Brownie Flashmite 20 (EKC): 107
Brownie Hawkeye (EKC): 108
Brownie Holiday (EKC): 108
Brownie Junior 620 (EKC): 109
Brownie Movie Camera (EKC): 413
Brownie Portrait (EKC): 109
Brownie Reflex (EKC): 109
Brownie Reflex 20 (EKC): 109
Brownie Scout Camera (Herbert George): 200
Brownie Six-20 (EKC): 109
Brownie Starflash (EKC): 110
Brownie Starflex (EKC): 110
Brownie Starlet (Kodak Ltd.) (EKC): 109-110
Brownie Starlet (USA) (EKC): 110
Brownie Starmatic (EKC): 110
Brownie Starmeter (EKC): 110
Brownie Starmite (EKC): 110
Brownie Super 27 (EKC): 110
Brownie Target Six-16 (EKC): 111
Brownie Target Six-20 (EKC): 111
Brownie Twin 20 (EKC): 111
Brownie Vecta (EKC): 111
BRUMBERGER (Movie): 411
Brumberger 8mm-E3L: 411
Brumberger 8mm-T3L: 411
Brumberger 35: 63
BRUNS: 63
Bruns Detective camera: 63
Buccaneer (Universal): 356
Buckeye (American Camera Mfg.): 25
Buckeye (Anthony): 34
Buckeye (Cardinal): 77
Buckeye (EKC): 111
Buckeye Special (American Camera Mfg.): 25
Buckles (Non-Camera Belt Buckles): 428
Budweiser: 63
Buena 35-S: 63
BUESS: 63-64
Buess Multiprint: 63-64

Camera Projector Midas: 411
Camera Repair: ADV
Camera-Robot (Non-Camera): 431
Camera Salt & Pepper Shakers
 (Non-Camera): 437
Camera-screwdriver-keychain
 (Non-Camera): 437
Camera Soap-on-a-Rope (Non-Camera):
 437
Camera-Viewer (Non-Camera): 440
Camera-Viewer Keychain: 440
Camera with Birdie (Non-Camera): 434
Cameradio (Universal Radio): 359
CAMERAS LTD. (Movie): 411-412
Cameras Ltd. Dekko: 411-412
Camerette: 69
Camerette (Yen-Kame): 382
Camex Reflex (Ercsam): 415
Camflex (National): 283
CAMOJECT: 69
Camp Fire Girl's Kodak (EKC): 112-113
Camp out (Non-Camera): 439
Campro: 412
CAMPRO LTD. (Movie): 412
Camro 28 (Argus): 41
Can Camera 110 TX Coca-Cola (Tizer): 349
Can Cameras (Eiko): 153
Can-Tex (Bellcraft): 50
CANADIAN CAMERA CO.: 69
Canadian Camera Co. Glenco: 69
Candex Jr. (General Products): 176
CANDID CAMERA CORP. OF AMERICA
 (Camera Corp. of America): 68
CANDID CAMERA SUPPLY CO.: 69
Candid Camera Supply Minifoto Junior: 69
Candid Flash Camera (Flash Camera Co.):
 168
Candid Shot (Non-Camera): 432
CANDY & GUM (Non-Camera): 428
Canon IIA: 73
Canon IIAF: 73
Canon IIB: 73
Canon IIC: 73
Canon IID: 73
Canon IID1: 73
Canon IID2: 73
Canon IIF: 73
Canon IIF2: 73
Canon III: 73-74
Canon IIIA: 74
Canon IIIA Signal Corps.: 74
Canon IIS: 73
Canon IIS2: 73
Canon IV: 74
Canon IVBS: 74
Canon IVF: 74
Canon IVS: 74
Canon IVSB2: 74
Canon 7: 76
Canon 7s: 76
Canon 7sZ: 76
CANON CAMERA CO.: 70-76
Canon Canonet: 76
Canon Canonex: 76
Canon Canonflex: 76
Canon Demi: 76
Canon Dial 35: 76

Canon EX-EE: 76
Canon FP: 76
Canon FT: 76
Canon FX: 76
Canon Hansa: 70-71
Canon J: 71
Canon J-II: 71-72
Canon JS: 71
Canon Kwanon: 70
Canon L-1: 75
Canon L-2: 75
Canon L-3: 75
Canon NS: 72
Canon Original: 70-71
Canon P: 75
Canon Pellix: 76
Canon Pellix QL: 76
Canon RF Wanted: ADV
Canon S: 72
Canon S-I (Canon S): 72
Canon S-II: 72
Canon Seiki S-II: 72
Canon TL: 76
Canon VI-L: 75
Canon VI-T: 75
Canon VL: 75
Canon VL-2: 75
Canon VT: 74-75
Canon VT-Deluxe: 75
Canon VT-Deluxe-M: 75
Canon VT-Deluxe-Z: 75
Canon X-Ray Cameras: 72
Canonet (Canon): 76
Canonex (Canon): 76
Canonflex (Canon): 76
Canter Beauty (Taiyodo Koki): 344
Capitol 120: 76
Capri (Keystone): 418
Capri Camera-Viewer (Non-Camera): 440
Captain (Agfa): 19
Carbine (Butcher): 66
Carbine (Houghton Ensign): 203
Carbine, Tropical (Houghton Ensign): 203
Cardinal: 77
Cardinal Buckeye: 77
Cardinal Cinex: 77
CARDINAL CORP.: 77
Cardinal Photo-Champ: 77
CARL ZEISS OPTICAL CO. (Zeiss): 382
Carlton (London Stereoscopic): 254
Carlton (Rochester Optical): 317
Carlton (Utility): 359
Carlton Reflex (Allied): 25
Carmen: 77
CARPENTIER: 77
Carpentier Photo Jumelle: 77
Cartridge Hawk-Eye (EKC): 122
Cartridge Kodak (EKC): 113
Cartridge Premo (EKC): 132
Casca I (Steinheil): 341
Casca II (Steinheil): 341
Century 35 (Graflex): 192
CENTURY CAMERA CO.: 77
Century Copy Camera: 77
Century Field cameras: 77
Century Grand: 77
Century Grand Sr.: 77

Criterion (Birmingham Photographic): 54
Croma Color 16: 90
CROWN CAMERA CO.: 90
Crown Camera Co. Dandy Photo Camera: 90
Crown View (Graflex): 192
CRUVER-PETERS: 90
Cruver-Peters Palko: 90-91
Crystar: 91
Crystarflex: 91
Cub (American Advertising & Research Corp.): 25
Cub (Burke & James): 64
Cub Scout Camera (Herbert George): 200
Cubex IV (Imperial): 216
Cupid (Houghton Ensign): 204
Cupido (Ica): 208
CURTIS: 91
Curtis Color Master: 91
Curtis Color Scout: 91
Cycle Graphic Cameras (Graflex): 190
Cycle Pocos (Rochester Camera): 317
Cycle Wizard (Manhattan): 258
Cyclographe a foyer fixe (Damoizeau): 93
Cyclone: 91
Cyclone Cameras (Rochester Optical): 317
Cyclone Jr. (Western): 374
Cyclone Junior (Rochester Optical): 317
Cyclone Senior (Rochester Optical): 317
Cyclone Sr. (Western): 374
Cyclops: 91
Da-Brite (Herold): 200
Daci (Dacora): 91
Dacora I: 91
Dacora Daci: 91
Dacora Dacora-Matic 4D: 91
Dacora Digna: 91
Dacora Dignette: 92
Dacora Instacora E: 92
DACORA KAMERAWERK: 91
Dacora-Matic 4D (Dacora): 91
Dacora Royal: 92
Daguerreotype camera (Lewis): 250
Daguerreotype cameras: 92
Daguerreotype cannon (replica) (Voigtlander): 365
Daguerrian Cameras Wanted: ADV
DAH YANG TOYS (Non-Camera): 431
DAIICHI KOGAKU: 92
Daiichi Zenobia: 92
Daiichi Zenobiaflex: 92
DAISHIN SEIKI K.K.: 92
Daishin Seiki Hobby Junior: 92
Dale: 92
DALLMEYER: 92
Dallmeyer Naturalist: 92
Dallmeyer Sliding Box Wet Plate Camera: 92
Dallmeyer Snapshot Camera: 92
Dallmeyer Speed Camera: 92
Dallmeyer Stereo Wet Plate camera: 92
Dame Hub (Box camera): 92
Dame Hub (Folding): 92
DAME, STODDARD & KENDALL: 92
Damen-Kamera (Certo): 78
DAMOIZEAU: 93
Damoizeau Cyclographe a foyer fixe: 93

DAN CAMERA WORKS: 93
Dan 35: 93
DANCER: 93
Dancer Stereo Camera: 93
Dandy Photo Camera (Crown Camera Co.): 90
Dangelmeier (Dacora): 93
DARIER: 93
Darier Escopette: 93
Darling-16 (Shincho): 335
DART CAMERAS (Non-Camera): 431
Dauphin (Alsaphot): 25
Davy Crockett: 93
Davy Crockett (Herbert George): 199
Day-Xit (Shew): 334
Daydark Photo Postcard Cameras: 93
DAYDARK SPECIALTY CO.: 93
Daydark Tintype Camera: 93
Daylight Enlarging Camera (Anthony): 35
Daylight Kodak (EKC): 114-115
DBGM: 93
DBP: 93
DBPa: 93
DEARDORFF: 93-95
Deardorff 4x5" Cameras: 94-95
Deardorff 5x7" Cameras: 94
Deardorff 8x10" Cameras: 93-94
Deardorff 11x14" Cameras: 95
Deardorff 12x20" View: 95
Deardorff 16x20" View: 95
Deardorff Commercial Cameras: 95
Deardorff Home Portrait: 95
Deardorff Refinishing: ADV
Deardorff Triamapro: 95
Debonair: 95
Debonair (Imperial): 216
DEBRIE: 95-96
DEBRIE (Movie): 412
Debrie Parvo Interview: 412
Debrie Sept: 95-96
Debrie Sept (Movie): 412
DECANTERS (Non-Camera): 432-433
Deceptive Angle Graphic (Graflex): 189
Deckrullo (Contessa): 87
Deckrullo (Nettel): 284
Deckrullo (Zeiss): 392
Deckrullo-Nettel (Contessa): 87
Deckrullo Nettel (Zeiss): 392
Deckrullo-Nettel Stereo (Contessa): 87
Deckrullo Nettel Tropical (Zeiss): 392
Deckrullo Stereo (Contessa): 87
Defiance Auto Fixt Focus: 96
DEFIANCE MFG. CO.: 96
Dehel (Demaria): 96
DEJUR-AMSCO CORP.: 96
Dejur D-1: 96
Dejur Reflex: 96
Dekko (Cameras Ltd.): 411-412
Delco 28 (Argus): 41
Delco 828 (Deluxe Products): 96
Delmar (Sears): 327
DELOYE: 96
Deloye Prismac: 96
Delta (Ica): 208
Delta (Imperial): 216
Delta (Krugener): 228
Delta Magazine (Krugener): 229

Duplex (Iso): 217
Duplex Novelette (Anthony): 36
Duplex Ruby Reflex (Thornton-Pickard): 346-347
Duplex Ruby Reflex, Tropical (Thornton-Pickard): 347
DURHAM INDUSTRIES INC. (Non-Camera): 435
Duroll (Contessa): 87
DURST S.A.: 99
Durst 66: 99
Durst Automatica: 99
Durst Duca: 99
DVPCA Lapel pin (Non-Camera Krugener Delta-Car): 433
Dynamatic (Voigtlander): 365
Dynamatic II (Voigtlander):
DZERZHINSKY COMMUNE (Fed): 166
EARL PRODUCTS CO.: 100
Earl Scenex: 100
EASTERN SPECIALTY MFG. CO.: 100
Eastern Specialty Springfield Union: 100
EASTMAN DRY PLATE & FILM CO.: 100
EASTMAN KODAK CO.: 100-151
EASTMAN KODAK CO. (Movie): 413-415
EKC A Daylight Kodak: 114
EKC A Ordinary Kodak: 129
EKC Anniversary Kodak: 101-102
EKC Autographic Kodak: 102
EKC Autographic Kodak Junior: 102
EKC Autographic Kodak Special: 102-103
EKC Automatic 35: 103
EKC Automatic 35B: 103
EKC Automatic 35F: 103
EKC Automatic 35R4: 103
EKC B Daylight Kodak: 114
EKC B Ordinary Kodak: 129
EKC Baby Brownie: 106
EKC Baby Brownie New York World's Fair Model: 106
EKC Baby Brownie Special: 106
EKC Bantam: 103-104
EKC Bantam Colorsnap: 104
EKC Bantam f4.5: 104
EKC Bantam f4.5 Military Model: 104
EKC Bantam f5.6: 103
EKC Bantam f6.3: 103
EKC Bantam f8: 103
EKC Bantam RF: 104
EKC Bantam Special: 104
EKC Beau Brownie: 106
EKC Boy Scout Brownie: 104
EKC Boy Scout Kodak: 104
EKC Brownie (Original): 104-105
EKC Brownie 127: 105
EKC Brownie Auto 27: 105
EKC Brownie Bull's-Eye: 106
EKC Brownie Bullet: 106
EKC Brownie Bullet II: 106
EKC Brownie Chiquita: 107
EKC Brownie Fiesta: 107
EKC Brownie Flash: 107
EKC Brownie Flash IV: 107
EKC Brownie Flash 20: 107
EKC Brownie Flash B: 107
EKC Brownie Flash Six-20: 107
EKC Brownie Flashmite 20: 107

EKC Brownie Hawkeye: 108
EKC Brownie Holiday: 108
EKC Brownie Junior 620: 109
EKC Brownie Movie Camera: 413
EKC Brownie Portrait: 109
EKC Brownie Reflex: 109
EKC Brownie Reflex 20: 109
EKC Brownie Six-20: 109
EKC Brownie Starflash: 110
EKC Brownie Starflex: 110
EKC Brownie Starlet (Kodak Ltd.): 109-110
EKC Brownie Starlet (USA): 110
EKC Brownie Starmatic: 110
EKC Brownie Starmeter: 110
EKC Brownie Starmite: 110
EKC Brownie Super 27: 110
EKC Brownie Target Six-16: 111
EKC Brownie Target Six-20: 111
EKC Brownie Twin 20: 111
EKC Brownie Vecta: 111
EKC Brownie: 104
EKC Buckeye: 111
EKC Bull's-Eye: 111
EKC Bull's-Eye Special: 112
EKC Bullet: 112
EKC Bullet (plastic): 112
EKC Bullet New York World's Fair: 112
EKC Bullet Special: 112
EKC C Daylight Kodak: 115
EKC C Ordinary Kodak: 129
EKC Camp Fire Girl's Kodak: 112-113
EKC Cartridge Hawk-Eye: 122
EKC Cartridge Kodak: 113
EKC Cartridge Premo: 132
EKC Century of Progress, World's Fair Souvenir: 113
EKC Chevron: 113
EKC Cine-Kodak: 413-414
EKC Cine Kodak 8: 414-415
EKC Cine Kodak Model BB Junior: 414
EKC Cine Kodak Model BB: 414
EKC Cine Kodak Model E: 414
EKC Cine Kodak Model K: 414
EKC Cine-Kodak Magazine 8: 415
EKC Cine-Kodak Magazine 16: 415
EKC Cine-Kodak Model B: 414
EKC Cine-Kodak Special, Special II: 415
EKC Cirkut Cameras: 113-114
EKC Cirkut Outfits: 113-114
EKC Cone Pocket Kodak: 114
EKC Coquette: 114
EKC Daylight Kodak: 114-115
EKC Duaflex: 115
EKC Duex: 115
EKC Duo Six-20: 115
EKC Duo Six-20 Series II: 115
EKC Duo Six-20 Series II w/ Rangefinder: 115
EKC Eastman Plate Camera: 115
EKC Ektra: 116
EKC Ektra 1: 116
EKC Ektra 2: 116
EKC Ektra II: 116
EKC Ektra 200: 116
EKC Empire State: 116
EKC Eureka: 116-117
EKC Falcon: 117

EKC No. 4 Cartridge Kodak: 113
EKC No. 4 Eureka: 117
EKC No. 4 Folding Hawk-Eye: 122
EKC No. 4 Folding Kodak: 118
EKC No. 4 Folding Kodet: 127
EKC No. 4 Folding Kodet Junior: 127
EKC No. 4 Folding Kodet Special: 127
EKC No. 4 Folding Pocket Kodak: 121
EKC No. 4 Kodak: 101
EKC No. 4 Kodak Jr.: 101
EKC No. 4 Kodet: 127
EKC No. 4 Panoram Kodak: 129
EKC No. 4 Premo Junior: 133
EKC No. 4 Screen Focus Kodak: 143
EKC No. 4 Speed Kodak: 146
EKC No. 4 Weno Hawk-Eye: 124
EKC No. 4A Autographic Kodak: 102
EKC No. 4A Folding Kodak: 119
EKC No. 5 Cartridge Kodak: 113
EKC No. 5 Cirkut Camera: 114
EKC No. 5 Folding Kodak: 118
EKC No. 5 Folding Kodet: 127
EKC No. 5 Folding Kodet Special: 127
EKC No. 5 Weno Hawk-Eye: 124
EKC No. 6 Cirkut Camera: 114
EKC No. 6 Cirkut Outfit: 114
EKC No. 6 Folding Kodak: 118
EKC No. 7 Weno Hawk-Eye: 124
EKC No. 8 Cirkut Outfit: 114
EKC No. 10 Cirkut Camera: 114
EKC No. 16 Cirkut Camera: 114
EKC Ordinary Kodak: 128-129
EKC Panoram Kodak: 129
EKC Peer 100: 129
EKC Petite: 129-130
EKC Pin-Hole Camera: 130
EKC Plate camera: 115
EKC Pocket Instamatic: 130
EKC Pocket Kodak: 131-132
EKC Pocket Kodak Junior: 131
EKC Pocket Kodak Series II: 131
EKC Pocket Kodak Special: 131-132
EKC Pocket Premo: 134
EKC Pocket Premo C: 134
EKC Pony II: 132
EKC Pony IV: 132
EKC Pony 135: 132
EKC Pony 828: 132
EKC Pony Premo: 134
EKC Pony Premo No. 1: 134
EKC Pony Premo No. 2: 134
EKC Pony Premo No. 3: 134
EKC Pony Premo No. 4: 134
EKC Pony Premo No. 5: 134
EKC Pony Premo No. 6: 134
EKC Pony Premo No. 7: 134
EKC Popular Brownie: 109
EKC Portrait Brownie: 109
EKC Premo: 132-135
EKC Premo Box Film: 132
EKC Premo Folding: 133
EKC Premo Junior: 133-134
EKC Premo No. 12: 133
EKC Premo No. 8: 133
EKC Premo No. 9: 133
EKC Premoette: 135
EKC Premoette Junior: 135

EKC Premoette Senior: 135
EKC Premoette Special: 135
EKC Premograph: 135-136
EKC Premograph No. 2: 136
EKC Pupille: 136
EKC Quick Focus Kodak: 136
EKC Rainbow Hawk-Eye: 123
EKC Ranca: 136
EKC Recomar 18: 136
EKC Recomar 33: 136
EKC Regent: 136-137
EKC Regent II: 137
EKC Regular Kodak: 137
EKC Retina: 137-141
EKC Retina (117): 137
EKC Retina (118): 137
EKC Retina I (010): 138
EKC Retina I (013): 138
EKC Retina I (119): 137
EKC Retina I (126): 137
EKC Retina I (141): 138
EKC Retina I (143): 138
EKC Retina I (148): 138
EKC Retina I (149): 138
EKC Retina Ia (015): 138
EKC Retina Ib (018): 138
EKC Retina IB (019): 138
EKC Retina IBS (040): 138
EKC Retina IF (046): 138
EKC Retina II (011): 139
EKC Retina II (014): 139
EKC Retina II (122): 138
EKC Retina II (142): 139
EKC Retina IIa (016): 139
EKC Retina IIa (150): 139
EKC Retina IIc (020): 139
EKC Retina IIC (029): 139
EKC Retina IIF (047): 140
EKC Retina IIS (024): 140
EKC Retina IIIc (021): 140
EKC Retina IIIC (028): 140
EKC Retina IIIC (1982): 140
EKC Retina IIIS (027): 140
EKC Retina Automatic I (038): 141
EKC Retina Automatic II (032): 141
EKC Retina Automatic III (039): 141
EKC Retina Reflex (025): 141
EKC Retina Reflex III (041): 142
EKC Retina Reflex IV (051): 142
EKC Retina Reflex S (034): 142
EKC Retina S1 (060): 141
EKC Retina S2 (061): 141
EKC Retinette: 142-143
EKC Retinette (012): 142
EKC Retinette (017): 142
EKC Retinette (022): 142
EKC Retinette (147): 142
EKC Retinette I (030): 142
EKC Retinette IA (035): 142
EKC Retinette IA (042): 142-143
EKC Retinette IA (044): 143
EKC Retinette IB (037): 143
EKC Retinette IB (045): 143
EKC Retinette II (026): 143
EKC Retinette II (160): 143
EKC Retinette IIA (036): 143
EKC Retinette IIB (031): 143

EKC Retinette F (022/7): 143
EKC Screen Focus Kodak: 143
EKC Signet 30: 144
EKC Signet 35: 144
EKC Signet 35 (Signal Corp.): 145
EKC Signet 40: 144
EKC Signet 50: 144
EKC Signet 80: 144
EKC Six-16 Brownie: 109
EKC Six-16 Brownie Junior: 109
EKC Six-16 Brownie Special: 109
EKC Six-16 Folding Hawk-Eye: 122
EKC Six-16 Target Hawk-Eye: 123
EKC Six-20 Boy Scout Brownie: 104
EKC Six-20 Brownie: 109
EKC Six-20 Brownie Junior: 109
EKC Six-20 Brownie Special: 109
EKC Six-20 Bull's-Eye Brownie: 109
EKC Six-20 Flash Brownie: 109
EKC Six-20 Folding Hawk-Eye: 122
EKC Six-20 Target Hawk-Eye: 123
EKC Six-Three Kodak No. 1A: 145
EKC Six-Three Kodak No. 3: 145
EKC Six-Three Kodak No. 3A: 145
EKC Special Kodak: 145-146
EKC Speed Kodak: 146
EKC Star Premo: 134-135
EKC Startech: 146
EKC Stereo Hawk-Eye: 123
EKC Stereo Kodak: 146-147
EKC Stereo Kodak Model 1: 147
EKC Super Kodak Six-20: 147
EKC Suprema: 147
EKC Target Brownie Six-16: 111
EKC Target Brownie Six-20: 111
EKC Target Hawk-Eye: 123
EKC Tele-Ektra 1, 2: 147-148
EKC Tele-Instamatic: 147-148
EKC Tourist: 148
EKC Tourist II: 148
EKC Trimlite Instamatic: 147-148
EKC Vanity Kodak: 148
EKC Vanity Kodak Ensemble: 148
EKC Vest Pocket Autographic Kodak
  Special: 149-150
EKC Vest Pocket Autographic Kodak: 149
EKC Vest Pocket Hawk-Eye: 123
EKC Vest Pocket Kodak: 148-149
EKC Vest Pocket Kodak Model B: 149
EKC Vest Pocket Kodak Series III: 149
EKC Vest Pocket Kodak Special: 149
EKC Vest Pocket Rainbow Hawk-Eye: 123
EKC View: 150
EKC Vigilant Junior Six-16: 150
EKC Vigilant Junior Six-20: 150
EKC Vigilant Six-16: 150
EKC Vigilant Six-20: 150
EKC Vollenda: 150-151
EKC Vollenda 620: 150
EKC Vollenda Junior 616: 150
EKC Vollenda Junior 620: 151
EKC Weno Hawk-Eye: 123-124
EKC Winner Pocket: 151
EKC World's Fair Flash: 151
EKC Zenith Kodak: 151
Easy-Load (Expo): 164
EBNER: 151

Ebony 35 (Hoei): 202
Ebony 35 De-Luxe (Hoei): 202
Ebony Deluxe IIS (Hoei): 202
Echo 8 (Suzuki): 344
Eclipse (Horsman): 203
Eclipse (Shew): 334
EDBAR INTERNATIONAL CORP.: 151
Edbar V.P. Twin: 151
Edelweiss (Zenith): 405
Eder-Patent Camera: 151-152
Edina (Wirgin): 377
Edinex (Wirgin): 377
Edinex 120 (Wirgin): 377
Edixa (Wirgin): 377
Edixa 16 (Wirgin): 377
Edixa 16M (Wirgin): 377
Edixa 16MB (Wirgin): 377
Edixa Electronica (Wirgin): 377
Edixa Reflex (Wirgin): 377
Edixa Stereo (Wirgin): 377
Edixa Stereo II, IIa (Wirgin): 377
Edixa Stereo III, IIIa (Wirgin): 377
Edixaflex (Wirgin): 377
EFS Camp out (Non-Camera): 439
EHIRA CAMERA WORKS (Ehira): 152
Ehira Chrome Six: 152
EHIRA K.S.K.: 152
Ehira-Six: 152
Ehira Weha Chrome Six: 152
EHO-ALTISSA: 152
Eho-Altissa Altiflex: 152
Eho-Altissa Altiscop: 152
Eho-Altissa Altissa: 152
Eho-Altissa Altix: 152
Eho-Altissa Altix IV: 152
Eho-Altissa Altix-N: 152
Eho-Altissa Altix NB: 152
Eho-Altissa Eho Baby Box: 152
Eho-Altissa Eho Box: 152
Eho-Altissa Eho Stereo Box: 153
Eho Baby Box (Eho-Altissa): 152
Eho Box (Eho-Altissa): 152
EHO KAMERAFABRIK (Eho-Altissa):
  152-153
Eho Stereo Box (Eho-Altissa): 153
Eight-20 Penguin (Kershaw): 220
Eiko Budweiser: 153
Eiko Can Cameras: 153
EIKO CO. LTD.: 153
Eiko Coca-Cola: 153
Eiko Mickey Mouse: 153
Eiko Pepsi-Cola: 153
Eiko 7-up: 153
Eiko Snoopy: 153
Eka (Krauss): 227
Ektra (EKC): 116
Ektra 1 (EKC): 116
Ektra 2 (EKC): 116
Ektra II (EKC): 116
Ektra 200 (EKC): 116
E.L.C.: 153
E.L.C. l'As: 153
Elca (Elop): 153
Elca II (Elop): 153
Electric Eye 127 (Bell & Howell): 49
Electro Shot (Minolta): 273
Electronic: 153

Gundlach Korona Banquet cameras: 195
Gundlach Korona Stereo: 195
Gundlach Korona View: 195
Gundlach Long Focus Korona: 195
GUNDLACH MANHATTAN OPTICAL CO.:
194-195
GUNDLACH OPTICAL CO.: 194-195
GUSTAV AMIGO (Movie): 417
Gustav Amigo: 417
Guthe & Thorsch (KW): 189
Hacon (Norisan): 291
Hadds Foto-Flex: 195
HADDS MFG. CO.: 195
Hadson: 195
HAKING: 195-196
Haking Halina 35: 195
Haking Halina 35X: 195
Haking Halina-Baby: 195
Haking Halina Viceroy: 196
Haking Kinoflex Deluxe: 196
Haking Prefect Senior: 196
Haking Votar Flex: 196
Halina 35 (Haking): 195
Halina 35X (Haking): 195
Halina-Baby (Haking): 195
Halina Viceroy (Haking): 196
HALL CAMERA CO.: 196
Hall Mirror Reflex Camera: 196
Hall Pocket Camera: 196
Halloh (Ica): 209
HAMAPHOT KG: 196
Hamaphot Modell P56L: 196
Hamco: 196
HANAU: 196
Hanau le Marsouin: 196
Hanau Passe-Partout: 196
Hand Camera (Chadwick): 80
Handy (Rochester Optical): 317
HANEEL TRI-VISION CO.: 196
Haneel Tri-Vision Stereo: 196
Hanken: 197
HANNA-BARBERA: 197
Hanna-Barbera Fred Flintstone: 197
Hanna-Barbera Huckelberry Hound: 197
Hanna-Barbera Yogi Bear: 197
Hansa (Canon): 70-71
Hapo (Photo-Porst): 300
Happi-Time (Herbert George): 199
Happy: 197
Happy (K.W.): 231
Happy (Minolta): 265
Happy Times Instant Camera (EKC): 122
HARBOE: 197
Harboe Wood box camera: 197
HARE: 197
Hare Stereo camera: 197
Hare Tourist camera: 197
Hare Tropical wet-plate stereo camera:
197
Hare Wet-plate stereo camera: 197
Harmony: 197
HARUKAWA: 197
Harukawa Septon Pen Camera: 197
Harvard camera (Mason): 260
HASBRO INDUSTRIES INC.
(Non-Camera): 440
HASSELBLAD: 197-198

Hasselblad 500C: 198
Hasselblad 1000F: 198
Hasselblad 1600F: 197
Hasselblad for sale: ADV
Hasselblad Plush Toy (Non-Camera): 435
Hasselblad Service: ADV
Hasselblad Super Wide Angle: 198
Hat Detective Camera (Adams & Co.): 16
Hawk-Eye (Blair): 55
Hawk-Eye (EKC): 122-124
Hawk-Eye Box (Blair): 56
Hawk-Eye Detective (Blair): 56
Hawk-Eye Detective (Boston): 61
Hawk-Eye Flashfun (EKC): 122
Hawk-Eye Flashfun II (EKC): 122
Hawk-Eye Junior (Blair): 56
Hawk-Eye Special (EKC): 122
Hawkette (EKC): 122
Heag (Ernemann): 157-160
Heag (tropical) (Ernemann): 160
Heag 0 (Ernemann): 157
Heag 00 (Ernemann): 158
Heag I (Ernemann): 158
Heag II (Ernemann): 158
Heag III (Ernemann): 158
Heag IV (stereo) (Ernemann): 158
Heag IX Universal (Ernemann): 159
Heag V (Ernemann): 158
Heag VI (Ernemann): 158
Heag VII (Ernemann): 158-159
Heag XI (Ernemann): 159
Heag XII (Ernemann): 159
Heag XII Model III (stereo) (Ernemann):
159
Heag XIV (Ernemann): 159
Heag XV (plate type) (Ernemann): 159
Heag XV (rollfilm type) (Ernemann): 160
HEALTHWAYS: 198
Healthways Mako Shark: 198
Heidescop (Franke & Heidecke): 170
HEILAND PHOTO PRODUCTS: 198
Heiland Premiere: 198
Heli-Clack (Rietzschel): 313
Heli-Clack Universal Type I, II (Rietzschel):
313-314
Heliar Reflex (Voigtlander): 365
HELIN-NOBLE INC.: 198
Helin-Noble Noble 126: 198
Heliomatic 8 S2R (Nizo): 420
Helios (Huttig): 207
Hello Kitty (Sanrio): 324
Helm Bugs Bunny: 198
Helm Mickey Mouse: 198
Helm Snoopy-Matic: 199
HELM TOY CORP.: 198
HENDREN ENTERPRISE: 199
Hendren Octopus "The Weekender": 199
Henry Clay Camera (American Optical): 26
Henso Reporter (Hensoldt): 199
HENSOLDT: 199
Hensoldt Henso Reporter: 199
HERBERT GEORGE CO.: 199-200
Herbert George Boy Scout Camera: 200
Herbert George Brownie Scout Camera:
200
Herbert George Cub Scout Camera: 200
Herbert George Davy Crockett: 199

I
N
D
E
X

479

Nitor (Agfa): 21
NITTO PHOTO PRODUCTS: 290
Nitto Elega-35: 290
Nixe (Ica): 211
Nixe (Zeiss): 398
NIZO (Movie): 420
Nizo Exposomat 8R: 420
Nizo Heliomatic 8 S2R: 420
No Name Contax (Zeiss): 389
No Need Dark Room (Yen-Kame): 382
No. 0 Brownie (EKC): 105
No. 0 Buster Brown (Ansco): 29
No. 0 Folding Pocket Kodak (EKC): 119
No. 0 Graphic (Graflex): 189
No. 0 Premo Junior (EKC): 133
No. 00 Cartridge Premo (EKC): 132
No. 1 Ansco Junior: 30
No. 1 Autographic Kodak Junior: 102
No. 1 Autographic Kodak Special: 102
No. 1 Brownie (EKC): 105
No. 1 Cone Pocket Kodak (EKC): 114
No. 1 Film Premo (EKC): 133
No. 1 Folding Ansco: 30
No. 1 Folding Buster Brown (Ansco): 29
No. 1 Folding Pocket Kodak (EKC): 119
No. 1 Goodwin Jr. (Ansco): 30
No. 1 Kodak (EKC): 100
No. 1 Kodak Junior (EKC): 125
No. 1 Kodak Series III (EKC): 126
No. 1 Panoram Kodak (EKC): 129
No. 1 Pocket Kodak (EKC): 131
No. 1 Pocket Kodak Junior (EKC): 131
No. 1 Pocket Kodak Series II (EKC): 131
No. 1 Pocket Kodak Special (EKC): 131
No. 1 Premo Junior (EKC): 133
No. 1 Premoette (EKC): 135
No. 1 Premoette Junior (EKC): 135
No. 1 Premoette Junior Special (EKC): 135
No. 1 Premoette Special (EKC): 135
No. 1 Seneca Junior (Seneca): 332
No. 1 Special Folding Ansco: 30
No. 1 Tourist Buckeye (American Camera Mfg.): 26
No. 1A Ansco Junior: 30
No. 1A Autographic Kodak (EKC): 102
No. 1A Autographic Kodak Junior: 102
No. 1A Autographic Kodak Special: 103
No. 1A Folding Ansco: 30
No. 1A Folding Goodwin (Ansco): 30
No. 1A Folding Hawk-Eye (EKC): 122
No. 1A Folding Pocket Kodak (EKC): 120
No. 1A Folding Pocket Kodak Special: 120
No. 1A Folding Rexo (Burke & James): 64
No. 1A Gift Kodak (EKC): 121
No. 1A Ingento Jr. (Burke & James): 64
No. 1A Kodak Junior (EKC): 125
No. 1A Kodak Series III (EKC): 126
No. 1A Pocket Kodak (EKC): 130-131
No. 1A Pocket Kodak Junior (EKC): 131
No. 1A Pocket Kodak Series II (EKC): 131
No. 1A Pocket Kodak Special (EKC): 132
No. 1A Premo Junior (EKC): 133
No. 1A Premoette (EKC): 135
No. 1A Premoette Junior (EKC): 135
No. 1A Premoette Junior Special (EKC): 135
No. 1A Premoette Special (EKC): 135

No. 1A Rexo Jr. (Burke & James): 64
No. 1A Special Kodak (EKC): 146
No. 1A Speed Kodak (EKC): 146
No. 2 Brownie (EKC): 105
No. 2 Buckeye (American Camera Mfg.): 25
No. 2 Bull's-Eye (EKC): 111
No. 2 Bull's-Eye Special (EKC): 112
No. 2 Bullet (EKC): 112
No. 2 Bullet Special (EKC): 112
No. 2 Buster Brown (Ansco): 29
No. 2 Cartridge Hawk-Eye (EKC): 122
No. 2 Cartridge Premo (EKC): 132
No. 2 Eureka (EKC): 116
No. 2 Eureka Jr. (EKC): 116
No. 2 Falcon (EKC): 117
No. 2 Film Pack Hawk-Eye (EKC): 122
No. 2 Flexo Kodak (EKC): 117
No. 2 Folding Autographic Brownie (EKC): 108
No. 2 Folding Brownie (EKC): 107
No. 2 Folding Bull's-Eye (EKC): 111
No. 2 Folding Cartridge Hawk-Eye (EKC): 122
No. 2 Folding Cartridge Premo (EKC): 133
No. 2 Folding Film Pack Hawk-Eye (EKC): 123
No. 2 Folding Hawk-Eye Special (EKC): 122
No. 2 Folding Pocket Brownie (EKC): 108
No. 2 Folding Pocket Kodak (EKC): 120
No. 2 Folding Rainbow Hawk-Eye (EKC): 123
No. 2 Folding Rainbow Hawk-Eye Special (EKC): 123
No. 2 Goodwin (Ansco): 30
No. 2 Hawk-Eye Special (EKC): 122
No. 2 Hawkette (EKC): 122
No. 2 Kewpie (Conley): 85
No. 2 Kodak (EKC): 101
No. 2 Rainbow Hawk-Eye (EKC): 123
No. 2 Stereo Brownie (EKC): 110
No. 2 Stereo Kodak (EKC): 147
No. 2 Target Hawk-Eye (EKC): 123
No. 2 Target Hawk-Eye Junior (EKC): 123
No. 2 Weno Hawk-Eye (Blair): 57
No. 2 Weno Hawk-Eye (EKC): 124
No. 2A Brownie (EKC): 105
No. 2A Buster Brown (Ansco): 29
No. 2A Cartridge Hawk-Eye (EKC): 122
No. 2A Cartridge Premo (EKC): 132
No. 2A Film Pack Hawk-Eye (EKC): 122
No. 2A Folding Autographic Brownie (EKC): 108
No. 2A Folding Buster Brown (Ansco): 29
No. 2A Folding Cartridge Hawk-Eye (EKC): 122
No. 2A Folding Cartridge Premo (EKC): 133
No. 2A Folding Hawk-Eye Special (EKC): 122
No. 2A Folding Pocket Brownie (EKC): 108
No. 2A Folding Rainbow Hawk-Eye (EKC): 123
No. 2A Folding Rainbow Hawk-Eye Special (EKC): 123

No. 2A Folding Scout (Seneca): 332
No. 2A Goodwin (Ansco): 30
No. 2A Hawk-Eye Special (EKC): 122
No. 2A Kewpie (Conley): 85
No. 2A Rainbow Hawk-Eye (EKC): 123
No. 2A Target Hawk-Eye (EKC): 123
No. 2C Ansco Junior: 30
No. 2C Autographic Kodak Junior: 102
No. 2C Autographic Kodak Special: 103
No. 2C Brownie (EKC): 105
No. 2C Buster Brown (Ansco): 29
No. 2C Cartridge Premo (EKC): 132
No. 2C Folding Autographic Brownie (EKC): 108
No. 2C Folding Cartridge Premo (EKC): 133
No. 2C Folding Scout (Seneca): 332
No. 2C Kewpie (Conley): 85
No. 2C Kodak Series III (EKC): 126
No. 2C Pocket Kodak (EKC): 131
No. 2C Pocket Kodak Special (EKC): 132
No. 2C Rexo Jr. (Burke & James): 64
No. 3 Ansco Junior: 30
No. 3 Autographic Kodak (EKC): 102
No. 3 Autographic Kodak Special: 103
No. 3 Brownie (EKC): 105
No. 3 Buckeye (American Camera Mfg.): 26
No. 3 Bull's-Eye (EKC): 111
No. 3 Buster Brown (Ansco): 29
No. 3 Cartridge Kodak (EKC): 113
No. 3 Combination Hawk-Eye (Blair): 55
No. 3 Eclipse (Horsman): 203
No. 3 Film Premo (EKC): 133
No. 3 Flush Back Kodak (EKC): 117
No. 3 Folding Ansco: 30
No. 3 Folding Brownie (EKC): 107
No. 3 Folding Buster Brown (Ansco): 29
No. 3 Folding Hawk-Eye (Blair): 55-56
No. 3 Folding Hawk-Eye (EKC): 122
No. 3 Folding Hawk-Eye Special (EKC): 122
No. 3 Folding Kodet (EKC): 127
No. 3 Folding Pocket Kodak (EKC): 120
No. 3 Folding Pocket Kodak, Deluxe: 121
No. 3 Folding Scout (Seneca): 332
No. 3 Goodwin (Ansco): 30
No. 3 Kewpie (Conley): 85
No. 3 Kodak (EKC): 101
No. 3 Kodak Jr. (EKC): 101
No. 3 Kodak Series III (EKC): 126
No. 3 Pocket Kodak Special (EKC): 132
No. 3 Premo Junior (EKC): 133
No. 3 Rexo (Burke & James): 64
No. 3 Rexo Jr. (Burke & James): 64
No. 3 Special Kodak (EKC): 146
No. 3 Weno Hawk-Eye (Blair): 57
No. 3 Zenith Kodak (EKC): 151
No. 3A Ansco Junior: 30
No. 3A Autographic Kodak (EKC): 102
No. 3A Autographic Kodak Junior: 102
No. 3A Autographic Kodak Special: 103
No. 3A Folding Ansco: 30
No. 3A Folding Autographic Brownie (EKC): 108
No. 3A Folding Brownie (EKC): 107
No. 3A Folding Buster Brown (Ansco): 29

No. 3A Folding Cartridge Hawk-Eye (EKC): 122
No. 3A Folding Cartridge Premo (EKC): 133
No. 3A Folding Hawk-Eye (EKC): 122
No. 3A Folding Ingento (Burke & James): 64
No. 3A Folding Pocket Kodak (EKC): 121
No. 3A Folding Scout (Seneca): 332
No. 3A Ingento Jr. (Burke & James): 64
No. 3A Kewpie (Conley): 85
No. 3A Kodak Series II (EKC): 126
No. 3A Kodak Series III (EKC): 126
No. 3A Panoram Kodak (EKC): 129
No. 3A Pocket Kodak (EKC): 131
No. 3A Rexo (Burke & James): 64
No. 3A Signal Corps Model K-3 (EKC): 103
No. 3A Special Kodak (EKC): 146
No. 3B Quick Focus Kodak (EKC): 136
No. 4 Autographic Kodak (EKC): 102
No. 4 Bull's-Eye (EKC): 111
No. 4 Bull's-Eye Special (EKC): 112
No. 4 Bullet (EKC): 112
No. 4 Bullet Special (EKC): 112
No. 4 Cartridge Kodak (EKC): 113
No. 4 Eureka (EKC): 117
No. 4 Folding Ansco: 30
No. 4 Folding Hawk-Eye (Blair): 56
No. 4 Folding Hawk-Eye (EKC): 122
No. 4 Folding Kodak (EKC): 118
No. 4 Folding Kodet (EKC): 127
No. 4 Folding Kodet Junior (EKC): 127
No. 4 Folding Kodet Special (EKC): 127
No. 4 Folding Pocket Kodak (EKC): 121
No. 4 Folding Weno Hawk-Eye (Blair): 55
No. 4 Kodak (EKC): 101
No. 4 Kodak Jr. (EKC): 101
No. 4 Kodet (EKC): 127
No. 4 Panoram Kodak (EKC): 129
No. 4 Premo Junior (EKC): 133
No. 4 Screen Focus Kodak (EKC): 143
No. 4 Speed Kodak (EKC): 146
No. 4 Weno Hawk-Eye (Blair): 57
No. 4 Weno Hawk-Eye (EKC): 124
No. 4A Autographic Kodak (EKC): 102
No. 4A Folding Kodak (EKC): 119
No. 5 Cartridge Kodak (EKC): 113
No. 5 Cirkut Camera (EKC): 114
No. 5 Folding Ansco: 30
No. 5 Folding Kodak (EKC): 118
No. 5 Folding Kodet (EKC): 127
No. 5 Folding Kodet Special (EKC): 127
No. 5 Weno Hawk-Eye (EKC): 124
No. 6 Cirkut Camera (EKC): 114
No. 6 Cirkut Outfit (EKC): 114
No. 6 Folding Ansco: 30
No. 6 Folding Kodak (EKC): 118
No. 6 Weno Hawk-eye (Blair): 57
No. 7 Folding Ansco: 30
No. 7 Weno Hawk-Eye (EKC): 124
No. 7 Weno Hawk-eye (Blair): 57
No. 8 Cirkut Outfit (EKC): 114
No. 8 Folding Buckeye (American Camera Mfg.): 25
No. 9 Ansco Model B: 30
No. 10 Ansco: 30

O.P.L. Focaflex: 293
OPTIKOTECHNA: 293
Optikotechna Spektaretta: 293
Optima (Agfa): 21
Optima Reflex (Agfa): 21
Optimus Camera Deluxe (Perken): 298
Optimus Detective (Perken): 298
Ordinary Kodak (EKC): 128-129
Orinox Binocular Camera (Asia American
 Industries): 43
Orion box camera: 294
Orion Camera, Model Simplicite: 294
ORION WERK: 294
Orion Rio folding plate cameras: 294
Orion Rio Tropical: 294
Orix (Pentacon): 296
Orix (Zeiss): 398
ORNAMENTAL (Non-Camera): 434-435
Ortho Jumelle Duplex (Joux): 218
O.T.A.G.: 294
O.T.A.G. Amourette: 294
O.T.A.G. Lutin: 294
OTTEWILL: 294
Ottewill Sliding-box camera: 294
OTTICO MECCANICA ITALIANA (OMI):
 293
OWLA: 294
Owla Stereo: 294
Oxford Minicam (Shaw): 334
Pacemaker Crown Graphic (Graflex): 190
Pacemaker Speed Graphic (Graflex): 191
Padie (Laack): 234
Paff (Ihagee): 215
Pajtas (Gamma): 175
Palko (Cruver-Peters): 90-91
Palmer (Rocket): 320
PALMER & LONGKING: 294
Palmer & Longking Lewis-style
 Daguerreotype: 294
Palmos Klapp-Stereo (Ica): 211
Palmos-O (Zeiss): 398
Panax: 294
Panda (Ansco): 32
Panomatic 126 (Non-Camera): 434
PANON CAMERA CO. LTD.: 294
Panon Wide Angle Camera: 294
Panon Widelux: 294
Panoram 120 (Burke & James): 64
Panoram Kodak (EKC): 129
Panoramic camera (Turret): 354
Panta (Rodehueser): 320
PAPIGNY: 294
Papigny Jumelle Stereo: 294
Paramat (Agfa): 21
Parat (Agfa): 21
Parcel Detective (Marion): 259
PARIS: 294
Paris GAP Box: 294
PARK: 294
Park Tailboard camera: 294
PARKER PEN CO.: 294-295
Parker: 294-295
Parva (San Giorgio): 323
Parvo Interview (Debrie): 412
Parvola (Ihagee): 215
Pascal (Japy): 217
Passe-Partout (Hanau): 196

Patent camera (Rouch): 322
Patent Camera Box (Bolles & Smith): 58
Patent Etui (K.W.): 231
Patent Klapp Reflex (Ihagee): 215-216
Patent Reflex Hand camera (Reflex
 Camera Co.): 311
Patent Stamp Camera (Hyatt): 208
Patent Three-Colour Separation Camera
 (Butler): 68
PATHE FRERES (Movie): 421-422
PATHE S.A. (Movie): 421-422
Pathe 28mm: 421
Pathe 35mm: 421
Pathe Baby: 421
Pathe Baby with Camo motor: 422
Pathe Baby with motor: 422
Pathe Mondial B: 422
Pathe Motocamera: 421
Pathe Motocamera 16: 421
Pathe Motocamera Luxe: 421
Pathe National I: 422
Pathe National II: 422
Pathfinder (Polaroid 110, 110A): 306
Pax (Braun): 62
Pax (Yamato): 380
Pax Golden View (Yamato): 380
Paxette (Braun): 62
Paxina (Braun): 63
PD-16 (Agfa): 21
PDQ (Anthony): 37
PDQ CAMERA CO.: 295
PDQ Mandel Automatic PDQ: 295
PDQ Photo Button Camera: 295
PDQ Street Camera (Chicago Ferrotype
 Co.): 80-81
Peace: 295
Peace (reflex): 295
Peace Baby Flex: 295
Peace-Gas Camera-Lighter
 (Non-Camera): 429
Pearl (Baby) (Konishiroku): 226
Pearl II (Konishiroku): 226
Pearlette (Konishiroku): 226
PEARSALL: 295
Pearsall Compact: 295
PECK: 295
Peck Ferrotype: 295
Peck Wet-plate camera: 295
Peckham Wray (Wray): 379
Pecto (Columbia Optical): 84
Peer 100 (EKC): 129
Peerflekta (Welta): 372
Peerless (Rochester Optical): 318
Peerless Box camera: 295
PEERLESS MFG. CO.: 295
Peggy I (Krauss): 228
Peggy II (Krauss): 228
PELLET SHOOTERS (Non-Camera): 431
Pellix (Canon): 76
Pen (Olympus): 293
Pen D (Olympus): 293
Pen F (Olympus): 293
Pen FT (Olympus): 293
PENCIL SHARPENER (Non-Camera): 435
Penny Picture camera (Gennert): 176
PENROSE: 295
Penrose Studio camera: 295

Photo Master: 300
Photo-Master (Herold): 200
Photo-Master Twin 620: 300
PHOTO MATERIALS CO.: 300
Photo Materials Trokonet: 300
PHOTO-PORST: 300
Photo-Porst Hapo: 300
Photo Postcard Cameras (Daydark): 93
Photo-Revolver (Krauss): 228
Photo Revolver de Poche (Enjalbert): 154
Photo-Second Hand Auction: ADV
PHOTO SEE CORP.: 300
Photo-See: 300
Photo Sniper (Zenit): 405
Photo-Ticket No. 2 (Turillon): 354
Photo Vanity (Ansco): 32
Photoette #115 (B & R Mfg.): 44
Photographic Mail Auction: ADV
Photographic Rifle (Thornton-Pickard):
  347
Photography on Bald Mountain: ADV
Photolet: 300
Photopal (Scott-Atwater): 325
Photorecord (Graflex): 193
Photoret Watch Camera (Magic
  Introduction): 256
Photoscopic: 301
Photosphere (Compagnie Francaise): 84
Photrix Quick B (Witt): 378
Physio-Pocket (Bloch): 58
Physiographe (Bloch): 58
Pic: 301
Piccochic (Balda): 46
Piccolette (Contessa): 88
Piccolette (Zeiss): 398-399
Piccolette Camera Bnak (Non-Camera):
  427
Piccolette Luxus (Contessa): 88
Piccolette-Luxus (Zeiss): 399
Pickwick (Monarch): 278
Pickwik (Galter): 175
Picny (Miyakawa): 277
Picture Master: 301
Picture-Quick (Non-Camera): 439
Pierrette (Balda): 46
Pigeon (Shinano): 334-335
Pigeon III (Shinano): 335
Pigeon 35 (Tomioka): 350
Pigeonflex (Yashina): 382
PIGGOTT: 301
Piggott Sliding-box wet-plate camera: 301
PIGNONS AG: 301-303
Pignons Alpa (I): 302
Pignons Alpa 4: 302
Pignons Alpa 4b: 302
Pignons Alpa 5: 302
Pignons Alpa 5b: 302
Pignons Alpa 6: 302
Pignons Alpa 6b: 302
Pignons Alpa 6c: 302
Pignons Alpa 7: 302
Pignons Alpa 7b: 302
Pignons Alpa 7s: 302
Pignons Alpa 8: 302
Pignons Alpa 8b: 302
Pignons Alpa 9d: 302
Pignons Alpa 9f: 302

Pignons Alpa 10d: 302
Pignons Alpa 10f: 303
Pignons Alpa 10s: 303
Pignons Alpa 11e: 302
Pignons Alpa 11el: 303
Pignons Alpa 11fs: 303
Pignons Alpa 11si: 303
Pignons Alpa 11z: 303
Pignons Alpa Prisma Reflex (III): 302
Pignons Alpa Reflex (II): 302
Pignons Bolca (Standard): 302
Pignons Bolca I: 302
Pilot 6 (K.W.): 231
Pilot Reflex (K.W.): 232
Pilot Super (K.W.): 232
Pin-Hole Camera (EKC): 130
Pin-Zip 126 (Time Field): 348
Pinhole camera (Mackenstein): 256
Pioneer: 303
Pioneer (Agfa): 21
Pioneer (Ansco): 32
PIPON: 303
Pipon Magazine camera: 303
Pipon Self-Worker: 303
Pistol camera (Mamiya): 257-258
Pistol camera (Williamson): 375-376
Pistolgraphe (Skaife): 337
Pixie (Whittaker): 375
Pixie Custom (Whittaker): 375
Pixie Slip-On (Baudinet): 47
Plan Primar (Bentzin): 51
PLANOVISTA SEEING CAMERA LTD.:
  303
Planovista (Bentzin): 51
PLANTERS (Non-Camera): 435
Plaskop (Ica): 211
Plaskop (Zeiss): 399
PLASMAT GmbH: 303
Plasmat Roland: 303
PLASTICS DEVELOPMENT CORP.: 303
Plastics Development Snapshooter: 303
Plastoscop (Krugener): 229
Plate (Non-Camera Kodak plate): 433
Plate camera (American Optical): 27
Plate cameras (Agfa): 21
PLAUBEL & CO.: 303-305
Plaubel Baby Makina: 303
Plaubel Folding-bed plate cameras: 303
Plaubel Makina: 303-304
Plaubel Makina II: 304
Plaubel Makina IIa: 304
Plaubel Makina IIS: 304
Plaubel Makina III: 304
Plaubel Makinette: 304
Plaubel Roll-Op: 304-305
Plaubel Stereo Makina: 305
Plaubel Veriwide 100: 305
Plavic: 305
Plenax (Agfa): 21
Plik (Industries Brazileira): 216-217
POCK: 305
Pock Detective camera: 305
Pocket (Yen-Kame): 382
Pocket Camera (Hall): 196
Pocket Camera-Viewer (Non-Camera):
  440
Pocket Coin Bank (Non-Camera): 427

Premoette (EKC): 135
Premoette Junior (EKC): 135
Premoette Senior (EKC): 135
Premoette Special (EKC): 135
Premograph (EKC): 135-136
Premograph (Rochester Optical): 319
Premograph No. 2 (EKC): 136
Press (Burke & James): 64
Press camera (Goldmann): 181
Press Flash (Spartus): 339
Press Graflex: 186
Press King (B & W Mfg.): 44
Press Van: 308
Press/View (Burke & James): 65
Pressman (Busch): 65
Presto (Magic Introduction): 257
PRESWITCH MFG. CO. (Movie): 422
Preswitch 35mm: 422
Primar (Bentzin): 51
Primar Folding Reflex (Bentzin): 51
Primar Reflex (Bentzin): 51
Primarette (Bentzin): 51
Primarflex (Bentzin): 51
Primo Jr. (Tokyo Kogaku): 350
Prince: 308
Prince Flex (Non-Camera): 434
Princess (Closter): 83
Princess May: 308
PRINTEX PRODUCTS: 308
Printex: 308
PRINTING FRAMES (Non-Camera): 435-436
Prismac (Deloye): 96
Prismotype (Fallowfield): 165
Pro (Beaurline): 47
Pro Camera: 308
Prominent (6x9) (Voigtlander): 366
Prominent (35mm) (Voigtlander): 366
Prominent II (Voigtlander): 366
Proud Chrome Six III: 308
Puck (Ising): 217
Puck Special (Thornton-Pickard): 347
Pullman Detective (Levi): 250
Pupille (EKC): 136
Pupille (Nagel): 282
Purma Plus (Hunter): 206
Purma Special (Hunter): 206-207
PUTNAM: 308
Putnam Marvel: 308
PUZZLES & GAMES (Non-Camera): 436
Pygmee (Carmen): 77
PYNE: 308
Pyne Stereoscopic Camera: 308
Q.P.: 309
Q.R.S. Kamra: 309
Q.R.S.-DeVRY CORP.: 309
Quad (Close & Cone): 83
Quick Focus Kodak (EKC): 136
Quigley Photographic Services: ADV
Raaco: 309
Radial Hand camera (Marion): 259
RADIOS (Non-Camera): 436
Radix: 309
Radix (Bilora): 54
Rainbow Hawk-Eye (EKC): 123
Rajar No. 6 (APeM): 37
Rakso: 309

Raleigh: 309
Rambler Flash Camera (Imperial): 216
Ramera (Kowa): 227
Ranca (EKC): 136
Ranca (Nagel): 282
Rapide (Coronet): 89
Rapide (Yashica): 381
Rapitake (La Rose): 234
RAY CAMERA CO.: 309
Ray Box camera: 309
Ray Jr.: 309
Ray No. 1: 309
Ray No. 2: 309
Ray No. 4: 309
Rayelle: 309
Rayflex (Fototechnica): 170
Raylo Color Camera (American Raylo Corp.): 27
R.B. Graflex Junior: 186-187
R.B. Graflex Series B: 187
R.B. Graflex Series C: 187
R.B. Graflex Series D: 187
R.B. Super D Graflex: 187
R.B. Tele Graflex: 188
Ready Ranger Tele-photo Camera Gun (Aurora): 43
Readyflash (Ansco): 32
Readyset (Ansco): 32
Readyset Royal (Ansco): 32
Readyset Traveler (Ansco): 32
Real Camera: 310
Realist 35 (White): 374
Realist 45 (White): 374
Recomar (Nagel): 282
Recomar 18 (EKC): 136
Recomar 33 (EKC): 136
Record (Ica): 211
Record Camera: 310
Record Stereo Camera (Huttig): 207
RECTAFLEX: 310
Rectaflex Junior: 310
Rectaflex Rotor: 310
Rectaflex Standard: 310
Recto (Contessa): 88
REDDING: 310
Redding's Patent Luzo: 310
Rediflex (Ansco): 32
Reflekta (Welta): 372
Reflex (Compco): 85
Reflex (Ernemann): 161
Reflex (Houghton Ensign): 204
Reflex (Ica): 211
Reflex (Imperial): 216
Reflex (Irwin): 217
Reflex (Murer): 281
Reflex I (Pho-Tak): 299
Reflex 66: 310
Reflex-Box (K.W.): 233-234
REFLEX CAMERA CO.: 310-311
Reflex Camera Co. Focal plane postcard camera: 311
Reflex Camera Co. Junior Reflex: 310
Reflex Camera Co. Patent Reflex Hand camera: 311
Reflex Camera Co. Reflex camera: 311
Reflex Carbine (Butcher): 67
Reflex Korelle (Kochmann): 224

490

Sida (Kaftanski): 219
Sida Extra (Kaftanski): 219
Sidax (Kaftanski): 219
SIEMENS & HALSKE (Movie): 422
Siemens B: 422
Siemens C: 422
Siemens C II: 422
Siemens F: 422
Sigma 3D Stereo Systems: ADV
Signal Corps Combat Camera (Simmon): 336
Signet 30 (EKC): 144
Signet 35 (EKC): 144
Signet 35 (Signal Corp.) (EKC): 145
Signet 40 (EKC): 144
Signet 50 (EKC): 144
Signet 80 (EKC): 144
SIGRISTE: 336
Sigriste Stereo: 336
Sil-Bear: 336
Silar (Meyer): 262
Silette (Agfa): 22
Silver King (Camera Man): 69
Silver Pocket Radio (Non-Camera): 436
SIMDA: 336
Simda Panorascope Stereo: 336
SIMMON BROTHERS, INC.: 336
Simmon Omega 120: 336
Simmon Signal Corps Combat Camera: 336
SIMONS: 336
Simons Sico: 336
Simplex (112/7) (Zeiss): 399
Simplex (511/2) (Zeiss): 399
Simplex Ernoflex (Ernemann): 161
Simplex Magazine (Krugener): 229
Simplex Pockette (International Projector): 418
Simplex Snapper (Lava-Simplex): 237
Simplex-Ernoflex (Zeiss): 399
SIMPRO CORP. of AMERICA: 336
SIMPRO INTERNATIONAL LTD.: 337
Simpro Slip-on: 337
Simpro-X: 336
SINCLAIR: 337
Sinclair Traveller Una: 337
Sinclair Tropical Una: 337
Sinclair Una: 337
Sinclair Una Cameo: 337
Sinclair Una Deluxe: 337
SINEMAT MOTION PICTURE CO.: 422
Sinemat Duplex 17½mm: 422-423
Sing 88: 337
Single lens stereo (Baird): 44
Single lens stereo (Derogy): 97
Single-lens Stereo (Moorse): 279
Sinnox (Jougla): 218
Sinox (Lumiere): 255
SIRCHIE FINGER PRINT LABORATORIES INC.: 337
Sirchie Finger Print Camera: 337
Sirene (Ica): 211
Sirene (Zeiss): 399
SIRIO: 337
Sirio Elettra I: 337
Sirio Elettra II: 337
SITACON CO. LTD.: 337

Sitacon ST-3: 337
Six-Three Kodak No. 1A (EKC): 145
Six-Three Kodak No. 3 (EKC): 145
Six-Three Kodak No. 3A (EKC): 145
Six-16 Brownie (EKC): 109
Six-16 Brownie Junior (EKC): 109
Six-16 Brownie Special (EKC): 109
Six-16 Folding Hawk-Eye (EKC): 122
Six-16 Target Hawk-Eye (EKC): 123
Six-20 Boy Scout Brownie (EKC): 104
Six-20 Brownie (EKC): 109
Six-20 Brownie Junior (EKC): 109
Six-20 Brownie Special (EKC): 109
Six-20 Bull's-Eye Brownie (EKC): 109
Six-20 Flash Brownie (EKC): 109
Six-20 Folding Hawk-Eye (EKC): 122
Six-20 Target Hawk-Eye (EKC): 123
Six-Twenty (Imperial): 216
Six-Twenty Reflex (Imperial): 216
SKAIFE: 337
Skaife Pistolgraphe: 337
Sky (Minolta): 268
Sky Scraper Camera (Folmer & Schwing): 168
Skylard (Mansfield): 258
SKYVIEW CAMERA CO.: 337
Skyview Aerial: 337
Sliding-box Daguerreotype (Kranz): 227
Sliding Box Wet Plate Camera (Dallmeyer): 92
Sliding-box wet-plate camera (Piggott): 301
Slip-on (Simpro): 337
Smena (Mashpriborintorg): 260
Smena Symbol (Mashpriborintorg): 260
SMITH: 337
Smith Detective Camera: 337
Smith Multiplying Camera: 337
S.M.R. (Non-Camera): 429
Smurf Musical Toy Camera (Non-Camera): 434
Snap 16: 337
Snap No. 2 (Conley): 86
Snap-Shot Secret Gun CH-337 (Non-Camera): 431
Snappa (Rochester Optical): 319
Snappy (Konishiroku): 226
Snapshooter (Plastics Development): 303
Snapshot (Dallmeyer): 92
Snapshot (La Crosse): 234
Snoop The Astronaut (Non-Camera): 439
Snoopy (Eiko): 153
Snoopy Counting Camera (Non-Camera): 440
Snoopy-Matic (Helm): 199
SOAP (Non-Camera): 437
SOCIETA CONSTRUZIONI-ARTICOLI-TECHNICI (S.C.A.T.): 325
SOCIETA GAMMA (Gamma): 175
SOCIETE d'APPAREILS MECANIQUES IDAM (Idam): 213
SOCIETE DE PHOTOGRAPHIE ET D'OPTIQUE (S.P.O.): 340-341
Society (Collins): 84
SOCIETY OF CINEMA PLATES (Movie): 423
Society of Cinema Olikos: 423

STEINHEIL: 341
Steinheil Casca I: 341
Steinheil Casca II: 341
Steinheil Detective camera: 341
Steinheil Multo-Nettel: 341
Steinheil Tropical camera: 341
Steky (Riken): 315
Stella Jumelle (Roussel): 322
Stellar Flash Camera: 342
Stellar: 341
Stellarflex: 342
Steno-Jumelle (Joux): 218
Steno-Jumelle Stereo (Joux): 218
Stere-all (Universal): 358
Stereax (Contessa): 88
Stereflektoskop (Voigtlander): 366
Sterelux (Lumiere): 255
Stereo (Murer): 281
Stereo (Scovill): 326
Stereo 33 (Revere): 312
Stereo 35 (Meopta): 261-262
Stereo Auto Graflex: 188
Stereo Bob (Ernemann Bob V Stereo): 155
Stereo Box (Murer): 281
Stereo Camera (Chadwick): 80
Stereo camera (Hare): 197
Stereo camera (Ihagee): 216
Stereo Camera (Negretti): 284
Stereo Camera (Ross): 321
Stereo Cameras Wanted: ADV
STEREO CORP.: 342
Stereo Corp. Contura: 342
Stereo Ernoflex (Ernemann): 161
Stereo-Ernoflex (Zeiss): 399
Stereo Graflex: 188
Stereo Graphic (Wray): 379
Stereo Graphic (35mm) (Graflex): 191
Stereo Hawk-Eye (Blair): 57
Stereo Hawk-Eye (EKC): 123
Stereo Hit (Tougodo): 351
Stereo Ideal (Ica): 212
Stereo Ideal (650) (Zeiss): 399
Stereo Ideal (651) (Zeiss): 399
Stereo Instantograph (Lancaster): 236
Stereo Jumelle (Bellieni): 50
Stereo Jumelle (Mackenstein): 256
Stereo Kern SS (Kern): 221
Stereo Kodak (EKC): 146-147
Stereo Kodak Model 1 (EKC): 147
Stereo Makina (Plaubel): 305
Stereo Mikroma (Meopta): 261
Stereo Mikroma (I, II (Meopta): 261
Stereo Muro (Suter): 344
Stereo Nettel (Zeiss): 399
Stereo Nettel, Tropical (Zeiss): 399
Stereo Palmos (Zeiss): 399-400
Stereo Palmos (Zeiss Minimum Palmos
  Stereo): 397
Stereo Panorama (Linhof): 251
Stereo Panoramique (Leroy): 249
Stereo Photo Binocle (Goerz): 180
Stereo Photosphere (Compagnie
  Francaise): 84
Stereo Physiographe (Bloch): 58
Stereo Pocket (Tiranty): 349
Stereo Puck (Thornton-Pickard): 348
Stereo Realist (White): 374-375

Stereo Realist Custom 1050 (White): 375
Stereo Realist Macro (White): 375
Stereo Realist Viewer (White): 375
Stereo Reflex (Bentzin): 51
Stereo Reflex (Ernemann): 161-162
Stereo Reflex (Murer): 281
Stereo Reicka (Ica): 212
Stereo Rokuwa (Rokuwa): 320
Stereo Simplex (Ernemann): 162
Stereo Simplex Ernoflex (Ernemann): 162
Stereo-Simplex-Ernoflex (Zeiss): 399
Stereo Solograph (Anthony): 37
Stereo Solograph (Scovill): 326
Stereo Tenax (Goerz): 181
Stereo Toska (Ica): 212
Stereo Tourist (McBean): 260
Stereo View (Seneca): 332
Stereo Weno (Blair): 57
Stereo Wet Plate camera (Dallmeyer): 92
Stereo wet-plate camera (Koch): 223
Stereo Wet-plate cameras (Stock): 342
STEREOCRAFTERS: 342
Stereocrafters Videon: 342
Stereocrafters Videon II: 342
Stereocycle (Bazin & Leroy): 47
Stereofix (Ica): 212
Stereolette (Butcher): 67
Stereolette (Huttig): 207
Stereolette (Ica): 212
Stereolette-Cupido (Ica): 212
Stereolette-Cupido (Zeiss): 400
Stereophot (Secam): 329-330
Stereophotoskop (Voigtlander): 366
Stereoplast (Krauss): 228
Stereoscop-Camera (Ernemann): 162
Stereoscopic Binocular Camera (Watson):
  371
Stereoscopic Camera (Pyne): 308
Stereoscopic Graphic (Graflex): 192
Stereoscopic Montauk (Gennert): 177
Stereoscopic Reflex (Frennet): 174
Sterling: 342
Steroco (Contessa): 88
Steroco (Zeiss): 400
STEVEN MFG. CO. (Non-Camera): 440
Stewart Radio-Light-Mirror (Non-Camera):
  436
STEWART-WARNER (Movie): 423
Stewart-Warner Companion 8 Model
  532B: 423
Stewart-Warner Hollywood Model 531-B:
  423
STIRN: 342
Stirn Concealed Vest Camera Nos. 1,2:
  342
Stirn Magazine camera: 342
STOCK: 342
Stock Stereo Wet-plate cameras: 342
STOECKIG: 342-343
Stoeckig Union: 342-343
Street Camera (Benson): 51
Studio camera (Gilles-Faller): 177
Stylex (Herbert George): 200
Stylophot Deluxe (Secam): 320
Stylophot Standard (Secam): 329
Subminiature Cameras Wanted: ADV
Suevia (Zeiss): 400

Zeiss Ikonette: 395
Zeiss Ikonette 35: 395
Zeiss Ikonta: 395
Zeiss Ikonta 35: 396
Zeiss Ikonta A: 395
Zeiss Ikonta B: 395-396
Zeiss Ikonta C: 396
Zeiss Ikonta D: 396
Zeiss Juwel: 396
Zeiss Kinamo S10: 426
Zeiss Kolibri: 396
Zeiss Kosmopolit: 396
Zeiss Liliput: 396
Zeiss Lloyd: 396
Zeiss Magnar-Kamera: 397
Zeiss Maixmar: 397
Zeiss Maximar A: 397
Zeiss Maximar B: 397
Zeiss Minimum Palmos Stereo: 397
Zeiss Miroflex A: 397
Zeiss Miroflex B: 397
Zeiss Movikon 8: 426
Zeiss Movikon 16: 426
Zeiss Nettar: 397
Zeiss Nettax (513/16): 398
Zeiss Nettax (538/24): 398
Zeiss Nettel: 398
Zeiss Nettel, Tropen: 398
Zeiss Nixe: 398
Zeiss No Name Contax: 389
Zeiss Onito: 398
Zeiss Orix: 398
Zeiss Palmos-O: 398
Zeiss Perfekt: 398
Zeiss Piccolette: 398-399
Zeiss Piccolette-Luxus: 399
Zeiss Plaskop: 399
Zeiss Polyskop: 399
Zeiss RF Wanted: ADV
Zeiss Simplex (112/7): 399
Zeiss Simplex (511/2): 399
Zeiss Simplex-Ernoflex: 399
Zeiss Sirene: 399
Zeiss Sonnet: 399
Zeiss Stereo-Ernoflex: 399
Zeiss Stereo Ideal: 399
Zeiss Stereo Nettel: 399
Zeiss Stereo Nettel, Tropical: 399
Zeiss Stereo Palmos: 399-400
Zeiss Stereo-Simplex-Ernoflex: 399
Zeiss Stereolette-Cupido: 400
Zeiss Steroco: 400
Zeiss Suevia: 400
Zeiss Super Ikomat: 400
Zeiss Super Ikonta A: 400
Zeiss Super Ikonta B: 400-401
Zeiss Super Ikonta BX: 401
Zeiss Super Ikonta C: 401-402
Zeiss Super Ikonta D: 402
Zeiss Super Ikonta III: 401
Zeiss Super Ikonta IV: 401
Zeiss Super Nettel: 402
Zeiss Super Nettel II: 402-403
Zeiss Symbolica: 403
Zeiss Taxo: 403
Zeiss Taxona: 403
Zeiss Tenax: 403

Zeiss Tenax I: 403
Zeiss Tenax II: 403
Zeiss Tenax Automatic: 403
Zeiss Tengoflex: 403-404
Zeiss Tessco: 404
Zeiss Trona: 404
Zeiss Tropen Adoro: 404
Zeiss Tropica: 404
Zeiss Unette: 404
Zeiss Universal Juwel: 396
Zeiss Victrix: 404
Zeiss Volta: 405
Zen 99 (Kowa): 227
ZENIT: 405
Zenit: 405
Zenit 3: 405
Zenit 3M: 405
Zenit B: 405
Zenit Photo Sniper: 405
Zenith (Universal): 359
ZENITH CAMERA CORP.: 405
Zenith Comet: 405
Zenith Comet Flash: 405
Zenith Edelweiss: 405
ZENITH FILM CORP.: 405
Zenith Kodak (EKC): 151
Zenith Sharpshooter: 405
Zenith Winpro 35, Synchro Flash: 405
Zenobia (Daiichi): 92
Zenobiaflex (Daiichi): 92
ZION: 405
Zion Pocket Z: 405
ZIX CO. (Movie): 426
Zix: 426
Zodel (Wallace): 370
Zodiac: 405
ZORKI: 405
Zorki 2: 405
Zorki 2C: 405
Zorki 3: 405
Zorki 4: 405
Zorki 5: 405
Zorki C: 405
ZUIKO OPTICAL CO.: 405
Zuiko Honor: 405
ZULAUF: 405
Zulauf Bebe: 405
Zwei-Verschluss-Camera, Model VI
   (Ernemann): 163
Zwei-Verschluss-Camera, Model VI
   (stereo) (Ernemann): 163

Key to Abbreviations / Abkürzungsverzeichnis / Table des Abbréviations

	Key to Abbreviations	Abkürzungsverzeichnis	Table des Abbréviations
An., anast	anastigmat	anastigmat	anastigmat
B	bulb (short time exposeres)	(kurze Zeitaufnahme)	(pose en un temps)
B & I	bulb & instant	Zeit & Momentverschluss	obturateur pose & inst.
B&L	Bausch & Lomb	Bausch & Lomb	Bausch & Lomb
BB	ball bearing (shutter)	Kugellager (Verschl.)	roulement à billes (obturat.)
BIM	built-in meter	eingebauter Belichtungs- messer	celule incorporée
CRF	coupled rangefinder	gekoppelter Entfernungs- messer	télémètre couplé
DEB	double extension bellows	doppelter Balgenauszug	double tirage du soufflet
ext.	extension	Auszug	tirage
GGB	ground glass back	Mattscheibenrückteil	corps arrière à verre dépoli
RF	rangefinder	Entfernungsmesser	télémètre
sh.	shutter	Verschluss	obturateur
SLR	single lens reflex	einaügige Spiegelreflex	appareil reflex a un objectif
T,B,I	Time, bulb, instant	Zeit & Momentverschl.	pose & instantanée
TLR	twin lens reflex	zweiaügige Spiegelreflex	Appareil reflex a deux obj.

IMPORTANT NOTICE !

The following four pages are for your personal notes and observations. We urge all readers to use this space to make corrections or additions which will make your guide better or easier to use. Then we ask that you pass your best notes along to us and we will use them to improve the next edition for you and your fellows collectors. THANKS!

NOTES

NOTES

NOTES

METRIC/ENGLISH EQUIVALENTS of camera image sizes

The sizes in this table are not always exact measurements, but are the equivalents used in popular parlance among collectors.

METRIC	ENGLISH	COMMENTS
5x8mm		Echo 8
8x11mm		Minox
10x14mm		many 16mm subminiatures
13x17mm		110 cassette
14x14mm		many 16mm subminiatures
16x22mm	⅝x⅞"	Expo watch camera
18x24mm	¾x15/16"	single frame 35mm
18x28mm	¾x1⅛"	Expo police camera
2x3cm	¾x1⅛"	
22x31mm	¾x1¼"	
22x33mm	⅞x1¼"	
22x35mm	⅞x1⅜"	
24x24mm	1x1"	35mm square format
24x30mm	15/16x1-3/16"	many 35mm stereo cameras
24x36mm	1x1⅜"	35mm standard format
25mm dia.	1" round	
28x28mm	1⅛x1⅛"	126 cassette
28x40mm	1⅛x1½"	828 full frame, 8 exp.
3x4cm	1-3/16x1½"	127 half frame, 16 exp.
32x45mm	1¼x1¾"	Cartridge Premo #00
35x45mm	1⅜x1¾"	
4x4cm	1⅝x1⅝"	127 square format, 12 exp.
4x5cm	1½x2"	
4x6cm	1½x2¼"	
4x6.5cm	1⅝x2½"	127 full frame, 8 exp.
4.5x6cm	1¾x2¼"	120/620 half frame, 16 exp.
4.5x6cm	1¾x2-5/16"	
4.5x6cm	1¾x2⅜"	Premo Jr. #0
4.5x6.5cm	1¾x2½"	
4.5x10.7cm	1¾x4¼"	popular stereo plate size
5x5cm	2x2"	
5x6.5cm	2x2½"	
5x7.5cm	2x3"	Houghton Ensignette #2
5x8cm	2x3⅛"	
5.5x6.5cm	2-1/16x2½"	116/616 half frame, 16 exp.
6x6cm	2¼x2¼"	120/620 square format, 12 exp.
6x6.5cm	2¼x2½"	National Graflex, 10 exp on 120
6x7cm	2¼x2¾"	1/9 plate, "Ideal format": 10 exp. on 120 or 21 exp. on 220
6x8.5cm	2¼x3¼"	
6x9cm	2¼x3¼", 2¼x3½"	120/620 full frame, 8 exp.
6x13cm	2¼x5⅛"	common stereo plate size
6x17cm	2¼x6¾"	Baby Al Vista
6x18cm	2¼x7"	panoramic
6.5x6.5cm	2½x2½"	
6.5x7.5cm	2½x3"	
6.5x9cm	2½x3½"	
6.5x11cm	2½x4¼"	1A or 116/616 full frame
7x8.4cm	2¾x3¼"	1/6 plate, or "A" Daylight or Ordinary Kodak
71x93mm	2¾x3⅝"	Kodak instant film (68x91mm actual)
7.25x12.5cm	2⅞x4⅞"	2C or 130 film
7.5x10cm	3x4"	
8x8cm	3⅛x3-3/16"	each image of stereo pair
8x10.5cm	3¼x4¼"	¼ plate (popular approximation), lantern slide
8x14cm	3¼x5½"	3A or 122 film, postcard size

METRIC	ENGLISH	COMMENTS
8x16cm	3⅛x6¼"	stereo pair
8x26cm	3¼x10⅜	panoram
8x46cm	3¼x18"	panoram
8.2x10.7cm	3¼x4¼"	literal measurement (The approxmiation 8x10.5cm is usually used.)
8.5x14.5cm	3⅜x5¾"	stereo format
9x9cm	3½x3½"	
9x10cm	3½x4"	"B" Daylight or Ordinary Kodak
9x12cm	3½x4¾"	popular European plate size
9x13cm	3½x5"	
9x14cm	3½x5½"	
9x15cm	3½x6"	stereo format
9x16cm	3½x6¼"	stereo format
9x18cm	3½x7"	stereo format
9x23cm	3½x9"	Al Vista 3B
9x30cm	3½x12"	#4 Panoram Kodak
9.5x12cm	3¾x4¾"	
10x13cm	4x5"	common plate and film size
10x15cm	4x6"	sometimes used as a metric equivalent for 4x5"
10x25cm	4x10"	
10x30cm	4x12"	
11x11cm	4¼x4¼"	
11x16.5cm	4¼x6½"	half plate
11.5x14cm	4½x5½"	
11.5x21.5cm	4½x8½"	Stock stereo wet-plate
12x16.5cm	4¾x6½"	
12x17cm	4¾x6¾"	
13x18cm	5x7"	popular plate and film size
13x19cm	5x7½"	
13x20cm	5x8"	popular size before 1900
13x30cm	5x12"	
14x16.5cm	5½x6½"	2/3 plate
16.5x21.5cm	6½x8½"	full plate
18x24cm	7x9½"	
18x25cm	7x10"	
18x28cm	7x11"	
18x43cm	7x17"	"banquet" cameras
19x24cm	7½x9½"	
20x25cm	8x10"	
20x50cm	8x20"	"banquet" cameras
24x30cm	9½x12"	
25x30cm	10x12"	
28x35.5cm	11x14"	large studio size

KODAK & ANSCO FILM NUMBERS AND IMAGE SIZES

KODAK	ANSCO	INCHES	METRIC
101	8A	3½x3½	9x9cm
103	10A	4x5	10x13cm
105	5A	2¼x3¼	6x9cm
116	6A,6B	2½x4¼	6.5x11cm
117	3A	2¼x2¼	6x6cm
118	7A	3¼x4¼	8x10.5cm
120	4A	2¼x3¼	6x9cm
122	18A	3¼x5½	8x14cm
124	7C	3¼x4¼	8x10.5cm
125	18C	3¼x5½	8x14cm
127	2C	1⅝x2½	4x6.5cm
130	26A	2⅞x4⅞	7.25x12.5cm

DATING CAMERAS BY UNITED STATES PATENT NUMBERS

Patent dates can often be helpful in dating cameras, shutters or other accessories. One must be careful, however, not to conclude that the item was manufactured in the year the patent was issued. This is usually not the case. The patent date serves to indicate the year *after* which the item was made. Often the patents had been issued for five years or more before an item was produced bearing the patent number. Many products continued to carry the patent numbers for many years after the patent was issued. Thus a camera manufactured in 1930 could have a 1905 patent date.

The first numbered patents were issued in 1836, just before the advent of photography. Originally the law required that the patent date (but not the number) be put on the product. The present requirement to place the patent number on the item or its container began on April 1, 1927. Many earlier products, however, bore the patent number even though it was not required by law.

The following table lists the first patent number for the indicated year.

YEAR	NUMBER	YEAR	NUMBER	YEAR	NUMBER
1836	1	1887	355,291	1938	2,104,004
1837	110	1888	375,720	1939	2,142,080
1838	546	1889	395,305	1940	2,185,170
1839	1,061	1890	418,665	1941	2,227,418
1840	1,465	1891	443,987	1942	2,268,540
1841	1,923	1892	466,315	1943	2,307,007
1842	2,413	1893	488,976	1944	2,338,081
1843	2,901	1894	511,744	1945	2,366,154
1844	3,395	1895	531,619	1946	2,391,856
1845	3,873	1896	552,502	1947	2,413,675
1846	4,348	1897	574,369	1948	2,433,824
1847	4,914	1898	596,467	1949	2,457,797
1848	5,409	1899	616,871	1950	2,492,941
1849	5,993	1900	640,167	1951	2,536,016
1850	6,891	1901	664,827	1952	2,580,379
1851	7,865	1902	690,385	1953	2,624,046
1852	8,622	1903	717,521	1954	2,664,562
1853	9,512	1904	748,567	1955	2,698,434
1854	10,358	1905	778,834	1956	2,728,913
1855	12,117	1906	808,618	1957	2,775,762
1856	14,009	1907	839,799	1958	2,818,567
1857	16,324	1908	875,679	1959	2,866,973
1858	19,010	1909	908,436	1960	2,919,443
1859	22,477	1910	945,010	1961	2,966,681
1860	26,642	1911	980,178	1962	3,015,103
1861	31,005	1912	1,013,095	1963	3,070,801
1862	34,045	1913	1,049,326	1964	3,116,487
1863	37,266	1914	1,083,267	1965	3,163,865
1864	41,047	1915	1,123,212	1966	3,226,729
1865	45,085	1916	1,166,419	1967	3,295,143
1866	51,784	1917	1,210,389	1968	3,360,800
1867	60,658	1918	1,251,458	1969	3,419,907
1868	72,959	1919	1,290,027	1970	3,487,470
1869	85,503	1920	1,326,899	1971	3,551,909
1870	98,460	1921	1,364,063	1972	3,631,539
1871	110,617	1922	1,401,948	1973	3,707,729
1872	122,304	1923	1,440,362	1974	3,781,914
1873	134,504	1924	1,478,996	1975	3,858,241
1874	146,120	1925	1,521,590	1976	3,930,271
1875	158,350	1926	1,568,040	1977	4,000,520
1876	171,641	1927	1,612,790	1978	4,065,812
1877	158,813	1928	1,654,521	1979	4,131,952
1878	198,733	1929	1,696,897	1980	4,180,167
1879	211,078	1930	1,742,181	1981	4,242,757
1880	223,211	1931	1,787,424	1982	4,308,622
1881	236,137	1932	1,839,190	1983	4,366,579
1882	251,685	1933	1,892,663	1984	4,423,523
1883	269,820	1934	1,941,449	1985	4,490,855
1884	291,016	1935	1,985,878		
1885	310,163	1936	2,026,516		
1886	333,494	1937	2,066,309		

DATING CAMERAS BY SHUTTER TYPE

Dating cameras by shutter type is a rather unreliable guide to dating, since shutters and lenses are easily interchanged, and photographers over the years have often made these changes. However, if the shutter has been determined to be original equipment, then the following dates serve the purpose of estimating a date AFTER WHICH the camera would have been made. Shutters are listed by manufacturer, either in alphabetical order by shutter name, or chronologically.

We are indebted to Dr. Rudolf Kingslake for the research on these shutters, particularly the Bausch & Lomb, Kodak, and Wollensak brands.

BAUSCH & LOMB (Rochester, NY)
Bausch & Lomb began as an optical company, at first making eyeglass lenses, then in 1883 adding photographic lenses. In 1888 they made their first shutters, and continued making shutters until 1935.

Iris Diaphragm Shutter - 1890-1904. Shutter blades act as diaphragm.

Victor-Unicum - 1893 (Patent Jan 6, 1891.)

"Star" - 1893. Has rotating disc with waterhouse stops.

Victor (Unicum with air retard cylinder) - 1894-1897. Iris diaphragm.

Unicum - 1897-past 1907. Iris diaphragm.

Vici - c1892.

Victor (1901 type) - 1901. Flat top with speed dial on it.

Argos - Patented 1900.

Volute - Patented 1902, continued until 1935.

AUTOMATIC SHUTTERS - *All B&L Shutters made after 1901, except for the Volute, were of the automatic type which did not require cocking.*

Auto - Patented Dec. 1900. Speed lever on bottom. Inverted a couple years later so speed dial was on top.

Gem - c1902 (Patented Feb. 1901). First model had TBI lever on left (viewed from front) and air retard cylinder on right. In 1903, the mechanism was reversed, so the positions of the TBI lever and air cylinder were also reversed. This was called the "Simplex".

Simplex - c1903. See "Gem" above.

Automat (1901 type) - Introduced late 1901, but not patented until December 1904. Speed control lever in a curved slot just below the lens.

Automat (1906 type) - c1906-1913. This popular style has a circular control lever at the top.

FPK Automatic - 1903-1913. Made for the Eastman Kodak Co. for use on the Folding Pocket Kodak cameras.

Automatic (1910) - Three distinct types.
- TBI. Two-blade shutter
- 1, 2, 5, 25, 50, 100, BT controlled by lever at top.
- Same speeds 1-100, BT but controlled by dial at top.

Compound - c1907 or 1908 on. Made under license from Deckel.
- c1907-1910. Speed dial has flat face with markings on face.
- c1910. Speed dial is conic section with markings on the edge.
- c1914. Pneumatic piston replaced by cable release.

B&L STEREO SHUTTERS
Iris Diaphragm Stereo - Intro. 1893. Two air cylinders between lenses.

Automat Stereo (slot below lens) - Intro. 1901.

Simplex Stereo - Intro. 1902. Air valve and TBI lever on face of left shutter (viewed from front.)

Automat Stereo (top dial) - Intro. 1904.

Single Valve Stereo - 1907.

Stereo Compound - 1911

DECKEL (Friedrich Deckel, Munich)
Bruns & Deckel founded 1903. F. Deckel firm established 1905. Following are major shutter types with approximate dates of introduction.
Compound - Introduced c1903.

Compour (Dial-set) - Introduced 1912.

Compur (Rim-set) - Introduced c1930.

Synchro Compur - c1951.

GAUTHIER (Alfred Gauthier, Calmbach)

Koilos (original with leather brake) - c1904.

Koilos (air piston) - c1906.

Ibso - c1908.

Ibsor - c1926. Gear control.

Prontor S - c1948.

Prontor SV - c1950. Full synchronization.

Prontor SKL - 1957. Meter-coupled

Prontormat-S - Fully automatic meter-controlled.

KODAK SHUTTERS - *This list includes only those shutters made by Kodak. They are listed in alphabetic order by shutter name.*
Automat - 1904-17. 5-speed, bulb release.

Automatic Flash - 1960-. Single-speed. For Automatic and Motormatic Cameras.

Ball Bearing shutters:
- #0 - 1914-26. 2-speed. For Vest Pocket cameras.
- #1 - 1909-24. 3-speed. Bulb or cable release.
- #2 - 1909-33. 3-speed. Bulb or cable release.
- Stereo Ball Bearing - 1919-24. 3-speed. Similar to the #2.

Brownie Automatic - 1904-15. Single-speed.

Brownie Automatic Stereo - 1905-15. Single-speed. For bulb operation.

Dak - 1940-1948. Single-speed.

Dakar #1 - 1935-36. 4-speed.

Dakon - 2-speed version 1940-48. 3-speed version 1946-48.

Diodak - 4-speed.
- #1 - 1932-35.
- #2 - 1932-33.
- #2A - 1936-41.

Diomatic top dial shutters - 4-speed.
- #0 - 1924-35.
- #1 - 1924-33.

Diomatic ring set shutters - These are similar to the Kodamatic #1 and #2 shutters.
- #1 - 3-speed version 1940-48. 4-speed version 1938-48.
- #2 - 1938-39. 4-speed.

Eastman Automatic - 1898-1906. Single-speed.

Flash 200 - 1949-59. 4-speed.

Flash 200 Stereo - 1954-59. 4-speed.

Flash 250 - 1957-61. 4-speed.

Flash 300 - 1953-58. 4-speed.

Flash Dakon - 1947-48. 3-speed

Flash Diomatic - 1946-52. 3 and 4-speed versions.

Flash Kodamatic - 5-speed version 1946-53. 7-speed version(for the Kodak Reflex Camera) 1946-54.

Flash Kodon - 1948-58. Single-speed, TBI. This is the "Dak" shutter with flash sync.

Flash Supermatic #1 - 1946-48. 9-speed.

Flash Supermatic #2 - 1946-52. 9-speed.

Hawk-Eye - 1923. Single-speed. A simplified Ball Bearing #0, T and I only.

Kodal #0 - 1932. Single-speed. Octagonal. T & I only.

Kodal #1 - 1932-40. Single-speed. Octagonal, B & I only.

Kodamatic (old style) - 1921-34. 7-speed. Small version was called the #1 or #1A. Large version was called #2 or #3A.

Kodamatic (ring set) #1 - 1937-48. 5-speed.

Kodamatic (ring set) #2 - 1937-47. 5-speed.

Kodex #0 - 1924-34. 2-speed.

Kodex #1 - Old style 1925-33; 2-speed. New style 1935-45; 3-speed.

Kodo #0 - 1929-40. Single-speed.

Kodo #1 - 1929-40. Single-speed.

Kodon #0 - 1932-40. 3-speed. Octagonal.

Kodon #1 - 1932-40. 3-speed. Octagonal.

Supermatic #0 - 1941-48. 9-speed. For the Bantam Special.

Supermatic #1 - 1939-48. 9-speed.

Supermatic #2 - 1939-47. 9-speed.

Supermatic #3 - 8-speed.

Supermatic X - 8-speed. Same as the #3 but with X sync.

Synchro 80 - 1959-. 2-speed. For the Automatic 35 Camera.

Synchro 250 - 1957-60. 7-speed. For the Signet 30 and 50 Cameras.

Synchro 300 - 1951-58. 4-speed. For the Signet 35 Camera.

Synchro 400 - 1956-59. 7-speed. For the Signet 40 Camera.

Synchro-Rapid 800 - 1949-56. 10-speed.

Triple Action - 1897-03. 3-speed. Made in small and large versions.

WOLLENSAK SHUTTERS
Actus - 1912-14. 3-speed, T,B.

Alphax - 1946-56. 5-speed, T,B.

Autex - 1908-13. 6-speed, T,B.

Auto A - 1913-18. 6-speed, T,B.

Auto B - 1918-22. 7-speed, T,B.

Automatic A - 1901-02. 8-speed, T,B.

Automatic B - 1902-08. 6-speed, T,B.

Automatic s.v. - 1900-02. 3-speed, T,B.

Betax - 1922-48. 6-speed, T,B.

Ballard Unique - 1901?. Single-speed, T,B.

Conley Safety - 1912?. 6-speed, T,B.

Deltax - 1922-42. 3-speed, T,B.

Gammax - 1922-42. 4-speed, T,B.

Graphex - 1946?. 9-speed, T,B.

Junior - 1901-11. Single-speed, T,B.

Optimo (Velosto) - 1909-30. 8-speed, T,B.

Optimo #0 - 1916-22. 7-speed, T,B.

Rapax - 1946-56. 9-speed, T,B.

Regno A - 1908-11. 6-speed, T,B.

Regno B - 1911-18. 6-speed, T,B.

(Original) - 1900-01. 8-speed, T,B.

Regular A - 1901-02. 8-speed, T,B.

Regular B - 1902-08. 6-speed, T,B.

Senior - 1903-07. Single-speed, T,B.

Skyshade - 1906-13. 6-speed, T,B.

Studio - 1906-40.

TIB - 1911-14. Single-speed, T,B.

Ultro A - 1914-19. Single-speed, T,B.

Ultro B - 1919-22. Single-speed, T,B.

Victo A - 1914-18. 4-speed, T,B.

Victo B - 1918-22. 4-speed, T,B.

Victus - 1908-12. 3-speed, T,B.

Winner A - 1901-02. 4-speed, T,B.

Winner B - 1902-08. 3-speed, T,B.

COLLECTORS' ORGANIZATIONS

This list was prepared by the Western Photographic Collectors' Assn. and updated by Centennial Photo Service. If your organization is not included in this listing, please contact either the WPCA or Centennial Photo.

AMERICAN PHOTOGRAPHIC HISTORICAL SOCIETY
P.O. Box 1775 Grand Central Station
New York, NY 10163

AMERICAN SOCIETY OF CAMERA COLLECTORS, Inc.
4918 Alcove Ave.
North Hollywood, CA 91607
(818) 769-6160

BAY AREA PHOTOGRAPHICA ASSN. (BAPA)
2538 34th Ave.
San Francisco, CA 94116
(415) 664-6498 or 387-7464

CHICAGO PHOTOGRAPHIC COLLECTORS SOCIETY
P.O. Box 375
Winnetka, IL 60093

CLUB DAGUERRE-DARRAH
2562 Victoria
Wichita, KS 67216
(316) 265-0393

DELAWARE VALLEY PHOTOGRAPHIC COLLECTORS ASSN.
P.O. Box 74
Delanco, NJ 08075

INTERNATIONAL PHOTOGRAPHIC HISTORICAL ORGANIZATION
P.O. Box 16074
San Francisco, CA 94116
(415) 681-4356

LEICA HISTORICAL SOC. of AMERICA
3327 So. Hametown Rd.
Norton, OH 44203
(216) 825-7364

MICHIGAN PHOTOGRAPHIC HISTORICAL SOCIETY
Box 202
Wayne, MI 48184
(313) 721-5126

MIDWEST PHOTOGRAPHIC HISTORICAL SOCIETY
19 Hazelnut Ct.
Florissant, MO 63033

NATIONAL STEREOSCOPIC ASSN.
Box 14801
Columbus, OH 43214

THE OHIO CAMERA COLLECTORS
P.O. Box 282
Columbus, OH 43216

PENNSYLVANIA PHOTOGRAPHIC HISTORICAL SOC., Inc.
P.O. Box 862
Beaver Falls, PA 15010-0862
(412) 843-5688

PHOTOGRAPHIC COLLECTORS of HOUSTON
P.O. Box 22914
Houston. TX 77227

PHOTOGRAPHIC COLLECTORS of TUCSON
P.O. Box 18646
Tucson, AZ 85731

THE PHOTOGRAPHIC HISTORICAL SOCIETY
P.O. Box 39563
Rochester, NY 14604

THE PHOTOGRAPHIC HISTORICAL SOCIETY of CANADA PHOTOGRAPHIC HISTORICAL SOCIETY of METROPOLITIAN TORONTO
P.O. Box 115, Postal Stn "S"
Toronto, Ont, CANADA M5M 4L6
(416) 243-1439 (Evenings)

PHOTOGRAPHIC HISTORICAL SOCIETY of NEW ENGLAND, Inc.
P.O. Box M, West Newton Branch
Boston, MA 02165
(617) 277-0207

THE PHOTOGRAPHIC HISTORICAL SOCIETY of the WESTERN RESERVE
P.O. Box 21174
Cleveland, OH 44121
(216) 382-6727 or 232-1827

PUGET SOUND PHOTOGRAPHIC COLLECTORS SOCIETY
10421 Delwood Dr. S.W.
Tacoma, WA 98498
(206) 582-4878

TRI-STATE PHOTOGRAPHIC COLLECTORS SOCIETY
8910 Cherry
Blue Ash, OH 45242
(513) 891-5266

WESTERN CANADA PHOTOGRAPHIC HISTORICAL ASSN.
Box 33742
Vancouver, B.C. CANADA V6J 4L6
(604) 873-2128

WESTERN PHOTOGRAPHIC COLLECTOR ASSN. Inc.
P.O. Box 4294
Whittier, CA 90607

ZEISS HISTORICAL SOCIETY
P.O. Box 631
Clifton, NJ 07012
(201) 472-1318

COLLECTORS' ORGANIZATIONS by STATE

NAME	DUES n=non-profit	MONTHLY Meeting/ Journal/ Newsletter	SHOW DATES	MEMBER- SHIP
--- ARIZONA ---				
PHOTOGRAPHIC COLLECTORS				
--- CALIFORNIA ---				
AMERICAN SOCIETY OF CAMERA COLLECTORS, Inc.	$15.00 n	M/N	Mar/Sept	271
BAY AREA PHOTOGRAPHIC ASSN.	$6.00 n	bi-mon/N	none	60
INTERNATIONAL PHOTOGRAPHIC HISTORICAL ORGANIZATION	$16.00	bi-mon/N/J		
WESTERN PHOTOGRAPHIC COLLECTORS ASSN, Inc.	$16 Reg, $13 Cor, $23 For n	M/N/*	May/Nov	400+
--- ILLINOIS ---				
CHICAGO PHOTOGRAPHIC COLLECTORS SOCIETY	$18.00	M/N/*	Spr/Fall	110
--- KANSAS ---				
CLUB DAGUERRE-DARRAH	$12.00	M/N	Feb	18
--- MASSACHUSETTS ---				
PHOTOGRAPHIC HISTORICAL SOC. OF NEW ENGLAND, Inc.	$15 Reg, $30 For n	M/N/*	Apr/Oct	350
--- MICHIGAN ---				
MICHIGAN PHOTOGRAPHIC HISTORICAL SOCIETY	$2.50 Reg, $10 Int n	bi-mon/N/J	Nov	70
--- MISSOURI ---				
MIDWEST PHOTOGRAPHIC HIST. SOC.	$10.00 n	M/N/*	Apr/Oct	80
--- NEW YORK ---				
AMERICAN PHOTOGRAPHIC HIST. SOC.	$22.50 n	M/N/*	May/Nov	600+
THE PHOTOGRAPHIC HISTORICAL SOCIETY	$12.00 n	M/N/*	Oct	60
--- OHIO ---				
THE OHIO CAMERA COLLECTORS	$10.00 n	M/N/J	May	100
THE PHOTOGRAPHIC HISTORICAL SOCIETY of the WESTERN RESERVE	$10.00 n	M/N	July	40
TRI-STATE PHOTOGRAPHIC COLLECTORS SOCIETY	$5.00 n	M	none	12
--- PENNSYLVANIA ---				
DELAWARE VALLEY PHOTOGRAPHIC COLL. ASSN.	$15.00 n	M/N/*	Feb/Jun/Aug/Nov	90
PENNSYLVANIA PHOTOGRAPHIC HISTORICAL SOCIETY, Inc.	$20 Fam, $15 Ind n	bi-mon/N	Aug/Oct	55
--- TEXAS ---				
PHOTOGRAPHIC COLLECTORS of HOUSTON	$10.00	M/N	Apr/Oct	80
--- WASHINGTON ---				
PUGET SOUND PHOTOGRAPHIC COLLECTORS SOCIETY	$10.00 n	M/N	May	65
--- CANADA ---				
PHOTOGRAPHIC HISTORICAL SOCIETY of METROPOLITAN TORONTO	$8.00 n	M/N	Fall/Win	150
THE PHOTOGRAPHIC HISTORICAL SOCIETY of CANADA	$20.00 n	J	May	250
WESTERN CANADA PHOTO. HISTORICAL ASSOCIATION.	$12 Act, $15 Fam, $7 Assoc	M/N	none	45
--- NATIONAL ---				
LEICA HISTORICAL SOCIETY of AMERICA	$20.00 n	N/J	Oct	660
NATIONAL STEREOSCOPIC ASSOCIATION	$20 Reg, $27 1stCl n	J	Aug	1600
ZEISS HISTORICA SOCIETY	$20.00 n	annual/N		155

* indicates the Photographica/Journal

EXCHANGE RATES

The prices in this guide represent prices in the U.S.A. market. There are definite variations from these figures in the foreign markets. Some cameras are more common in one country than another. Collectors' interests are different in various parts of the world, and "trends" or "fads" affect different markets at different times. However, none of the world's markets are closed to outside influence, and the fluctations have a tendency to level off on a world wide scale. A higher price in one country will tend to draw more cameras to that area and the world price rises until that demand eventually becomes satisfied, usually between the earlier norm and the "fad" high. Keeping this general background in mind, the following chart will prove useful to people dealing across national boundaries. The following figures are for the U.S. Dollar values of the indicated currencies as of April 19, 1985. Multiplying these factors* times the U.S. Dollar price gives the value in the foreign currencies.

CURRENCY	EXCHANGE RATE	MULTIPLCATION FACTOR *
Australian $	.6589	1.5177
Canadian $	.7555	1.3236
British £	1.3184	.7585
French Franc	.1123	8.9047
German DM	.3426	2.9188
Japanese Yen	.004121	242.65

OFFICIAL DEALERS BLUE BOOK
OF CURRENT CAMERA VALUES

Buying or selling a camera can be as complicated as trading up to a new car. With hundreds of new models added each year, this extensive guide fills a critical need for camera dealers and photographers. The *Dealer Blue Book* takes over where the *Price Guide to Cameras* leaves off, covering primarily **usable** rather than collectible cameras. Thousands of cameras and lenses including current models through 1981, used equipment, and a few collectibles are all put in perspective for the first time in a single guide. Original prices and current trade-in values.

64 pages, pocket size. $8.95. Published in 1981. ISBN 0-931838-03-7

COLLECTORS GUIDE TO KODAK CAMERAS

Millions of Americans own antique Kodak cameras, and this is the first comprehensive guide which describes and illustrates most of these family heirlooms. Large, clear photos and easy to use index make it an ideal guide for the novice or expert alike. Identification features have been included for each camera model as well as technical specifications and original prices. Virtually all Kodak and Brownie cameras are listed along with the shutter and lens variations and the years of production for each variation.

176 pages, 5.5x8.5 inches. $12.95. ISBN 0-931838-02-9

Add $1.00 for postage for a single title, $2.00 for any multiple-book order. We will ship by 4th Class Book Rate in the USA and by Surface Mail to foreign countries. If other method of shipping is requested, please include an appropriate amount to cover the cost. Foreign orders, please pay in U.S. Dollars, preferably in currency to avoid excessive bank charges. We accept VISA and MasterCard. Include card number, expiration date, and name of cardholder.

OTHER TITLES ARE UNDER PREPARATION, including:
Collectors Guide to Rollei Cameras, Collectors Guide to Subminiature Cameras and others. Please send self-addressed stamped envelope for complete list of books available.

**Centennial Photo
Rt. 3, Box 1125
Grantsburg, WI 54840-9136**

BURTON TILLEY
BUYS CAMERAS!
TOLL FREE
1-800-525-0359

We Will Buy The Following Cameras
in Ex+ or Better Condition
at Prevailing Prices.

JAPANESE CAMERAS

Acro 35 w/top viewer
Hansa Canon
Canon S or S-2 any cond.
Canon J or J2, any cond.
Canon Seiki Serenar Lenses
Canon VI or VIT w/Lens
Honor w/lens (Leica copy)
Nikon I Serial #609-1 to 609-759, any cond.
Nikon M Serial #M609-759 to M609-2000, any
cond., no sync.
Nikon M Serial #M6092000 to M6094000, any
cond. (factory sync) WL
Nikon 50mm lens only, for above, says "Tokyo" not
"Japan", some are rare.
Nikon S2, S2 Black, w/lens. Exc+
Nikon S3 w/lens. like new
Nikon S3 Black, w/lens. Exc+
Nikon S4, SP w/lens. Mint
Nikon SP Black, w/lens. Exc++
Nikon S-3M Half frame
Nippon Kogaku "Tokyo" lenses
Nikon 21mm or 25mm lens w/finder for RF
Nikon 50/3.5 Macro, or 50/1.1 SM or BM for RF
Nikon RF any camera accessories
Nippon Camera (Leica copy)
Nippon Camera collapsible fixed lens, any cond.
Look, Leica copy
Peerless, Leica copy

EUROPEAN EQUIPMENT

Alpa-Reflex I, ca. 1947
Bertram (3 lens set) Mint
Casca (no rangefinder) or Casca II (w/RF)
Exakta 6x6 Pre or Post War
Ernemann Cameras, many types
Gami (complete)
Ihagee Patent Klapp Reflex
Kardon Military or Civilian
Minox B new type, Mint
Minx III or IIIS
Pilot TLR
Plaubel Makinette
Cart Bentzin Primarette
Roland
Rolleiflex 4x4 black or grey
Grey Rollei T
Rollei 2.8F or 3.5F, newest, truly Mint, 120/220 Planar
Rolleiwide w/case. Mint
Sept. Exc+
Sybil Baby and all other sizes
Vollenda w/Elmar lens. Exc++

LEICAS

Leitz plastic stereoviewer
Leica IIIc Wartime. Must be Exc+

Leica IIIf RD ST. Must be Mint
Leica Ig. Must be Exc+
Leica M2. Must be Mint
Leica M3 under SR #700200, any cond.
Leica M3 above #1,100,000. Mint
Leica M5 chrome, 3 lug. Mint
Leica Brightline finders 21, 28, 35
Leitz 15 Hologon w/finder
Leitz 28/5.6 Summaron or 28/6.3 Hektor
Leitz 33/2.5 Stemar Stereo. Set.
Leitz 35/2 Summicron. Germany or no eyes-SM
Leitz 50/2 Summicron Rigid, BM
Leitz 50/3.5 Red Dial, Elmar, SM
Leitz 90/2.8 Elmarit or 90/4 Elmarit
Leitz 90/4 Elmar collapsible or SM
Leitz 125/2.5 Hektor w/hood & caps
Leitz 135 Elmar
Leica All Viewfinders, many types

VOIGTLANDER

Bessas, many types, I, II, II Apo-Lanthar
Bergheil green & black
Perkeo Pre War black body, or w/rangefinder
Prominent, Prewar folding or Prominent II
Superb, Heliar or Skopar lens, like new
Virtus Prewar, Exc+

ZEISS

Contaflex Twin lens truly Mint
35/2.8 Biogon for above w/finder
Contarex Professional, Special, or SE Electronic
Exc++
Contarex Super, new type
Contarex 16mm or 18/4 Distagon, black
Contarex 25/2.8 or 35/2 Distagon, black
Contarex 35/4 Curtagon, PA
Contarex 85/1.4 black
Contarex 180/2.8, black RARE
250/4 Sonnar w/knob focus black
Contarex 1000mm or 500mm Mirotar, Valuable
Contarex Vario Sonnar S. Valuable
Contax D, Contax F, Contax S
Contax IIa full sync Exc++, 50/1.5 "Carl Zeiss" lens
Contax IIIa full sync Exc+, 50/1.5
Contax 21mm lens w/finder
Contax 25mm Topogon
Contax 28mm Black Tessar
Contax 35mm Orthometer or Biometer
Contax 35mm Biogon (post war) or Planar
Contax 40mm or 75mm Biotar. Rare
Contax Long Lenses and Contax Reflex Housings
Icarex
Hologon w/grip filter
Baby Ikonta w/Tessar
Super Ikonta A or C w/MX Tessar
Zeiss plastic stereoviewer for Stereotar C

Burton Tilley's
World Cameras
1625 Larimer, Suite 3003 (30th Floor), Denver, CO 80202
TOLL FREE 1-800-525-0359 or (303) 892-6656

Vintage Cameras Ltd.

Antique and Classic Cameras Ltd. **ENGLAND** Antique and Vintage Images Ltd.

254 - 256 Kirkdale Corner, London SE26 4NL Tel. 01-778 9052/5416/5841 Telex: 896691 TLIXIR G VINCAM

MANY   OF

THE   ITEMS

LISTED   IN

THIS   GUIDE

CAN   BE

OBTAINED

FROM   US.

WE ALWAYS

CARRY A LARGE

STOCK OF:

C O L L E C T O R S   C A M E R A S

and   P H O T O G R A P H I C A

on display in our extensive showroom.

REGULAR LISTS SENT
TO SUBSCRIBERS.
Hours: 9am to 5pm.
Monday to Saturday.

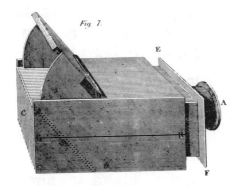

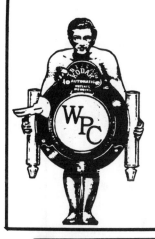

535

**YOU ARE INVITED TO BECOME A MEMBER OF
THE INTERNATIONAL MUSEUM OF PHOTOGRAPHY
AT GEORGE EASTMAN HOUSE - ROCHESTER, N.Y.**

★ ★ ★ ★ ★ ★ ★ ★ ★ ★ ★ ★ ★ ★ ★ ★ ★ ★

As a result of a decision made by the acquistions committee, George Eastman House will be selling a large number of duplicate items from the technology collections.

The first list with not less than 150 items, ranging in price from $5.00 to $400.00 will become available early in June 1985. Subsequent lists will be published as we complete the process of re-inventorying the collections and will be mailed upon request.

They will be available for $3.00 each. This amount is refundable if your purchase equals or exceeds $50.00.

**MEMBERS OF GEORGE EASTMAN HOUSE
ARE ENTITLED TO A 25% OVERALL DISCOUNT ON ANY
ITEMS PURCHASED**

Each item will come with a document stating that it has been formally de-accessioned from the collections of George Eastman House.

Membership Categories   **(VISA or MasterCard accepted)**
☐ Student $20.00   ☐ Senior Citizen $20.00
☐ Individual $30.00   ☐ Family $40.00

In addition to other benefits, members will receive four issues annually of the museum publication "Image".

For additional information write the International Museum of Photography at George Eastman House, attention Director of Technology Collections.

**International Museum of Photography
at George Eastman House
900 East Avenue
Rochester, New York 14607**

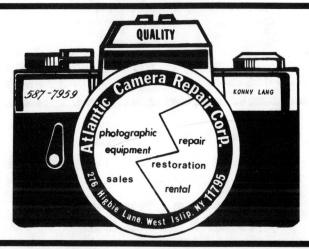

A PHOTOGRAPHIC EXHIBITION
FOR COLLECTORS AND HISTORIANS

HAROLD B. LEWIS PHOTO

Jack Naylor Collection
OF CAMERAS AND IMAGES

- **PRE-PHOTOGRAPHY**

  - **THE FIRST PHOTOGRAPHY**

    - **WET and DRY PLATE, ROLL FILM and CONTEMPORARY PHOTOGRAPHY**

    - **RESEARCH LIBRARY**

INFORMATION:

Jack Naylor
CAMERAS and IMAGES INTERNATIONAL, INC.
P.O. BOX 23, WALTHAM STATION
BOSTON, MASSACHUSETTS 02254
617-277-0207   617-277-7878

A Private Museum

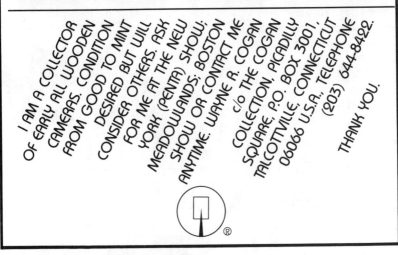

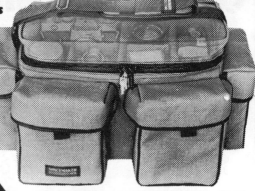

ADORAMA
THE PHOTOGRAPHY PEOPLE

138 West 34th Street   212/564-4465
New York, N.Y. 10001   800/223-2500

We are specializing in professional used camera
equipment—buying, selling, trading. The full
product line of:
Leica, Rolleiflex, ZeissContax, Voigtlander,
Tessina, Minox, Alpa, Hasselblad, Linhof, Canon
& Nikon range finders, Kodak Retinas, Robot,
Stereo Realist, etc. Lenses and accessories.

TOP DOLLARS FOR YOUR EQUIPMENT!

Dear Reader,

For your convenience we have a Trade-in Service.
Your old or unwanted equipment, that might have
a greater value than you think, will be gladly traded
or bought by us. Please mail your items with your
name, address and phone number to my attention.

We will evaluate it and make an offer as soon as
possible, assuring you the fairest and highest prices.
If you would not be satisfied, we will return your items
prepaid and insured.

We hope you will take advantage of this excellent
service.

Cordially yours,

Trade & Used Department Manager